Elementary Differential Equations
and Boundary Value Problems

ELEMENTARY DIFFERENTIAL EQUATIONS AND BOUNDARY VALUE PROBLEMS

William E. Boyce

and

Richard C. DiPrima

Rensselaer Polytechnic Institute

Second Edition

John Wiley & Sons, Inc.,
New York · London · Sydney · Toronto

Library of Congress Catalog Card Number: 69-16043
SBN 471 09331 9
Printed in the United States of America

To My Mother, Ethel DiPrima,
and in Loving Memory
of My Father, Clyde DiPrima

Richard C. DiPrima

To My Mother, Marie S. Boyce,
and My Father, Edward G. Boyce

William E. Boyce

Preface

A course in elementary differential equations is an excellent vehicle through which to convey to the student a feeling for the interrelation between pure mathematics, on the one hand, and the physical sciences or engineering, on the other. Before the engineer can proceed confidently to use differential equations in his work, he must have at least a rudimentary knowledge of the basic theory, including some facts about the existence and uniqueness of solutions. Conversely, the student of pure mathematics often benefits greatly by a knowledge of some of the ways in which the necessity for solving specific problems has stimulated work of a more abstract nature.

We wrote this book from the intermediate viewpoint of the applied mathematician, whose interest in differential equations may, at the same time, be quite theoretical as well as intensely practical. We have therefore sought to combine a sound and accurate (but not particularly abstract) exposition of the elementary theory of differential equations with considerable material on methods of solution that have proved useful in a wide variety of applications. We have given principal attention to those methods that are capable of broad application and that can be extended to problems beyond the range of our book. We emphasize that these methods have a systematic and orderly structure, and are not merely a miscellaneous collection of unrelated mathematical tricks. At some point, however, the student should realize that many problems cannot be satisfactorily solved by more or less elementary analytical techniques. Therefore, we have also treated questions related to the qualitative behavior of solutions and have discussed ways of approximating solutions numerically.

As soon as one is faced with a problem whose solution cannot be simply found, questions arise as to the existence and/or uniqueness of solutions. We answer these by stating the relevant theorems, although not necessarily in their most general form, and discussing their significance. In particular, the differences between linear and nonlinear equations, and between initial and boundary value problems are examined.

Although we believe that most students at this level can begin to grasp the importance and applications of the various theorems, the proofs in many cases involve concepts unknown to them, such as uniform convergence. Where this is the case, we have omitted the proofs without apology. For example, we discuss some of the problems involved in proving the fundamental existence and uniqueness theorem for a first order initial value problem by the method of successive approximations; our approach, however, is rather intuitive, and the more difficult analytical details are avoided.

We have written this book primarily for students who have a knowledge of calculus gained from a normal two- or three-semester course; most of the book is well within the capabilities of such students. In Chapter 7 (Systems of Equations), experience with matrix algebra will be helpful, although we include two sections on matrices that summarize the information necessary to read the rest of the chapter. A few sections are indicated by an asterisk; these probably require greater mathematical sophistication (although, strictly speaking, no more knowledge) than the rest of the book.

Students frequently feel that courses and books on differential equations tend to be "cookbookish," and we have made a special effort to combat this tendency. Whenever possible, the student's prior knowledge is drawn upon to suggest a method of attack for a new type of problem. Moreover, the discussions of applications are usually accompanied by a careful derivation of the relevant equations. In an elementary book, we do not believe that terseness is a primary virtue and, in general, we have striven for clarity rather than conciseness. We hope that whatever may have been lost in elegance has been regained in readability.

While the scope of the book can better be judged from the Table of Contents, it may be worthwhile to note here some of its principal features. Chapter 1 is a brief introduction to some of the terminology and history of differential equations. Chapter 2 deals with first order equations. The differences between linear and nonlinear equations are emphasized in the first three sections. This is followed by a discussion of the standard elementary integration methods and a consideration of several applications, including the straight line motion of a body with variable mass. The chapter closes with a discussion of the Picard theorem both from a classical and from a modern point of view.

Chapters 3 to 7 deal with linear ordinary differential equations. In Chapter 3 we discuss second order linear equations. The concepts of fundamental sets of solutions, linear independence, and superposition are emphasized, together with methods of solution. Examples are drawn from the fields of mechanical vibrations and electrical networks. The ideas of this chapter are extended to higher order linear equations in Chapter 5. In Chapter 4, on power series solutions, we show why the classification of points as ordinary, regular singular, or irregular singular is necessary and natural, rather than arbitrary. We use the Euler equation as a model for handling more general equations having a regular singular point. The cases in which the roots of the indicial equation are equal, or differ by an integer, are thoroughly treated and are illustrated by appropriate forms of the Bessel equation. In Chapter 6 the Laplace transform is introduced, and its usefulness in solving initial value problems having piecewise continuous or impulsive forcing terms is emphasized. Chapter 7 deals with systems of first order linear equations. The first two sections provide a brief introduction to systems and their solution by elimination methods, and can be read without any knowledge of matrices. In the remainder of the chapter we use vector-matrix notation. This brings out clearly the close relationship between the theory of single equations and that of systems.

In Chapters 8 and 9 we discuss problems, especially nonlinear ones, for which the previous methods fail. In Chapter 8 there is a careful treatment of discrete numerical techniques for solving initial value problems. Procedures ranging from the Euler tangent line method to the Runge-Kutta and Milne predictor-corrector methods are discussed and compared. A great deal of emphasis is given to the underlying principles governing numerical procedures and their refinement, and to a consideration of the kinds, sources, and control of errors. Chapter 9 is an introduction to the qualitative theory of differential equations, with emphasis on stability questions for autonomous systems. Critical points of linear systems are classified, and almost linear systems are studied with reference to a neighboring linear system. Liapounov's second method is introduced from a physical point of view, and the chapter ends with a brief investigation of limit cycles.

In the remaining chapters, we take up partial differential equations, Fourier series, and Sturm-Liouville boundary value prolems. In Chapter 10, the solution of the heat equation by the method of separation of variables leads to a discussion of the elementary properties of Fourier series. Afterward, the same methods are applied to the solution of typical problems for the wave equation and potential equation. Chapter 11 contains a treatment of more general Sturm-Liouville boundary value problems, singular as well as regular. The eigenvalues and eigenfunctions of such problems are discussed, and eigenfunction series are employed to extend the method of separation of variables to more general problems in partial differential equations.

Readers familiar with the first edition will notice three major changes in this revision; these result largely from changes in the pattern of elementary mathematical instruction in many colleges.

1. We have rewritten the chapter on systems of equations to take advantage of the fact that many students of elementary differential equations are now acquainted with matrices. However, for other students we have provided two sections which summarize the properties of matrices that we require.

2. We have added a chapter on stability theory for linear and nonlinear equations. This is prompted by the increasing importance of nonlinear phenomena in many fields and the study of such phenomena at earlier stages of the educational process—for example, the study of automatic control systems in engineering curricula.

3. We have reorganized the material on partial differential equations, Fourier series, and eigenvalue problems in order to show more clearly the connections among these topics. We have also included a brief survey of the theory of Sturm-Liouville boundary value problems.

In addition we have made minor changes throughout—wherever it seemed possible to improve upon the clarity or accuracy of the previous text.

For classroom use, we believe that this book has more than average flexibility. Beginning with Chapter 4, the chapters are substantially independent of each other, although Chapter 11 logically follows Chapter 10. Furthermore, in most chapters the principal ideas are developed in the first few sections; the remaining ones are devoted to extensions and applications. Thus the instructor has maximum control over the selection and arrangement of course material, and over the depth to which the various topics are to be explored.

At Rensselaer we have found it possible to cover approximately the following material in a three-hour one-semester course:

1.1, 1.2	5.1–5.4
2.1–2.7, 2.9	7.1–7.4
3.1–3.6.2	8.1–8.3
4.1–4.5	10.1–10.8

A variety of other arrangements are also possible. For example, courses oriented toward systems analysis would probably emphasize Chapters 6, 7, and 9. Finally, we mention that if the students have been exposed to differential equations in their calculus course, then some of the introductory material in Chapters 2 and 3 can be dispensed with, and later chapters taken up more thoroughly.

As far as the physical layout of this book is concerned, sections are numbered in decimal form. Theorems, figures, etc., are numbered consecutively in each chapter. Thus, Theorem 3.7 is the seventh theorem in Chapter 3, but is not necessarily in Section 3.7. References are given at the end of each chapter. Most sections are followed by problem sets for the student, with all answers collected at the end of the book. Some of the more difficult problems are indicated by an asterisk. Certain sections are also designated by an asterisk. These contain more advanced material, which can be omitted by a beginning student in his first reading.

In addition to those people mentioned in the preface to the first edition, we express our appreciation to the following individuals, who assisted us in preparing this edition: Professors Donald G. Aronson, Donald S. Cohen, Bernard A. Fleishman, Mark A. Pinsky, and Lee A. Segel, who read and offered critical commentary on portions of the manuscript; Professor George J. Habetler, for many helpful discussions; Professor Paul A. McGloin, for additional numerical computations; Mr. Donald A. Drew, for help in proofreading and in checking answers; and Mrs. Helen D. Hayes, who very quickly and efficiently typed a rather messy manuscript.

We also thank Professor George H. Handelman, who kindly placed the resources of Rensselaer's Department of Mathematics at our disposal in a variety of ways. Finally, we thank the editorial and production staff of John Wiley and Sons, Inc. for their assistance and cooperation.

Troy, New York January, 1969

William E. Boyce

Richard C. DiPrima

Contents

*Elementary Differential Equations
and Boundary Value Problems*

CHAPTER 1

Introduction

Many important and significant problems in engineering, the physical sciences, and the social sciences, when formulated in mathematical terms, require the determination of a function satisfying an equation containing derivatives of the unknown function. Such equations are called *differential equations*. Perhaps the most familiar example is Newton's law

$$m\frac{d^2u(t)}{dt^2} = F\left[t, u(t), \frac{du(t)}{dt}\right] \tag{1}$$

for the position $u(t)$ of a particle acted on by a force F, which may be a function of time t, the position $u(t)$, and the velocity $du(t)/dt$. To determine the motion of a particle acted on by a given force F it is necessary to find a function u satisfying Eq. (1). If the force is that due to gravity, then

$$m\frac{d^2u(t)}{dt^2} = -mg. \tag{2}$$

On integrating Eq. (2) we have

$$\frac{du(t)}{dt} = -gt + c_1,$$

$$u(t) = -\tfrac{1}{2}gt^2 + c_1t + c_2, \tag{3}$$

where c_1 and c_2 are constants. To determine $u(t)$ completely it is necessary to specify two additional conditions, such as the position and velocity of the particle at some instant of time. These conditions can be used to determine the constants c_1 and c_2.

In developing the theory of differential equations in a systematic manner it is helpful to classify different types of equations. One of the more obvious classifications is based on whether the unknown function depends on a single independent variable or on several independent variables. In the first case only ordinary derivatives appear in the differential equation and it is said to be an *ordinary differential equation*. In the second case the derivatives are partial derivatives and the equation is called a *partial differential equation*.

Two examples of ordinary differential equations, in addition to Eq. (1), are

$$L\frac{d^2Q(t)}{dt^2} + R\frac{dQ(t)}{dt} + \frac{1}{C}Q(t) = E(t), \tag{4}$$

for the charge $Q(t)$ on a condenser in a circuit with capacitance C, resistance R, inductance L, and impressed voltage $E(t)$; and the equation governing the decay with time of an amount $R(t)$ of a radioactive substance, such as radium,

$$\frac{dR(t)}{dt} = -kR(t), \tag{5}$$

where k is a known constant. Typical examples of partial differential equations are Laplace's (1749–1827) or the potential equation

$$\frac{\partial^2 u(x, y)}{\partial x^2} + \frac{\partial^2 u(x, y)}{\partial y^2} = 0, \tag{6}$$

the diffusion or heat equation

$$\alpha^2\frac{\partial^2 u(x, t)}{\partial x^2} = \frac{\partial u(x, t)}{\partial t}, \tag{7}$$

and the wave equation

$$a^2\frac{\partial^2 u(x, t)}{\partial x^2} = \frac{\partial^2 u(x, t)}{\partial t^2}. \tag{8}$$

Here α^2 and a^2 are certain constants. The potential equation, the diffusion equation, and the wave equation arise in a variety of problems in the fields of electricity and magnetism, elasticity, and fluid mechanics. Each is typical of distinct physical phenomena (note the names), and each is representative of a large class of partial differential equations. While we will primarily be concerned with ordinary differential equations we will also consider partial differential equations, in particular the three important equations just mentioned.

1.1 ORDINARY DIFFERENTIAL EQUATIONS

The *order* of an ordinary differential equation is the order of the highest derivative that appears in the equation. Thus Eqs. (1) and (4) of the previous section are second order ordinary differential equations, and Eq. (5) is a first order ordinary differential equation. More generally, the equation

$$F[x, u(x), u'(x), \ldots, u^{(n)}(x)] = 0 \tag{1}$$

is an ordinary differential equation of the nth order. Equation (1) represents a relation between the independent variable x and the values of the function u and its first n derivatives u', u'', $\ldots$, $u^{(n)}$. It is convenient and follows the usual notation in the theory of differential equations to write y for $u(x)$, with $y', y'', \ldots, y^{(n)}$ standing for $u'(x), u''(x), \ldots, u^{(n)}(x)$. Thus Eq. (1) is written as

$$F(x, y, y', \ldots, y^{(n)}) = 0. \tag{2}$$

Occasionally, other letters will be used instead of y; the meaning will be clear from the context.

We shall assume that it is always possible to solve a given ordinary differential equation for the highest derivative, obtaining

$$y^{(n)} = f(x, y, y', y'', \ldots, y^{(n-1)}). \tag{3}$$

We will only study equations of the form (3). This is mainly to avoid the ambiguity that may arise because a single equation of the form (2) may correspond to several equations of the form (3). For example, the equation

$$y'^2 + xy' + 4y = 0$$

leads to the two equations

$$y' = \frac{-x + \sqrt{x^2 - 16y^2}}{2} \quad \text{or} \quad y' = \frac{-x - \sqrt{x^2 - 16y^2}}{2}.$$

The fact that we have written Eq. (3) does not necessarily mean that there is a function $y = \phi(x)$ which satisfies it. Indeed this is one of the questions that we wish to investigate. By a *solution* of the ordinary differential equation (3) on the interval $\alpha < x < \beta$ we mean a function ϕ such that $\phi', \phi'', \ldots, \phi^{(n)}$ exist and satisfy

$$\phi^{(n)}(x) = f[x, \phi(x), \phi'(x), \ldots, \phi^{(n-1)}(x)] \tag{4}$$

for every x in $\alpha < x < \beta$. Unless stated otherwise, we shall assume that the function f of Eq. (3) is a real-valued function, and we will be interested in obtaining real-valued solutions $y = \phi(x)$.

It is easily verified that the first order equation

$$\frac{dR}{dt} = -kR \tag{5}$$

has the solution

$$R = \phi(t) = ce^{-kt}, \quad -\infty < t < \infty, \tag{6}$$

where c is an arbitrary constant. Similarly the functions $y_1(x) = \cos x$ and $y_2(x) = \sin x$ are solutions of

$$y'' + y = 0 \tag{7}$$

for all x.

One question that might come to mind is whether there are other solutions of Eq. (5) besides those given by Eq. (6), and whether there are other solutions of Eq. (7) besides $y_1(x) = \cos x$ and $y_2(x) = \sin x$. A question that might occur even earlier is the following: Given an equation of the form (3), how do we know whether it even has a solution? This is the question of the *existence* of a solution. Not all differential equations have solutions; nor is the question of existence purely mathematical. If a meaningful physical problem is correctly formulated mathematically as a differential equation, then the mathematical problem should have a solution. In this sense an engineer or scientist has some check upon the validity of his mathematical formulation.

Second, assuming a given equation has one solution, does it have other solutions? If so, what type of additional conditions must be specified in order to single out a particular solution? This is the question of *uniqueness*. Notice that there is an infinity of solutions of the first order equation (5) corresponding to the infinity of possible choices of the constant c in Eq. (6). If R is specified at some time t, this condition will determine a value for c; even so, however, we do not know yet that there may not be other solutions of Eq. (5) which also have the prescribed value of R at the prescribed time t. The questions of existence and uniqueness are difficult questions; they and related questions will be discussed as we proceed.

A third question, a more practical one, is: Given a differential equation of the form (3), how do we actually determine a solution? We might note that if we find a solution of the given equation we have at the same time answered the question of the existence of a solution. On the other hand, without knowledge of existence theory we might, for example, use a large computing machine to find an approximation to a "solution" that does not exist. Even though we may know that a solution exists, it may be that the solution is not expressible in terms of the usual elementary functions— polynomial, trigonometric, exponential, logarithmic, and hyperbolic functions. Unfortunately this is the situation for most differential equations. However, before we can consider difficult problems it is first necessary to master some of the elementary theory of ordinary differential equations.

Linear and Nonlinear Equations. A second important classification of ordinary differential equations is according to whether they are linear or nonlinear. The differential equation

$$F(x, y, y', \ldots, y^{(n)}) = 0$$

is said to be *linear* if F is a linear function of the variables $y, y', \ldots, y^{(n)}$. Thus the general linear ordinary differential equation of order n is

$$a_0(x)y^{(n)} + a_1(x)y^{(n-1)} + \cdots + a_n(x)y = g(x). \tag{8}$$

Equations (2), (4), and (5) of the previous section are linear ordinary differential equations. An equation which is not of the form (8) is a *nonlinear* equation. For example, the angle θ that an oscillating pendulum of length l

makes with the vertical direction (see Figure 1.1) satisfies the nonlinear equation

$$\frac{d^2\theta}{dt^2} + \frac{g}{l} \sin \theta = 0. \tag{9}$$

FIGURE 1.1

The mathematical theory and the techniques for solving linear equations are highly developed. In contrast, for nonlinear equations the situation is not as satisfactory. General techniques for solving nonlinear equations are largely lacking, and the theory associated with such equations is also more complicated than the theory for linear equations. In view of this it is fortunate that many significant problems lead to linear ordinary differential equations or, at least, in the first approximation to linear equations. For example, for the pendulum problem, if the angle θ is small, then $\sin \theta \simeq \theta$ and Eq. (9) can be replaced by the linear equation

$$\frac{d^2\theta}{dt^2} + \frac{g}{l} \theta = 0.$$

On the other hand, there are important physical phenomena, such as the current flow in an electron tube, in which it is not possible to approximate the governing nonlinear differential equation by a linear one—the nonlinearity is crucial.

In an elementary text it is natural to emphasize the discussion of linear equations. The greater part of this book is therefore devoted to linear equations and to various methods for solving them. However, Chapters 8 and 9, as well as a large part of Chapter 2, are concerned with nonlinear equations. Throughout the text we attempt to show why nonlinear equations are, in general, more difficult, and why many of the techniques that are useful in solving linear equations cannot be applied to nonlinear equations.

1.2 HISTORICAL REMARKS

Without knowing something about differential equations and methods of solving them it is difficult to discuss the history and development of this important branch of mathematics. Further, the development of the theory of differential equations is intimately interwoven with the general development of mathematics and cannot be divorced from it. In these brief comments we will just mention a few, certainly not all, of the famous mathematicians of the seventeenth and eighteenth centuries who made important contributions in this area. We will follow closely the brief historical survey given by Ince* [Appendix A] in his authoritative treatise on ordinary differential equations, and the discussion by Cajori.

The theory of differential equations dates back to the beginnings of the calculus with Newton (1642–1727) and Leibniz (1646–1716) in the seventeenth century. Indeed Ince states,

> Yet our hazy knowledge of the birth and infancy of the science of differential equations condenses upon a remarkable date, the eleventh day of November, 1675, when Leibniz first set down on paper the equation
>
> $$\int y \, dy = \tfrac{1}{2}y^2,$$
>
> thereby not merely solving a simple differential equation, which was in itself a trivial matter, but what was an act of great moment, forging a powerful tool, the integral sign.

Following Newton and Leibniz come the names of the Bernoulli brothers Jakob (1654–1705) and Johann (1667–1748) and Johann's son Daniel (1700–1782). These are just three of eight members of the Bernoulli family who were prominent scientists and mathematicians in their time. With the aid of the calculus, they formulated as differential equations and solved a number of problems in mechanics, including that of the determination of the curve of most rapid descent for the motion of a particle under the influence of gravity. It was Daniel whose name is associated with the famous Bernoulli equation in fluid mechanics. In 1690 Jakob Bernoulli published the solution of the differential equation, written in differential form, $(b^2y^2 - a^3)^{\frac{1}{2}} \, dy = (a^3)^{\frac{1}{2}} \, dx$. Today this is a simple exercise but at that time to go from the equation $y' = [a^3/(b^2y^2 - a^3)]^{\frac{1}{2}}$ to the differential form, and then to assert that the integrals† of each side must be equal except for a constant was a major step. Indeed, for example, while Johann Bernoulli knew that $ax^p \, dx = d[ax^{p+1}/(p + 1)]$ was not meaningful for $p = -1$, he did not know that $dx/x = d(\ln x)$. Nevertheless he was able to show that the equation $dy/dx = y/ax$, which we could solve by writing it as

$$a\frac{dy}{y} = \frac{dx}{x},$$

has the solution $y^a/x = c$ where c is a constant of integration. See Section 2.4.

By the end of the seventeenth century most of the elementary methods of solving first order ordinary differential equations (Chapter 2) were known, and attention was centered on higher order ordinary differential equations and partial differential equations. Riccati (1676–1754), an Italian mathematician, considered equations of the form $f(y, y', y'') = 0$ (Section 3.1). He

---

* References are listed at the end of each chapter.
† Jakob Bernoulli appears to be the first person to have used the word integral.

also considered the nonlinear equation known as the Riccati equation, $dy/dx = a_0(x) + a_1(x)y + a_2(x)y^2$, though not in such a general form.

Euler,[*] one of the greatest mathematicians of all time, also lived during the eighteenth century. Of particular interest here is his work on the formulation of problems in mechanics in mathematical language, and his development of methods of solving these mathematical problems. Lagrange (1736–1813) said of Euler's work in mechanics, "The first great work in which analysis is applied to the science of movement." Euler also considered such questions as the possibility of reducing second order equations to first order equations by a suitable change of variables; he introduced the concept of an integrating factor (Section 2.6), and he gave a general treatment of linear ordinary differential equations with constant coefficients (Chapters 3 and 5) in 1739. Later in the eighteenth century the great French mathematicians Lagrange and Laplace made important contributions to the theory of ordinary differential equations and gave the first scientific treatment of partial differential equations. Indeed, possibly the most famous partial differential equation in mathematical physics, $u_{xx} + u_{yy} = 0$, where subscripts denote partial derivatives, is known as Laplace's equation. The student who is interested in the history of the theory of differential equations might wish to refer to one of the many books[†] dealing with the development of mathematics.

In more recent years part of the effort of mathematicians in the areas of ordinary and partial differential equations has been to develop a rigorous, systematic (but general) theory. The goal is not so much to construct solutions of particular differential equations, but rather to develop techniques suitable for treating classes of equations.

PROBLEMS

1. For each of the following differential equations determine its order and whether or not the equation is linear.

(a) $x^2 \dfrac{d^2y}{dx^2} + x \dfrac{dy}{dx} + 2y = \sin x$

(b) $(1 + y^2) \dfrac{d^2y}{dx^2} + x \dfrac{dy}{dx} + y = e^x$

(c) $\dfrac{d^4y}{dx^4} + \dfrac{d^3y}{dx^3} + \dfrac{d^2y}{dx^2} + \dfrac{dy}{dx} + y = 1$

(d) $\dfrac{dy}{dx} + xy^2 = 0$

(e) $\dfrac{d^2y}{dx^2} + \sin(x + y) = \sin x$

(f) $\dfrac{d^3y}{dx^3} + x \dfrac{dy}{dx} + (\cos^2 x)y = x^3$

---

[*] Euler (1707–1783) was a prolific mathematician. His collected works fill over sixty volumes. Even though blind during the last seventeen years of his life his work continued undiminished.

[†] The books by Ince and Cajori have already been mentioned. See also Bell and Struik.

2. Verify for each of the following that the given function or functions are solutions of the differential equation.

(a) $y'' - y = 0$; $y_1(x) = e^x, y_2(x) = \cosh x$

(b) $y'' + 2y' - 3y = 0$; $y_1(x) = e^{-3x}$, $y_2(x) = e^x$

(c) $y'''' + 4y''' + 3y = x$; $y_1(x) = x/3, y_2(x) = e^{-x} + x/3$

(d) $2x^2 y'' + 3xy' - y = 0, x > 0$; $y_1(x) = x^{1/2}, y_2(x) = x^{-1}$

(e) $x^2 y'' + 5xy' + 4y = 0, x > 0$; $y_1(x) = x^{-2}, y_2(x) = x^{-2} \ln x$

(f) $y'' + y = \sec x, 0 < x < \pi/2$; $y = \phi(x) = (\cos x) \ln \cos x + x \sin x$

(g) $y' - 2xy = 1$; $y = \phi(x) = e^{x^2} \int_0^x e^{-t^2} \, dt + e^{x^2}$

3. Determine for what values of r each of the following linear differential equations has solutions of the form $y = e^{rx}$.

(a) $y' + 2y = 0$ (b) $y'' - y = 0$

(c) $y'' + y' - 6y = 0$ (d) $y''' - 3y'' + 2y' = 0$

4. Determine for what values of r each of the following linear differential equations has solutions of the form $y = x^r$.

(a) $x^2 y'' + 4xy' + 2y = 0$, $x > 0$

(b) $x^2 y'' - 4xy' + 4y = 0$, $x > 0$

5. The *order* of a partial differential equation is defined as the order of the highest partial derivative that appears in the equation. Similarly the equation is said to be *linear* if the equation is linear in the dependent function and its derivatives. For each of the following equations determine the order and whether or not the equation is linear.

(a) $u_{xx} + u_{yy} + u_{zz} = 0$ (b) $\alpha^2 u_{xx} = u_t$

(c) $a^2 u_{xx} = u_{tt}$ (d) $u_{xx} + u_{yy} + uu_x + uu_y + u = 0$

(e) $u_{xxxx} + 2u_{xxyy} + u_{yyyy} = 0$ (f) $u_t + uu_x = 1 + u_{xx}$

6. Verify for each of the following differential equations that the given function or functions are solutions.

(a) $u_{xx} + u_{yy} = 0$; $u_1(x, y) = x^2 - y^2$, $u_2(x, y) = \cos x \cosh y$

(b) $\alpha^2 u_{xx} = u_t$; $u_1(x, t) = e^{-\alpha^2 t} \sin x$,

          $u_2(x, t) = e^{-\alpha^2 \lambda^2 t} \sin \lambda x$, λ a real constant

(c) $a^2 u_{xx} = u_{tt}$; $u_1(x, t) = \sin \lambda x \sin \lambda at$, λ a real constant,

          $u_2(x, t) = \sin (x - at)$

7. Verify for each of the following differential equations that the given function is a solution.

(a) $u_{xx} + u_{yy} + u_{zz} = 0$; $u = \phi(x, y, z) = (x^2 + y^2 + z^2)^{-\frac{1}{2}}$,

$$(x, y, z) \neq (0, 0, 0)$$

(b) $\alpha^2 u_{xx} = u_t$; $u = \phi(x, t) = (\pi/t)^{\frac{1}{2}} e^{-x^2/4\alpha^2 t}$, $t > 0$

(c) $a^2 u_{xx} = u_{tt}$; $u = f(x - at) + g(x + at)$, where f and g are twice differentiable functions

REFERENCES

Bell, E. T., *Men of Mathematics*, Simon and Schuster, New York, 1937.
Cajori, Florian, *A History of Mathematics*, 2nd ed., Macmillan, New York, 1919.
Ince, E. L., *Ordinary Differential Equations*, Longmans, Green, London, 1927.
Struik, D. J., *A Concise History of Mathematics*, Dover, New York, 1948.

First Order Differential Equations

2.1 LINEAR EQUATIONS

This chapter deals with differential equations of first order, that is, equations of the form

$$y' = f(x, y), \tag{1}$$

where f is a given function of two variables. Any function $y = \phi(x)$, which with its derivative y' identically satisfies Eq. (1), is called a solution, and our object is to try to determine whether such functions exist and, if so, how to find them. In order to gain some familiarity with differential equations and their solutions, we will first consider the linear first order equation

$$y' + p(x)y = g(x), \tag{2}$$

where p and g are given continuous functions on some interval $\alpha < x < \beta$. In this section we will be concerned with methods for solving Eq. (2). More theoretical questions involving the existence and uniqueness of solutions in general will be discussed in Section 2.2.

Let us begin with the equation

$$y' + ay = 0, \tag{3}$$

where a is a real constant. This equation can be solved by inspection. What function has a derivative which is a multiple of the original function? Clearly $y = e^{-ax}$ satisfies Eq. (3); furthermore

$$y = ce^{-ax}, \tag{4}$$

where c is an arbitrary constant, also does so. Since c is arbitrary, Eq. (4) represents infinitely many solutions of the differential equation (3). It is natural to ask whether Eq. (3) has any solutions other than those given by Eq. (4). We will show in the next section that there are no other solutions, but for the time being this question remains open.

Geometrically, Eq. (4) represents a one-parameter family of curves, called *integral curves* of Eq. (3). For $a = 1$ several members of this family

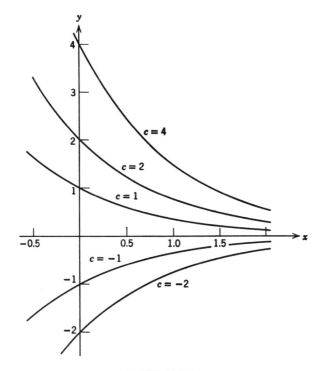

FIGURE 2.1

are sketched in Figure 2.1. Each integral curve is the geometric representation of the corresponding solution of the differential equation. Specifying a particular solution is equivalent to picking out a particular integral curve from the one-parameter family. It is usually convenient to do this by prescribing a point (x_0, y_0) through which the integral curve must pass; that is, we seek a solution $y = \phi(x)$ such that

$$\phi(x_0) = y_0.$$

Such a condition is called an *initial condition.* Since y stands for $\phi(x)$ we could also write

$$y = y_0 \quad \text{at} \quad x = x_0.$$

However, it is common practice to express the initial condition in the form

$$y(x_0) = y_0, \tag{5}$$

and this is the notation we will usually use in this book. A first order differential equation together with an initial condition form an *initial value problem.**

---

* This terminology is suggested by the fact that the independent variable often denotes time, the initial condition defines the situation at some fixed instant, and the solution of the initial value problem describes what happens later.

For example, the differential equation (3),

$$y' + ay = 0,$$

and the initial condition

$$y(0) = 2, \tag{6}$$

form an initial value problem. As noted above, all solutions of the differential equation (3) are given by Eq. (4). The particular solution satisfying the initial condition (6) is found by substituting $x = 0$ and $y = 2$ in Eq. (4). Then c equals 2 and the desired solution is the function

$$y = \phi(x) = 2e^{-ax}. \tag{7}$$

This is the unique solution of the given initial value problem. More generally, it is possible to show that the initial value problem composed of the differential equation (2) and the initial condition (5) will have a unique solution whenever the coefficients p and g are continuous functions. This is discussed in the next section.

In order to develop a systematic method for solving first order linear equations it is convenient first to work backward. Thus we rewrite the solution (4) of the differential equation (3) in the form

$$ye^{ax} = c. \tag{8}$$

On differentiating the left side of Eq. (8) we obtain

$$(ye^{ax})' = y'e^{ax} + aye^{ax} = e^{ax}(y' + ay), \tag{9}$$

and hence Eq. (8) implies that

$$e^{ax}(y' + ay) = 0. \tag{10}$$

Cancellation of the positive factor e^{ax} yields the differential equation (3). It is important to note that the solution of Eq. (3) can be constructed by reversing the above process, that is, we multiply Eq. (3) by e^{ax}, obtaining Eq. (10), from which Eq. (8) follows by using Eq. (9). Finally, solving Eq. (8) for y gives Eq. (4).

The same procedure can be used to solve the more general equation

$$y' + ay = g(x). \tag{11}$$

Multiplying by e^{ax} gives

$$e^{ax}(y' + ay) = e^{ax}g(x),$$

or, using Eq. (9),

$$(ye^{ax})' = e^{ax}g(x).$$

Hence

$$ye^{ax} = \int^x e^{at}g(t)\, dt + c,$$

where c is an arbitrary constant. Hence a solution of Eq. (11) is the function

$$y = \phi(x) = e^{-ax} \int^x e^{at} g(t) \, dt + c e^{-ax}. \tag{12}$$

In Eq. (12) and elsewhere in this book we use the notation $\int^x f(t) \, dt$ to denote an antiderivative of the function f, that is, $F(x) = \int^x f(t) \, dt$ designates some particular representative of the class of functions whose derivatives are equal to f. All members of this class are included in the expression $F(x) + c$, where c is arbitrary.

Thus, for a given function g the problem of determining a solution of Eq. (11) is reduced to that of evaluating the antiderivative in Eq. (12). The difficulty involved in this depends on g; nevertheless Eq. (12) gives an explicit formula for the solution $y = \phi(x)$. The constant c can be determined if an initial condition is prescribed.

Now let us turn to the general first order linear equation (2),

$$y' + p(x)y = g(x).$$

By analogy with the foregoing process we would like to choose a function μ so that if Eq. (2) is multiplied by $\mu(x)$, the left-hand side of Eq. (2) becomes the derivative* of $\mu(x)y$. That is, we want to choose μ, if possible, so that

$$\mu(x)[y' + p(x)y] = [\mu(x)y]'$$
$$= \mu(x)y' + \mu'(x)y.$$

Thus $\mu(x)$ must satisfy

$$p(x)y\mu(x) = y\mu'(x).$$

Assuming for the moment that $\mu(x) > 0$, we obtain†

$$\frac{\mu'(x)}{\mu(x)} = [\ln \mu(x)]' = p(x). \tag{13}$$

Hence

$$\ln \mu(x) = \int^x p(t) \, dt,$$

and finally

$$\mu(x) = \exp \left[\int^x p(t) \, dt \right]. \tag{14}$$

* A function μ having this property is called an integrating factor. Integrating factors are discussed more fully in Section 2.6.

† Recall that $\displaystyle \int^x \frac{dt}{t} = \ln |x|$.

Note that $\mu(x)$, as defined by Eq. (14), is indeed positive. Further, since $\int^x p(t)\,dt$ may denote any one of the antiderivatives of p, $\mu(x)$ is determined only up to an arbitrary multiplicative constant.

Returning to Eq. (2) and multiplying by $\mu(x)$ gives

$$[\mu(x)y]' = \mu(x)g(x).$$

Therefore

$$\mu(x)y = \int^x \mu(s)g(s)\,ds + c,$$

or

$$y = \frac{1}{\mu(x)}\left[\int^x \mu(s)g(s)\,ds + c\right], \tag{15}$$

where $\mu(x)$ is given by Eq. (14). Equation (15) provides an explicit formula for the solution of the general first order linear equation (2), where p and g are given continuous functions. Two integrations are required, one to obtain $\mu(x)$ from Eq. (14), and the other to determine y from Eq. (15). The arbitrary constant c can be used to satisfy an initial condition.

Example 1.   Find the solution of the initial value problem

$$y' - 2xy = x, \qquad y(0) = 1. \tag{16}$$

For this equation the function μ is given by

$$\mu(x) = \exp\left(-\int^x 2t\,dt\right) = e^{-x^2}.$$

Hence

$$e^{-x^2}(y' - 2xy) = xe^{-x^2},$$

so that

$$(ye^{-x^2})' = xe^{-x^2}.$$

Therefore

$$ye^{-x^2} = \int^x te^{-t^2}\,dt + c = -\tfrac{1}{2}e^{-x^2} + c,$$

and finally

$$y = -\tfrac{1}{2} + ce^{x^2}.$$

To satisfy the initial condition $y(0) = 1$ we must choose $c = \tfrac{3}{2}$. Hence

$$y = -\tfrac{1}{2} + \tfrac{3}{2}e^{x^2} \tag{17}$$

is the solution of the given initial value problem.

Example 2.   Find the solution of the initial value problem

$$y' - 2xy = 1, \qquad y(0) = 1. \tag{18}$$

As in the previous example $\mu(x)$ is e^{-x^2}, and we obtain

$$ye^{-x^2} = \int^x e^{-t^2} dt + c. \tag{19}$$

To evaluate c it is convenient to take the lower limit of integration* as the initial point $x = 0$. Then, multiplying Eq. (19) by e^{x^2} we obtain

$$y = e^{x^2} \int_0^x e^{-t^2} dt + ce^{x^2}.$$

The initial condition $y(0) = 1$ requires that $c = 1$ and hence

$$y = e^{x^2} \int_0^x e^{-t^2} dt + e^{x^2} \tag{20}$$

is the solution of the given problem.

Note that in the solution of Example 2 the integral of e^{-t^2} is not expressible as an elementary function. This illustrates the fact that it may be necessary to leave the solution of even a very simple problem in integral form. However, the function

$$\text{erf}(x) = \frac{2}{\sqrt{\pi}} \int_0^x e^{-t^2} dt, \tag{21}$$

known as the *error function*, has been extensively tabulated and can be regarded as a known function. From a computational point of view, therefore, Eq. (20) is a perfectly satisfactory expression for the solution of the initial value problem (18). It is just as satisfactory, in fact, as the solution $y = -\frac{1}{2} + \frac{3}{2}e^{x^2}$ of the initial value problem (16). In order to evaluate e^{x^2} for a given value of x we ordinarily consult a table, and it is no more difficult to look up erf (x) in a different table.

PROBLEMS

In each of Problems 1 through 4 solve the given differential equation.

1. $y' + 3y = x + e^{-2x}$ 2. $y' - 2y = x^2 e^{2x}$

3. $y' + y = xe^{-x} + 1$ 4. $y' + (1/x)y = 3 \cos 2x, \qquad x > 0$

---

* The choice of the lower limit of integration is actually immaterial since the difference between $\int_a^x e^{-t^2} dt$ and $\int_b^x e^{-t^2} dt$ is merely a constant, which can be added to c.

In each of Problems 5 through 8 find the solution of the given initial value problem.

5. $y' - y = 2xe^{2x}$, $y(0) = 1$ 6. $y' + 2y = xe^{-2x}$, $y(1) = 0$

7. $y' + y = \dfrac{1}{1 + x^2}$, $y(0) = 0$

8. $y' + \dfrac{2}{x} y = \dfrac{\cos x}{x^2}$, $y(\pi) = 0$, $x > 0$

9. Find the solution of

$$\frac{dy}{dx} = \frac{1}{e^y - x}.$$

Hint: Consider x as the dependent variable instead of y.

10. (a) Show that $\phi(x) = e^{2x}$ is a solution of

$$y' - 2y = 0,$$

and that $y = c\phi(x)$ is also a solution of this equation for any value of the constant c.

(b) Show that $\phi(x) = 1/x$ is a solution of

$$y' + y^2 = 0,$$

for $x > 0$, but that $y = c\phi(x)$ is not a solution of this equation. Note that the equation of part (b) is nonlinear while that of part (a) is linear.

11. Show that if $y = \phi(x)$ is a solution of

$$y' + p(x)y = 0,$$

then $y = c\phi(x)$ is also a solution for any value of the constant c.

12. Let $y = y_1(x)$ be a solution of

$$y' + p(x)y = 0, \tag{i}$$

and let $y = y_2(x)$ be a solution of

$$y' + p(x)y = g(x). \tag{ii}$$

Show that $y = y_1(x) + y_2(x)$ is also a solution of Eq. (ii).

*13. Consider the following method of solving the general linear equation of first order:

$$y' + p(x)y = g(x). \tag{i}$$

(a) If $g(x)$ is identically zero, show that the solution is

$$y = A \exp\left[-\int^x p(t)\, dt\right], \tag{ii}$$

where A is a constant.

(b) If $g(x)$ is not identically zero, assume that the solution is of the form

$$y = A(x) \exp\left[-\int^x p(t)\, dt\right]. \tag{iii}$$

By substituting for y in the given differential equation show that $A(x)$ must satisfy the condition

$$A'(x) = g(x) \exp\left[\int^x p(t)\, dt\right]. \tag{iv}$$

(c) Find $A(x)$ from Eq. (iv). Then substitute for $A(x)$ in Eq. (iii) and determine y. Verify that the solution obtained in this manner agrees with that of Eq. (15) in the text. This technique is known as the method of *variation of parameters;* it is discussed in detail in Section 3.6.2 in connection with second order linear equations.

*14. Use the method of Problem 13 to solve each of the following differential equations.

(a) $y' - 2y = x^2 e^{2x}$ (b) $y' + (1/x)y = 3 \cos 2x$, $x > 0$

2.2 FURTHER DISCUSSION OF LINEAR EQUATIONS

In Section 2.1 we showed how to construct solutions of first order linear differential equations. Now we turn to a study of certain more theoretical questions. We will first state a fundamental theorem giving conditions under which an initial value problem for a first order linear equation will always have one and only one solution. The rest of the section will be devoted to a consideration of some of the implications of this theorem.

Theorem 2.1. If the functions p and g are continuous on an open interval $\alpha < x < \beta$ containing the point $x = x_0$, then there exists a unique function $y = \phi(x)$ which satisfies the differential equation

$$y' + p(x)y = g(x) \tag{1}$$

for $\alpha < x < \beta$, and which also satisfies the initial condition

$$y(x_0) = y_0, \tag{2}$$

where y_0 is an arbitrary prescribed initial value.

The proof of this theorem is essentially contained in the discussion in the last section leading to the formula

$$y = \frac{1}{\mu(x)}\left[\int^x \mu(s)g(s)\, ds + c\right], \tag{3}$$

where

$$\mu(x) = \exp\int^x p(t)\, dt. \tag{4}$$

Assuming that Eq. (1) has a solution, the derivation in Section 2.1 shows that it must be of the form (3). Note that since p is continuous for $\alpha < x < \beta$, it follows that μ is defined in this interval, and is a nonzero differentiable function. This justifies the conversion of Eq. (1) into the form

$$[\mu(x)y]' = \mu(x)g(x). \tag{5}$$

The function μg has an antiderivative since μ and g are continuous, and Eq. (3) follows from Eq. (5). The initial assumption—that there is at least one solution of Eq. (1)—can now be verified by substituting the expression for y in Eq. (3) back into the differential equation. Finally, the initial condition (2) determines the constant c uniquely, thus completing the proof. Since Eq. (3) contains *all* solutions of Eq. (1), it is customary to call Eq. (3) the *general solution* of Eq. (1).

There are several aspects of the above theorem which should be noted. In the first place, it states that the given initial value problem *has* a solution and also that the problem has *only one* solution. In other words, the theorem asserts both the *existence* and *uniqueness* of the solution of the initial value problem (1) and (2). Further, the solution $y = \phi(x)$ is a differentiable function and, in fact, since $y' = -p(x)y + g(x)$, the derivative $y' = \phi'(x)$ is continuous. Finally, the solution satisfies the differential equation (1) throughout the interval $\alpha < x < \beta$ in which the coefficients p and g are continuous. This means that the solution will break down, if at all, only at points where either p or g is discontinuous. Thus a certain amount of qualitative information about the solution is obtained merely by identifying points of discontinuity of p and g.

As an example consider the initial value problem

$$xy' + 2y = 4x^2, \tag{6}$$

$$y(1) = 2. \tag{7}$$

Proceeding as in Section 2.1, we rewrite Eq. (6) as

$$y' + \frac{2}{x}y = 4x, \tag{8}$$

and seek a solution in an interval containing $x = 1$. Since the coefficients in Eq. (8) are continuous except at $x = 0$, it follows from Theorem 2.1 that the solution of the given initial value problem is valid at least in the interval $0 < x < \infty$. To find this solution we first compute $\mu(x)$:

$$\mu(x) = \exp\left(\int^x \frac{2}{t}\,dt\right) = e^{2\ln x}$$

$$= x^2. \tag{9}$$

Multiplying Eq. (8) by $\mu(x)$ gives

$$x^2y' + 2xy = 4x^3,$$

or

$$(x^2y)' = 4x^3.$$

Hence

$$y = x^2 + \frac{c}{x^2}, \tag{10}$$

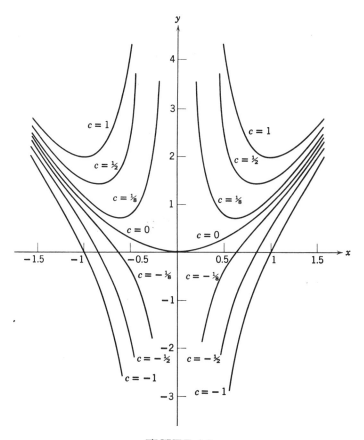

FIGURE 2.2

where c is arbitrary, is the general solution of Eq. (6). Integral curves of Eq. (6) for several values of c are sketched in Figure 2.2. In order to satisfy the initial condition (7) it is necessary that $c = 1$; thus

$$y = x^2 + \frac{1}{x^2} \tag{11}$$

is the solution of the initial value problem (6), (7).

Note that the solution (11) becomes unbounded as $x \to 0$. This is not surprising since $x = 0$ is a point of discontinuity of the coefficient of y in the differential equation (8). However, if the initial condition (7) is changed to

$$y(1) = 1, \tag{12}$$

then it follows from Eq. (10) that $c = 0$. Hence the solution of the initial value problem (6), (12) is

$$y = x^2, \tag{13}$$

which is perfectly well behaved as $x \to 0$. This illustrates that Theorem 2.1 does not assert that the solution of an initial value problem must become singular whenever the functions p and g become discontinuous; rather, it asserts that the solution cannot become singular at other points.

The possible behavior of solutions of initial value problems for first order linear equations in the neighborhood of points where p and g are discontinuous is more varied than the previous discussion suggests. The possibilities are explored to some extent in Problems 9 through 12; a more detailed treatment appears in Chapter 4 in connection with second order linear equations.

Sometimes, equations that are not linear can be solved by first making a substitution that converts the given equation into a linear equation. One type of equation for which this is possible is known as Bernoulli's equation; see Problems 15 and 16.

PROBLEMS

In each of Problems 1 through 4 find the general solution of the given differential equation.

1. $y' + (1/x)y = \sin x, \qquad x > 0$
2. $x^2 y' + 3xy = (\sin x)/x, \qquad x < 0$
3. $y' + (\tan x)y = x \sin 2x, \qquad -\pi/2 < x < \pi/2$
4. $xy' + 2y = e^x, \qquad x > 0$

In each of Problems 5 through 8 find the solution of the given initial value problem. State the interval in which the solution is valid.

5. $xy' + 2y = x^2 - x + 1, \qquad y(1) = \frac{1}{2}$
6. $xy' + y = e^x, \qquad y(1) = 1$
7. $y' + (\cot x)y = 2 \csc x, \qquad y(\pi/2) = 1$
8. $xy' + 2y = \sin x, \qquad y(\pi) = 1/\pi$

Each of the equations in Problems 9 through 12 has at least one discontinuous coefficient at $x = 0$. Solve each equation for $x > 0$ and describe the behavior of the solution as $x \to 0$ for various values of the constant of integration. Sketch several members of the family of integral curves.

9. $y' + (2/x)y = 1/x^2$ 10. $y' - (1/x)y = x$

11. $y' - (1/x)y = x^{1/2}$ 12. $y' + (1/x)y = (\cos x)/x$

13. Solve the initial value problem

$$y' + 2y = g(x), \qquad y(0) = 0$$

where

$$g(x) = \begin{cases} 1, & 0 \le x \le 1, \\ 0, & x > 1. \end{cases}$$

Hint: Solve the differential equation separately for $0 < x < 1$ and for $x > 1$. Then match the solutions so that y is continuous at $x = 1$. Note that it is impossible to make both y and y' continuous at $x = 1$.

14. Consider the equation

$$y' + ay = be^{-\lambda x}$$

where a and λ are positive constants, and b is any real number. Determine the behavior of y as $x \to \infty$.

*15. Consider the equation

$$y' + p(x)y = q(x)y^n,$$

where n is a constant but not necessarily an integer and p and q are given functions; this equation is known as Bernoulli's equation, after Jakob Bernoulli (1654–1705).

(a) Solve Bernoulli's equation when $n = 0, 1$.

(b) Show that, if $n \neq 0, 1$, the substitution $v = y^{1-n}$ reduces Bernoulli's equation to a linear equation. This method of solution was found by Leibniz (1646–1716) in 1696.

*16. Find the general solution of

$$x^2 y' + 2xy - y^3 = 0.$$

Hint: See Problem 15.

2.3 NONLINEAR EQUATIONS

We now turn to a study of differential equations of the form

$$y' = f(x, y), \tag{1}$$

subject to an initial condition

$$y(x_0) = y_0. \tag{2}$$

The differential equation (1) and the initial condition (2) together constitute an initial value problem. The basic questions to be considered are whether there exists a solution of this initial value problem, whether such a solution is unique, over what interval a solution is defined, and how to construct a useful formula for the solution. All of these questions were answered with relative ease in Sections 2.1 and 2.2 for the case in which Eq. (1) is linear. However, if f is not a linear function of the dependent variable y, then our earlier treatment no longer applies. In this section we will discuss in a general way some features of nonlinear initial value problems. In particular, we will note several important differences between the nonlinear problem (1), (2) and the linear problem consisting of the differential equation

$$y' + p(x)y = g(x) \tag{3}$$

and the initial condition (2).

The reason why first order linear differential equations are relatively simple is that there is a formula giving the solution of such an equation in all cases. In contrast, there is no corresponding general method for solving first order nonlinear equations. In fact, the analytic determination of the solution $y = \phi(x)$ of a nonlinear equation is usually very difficult, and often impossible.

The lack of a general formula for the solution of a nonlinear equation has at least two important consequences. In the first place, methods which yield approximate, perhaps numerical, solutions and qualitative information about solutions assume greater significance for nonlinear equations than for linear ones. Chapters 8 and 9 contain an introduction to some of these methods. Secondly, questions dealing with the existence and uniqueness of solutions must now be dealt with by indirect methods, since a direct construction of the solution cannot be carried out in general.

Existence and Uniqueness. The following fundamental existence and uniqueness theorem is analogous to Theorem 2.1 for linear equations. However, its proof is a great deal more complicated, and is postponed until Section 2.11.

Theorem 2.2. *Let the functions f and $\partial f / \partial y$ be continuous in some rectangle $\alpha < x < \beta, \gamma < y < \delta$ containing the point (x_0, y_0). Then, in some interval $x_0 - h < x < x_0 + h$ contained in $\alpha < x < \beta$, there is a unique solution $y = \phi(x)$ of the differential equation (1)*

$$y' = f(x, y)$$

which also satisfies the initial condition (2)

$$y(x_0) = y_0.$$

The conditions stated in Theorem 2.2 are sufficient to guarantee the existence of a unique solution of the initial value problem (1), (2). However, even if f does not satisfy the hypotheses of the theorem, it is still possible that a unique solution may exist. Indeed, the conclusion of the theorem remains true if the hypothesis about the continuity of $\partial f / \partial y$ is replaced by certain weaker conditions. Further, the existence of a solution (but not its uniqueness) can be established on the basis of the continuity of f alone, without any additional hypotheses at all. The present form of the theorem, however, is satisfactory for most purposes.

It can be shown by means of examples that some conditions on f are essential in order to obtain the result stated in the theorem. For instance, the following example shows that the initial value problem (1), (2) may have more than one solution if the hypotheses of Theorem 2.2 are violated.

Example 1. Find the solution of

$$y' = y^{1/3}, \qquad y(0) = 0 \tag{4}$$

for $x \geq 0$.

This problem is easily solved by the method of Section 2.4. For the present we can verify that the function

$$y = \phi(x) = (\tfrac{2}{3}x)^{3/2}, \quad x \geq 0$$

satisfies both of Eqs. (4). On the other hand, the function

$$y = \psi(x) = 0$$

is also a solution of the given initial value problem. Hence this problem does not have a unique solution. This fact does not contradict the existence and uniqueness theorem since

$$\frac{\partial}{\partial y} f(x, y) = \frac{\partial}{\partial y} (y^{1/3}) = \tfrac{1}{3} y^{-2/3},$$

and this function is not continuous, or even defined, at any point where $y = 0$. Hence the theorem does not apply in any region containing any part of the x axis. If (x_0, y_0) is any point not on the x axis, however, then there is a unique solution of Eqs. (4) passing through (x_0, y_0).

Interval of Definition.   For the linear problem (2), (3) the solution exists throughout any interval about $x = x_0$ in which the functions p and g are continuous. On the other hand, for the nonlinear initial value problem (1), (2) the interval in which a solution exists may be difficult to determine. The solution $y = \phi(x)$ exists as long as the point $[x, \phi(x)]$ remains within the region in which the hypotheses of the theorem are satisfied; however, since $\phi(x)$ is usually not known, it may be impossible to locate the point $[x, \phi(x)]$ with respect to this region. In any case, the interval in which a solution exists may have no simple relationship to the function f in Eq. (1). This is illustrated by the following example.

Example 2.   Consider the initial value problem

$$y' = y^2, \qquad y(0) = 1. \tag{5}$$

It can be readily verified by direct substitution that

$$y = \frac{1}{1 - x} \tag{6}$$

is the solution of this initial value problem. Clearly the solution becomes unbounded as $x \to 1$, and therefore it is valid only for $-\infty < x < 1$. There is no indication from the differential equation itself, however, that the point $x = 1$ is in any way remarkable. Moreover, if the initial condition is replaced by

$$y(0) = 2, \tag{7}$$

it is again easy to verify that the solution of the differential equation (5) satisfying the initial condition (7) is

$$y = \frac{2}{1 - 2x},$$ (8)

and that the solution now becomes unbounded as $x \to \frac{1}{2}$. This illustrates another disturbing feature of initial value problems for nonlinear equations, namely, the singularities of the solution may move about depending on the initial condition.

General Solution.   Another way in which linear and nonlinear equations differ is in connection with the concept of a general solution. For a first order linear equation it is possible to obtain a solution containing one arbitrary constant, from which all possible solutions follow by specifying values for this constant. For nonlinear equations this may not be the case; even though a solution containing an arbitrary constant may be found, there may be other solutions that cannot be obtained by giving values to this constant. A specific example is given in Problem 6. Thus we will use the term "general solution" only when discussing linear equations.

Implicit Solutions.   We recall again that for a first order linear equation there is an explicit formula [Eq. (15) of Section 2.1] for the solution $y = \phi(x)$. As long as the necessary antiderivatives can be determined, the value of the solution at any point can be found merely by substituting the appropriate value of x into the formula. For a nonlinear equation it is rarely possible to find such an explicit solution. Often the best that we can do is to eliminate the derivative that appears in Eq. (1), thereby obtaining in place of the differential equation a derivative-free equation of the form

$$\psi[x, \phi(x)] = 0$$ (9)

which is satisfied by some, perhaps all, solutions $y = \phi(x)$ of Eq. (1). Even this cannot be accomplished in most cases for nonlinear equations. However, if a relation such as Eq. (9) can be found, it is customary to say that we have an *implicit formula* for the solutions of Eq. (1). An equation of the form (9) is also called an *integral* (or first integral) of Eq. (1).

For example, consider the simple nonlinear equation

$$y' = -\frac{x}{y}.$$ (10)

Using the methods of the next section it is not hard to show that all solutions of Eq. (10) also satisfy the algebraic equation

$$x^2 + y^2 = c^2,$$ (11)

where c is an arbitrary constant. To verify this statement we can differentiate Eq. (11) with respect to x, thereby obtaining $2x + 2yy' = 0$, or $y' = -x/y$, which is Eq. (10). Equation (11) therefore is an implicit formula for solutions of Eq. (10). For $x^2 \leq c^2$, there are many functions $y = \phi(x)$ that satisfy Eq. (11). Some of these are:

$$y = \phi_1(x) = \sqrt{c^2 - x^2}, \qquad -c \leq x \leq c \qquad (12)$$

$$y = \phi_2(x) = -\sqrt{c^2 - x^2}, \qquad -c \leq x \leq c \qquad (13)$$

$$y = \phi_3(x) = \begin{cases} \sqrt{c^2 - x^2}, & -c \leq x \leq 0 \\ -\sqrt{c^2 - x^2}, & 0 < x \leq c \end{cases} \qquad (14)$$

$$y = \phi_4(x) = \begin{cases} -\sqrt{c^2 - x^2}, & -c \leq x \leq -c/2 \\ \sqrt{c^2 - x^2}, & -c/2 < x < c/2 \\ -\sqrt{c^2 - x^2}, & c/2 \leq x \leq c. \end{cases} \qquad (15)$$

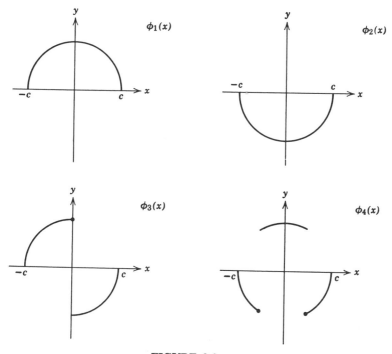

FIGURE 2.3

See Figure 2.3 for graphs of the functions given by Eqs. (12) to (15). However, only two of these functions satisfy the differential equation (10) over the entire interval $-c < x < c$, namely those given by Eqs. (12) and (13). If an initial condition is also given, then we want to select whichever of the functions ϕ_1 and ϕ_2 satisfies the specified condition, and also select the proper value of c. For example, if the initial condition is

$$y(0) = 3, \tag{16}$$

then we must discard ϕ_2, and keep ϕ_1 with c chosen to be 3. Hence

$$y = \sqrt{9 - x^2}, \qquad -3 < x < 3 \tag{17}$$

is a solution of the initial value problem (10) and (16). According to Theorem 2.2 there is no other solution of this problem on the interval $-3 < x < 3$.

In the foregoing example the explicit solutions given by Eqs. (12) and (13) were easily obtainable because the implicit relation (11) was quadratic in y. However, a little imagination will suggest that an implicit relation (9), assuming it can be found, will often be much more complicated than Eq. (11). If so, it will probably be impossible to solve it (analytically) for y; it may be quite difficult even to determine the intervals in which solutions exist. Furthermore, it must be kept in mind that there may be solutions of the implicit relation (9) which do not satisfy the differential equation; also, in some cases the differential equation may have other solutions that do not satisfy the implicit relation.

Graphical Construction of Integral Curves.   Since there is no way, in general, to obtain exact analytic solutions of nonlinear differential equations, methods that yield approximate solutions or other qualitative information about solutions may be of great importance. One such method involves the graphical approximation of integral curves. At each point in the xy plane where $f(x, y)$ is defined, the differential equation (1)

$$y' = f(x, y)$$

provides a value for y', which can be thought of as the slope of a line segment through that point. The totality of all such line segments form the *direction field* for the given differential equation. The integral curves are curves which, at every point, are tangent to the element of the direction field associated with that point.

The general shape of the integral curves can sometimes be visualized by drawing the elements of the direction field at a sufficiently large number of points. For example, consider

$$y' = 4y(1 - y), \tag{18}$$

a simple but important type of nonlinear equation. The construction of the direction field is greatly simplified by noting that the right-hand side of Eq. (18) is independent of x. Therefore, the elements of the direction field at all points on any line parallel to the x axis are themselves parallel. Further, two special solutions of Eq. (18) can be found by inspection, namely the constant solutions $y = \phi_1(x) = 0$ and $y = \phi_2(x) = 1$. These special solutions separate the xy plane into three zones, in each of which y' is of one sign. In fact,

$$\text{for} \qquad\quad y < 0, \qquad y' < 0;$$
$$\text{for} \qquad 0 < y < 1, \qquad y' > 0;$$
$$\text{for} \qquad\quad y > 1, \qquad y' < 0.$$

Using this information it is relatively simple to construct Figure 2.4, which depicts the direction field for Eq. (18).

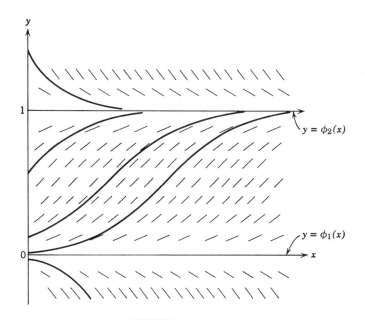

FIGURE 2.4

From this sketch certain qualitative properties of solutions can be easily deduced. In the first place, consider the solution corresponding to the initial condition $y(x_0) = y_0$ with $0 < y_0 < 1$. Such a solution tends to increase since $y' > 0$ in the vicinity of the initial point. However, this solution cannot increase beyond $y = 1$ because, if it reached $y = 1$, its slope would have become (and would remain) zero. In fact, the given solution cannot reach $y = 1$ for any finite value of x; if it did, then from that point as the initial point there would emanate two solutions [the solution in question and the solution $y = \phi_2(x)$] in contradiction to Theorem 2.2. Thus a solution starting in the interval $0 < y < 1$ approaches $y = 1$ as $x \to \infty$. Similarly, a solution starting above $y = 1$ must decrease and approach $y = 1$ from above as $x \to \infty$. Finally, a solution that is originally negative tends to decrease further.

It happens that Eq. (18) can be solved by the method of Section 2.4, and a few solutions are plotted in Figure 2.4. However, we emphasize that the qualitative behavior of the solutions of Eq. (18) was determined without solving the equation. The ideas touched on here are related to the concepts of stability and instability of solutions of differential equations, and are elaborated upon in Chapter 9.

PROBLEMS

1. For each of the following differential equations state the region in the xy plane where the existence of a unique solution through any specified point is guaranteed by the fundamental existence and uniqueness theorem.

(a) $y' = \dfrac{x - y}{2x + 5y}$

(b) $y' = (1 - x^2 - y^2)^{\frac{1}{2}}$

(c) $y' = \dfrac{2xy}{1 + y^2}$

(d) $y' = 3(x + y)^{-2}$

(e) $y' = \dfrac{\ln |xy|}{1 - x^2 + y^2}$

(f) $y' = (x^2 + y^2)^{\frac{3}{2}}$

2. Show that $y = \phi(x) = (1 - x^2)^{-1}$ is a solution of the initial value problem

$$y' = 2xy^2, \qquad y(0) = 1.$$

In what interval is this solution valid?

3. Show that $y = \phi(x) = [2(x + c)]^{-\frac{1}{2}}$, where c is an arbitrary constant, satisfies the differential equation

$$y' + y^3 = 0.$$

Find the solution which satisfies the initial condition $y(1) = 2$. Where is this solution valid?

4. Verify that

$$y = \phi(x) = [1 + \tfrac{2}{3} \ln (1 + x^3)]^{\frac{1}{2}}$$

is a solution of the initial value problem

$$y' = \dfrac{x^2}{y(1 + x^3)}, \qquad y(0) = 1.$$

For what interval is this solution valid?

5. Verify that

$$y = (c^2 - 4x^2)^{\frac{1}{2}}, \qquad y = -(c^2 - 4x^2)^{\frac{1}{2}}$$

are solutions of the differential equation

$$y' = -4x/y.$$

For what parts of the xy plane are these solutions valid? Find the particular solution passing through the point $(0, 4)$; through the point $(1, -1)$.

6. (a) Verify that both $y_1(x) = 1 - x$ and $y_2(x) = -x^2/4$ are solutions of the initial value problem

$$y' = \frac{-x + (x^2 + 4y)^{1/2}}{2}, \qquad y(2) = -1.$$

Where are these solutions valid?

(b) Explain why the existence of two solutions of the given problem does not contradict the uniqueness part of Theorem 2.2.

(c) Show that $y = cx + c^2$, where c is an arbitrary constant, satisfies the differential equation in part (a). If $c = -1$, the initial condition is also satisfied, and the solution $y = y_1(x)$ is obtained. Show that there is no choice of c which gives the second solution $y = y_2(x)$.

7. For each of the following differential equations, construct the direction field sufficiently well to be able to visualize the general behavior of the family of integral curves.

(a) $y' = x^2 + y^2$ (b) $y' = x^2 - xy + y^2 - 1$

(c) $y' = \dfrac{xy}{1 + x^2}$ (d) $y' = \dfrac{2x - 3y}{x + y}$

In each of Problems 8 through 11:

(a) Sketch the direction field.

(b) Sketch several members of the family of integral curves without solving the differential equation.

(c) Solve the given initial value problem.

(d) Sketch the solution obtained in (c) and compare with those obtained in (b).

8. $y' = -1, \qquad y(1) = 2$ 9. $y' = x + 1, \qquad y(0) = 1$

10. $y' + xy = 1, \qquad y(1) = 0$ 11. $y' - y = 1 - e^x, \qquad y(0) = 0$

12. For each of the following differential equations determine the general pattern of the integral curves by a consideration of the direction field. Let $y = \phi(x; y_0)$ be the solution corresponding to the initial condition $y(0) = y_0$. For what values of y_0 does $\lim_{x \to \infty} \phi(x; y_0)$ exist? Evaluate this limit in those cases.

(a) $y' = (1 - y)(2 - y)$

(b) $y' = y(1 - y^2)$

(c) $y' = -y(1 + y^2)$

(d) $y' = \epsilon y - \sigma y^2; \qquad \sigma > 0$ and $\epsilon > 0$

2.4 SEPARABLE EQUATIONS

It is often convenient to write the equation

$$\frac{dy}{dx} = f(x, y) \tag{1}$$

in the form

$$M(x, y) + N(x, y)\frac{dy}{dx} = 0. \tag{2}$$

It is always possible to do this by setting $M(x, y)$ equal to $-f(x, y)$ and $N(x, y)$ equal to 1, but there may be other ways as well. In the event that M is a function of x only and N is a function of y only, then Eq. (2) takes the form

$$M(x) + N(y)\frac{dy}{dx} = 0. \tag{3}$$

For example, the equation

$$\frac{dy}{dx} = \frac{x^2}{1 + y^2}$$

can be written as

$$-x^2 + (1 + y^2)\frac{dy}{dx} = 0.$$

A differential equation which can be put in the form (3) is said to be *separable*; the reason for this name is clear if Eq. (3) is written in the differential form

$$M(x)\, dx = -N(y)\, dy. \tag{4}$$

Now suppose that H_1 and H_2 are any functions such that

$$H_1'(x) = M(x), \qquad H_2'(y) = N(y); \tag{5}$$

then Eq. (3) becomes

$$H_1'(x) + H_2'(y)\frac{dy}{dx} = 0. \tag{6}$$

If $y = \phi(x)$ is a differentiable function of x, then according to the chain rule

$$H_2'(y)\frac{dy}{dx} = \frac{d}{dx}H_2[\phi(x)]. \tag{7}$$

Consequently, if $y = \phi(x)$ is a solution of the differential equation (3), then Eq. (6) becomes

$$H_1'(x) + \frac{d}{dx}H_2[\phi(x)] = 0,$$

or

$$\frac{d}{dx}\{H_1(x) + H_2[\phi(x)]\} = 0. \tag{8}$$

Integrating Eq. (8) gives

$$H_1(x) + H_2[\phi(x)] = c, \tag{9}$$

or

$$H_1(x) + H_2(y) = c, \tag{10}$$

where c is an arbitrary constant. Thus the solution $y = \phi(x)$ of the differential equation (3) has been obtained in implicit form. The functions H_1 and H_2 are any functions satisfying Eq. (5), that is, any antiderivatives of M and N, respectively. In practice the solution (10) is generally obtained from

Eq. (4) by integrating the left side with respect to x and the right side with respect to y; the justification for this is the argument just given.

If, in addition to the differential equation, an initial condition

$$y(x_0) = y_0 \tag{11}$$

is prescribed, the particular solution of Eq. (3) satisfying this condition is obtained by setting x equal to x_0 and y equal to y_0 in Eq. (10). This gives

$$c = H_1(x_0) + H_2(y_0). \tag{12}$$

Substituting this value for c in Eq. (10), and noting that

$$H_1(x) - H_1(x_0) = \int_{x_0}^x M(t)\, dt, \qquad H_2(y) - H_2(y_0) = \int_{y_0}^y N(t)\, dt,$$

we obtain

$$\int_{x_0}^x M(t)\, dt + \int_{y_0}^y N(t)\, dt = 0. \tag{13}$$

Equation (13) is an implicit representation of the solution of the differential equation (3) which also satisfies the initial condition (11). The reader should bear in mind that the determination of the solution in explicit form, or even the determination of the precise interval in which the solution exists, generally requires that Eq. (13) be solved for y as a function of x. This may present formidable difficulties.

Example.   Solve the initial value problem

$$\frac{dy}{dx} = \frac{3x^2 + 4x + 2}{2(y - 1)}, \qquad y(0) = -1. \tag{14}$$

The differential equation can be written as

$$2(y - 1)\, dy = (3x^2 + 4x + 2)\, dx.$$

Integrating the left-hand side with respect to y and the right-hand side with respect to x gives

$$y^2 - 2y = x^3 + 2x^2 + 2x + c, \tag{15}$$

where c is an arbitrary constant. To determine the particular solution satisfying the prescribed initial condition we substitute $x = 0$ and $y = -1$ into Eq. (15), obtaining $c = 3$. Hence the desired particular solution is given implicitly by

$$y^2 - 2y = x^3 + 2x^2 + 2x + 3. \tag{16}$$

To obtain the solution explicitly, we must solve Eq. (16) for y in terms of x. This is a simple matter in this case since Eq. (16) is quadratic in y, and we obtain

$$y = 1 \pm \sqrt{x^3 + 2x^2 + 2x + 4}. \tag{17}$$

Thus Eq. (17) gives two solutions of the differential equation, only one of which, however, satisfies the given initial condition. This is the solution corresponding to the minus sign in Eq. (17), so that we finally obtain

$$y = \phi(x) = 1 - \sqrt{x^3 + 2x^2 + 2x + 4} \qquad (18)$$

as the solution of the initial value problem (14). Note that if the plus sign is chosen by mistake in Eq. (17), then we will obtain the solution of the same differential equation that satisfies the initial condition $y(0) = 3$. Finally, in order to determine the interval in which the solution (18) is valid, we must find the interval in which the quantity under the radical is nonnegative. By plotting this expression as a function of x, the reader can show that the desired interval is $x > -2$.

In this example it was not difficult to solve explicitly for y as a function of x and to determine the exact interval in which the solution exists. However, this situation is exceptional and often it will be necessary to leave the solution in implicit form. Thus, in the problems below and in those following Sections 2.5 through 2.8, the terminology "Solve the following differential equation" means to find the solution explicitly if it is convenient to do so, but otherwise to find an implicit relation for the solution.

PROBLEMS

Solve each of the equations in Problems 1 through 8. State the regions of the xy plane in which the conditions of the fundamental existence and uniqueness theorem are satisfied.

1. $\dfrac{dy}{dx} = \dfrac{x^2}{y}$

2. $\dfrac{dy}{dx} = \dfrac{x^2}{y(1 + x^3)}$

3. $\dfrac{dy}{dx} + y^2 \sin x = 0$

4. $\dfrac{dy}{dx} = 1 + x + y^2 + xy^2$

5. $\dfrac{dy}{dx} = (\cos^2 x)(\cos^2 2y)$

6. $x\dfrac{dy}{dx} = (1 - y^2)^{1/2}$

7. $\dfrac{dy}{dx} = \dfrac{x - e^{-x}}{y + e^y}$

8. $\dfrac{dy}{dx} = \dfrac{x^2}{1 + y^2}$

For each of Problems 9 through 14 find the solution of the given initial value problem in explicit form, and determine (at least approximately) the interval in which it is defined.

9. $\sin 2x \, dx + \cos 3y \, dy = 0,$ $y(\pi/2) = \pi/3$

10. $x \, dx + ye^{-x} \, dy = 0,$ $y(0) = 1$

11. $\dfrac{dr}{d\theta} = r,$ $r(0) = 2$

12. $\dfrac{dy}{dx} = \dfrac{2x}{y + x^2 y}$, $y(0) = -2$

13. $\dfrac{dy}{dx} = xy^3(1 + x^2)^{-\frac{1}{2}}$, $y(0) = 1$

14. $\dfrac{dy}{dx} = \dfrac{2x}{1 + 2y}$, $y(2) = 0$

15. Solve the equation

$$y^2(1 - x^2)^{\frac{1}{2}} \, dy = \sin^{-1} x \, dx$$

in the interval $-1 < x < 1$.

16. Solve the equation

$$\frac{dy}{dx} = \frac{ax + b}{cx + d},$$

where a, b, c, and d are constants.

17. Solve the equation

$$\frac{dy}{dx} = \frac{ay + b}{cy + d},$$

where a, b, c, and d are constants.

*18. Show that the equation

$$\frac{dy}{dx} = \frac{y - 4x}{x - y}$$

is not separable, but that if the variable y is replaced by a new variable v defined by $v = y/x$, then the equation is separable in x and v. Find the solution of the given equation by this technique.

*19. (a) Solve the initial value problem $y' = \epsilon y$, $y(0) = y_0$, where ϵ is a positive constant. Show that the solution $y = \phi(x)$ has the following limiting behavior as $x \to \infty$:

$$\text{if } y_0 > 0, \qquad \lim_{x \to \infty} \phi(x) = \infty;$$

$$\text{if } y_0 = 0, \qquad \lim_{x \to \infty} \phi(x) = 0;$$

$$\text{if } y_0 < 0, \qquad \lim_{x \to \infty} \phi(x) = -\infty.$$

(b) Now suppose that the differential equation is changed by the addition of the term $-\sigma y^2$ where σ is a (small) positive number. Solve the initial value problem

$$y' = \epsilon y - \sigma y^2, \qquad y(0) = y_0.$$

Show that $y = \phi(x)$ now has the following behavior as $x \to \infty$:

$$\text{if } y_0 > 0, \qquad \lim_{x \to \infty} \phi(x) = \frac{\epsilon}{\sigma};$$

$$\text{if } y_0 = 0, \qquad \lim_{x \to \infty} \phi(x) = 0.$$

Show that if $y_0 < 0$ then $\phi(x)$ becomes unbounded as x approaches a certain finite value depending on y_0. The nonlinear equation in part (b) is important in many applications; see Sections 2.9 and 9.1. Also see Problem 12(d) of Section 2.3.

2.5 EXACT EQUATIONS

Let us first consider the equation

$$\psi(x, y) = c \tag{1}$$

where c is a constant. Assuming that Eq. (1) defines y implicitly as a differentiable function of x, we can differentiate Eq. (1) with respect to x and obtain*

$$\psi_x(x, y) + \psi_y(x, y)y' = 0. \tag{2}$$

Equation (2) is the differential equation whose solution is defined by Eq. (1).
Conversely, suppose that the differential equation

$$M(x, y) + N(x, y)y' = 0 \tag{3}$$

is given. If there exists a function ψ such that

$$\psi_x(x, y) = M(x, y), \qquad \psi_y(x, y) = N(x, y), \tag{4}$$

and such that $\psi(x, y) = c$ defines $y = \phi(x)$ implicitly as a differentiable function of x, then

$$M(x, y) + N(x, y)y' = \psi_x(x, y) + \psi_y(x, y)y'$$
$$= \frac{d}{dx}\{\psi[x, \phi(x)]\}. \tag{5}$$

As a result Eq. (3) becomes

$$\frac{d}{dx}\{\psi[x, \phi(x)]\} = 0. \tag{6}$$

In this case Eq. (3) is said to be an *exact differential equation*. The solution of Eq. (3), or the equivalent Eq. (6), is given implicitly by Eq. (1),

$$\psi(x, y) = c,$$

where c is an arbitrary constant. In practice the differential equation (3) is often written in the symmetric differential form

$$M(x, y)\, dx + N(x, y)\, dy = 0. \tag{7}$$

Example 1. Solve the differential equation

$$2xy^3 + 3x^2y^2\frac{dy}{dx} = 0.$$

By inspection it can be seen that the left-hand side is the derivative of x^2y^3.

* Subscripts denote partial derivatives with respect to the variable indicated by the subscript.

Thus the given equation can be rewritten as

$$\frac{d}{dx}(x^2y^3) = 0$$

and the solution is given implicitly by

$$x^2y^3 = c.$$

In this simple example it was easy to see that the differential equation was exact and, in fact, easy to find its solution, by recognizing that the left-hand side was the derivative of x^2y^3. For more complicated equations it may not be possible to do this. A systematic procedure for determining whether a given differential equation is exact is provided by the following theorem.

Theorem 2.3.   *Let the functions M, N, M_y, and N_x be continuous in the rectangular* region R: $\alpha < x < \beta, \gamma < y < \delta$. Then Eq. (3),*

$$M(x, y) + N(x, y)y' = 0,$$

is an exact differential equation in R if and only if

$$M_y(x, y) = N_x(x, y) \tag{8}$$

at each point of R. That is, there exists a function ψ satisfying Eqs. (4),

$$\psi_x(x, y) = M(x, y), \qquad \psi_y(x, y) = N(x, y),$$

if and only if M and N satisfy Eq. (8).

The proof of this theorem is in two parts. First we will show that if there is a function ψ such that Eq. (4) is true, then it follows that Eq. (8) is satisfied. Computing M_y and N_x from Eq. (4) yields

$$M_y(x, y) = \psi_{xy}(x, y), \qquad N_x(x, y) = \psi_{yx}(x, y). \tag{9}$$

The continuity of ψ_{xy} and ψ_{yx} guarantees their equality,† and Eq. (8) follows.

We will now show that if M and N satisfy Eq. (8), then Eq. (3) is exact. The proof involves the construction of a function ψ satisfying Eqs. (4),

$$\psi_x(x, y) = M(x, y), \qquad \psi_y(x, y) = N(x, y).$$

Integrating the first of Eqs. (4) with respect to x, holding y constant, gives

$$\psi(x, y) = \int^x M(t, y)\, dt + h(y). \tag{10}$$

---

* It is not essential that the region R be rectangular, but only that it be simply connected; see Problem 16 for a discussion of the meaning of this term.
† The hypothesis of continuity is required, since otherwise ψ_{xy} and ψ_{yx} are not always equal. The exceptions are rather peculiar functions, however, and are seldom encountered.

The function h is an arbitrary function of y, playing the role of the arbitrary constant. Now we must show that it is always possible to choose $h(y)$ so that $\psi_y = N$. From Eq. (10)

$$\psi_y(x, y) = \frac{\partial}{\partial y} \int^x M(t, y)\, dt + h'(y)$$

$$= \int^x M_y(t, y)\, dt + h'(y).$$

Setting $\psi_y = N$ and solving for $h'(y)$ gives

$$h'(y) = N(x, y) - \int^x M_y(t, y)\, dt. \tag{11}$$

In order to determine $h(y)$ from Eq. (11) it is essential that, despite its appearance, the right side of Eq. (11) be a function of y only. To establish this fact we can differentiate the quantity in question with respect to x, obtaining

$$N_x(x, y) - M_y(x, y),$$

which vanishes on account of Eq. (8). Hence, despite its apparent form, the right side of Eq. (11) does not in fact depend on x, and a single integration then gives $h(y)$. Substituting for $h(y)$ in Eq. (10), we obtain as the solution of Eqs. (4)

$$\psi(x, y) = \int^x M(t, y)\, dt + \int^y \left[N(x, s) - \int^x M_s(t, s)\, dt \right] ds. \tag{12}$$

It should be noted that this proof contains a method for the computation of $\psi(x, y)$ and thus for solving the original differential equation (3). It is usually better to go through this process each time it is needed rather than to try to remember the result given in Eq. (12). Note also that the solution is obtained in implicit form. As in the previous section it may or may not be feasible to find the solution explicitly.

Example 2. Solve

$$(y \cos x + 2xe^y) + (\sin x + x^2 e^y + 2)y' = 0. \tag{13}$$

It is clear that

$$M_y(x, y) = \cos x + 2xe^y = N_x(x, y),$$

and the given equation is exact. Thus there is a $\psi(x, y)$ such that

$$\psi_x(x, y) = y \cos x + 2xe^y,$$

$$\psi_y(x, y) = \sin x + x^2 e^y + 2.$$

Integrating the first of these equations gives

$$\psi(x, y) = y \sin x + x^2 e^y + h(y). \tag{14}$$

Setting $\psi_y = N$ gives

$$\psi_y(x, y) = \sin x + x^2 e^y + h'(y) = \sin x + x^2 e^y + 2.$$

Thus

$$h'(y) = 2,$$

and

$$h(y) = 2y.$$

The constant of integration can be omitted since any solution of the previous differential equation will suffice; we do not require the most general one. Substituting for $h(y)$ in Eq. (14) gives

$$\psi(x, y) = y \sin x + x^2 e^y + 2y;$$

hence the solution of the original equation is given implicitly by

$$y \sin x + x^2 e^y + 2y = c. \tag{15}$$

Example 3.   Solve

$$(3x^2 + 2xy) + (x + y^2)y' = 0. \tag{16}$$

Here

$$M_y(x, y) = 2x, \qquad N_x(x, y) = 1;$$

since M_y is not equal to N_x, the given equation is not exact. To see that it cannot be solved by the procedure described above, let us suppose that there is a function ψ such that

$$\psi_x(x, y) = 3x^2 + 2xy, \qquad \psi_y(x, y) = x + y^2. \tag{17}$$

Integrating the first of Eqs. (17) gives

$$\psi(x, y) = x^3 + x^2 y + h(y), \tag{18}$$

where h is an arbitrary function of y only. To try to satisfy the second of Eqs. (17) we compute ψ_y from Eq. (18) and set it equal to N, obtaining

$$\psi_y(x, y) = x^2 + h'(y) = x + y^2$$

or

$$h'(y) = x + y^2 - x^2. \tag{19}$$

Since the right-hand side of Eq. (19) depends on x as well as y, it is impossible to solve Eq. (19) for $h(y)$. Thus there is no $\psi(x, y)$ satisfying both of Eqs. (17).

PROBLEMS

Determine whether or not each of the equations in Problems 1 through 12 is exact. If exact, find the solution.

1. $(2x + 3) + (2y - 2)y' = 0$ 2. $(2x + 4y) + (2x - 2y)y' = 0$
3. $(9x^2 + y - 1) - (4y - x)y' = 0$ 4. $(2xy^2 + 2y) + (2x^2 y + 2x)y' = 0$

5. $\dfrac{dy}{dx} = -\dfrac{ax + by}{bx + cy}$ 6. $\dfrac{dy}{dx} = -\dfrac{ax - by}{bx - cy}$

7. $(e^x \sin y - 2y \sin x)\, dx + (e^x \cos y + 2 \cos x)\, dy = 0$

8. $(e^x \sin y + 3y)\, dx - (3x - e^x \sin y)\, dy = 0$

9. $(ye^{xy} \cos 2x - 2e^{xy} \sin 2x + 2x)\, dx + (xe^{xy} \cos 2x - 3)\, dy = 0$

10. $\left(\dfrac{y}{x} + 6x\right) dx + (\ln x - 2)\, dy = 0,$ $x > 0$

11. $(x \ln y + xy)\, dx + (y \ln x + xy)\, dy = 0;$ $x > 0,$ $y > 0$

12. $\dfrac{x\, dx}{(x^2 + y^2)^{3/2}} + \dfrac{y\, dy}{(x^2 + y^2)^{3/2}} = 0$

13. Find the value of b for which the following equations are exact, and then solve them for that value of b.

(a) $(xy^2 + bx^2y)\, dx + (x + y)x^2\, dy = 0$

(b) $(ye^{2xy} + x)\, dx + bxe^{2xy}\, dy = 0$

14. Consider the exact differential equation

$$M(x, y)\, dx + N(x, y)\, dy = 0.$$

Find an implicit formula $\psi(x, y) = c$ for the solution analogous to Eq. (12) by first integrating the equation $\psi_y = N$, rather than $\psi_x = M$, as in the text.

15. Show that any equation which is separable, that is, of the form

$$M(x) + N(y)y' = 0,$$

is also exact.

*16. In this problem we will point out the reason why it is necessary to have some restriction on the region R in Theorem 2.3. Let us consider the differential equation

$$\dfrac{x\, dy - y\, dx}{x^2 + y^2} = 0, \qquad (x, y) \neq (0, 0).$$

(a) Show that $M_y - N_x = 0$ at all points except the origin.

(b) Show that, except at $(0, 0)$, the given equation can be written as

$$d[\tan^{-1}(y/x)] = 0,$$

or, in polar coordinates

$$d\theta = 0.$$

(c) Now consider the solution of the given equation in the region R' (see Figure 2.5) interior to the square bounded by $|x| = 2$ and $|y| = 2$, but exterior to the circle $x^2 + y^2 = 1$. For this region the condition for exactness is satisfied at all points. From part (b) we obtain

$$\psi(x, y) = \tan^{-1}(y/x) = c$$

or

$$\theta = c,$$

where c is arbitrary. However, the expression $\psi(x, y)$ is not single-valued and hence does not define a function. For example, $\psi(1, 1) = (\pi/4) + 2n\pi$, where n is any

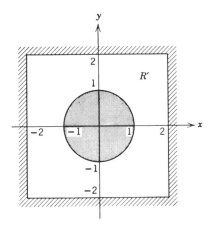

FIGURE 2.5

integer. Thus there is no *function* ψ that satisfies Eqs. (4) in R', notwithstanding the fact that Eqs. (8) are satisfied throughout R'. The explanation is that the region R' is not the proper kind of region.

(d) The expression of part (c) can be made single-valued by requiring that $\psi(x, y) = 0$ only take on values in some interval of length 2π, for example $-\pi \leq 0 < \pi$. This introduces a line, in this case the negative x axis, at every point of which $\psi(x, y)$ jumps discontinuously as (x, y) passes from one side of the line to the other. In the present problem this means that ψ is not differentiable on the negative x axis, and hence $\psi(x, y) = c$ cannot be an implicit formula for the solution of the given differential equation. This behavior is due to the nature of the region R', and the hypothesis about the region R in the theorem is included precisely to exclude such regions as R'. Actually, R need not be rectangular, as long as it is bounded by a single continuous closed curve which does not cross itself. Mathematicians say that such regions are *simply connected.*

Simply connected regions can also be thought of as those into which a perfectly elastic circular rubber sheet can be deformed by stretching without tearing, or those into which a circle can be continuously deformed. In other words, simply connected regions are regions without holes. Such matters are studied in the branch of mathematics known as topology.

2.6 INTEGRATING FACTORS

We will now show how the methods of Section 2.5 can be extended to a somewhat larger class of problems. Consider an equation of the form

$$M(x, y)\, dx + N(x, y)\, dy = 0. \tag{1}$$

If this equation is not already exact, we will try to choose a function μ, which may depend on both x and y, so that the equation

$$\mu(M\, dx + N\, dy) = 0 \tag{2}$$

is exact. The function μ is called an *integrating factor*. Equation (2) can then be solved by the methods of Section 2.5, and its solutions will also satisfy the original equation (1). This approach is an extension of the method developed in Section 2.1 for linear equations.

In order to investigate the possibility of carrying out this procedure, we recall from Section 2.5 that Eq. (2) is exact if and only if

$$(\mu M)_y = (\mu N)_x. \tag{3}$$

Since M and N are given functions, the integrating factor μ must satisfy the first order partial differential equation

$$M\mu_y - N\mu_x + (M_y - N_x)\mu = 0. \tag{4}$$

If a function μ satisfying Eq. (4) can be found, then Eq. (2) will be exact. The solution of Eq. (2) can then be obtained by the method of Section 2.5 and will be given implicitly by

$$\psi(x, y) = c.$$

This relation also defines the solution of Eq. (1), since the integrating factor μ can be canceled out of all terms in Eq. (2).

A partial differential equation of the form (4) may have more than one solution; if this is the case, any such solution may be used as an integrating factor of Eq. (1). This possible nonuniqueness of the integrating factor is illustrated in Example 3.

Unfortunately, Eq. (4), which determines the integrating factor, is ordinarily at least as difficult to solve as the original equation (1). Therefore, while in principle integrating factors are powerful tools for solving differential equations, in practice they can usually be found only in special cases. Some of these cases are indicated in the following examples, and in Problems 10 and 11 at the end of the section.

Example 1. Verify that $\mu(x, y) = (xy^2)^{-1}$ is an integrating factor for the differential equation

$$(y^2 + xy)\,dx - x^2\,dy = 0, \tag{5}$$

and then find its solution.

Since $M(x, y) = y^2 + xy$, and $N(x, y) = -x^2$, it follows that $M_y(x, y) = 2y + x$, and $N_x(x, y) = -2x$; thus the given equation is not exact. To show that $\mu(x, y) = (xy^2)^{-1}$ is an integrating factor for this equation, it is sufficient to multiply Eq. (5) by $\mu(x, y)$, thus obtaining

$$\left(\frac{1}{x} + \frac{1}{y}\right) dx - \frac{x}{y^2}\,dy = 0;$$

this latter equation is easily verified to be exact. By the method of Section

2.5 its solution is found to be given implicitly by

$$\ln |x| + \frac{x}{y} = c; \qquad x \neq 0, \qquad y \neq 0. \tag{6}$$

Note that $y = 0$ is also a solution, although it is not given by Eq. (6).

Example 2. The two most important situations in which simple integrating factors can be found occur when μ is a function of only one of the variables x, y, instead of both. Let us determine necessary conditions on M and N so that $M\,dx + N\,dy = 0$ has an integrating factor μ which depends on x only.

Assuming that μ is a function of x only, we have

$$(\mu M)_y = \mu M_y, \qquad (\mu N)_x = \mu N_x + N\frac{d\mu}{dx}.$$

Thus, if $(\mu M)_y$ is to equal $(\mu N)_x$, it is necessary that

$$\frac{d\mu}{dx} = \frac{M_y - N_x}{N}\mu. \tag{7}$$

If $(M_y - N_x)/N$ is a function of x only, then there is an integrating factor μ which also depends only on x; furthermore, $\mu(x)$ can be found by solving the first order *linear* equation (7).

Example 3. Find an integrating factor for the equation

$$(3xy + y^2) + (x^2 + xy)\frac{dy}{dx} = 0, \tag{8}$$

and then solve the equation.

On computing the quantity $(M_y - N_x)/N$ we find that

$$\frac{M_y(x, y) - N_x(x, y)}{N(x, y)} = \frac{3x + 2y - (2x + y)}{x^2 + xy} = \frac{1}{x}.$$

Thus according to Example 2, there is an integrating factor μ which is a function of x only, and satisfies the differential equation

$$\frac{d\mu}{dx} = \frac{\mu}{x}.$$

Hence

$$\mu(x) = x. \tag{9}$$

Multiplying Eq. (8) by this integrating factor yields

$$(3x^2y + xy^2) + (x^3 + x^2y)\frac{dy}{dx} = 0, \tag{10}$$

which is an exact equation. Its solution is easily found by the method of Section 2.5 to be given implicitly by

$$x^3y + \tfrac{1}{2}x^2y^2 = c. \tag{11}$$

The reader may also verify, as in Example 1, that a second integrating factor of Eq. (8) is given by $\mu(x, y) = 1/xy(2x + y)$, and that the same solution is obtained, though with much greater difficulty, if this integrating factor is used (see Problem 12).

PROBLEMS

Show that the equations in Problems 1 through 3 are not exact, but become exact when multiplied by the given integrating factor. Then solve the equations.

1. $x^2y^3 + x(1 + y^2)y' = 0$; $\mu(x, y) = 1/xy^3$

2. $\left(\dfrac{\sin y}{y} - 2e^{-x} \sin x\right) dx + \left(\dfrac{\cos y + 2e^{-x} \cos x}{y}\right) dy = 0$; $\mu(x, y) = ye^x$

3. $y \, dx + (2x - ye^y) \, dy = 0$; $\mu(x, y) = y$

In each of Problems 4 through 9 find an integrating factor, and solve the given equation.

4. $(3x^2y + 2xy + y^3) \, dx + (x^2 + y^2) \, dy = 0$

5. $y' = e^{2x} + y - 1$

6. $dx + \left(\dfrac{x}{y} - \sin y\right) dy = 0$

7. $y \, dx + (2xy - e^{-2y}) \, dy = 0$

8. $e^x \, dx + (e^x \cot y + 2y \csc y) \, dy = 0$

9. $\left(3x + \dfrac{6}{y}\right) dx + \left(\dfrac{x^2}{y} + 3\dfrac{y}{x}\right) dy = 0$

10. Show that if $(N_x - M_y)/M = Q$, where Q is a function of y only, then the differential equation

$$M + Ny' = 0$$

has an integrating factor of the form

$$\mu(y) = \exp \int^y Q(t) \, dt.$$

*11. Show that if $(N_x - M_y)/(xM - yN) = R$, where R depends on the quantity xy only, then the differential equation

$$M + Ny' = 0$$

has an integrating factor of the form $\mu(xy)$. Find a general formula for this integrating factor.

*12. Solve the differential equation

$$(3xy + y^2) + (x^2 + xy)y' = 0,$$

using the integrating factor

$$\mu(x, y) = [xy(2x + y)]^{-1}.$$

Verify that the solution is the same as that obtained in Example 3 with a different integrating factor.

2.7 HOMOGENEOUS EQUATIONS

The two main types of nonlinear first order equations that can be solved by direct processes of integration are those in which the variables separate, and those which are exact. Section 2.6 dealt with the use of integrating factors to solve certain types of equations by reducing them to exact equations. This section will introduce another technique, that of changes of variables, which can sometimes be used to simplify a differential equation and thus make its solution possible (or more convenient). Generally speaking, the appropriate substitution will have to be suggested by the repeated appearance of some combination of the variables, or some other peculiarity in the structure of the equation.

The most important class of equations for which a definite rule can be laid down is the class of homogeneous* differential equations. An equation of the form

$$\frac{dy}{dx} = f(x, y)$$

is said to be homogeneous whenever the function f does not depend on x and y separately, but only on their ratio y/x or x/y. Thus homogeneous equations are of the form

$$\frac{dy}{dx} = F\left(\frac{y}{x}\right). \tag{1}$$

Consider the following examples:

(a) $\dfrac{dy}{dx} = \dfrac{y^2 + 2xy}{x^2} = \left(\dfrac{y}{x}\right)^2 + 2\dfrac{y}{x}$;

(b) $\dfrac{dy}{dx} = \ln x - \ln y + \dfrac{x + y}{x - y} = \ln\dfrac{1}{y/x} + \dfrac{1 + (y/x)}{1 - (y/x)}$;

(c) $\dfrac{dy}{dx} = \dfrac{y^3 + 2xy}{x^2}$.

Thus (a) and (b) are homogeneous, since the right-hand side of each can be expressed as a function of y/x; since (c) cannot be so written, it is not homogeneous. Usually it is easy to tell by inspection whether or not a given equation is homogeneous; for complicated equations the criterion given in Problem 15 may be useful.

The form of a homogeneous equation suggests that it may be simplified by introducing a new variable,† which we will denote by v, to represent the

---

* The word homogeneous is used in more than one way in the study of differential equations. The reader must be alert to distinguish these as they occur.
† Leibniz in 1691 was the first to use this technique.

ratio of y to x. Thus

$$y = xv, \tag{2}$$

and Eq. (1) becomes

$$\frac{dy}{dx} = F(v). \tag{3}$$

Looking on v as the new dependent variable (replacing y), we must consider v as a function of x, and replace dy/dx in Eq. (3) by a suitable expression in terms of v. Differentiating Eq. (2) gives

$$\frac{dy}{dx} = x\frac{dv}{dx} + v,$$

and hence Eq. (3) becomes

$$x\frac{dv}{dx} + v = F(v). \tag{4}$$

The most significant fact about Eq. (4) is that the variables x and v can *always* be separated, regardless of the form of the function F; in fact,

$$\frac{dx}{x} = \frac{dv}{F(v) - v}. \tag{5}$$

Solving Eq. (5) and then replacing v by y/x gives the solution of the original equation.

Thus any homogeneous equation can be transformed into one whose variables are separated by the substitution (2). As a practical matter, of course, it may or may not be possible to evaluate the integral required in solving Eq. (5) by elementary methods. Moreover, a homogeneous equation may also belong to one of the classes already discussed; it may well be exact, or even linear, for example. In such cases there is a choice of methods for finding its solution.

Example. Solve the differential equation

$$\frac{dy}{dx} = \frac{y^2 + 2xy}{x^2}. \tag{6}$$

Writing this equation as

$$\frac{dy}{dx} = \left(\frac{y}{x}\right)^2 + 2\frac{y}{x}$$

shows that it is homogeneous. The variables cannot be separated, nor is the equation exact, nor is an integrating factor obvious. Thus we are led to the substitution (2), which transforms the given equation into

$$x\frac{dv}{dx} + v = v^2 + 2v.$$

Hence

$$x \frac{dv}{dx} = v^2 + v$$

or, separating the variables,

$$\frac{dx}{x} = \frac{dv}{v(v+1)}.$$

Expanding the right-hand side by partial fractions gives

$$\frac{dx}{x} = \left(\frac{1}{v} - \frac{1}{v+1}\right) dv.$$

Integrating both sides yields

$$\ln|x| + \ln|c| = \ln|v| - \ln|v+1|,$$

where c is an arbitrary constant. Hence, combining the logarithms and taking the exponential of both sides, we obtain

$$cx = \frac{v}{v+1}.$$

Finally, substituting for v in terms of y gives the solution of Eq. (6) in the form

$$cx = \frac{y/x}{(y/x)+1} = \frac{y}{y+x}.$$

Solving for y we obtain

$$y = \frac{cx^2}{1-cx}.$$

Sometimes it is helpful to transform both the independent and dependent variables. For example, in Problems 9, 10, 11, and 14 a change of both variables is required to make the equation homogeneous, after which a further change of the dependent variable leads to a solution of the problem.

PROBLEMS

Show that the equations in Problems 1 through 8 are homogeneous, and find their solutions.

1. $\dfrac{dy}{dx} = \dfrac{x+y}{x}$

2. $2y\,dx - x\,dy = 0$

3. $\dfrac{dy}{dx} = \dfrac{x^2 + xy + y^2}{x^2}$

4. $\dfrac{dy}{dx} = \dfrac{x^2 + 3y^2}{2xy}$

5. $\dfrac{dy}{dx} = \dfrac{4y - 3x}{2x - y}$

6. $\dfrac{dy}{dx} = -\dfrac{4x + 3y}{2x + y}$

7. $\dfrac{dy}{dx} = \dfrac{x + 3y}{x - y}$ 8. $(x^2 + 3xy + y^2)\, dx - x^2\, dy = 0$

*9. (a) Find the solution of the equation

$$\frac{dy}{dx} = \frac{2y - x}{2x - y}.$$

(b) Find the solution of the equation

$$\frac{dy}{dx} = \frac{2y - x + 5}{2x - y - 4}.$$

Hint: In order to reduce the equation of part (b) to that of part (a), consider a preliminary substitution of the form

$$x = X - h, \qquad y = Y - k.$$

Choose the constants h and k so that the equation is homogeneous in the variables X and Y.

*10. Solve $\dfrac{dy}{dx} = -\dfrac{4x + 3y + 15}{2x + y + 7}$.   See Hint, Problem 9b.

*11. Solve $\dfrac{dy}{dx} = \dfrac{x + 3y - 5}{x - y - 1}$.   See Hint, Problem 9b.

12. Find the solution of the equation

$$(3xy + y^2)\, dx + (x^2 + xy)\, dy = 0,$$

and compare it with the solution obtained by other methods in Example 3 and Problem 12 of Section 2.6.

*13. Show that if

$$M(x, y)\, dx + N(x, y)\, dy = 0$$

is a homogeneous equation, then it has

$$\mu(x, y) = \frac{1}{xM(x, y) + yN(x, y)}$$

for an integrating factor.

*14. (a) Prove that the equation

$$\frac{dy}{dx} = \frac{ax + by + m}{cx + dy + n},$$

where a, b, c, d, m, and n are constants, can always be reduced to a homogeneous equation by an appropriate transformation of the form

$$x = X - h, \qquad y = Y - k,$$

as long as $ad - bc \neq 0$.

(b) Find a transformation which will reduce the given equation to a form in which the variables are separable when $ad - bc = 0$. Find the solution of the equation in this case.

*15. Show that the equation $y' = f(x,y)$ is homogeneous if $f(x, y)$ is such that

$$f(x, tx) = f(1, t),$$

where t is a real parameter. Use this fact to determine whether each of the following equations is homogeneous.

(a) $y' = \dfrac{x^3 + xy + y^3}{x^2y + xy^2}$

(b) $y' = \ln x - \ln y + \dfrac{x + y}{x - y}$

(c) $y' = \dfrac{(x^2 + 3xy + 4y^2)^{1/2}}{x + 2y}$

(d) $y' = \dfrac{\sin (xy)}{x^2 + y^2}$

2.8 MISCELLANEOUS PROBLEMS

This section consists of a list of problems. The first 32 problems can be solved by the methods of the previous sections. They are presented so that the reader may have some practice in identifying the method or methods applicable to a given equation. At the end of the list are a number of problems suggesting specialized techniques which are useful for certain types of equations. In particular, Problems 35 through 38 are concerned with Clairaut (1713–1765) equations; Problems 39 and 40 deal with Riccati (1676–1754) equations.

1. $\dfrac{dy}{dx} = \dfrac{x^3 - 2y}{x}$

2. $(x + y) \, dx - (x - y) \, dy = 0$

3. $\dfrac{dy}{dx} = \dfrac{2x + y}{3 + 3y^2 - x}, \quad y(0) = 0$

4. $(x + e^y) \, dy - dx = 0$

5. $\dfrac{dy}{dx} = -\dfrac{2xy + y^2 + 1}{x^2 + 2xy}$

6. $x \dfrac{dy}{dx} + xy = 1 - y, \quad y(1) = 0$

7. $\dfrac{dy}{dx} = \dfrac{x}{x^2y + y^3}$ $\quad$ Hint: Let $u = x^2$.

8. $x \dfrac{dy}{dx} + 2y = \dfrac{\sin x}{x}, \quad y(2) = 1$

9. $\dfrac{dy}{dx} = -\dfrac{2xy + 1}{x^2 + 2y}$

10. $(3y^2 + 2xy) \, dx - (2xy + x^2) \, dy = 0$

11. $(x^2 + y) \, dx + (x + e^y) \, dy = 0$

12. $\dfrac{dy}{dx} + y = \dfrac{1}{1 + e^x}$

13. $x \, dy - y \, dx = (xy)^{1/2} \, dx$

14. $(x + y) \, dx + (x + 2y) \, dy = 0, \quad y(2) = 3$

15. $(e^x + 1) \dfrac{dy}{dx} = y - ye^x$

16. $\dfrac{dy}{dx} = \dfrac{x^2 + y^2}{x^2}$

17. $\dfrac{dy}{dx} = e^{2x} + 3y$

18. $(2y + 3x) \, dx = -x \, dy$

19. $x\,dy - y\,dx = 2x^2y^2\,dy$, $y(1) = -2$

20. $y' = e^{x+y}$ 21. $xy' = y + xe^{y/x}$

22. $\dfrac{dy}{dx} = \dfrac{x^2 - 1}{y^2 + 1}$, $y(-1) = 1$ 23. $xy' + y - y^2e^{2x} = 0$

24. $2 \sin y \cos x\,dx + \cos y \sin x\,dy = 0$

25. $\left(2\dfrac{x}{y} - \dfrac{y}{x^2 + y^2}\right)dx + \left(\dfrac{x}{x^2 + y^2} - \dfrac{x^2}{y^2}\right)dy = 0$

26. $(2y + 1)\,dx + \left(\dfrac{x^2 - y}{x}\right)dy = 0$

27. $(\cos 2y - \sin x)\,dx - 2 \tan x \sin 2y\,dy = 0$

28. $\dfrac{dy}{dx} = \dfrac{3x^2 - 2y - y^3}{2x + 3xy^2}$ 29. $\dfrac{dy}{dx} = \dfrac{2y + \sqrt{x^2 - y^2}}{2x}$

30. $\dfrac{dy}{dx} = \dfrac{y^3}{1 - 2xy^2}$, $y(0) = 1$

31. $(x^2y + xy - y)\,dx + (x^2y - 2x^2)\,dy = 0$

32. $\dfrac{dy}{dx} = -\dfrac{3x^2y + y^2}{2x^3 + 3xy}$, $y(1) = -2$

33. Show that an equation of the form

$$y = G(p),$$

where $p = dy/dx$, can be solved in the following manner.

(a) Differentiate with respect to x.

(b) Integrate the equation of part (a) to obtain x as a function of p. This equation and the original equation $y = G(p)$ form a parametric representation of the solution.

34. Solve the differential equation

$$y - \ln p = 0,$$

where $p = dy/dx$, by the method of Problem 33. Also solve this equation directly, and verify that the solutions are the same.

35. Any equation of the form

$$y = xp + f(p),$$

where $p = dy/dx$, is known as a Clairaut equation. Consider the particular example

$$y = xp + p^2. \tag{i}$$

(a) Differentiate (i) with respect to x, obtaining

$$(x + 2p)\dfrac{dp}{dx} = 0. \tag{ii}$$

Equation (ii) will be satisfied either if $dp/dx = 0$, or if $x + 2p = 0$.

(b) Show that if $dp/dx = 0$, then $p = c$, where c is an arbitrary constant, and Eq. (i) then implies that

$$y = cx + c^2. \tag{iii}$$

Note that if we integrate $p = dy/dx = c$, we obtain $y = cx + k$, a solution which apparently contains two arbitrary constants. However, substituting this expression for y in Eq. (i) gives $k = c^2$.

(c) Show that if $x + 2p = 0$, then elimination of the parameter p between this equation and Eq. (i) leads to

$$y = -\tfrac{1}{4}x^2. \tag{iv}$$

Verify that Eq. (iv) is another solution of Eq. (i); however, it is not obtainable from the solution (iii) for any choice of c. Equation (iv) is called the *singular*

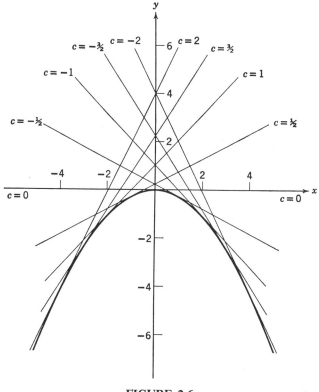

FIGURE 2.6

solution of Eq. (i). The singular solution is tangent at each point to some member of the family of straight lines given by Eq. (iii), and is called the *envelope* of that one-parameter family of lines. This is shown graphically in Figure 2.6, where several members of the family of straight lines given by Eq. (iii) and the parabola given by Eq. (iv) are sketched. See also Problem 6 in Section 2.3.

36. Consider the Clairaut equation

$$y = xp + f(p),$$

where $p = dy/dx$. Show that

$$y = cx + f(c),$$

where c is an arbitrary constant, is a one-parameter family of solutions of the given equation.

37. Consider the Clairaut equation

$$(y')^3 - 3xy' + 3y = 0.$$

Find a one-parameter family of solutions and also a singular solution not obtainable from the one-parameter family. Show geometrically how they are related.

38. Consider the Clairaut equation

$$xp - e^p - y = 0,$$

where $p = dy/dx$. Find a one-parameter family of solutions and a singular solution. Show geometrically how they are related. Pay particular attention to the interval $x < 0$.

39. The equation

$$\frac{dy}{dx} = q_1(x) + q_2(x)y + q_3(x)y^2$$

is known as Riccati's equation. Suppose that some particular solution y_1 of this equation is known. A more general solution containing one arbitrary constant can be obtained through the substitution

$$y = y_1(x) + \frac{1}{v(x)}.$$

Show that $v(x)$ satisfies the first order *linear* equation

$$\frac{dv}{dx} = -(q_2 + 2q_3 y_1)v - q_3.$$

Note that $v(x)$ will contain a single arbitrary constant.

40. Using the method of Problem 39 and the given particular solution, solve each of the following equations.

(a) $y' = 1 + x^2 - 2xy + y^2$; $y_1(x) = x$

(b) $y' = -\dfrac{1}{x^2} - \dfrac{y}{x} + y^2$; $y_1(x) = 1/x$

(c) $\dfrac{dy}{dx} = \dfrac{2\cos^2 x - \sin^2 x + y^2}{2\cos x}$; $y_1(x) = \sin x$

2.9 APPLICATIONS OF FIRST ORDER EQUATIONS

Differential equations are of interest to nonmathematicians primarily because of the possibility of using them to investigate a wide variety of problems in the physical, biological, and social sciences. There are three identifiable steps in this process, which are present regardless of the specific field of application.

In the first place, it is necessary to translate the physical situation into mathematical terms. This is generally done by making assumptions about what is happening that appear to be consistent with the observed phenomena. For example, it has been observed that radioactive materials decay at a rate proportional to the amount of the material present, that heat passes from a warmer to a cooler body at a rate proportional to the temperature difference, that objects move about in accordance with Newton's laws of motion, and that isolated insect populations grow at a rate proportional to the current population. Each of these statements involves a rate of change (derivative) and consequently, when expressed mathematically, takes the form of a differential equation.

It is important to realize that the mathematical equations are almost always only an approximate description of the actual process because they are based on observations that are themselves approximations. For example, bodies moving at speeds comparable to the speed of light are not governed by Newton's laws, insect populations do not grow indefinitely as stated because of eventual limitations on their food supply, and heat transfer is affected by factors other than the temperature difference. Moreover, the process of formulating a physical problem mathematically often involves the conceptual replacement of a discrete process by a continuous one. For instance, the number of members in an insect population changes by discrete amounts; however, if the population is large, it seems reasonable to consider it as a continuous variable and even to speak of its derivative. Alternatively, one can adopt the point of view that the mathematical equations exactly describe the operation of a simplified model, which has been constructed (or conceived of) so as to embody the most important features of the actual process.

In any case, once the problem has been formulated mathematically, one is often faced with the problem of solving one or more differential equations or, failing that, of finding out as much as possible about the properties of the solution. It may happen that this mathematical problem is quite difficult and, if so, further approximations may be indicated at this stage in order to make the problem mathematically tractable. For example, a nonlinear equation may be approximated by a linear one, or a slowly varying function may be replaced by its average value. Naturally, any such approximations must also be examined from the physical point of view to make sure that the simplified mathematical problem still reflects the essential features of the physical process under investigation. At the same time, an intimate knowledge of the physics of the problem may suggest reasonable mathematical approximations that will make the mathematical problem more amenable to analysis. This interplay of understanding of physical phenomena and knowledge of mathematical techniques and their limitations is characteristic of applied mathematics at its best, and is indispensable in successfully constructing mathematical models of intricate physical processes.

Finally, having obtained the solution (or at least some information about it), it must be interpreted in terms of the context in which the problem arose. In particular, one should always check as to whether the mathematical solution appears physically reasonable. This requires, at the very least, that the solution exist, that it be unique, and that it depend continuously upon the data of the problem. This last consideration is important because the coefficients in the differential equation and initial conditions are often obtained as a result of measurements of some physical quantity, and therefore are susceptible to small errors. If these small errors lead to large (or discontinuous) changes in the solution of the corresponding mathematical problem, which are not observed physically, then the relevance of the mathematical model to the physical problem must be reexamined. Of course, the fact that the mathematical solution appears to be reasonable does not guarantee that it is correct. However, if it is seriously inconsistent with careful observations of the physical system it purports to describe, this suggests either that errors have been made in solving the mathematical problem or that the mathematical model itself is too crude.

The examples which follow in this section and in the next are typical of applications in which first order differential equations arise.

Example 1 (Radioactive Decay).   A certain radioactive material is known to decay at a rate proportional to the amount present. A block of this material originally having a mass of Q_0 grams is observed, after 24 hours, to have experienced a reduction in mass of 10 percent. Find an expression for the mass of the block at any time. Also find the time interval that must elapse in order for the block to decay to one half of its original mass.

Let $Q(t)$ denote the mass of the material present at time t. Since the rate of change of Q is proportional to Q itself, we have

$$Q'(t) = kQ(t), \tag{1}$$

where k is a constant proportionality factor. Equation (1) can be solved either as a linear equation or by separating the variables, and its general solution is

$$Q(t) = ce^{kt}. \tag{2}$$

If the origin on the time scale is chosen to be the instant when the mass of the material is Q_0, then the initial condition is $Q(0) = Q_0$. Hence c is equal to Q_0, and Eq. (2) becomes

$$Q(t) = Q_0 e^{kt}. \tag{3}$$

If k is known, then Eq. (3) provides a formula for the mass Q present at any time. If k is not known in advance, then a second observation is needed to determine it. In the given problem $Q(24)$ is equal to $9Q_0/10$. Hence

$$\tfrac{9}{10}Q_0 = Q_0 e^{24k},$$

and

$$k = -\tfrac{1}{24} \ln (10/9) \simeq -0.00439. \tag{4}$$

Using this value of k in Eq. (3) gives the desired expression for $Q(t)$.

The time period during which the mass is reduced to one half of its original value is known as the *half-life* of the material. Let t_1 be the time at which $Q(t)$ is equal to $Q_0/2$. Then, from Eq. (3),

$$\frac{Q_0}{2} = Q_0 e^{kt_1},$$

or

$$t_1 = -\frac{1}{k} \ln 2. \tag{5}$$

Equation (5) is the relation between the half-life and the rate of decay for any material that obeys the differential equation (1). Using the value of k given by Eq. (4) we find that

$$t_1 = \frac{24 \ln 2}{\ln (10/9)} \simeq 158 \text{ (hours)}. \tag{6}$$

Example 2 (*Compound Interest*). Suppose that a sum of money S_0 is invested so that it draws interest at a rate of 4 percent compounded quarterly. The value of the investment $S(t)$ at any time can be computed algebraically or by reference to compound-interest tables. However, let us approximate the true situation by a mathematical model in which we assume that the interest is compounded *continuously*. Although this assumption is apparently rather extreme, it does permit us to write the law of growth of the investment as a differential equation, namely,

$$S'(t) = 0.04S(t). \tag{7}$$

The solution of the linear differential equation (7), which also satisfies the initial condition $S(0) = S_0$, is

$$S(t) = S_0 e^{0.04t}. \tag{8}$$

In Table 2.1 we list the values of $S(t)/S_0$ as given by Eq. (8) for various values of t. The exact values of $S(t)/S_0$ for an interest rate of 4 percent compounded quarterly are also given for comparison.

TABLE 2.1

Years	$S(t)/S_0$ Exact	$S(t)/S_0$ from Eq. (8)	Error (Percent)
2	1.0829	1.0833	0.04
5	1.2202	1.2214	0.1
10	1.4889	1.4918	0.2
20	2.2168	2.2255	0.4
40	4.9142	4.9530	0.8
80	24.149	24.533	1.5
200	2866	2981	4.0
400	8,214,000	8,886,000	8.2

For relatively small values of t the continuous mathematical model yields results which are close to the actual values. However, if the time period is measured in centuries the pyramiding effect of continuously compounding interest eventually causes serious discrepancies. This example illustrates that some care may be needed to determine the range within which simplifying assumptions are reasonably valid. However, it also illustrates that over limited but sometimes fairly long intervals drastic assumptions can sometimes be made without seriously affecting the accuracy of the results.

Example 3 (Mixing). Consider a tank containing, at time $t = 0$, Q_0 lb of salt dissolved in 100 gal of water. Assume that water containing $\frac{1}{4}$ lb of salt per gallon is entering the tank at a rate of 3 gal/min, and that the well-stirred solution is leaving the tank at the same rate. Find an expression for the amount of salt $Q(t)$ in the tank at time t.

The rate of change of salt in the tank at time t, $Q'(t)$, must equal the rate at which salt enters the tank minus the rate at which it leaves. The rate at which salt enters is $\frac{1}{4}$ lb/gal times 3 gal/min. The rate at which salt leaves is $(Q(t)/100)$ lbs/gal times 3 gal/min. Thus

$$Q'(t) = \tfrac{3}{4} - \tfrac{3}{100}Q(t) \tag{9}$$

is the differential equation governing this process. Equation (9) is linear and its solution is

$$Q(t) = 25 + ce^{-0.03t}, \tag{10}$$

where c is arbitrary. The initial condition

$$Q(0) = Q_0 \tag{11}$$

requires that c equal $Q_0 - 25$, and hence

$$Q(t) = 25(1 - e^{-0.03t}) + Q_0 e^{-0.03t}. \tag{12}$$

The second term on the right side of Eq. (12) represents the portion of the original salt remaining in the tank at time t. This term becomes very small with the passage of time as the original solution is drained from the tank. The first term on the right side of Eq. (12) gives the amount of salt in the tank at time t due to the action of the flow processes. As t becomes large this term approaches the constant value 25 (pounds). It is also clear physically that this must be the limiting value of Q as the original solution in the tank is more and more completely replaced by that entering with a concentration of $\frac{1}{4}$ lb/gal.

Example 4 (Epidemics).   A mathematical theory of epidemics has been developed along the following lines. Assume that there is a community of n members containing p infected individuals and q uninfected but susceptible individuals, where $p + q = n$. Alternatively, let x be the proportion of sick members and y the proportion of well members. Then $x = p/n, y = q/n$, and $x + y = 1$. If n is large it is reasonable to think of x and y as continuous variables; then the rate at which the disease spreads is dx/dt. Assuming that the disease spreads by contact between sick and well members of the community, then dx/dt is proportional to the number of contacts. If members of both groups move about freely among each other, the number of contacts in turn is proportional to the product of x and y. Thus we arrive at the differential equation

$$\frac{dx}{dt} = \beta xy$$

or

$$\frac{dx}{dt} = \beta x(1 - x), \tag{13}$$

where β is a positive proportionality factor. The initial condition is

$$x(0) = x_0, \tag{14}$$

where x_0 is the density of infected individuals at $t = 0$.

Equation (13) is separable, and may be written as

$$\frac{dx}{x(1 - x)} = \beta \, dt,$$

or, using a partial fraction expansion, in the form

$$\left(\frac{1}{x} + \frac{1}{1 - x} \right) dx = \beta \, dt.$$

Hence

$$\ln x - \ln (1 - x) = \beta t + C; \tag{15}$$

note that x and $1 - x$ are intrinsically positive so that absolute values are not needed. From Eq. (15) it follows that

$$\frac{x}{1 - x} = ce^{\beta t}, \tag{16}$$

where $c = e^C$. The initial condition requires that $c = x_0/(1 - x_0)$. Using this value of c in Eq. (16) and solving for x, we obtain

$$x = \frac{x_0 e^{\beta t}}{1 - x_0 + x_0 e^{\beta t}} = \frac{x_0}{x_0 + (1 - x_0)e^{-\beta t}}. \tag{17}$$

If $x_0 > 0$, then $x \to 1$ as $t \to \infty$ regardless of the actual value of x_0. Thus, no matter how small the initial number of infected individuals, the epidemic ultimately spreads throughout the entire population.

The mathematical model described above is clearly unrealistic in some respects. For one thing, if the disease is at all serious, a partial quarantine will occur naturally to the extent that sick individuals are restricted in their activities. An additional quarantine may be imposed by health authorities to further restrict the possibility of contact between sick and well individuals. Finally, many diseases are contagious only for a limited period of time, whereas in the model used here sick individuals are assumed to remain so indefinitely. All of these factors would tend to slow the spread of the disease as compared to the rate predicted above.

Example 5 (Orthogonal Trajectories).   Consider the family of parabolas defined by

$$y = kx^2, \tag{18}$$

where k is an arbitrary constant. If $k > 0$, the parabolas open upward, and if $k < 0$, they open downward, as shown by the dashed curves in Figure 2.7. Find the family of curves which intersects the given family of parabolas orthogonally at each point.

The first step is to obtain an expression for the slope at a given point (x, y) of the parabola which passes through that point. By differentiating Eq. (18) we find that

$$\frac{dy}{dx} = 2kx, \tag{19}$$

an expression which depends upon k as well as upon x and y. However, it follows from Eq. (18) that k equals y/x^2, and substituting for k in Eq. (19) then yields

$$\left(\frac{dy}{dx}\right)^{(1)} = \frac{2y}{x}. \tag{20}$$

The superscript (1) is merely to identify that these are the slopes of the first family of curves. The desired orthogonal family of curves is characterized by the fact that its slopes, denoted by $(dy/dx)^{(2)}$, are negative reciprocals of those

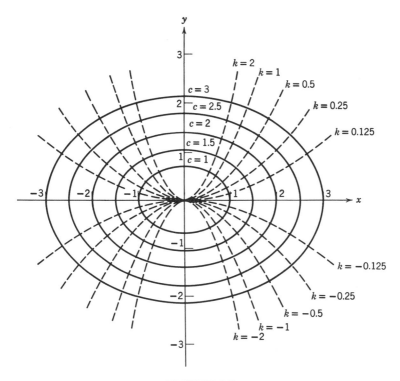

FIGURE 2.7

given by Eq. (20). Thus

$$\left(\frac{dy}{dx}\right)^{(2)} = -\frac{x}{2y}.$$ (21)

Equation (21) can be solved by separating the variables, with the result that

$$x^2 + 2y^2 = c,$$ (22)

where c is an arbitrary (nonnegative) constant. This family of curves is the family of ellipses indicated by the solid curves in Figure 2.7.

Families of curves which are mutually orthogonal are said to be orthogonal trajectories of each other. Such families of orthogonal trajectories occur naturally in several branches of physics. For instance, in an electrostatic field the lines of force and the lines of constant potential are everywhere orthogonal to each other.

PROBLEMS

1. Suppose a sum of money draws interest compounded continuously. If the original amount is S_0, when will the principal S attain the value $2S_0$ if the annual interest rate is 3%? 4%? 5%?

2. A certain man has a fortune which increases at a rate proportional to the square of his present wealth. If he had one million dollars a year ago, and has two million dollars today, how much will he be worth in six months? in two years?

3. A certain radioactive material is known to decay at a rate proportional to the amount present. A block of this material originally having a mass of 100 grams is observed, after 20 years, to have a mass of only 80 grams. Find an expression for the mass of the material at any time. Also find the half-life of the material.

4. A certain radioactive material has a half-life of 2 hours. Find the time interval required for a given amount of this material to decay to one-tenth of its original mass.

5. A radioactive isotope of carbon, known as carbon 14, obeys the law of radioactive decay

$$\frac{dQ}{dt} = kQ,$$

where $Q(t)$ denotes the amount of carbon 14 present at time t.

(a) Determine k if the half-life of carbon 14 is 5568 years.

(b) Let Q_0 represent the amount of carbon 14 present at time $t = 0$. Find an expression for Q at any time t.

(c) In recent years it has become possible to make measurements leading to knowledge of $Q(t)/Q_0$ for some wood and plant remains containing residual amounts of carbon 14. The results of (a) and (b) can then be used to determine the elapsed time since the death of these remains; that is, the period during which decay has been taking place. Find an expression for t in terms of Q, Q_0, and k. Find the interval since the beginning of decay if the current value of Q/Q_0 is 0.20. This technique of radiocarbon dating is of great value to archaeologists. It is limited, however, to intervals of about 30,000 years or less since after longer periods the amount of carbon 14 present is too small to yield accurate results.

6. Assume the population of the earth changes at a rate proportional to the current population. (A more accurate hypothesis concerning the law of population growth is considered in Problem 7.) Assume further that at time $t = 0$ (A.D. 1650) the earth's population was 250 million (2.5×10^8); at time $t = 300$ (A.D. 1950) its population was 2.5 billion (2.5×10^9). Find an expression giving the population of the earth at any time. Assuming that the greatest population the earth can support is 25 billion (2.5×10^{10}), when will this limit be reached?

7. In a certain isolated population $p(t)$ the rate of population growth dp/dt is a function of the population; thus

$$\frac{dp}{dt} = f(p).$$

(a) The simplest expression for $f(p)$ is $f(p) = \epsilon p$, where ϵ is a positive constant. Find $p(t)$ in this case if $p(0) = p_0$. What is $\lim_{t\to\infty} p(t)$?

(b) A better assumption in many situations is that $f(p) = \epsilon p - kp^2$, where ϵ and k are both positive constants. The term $-kp^2$ may be needed, for example, if overcrowded conditions for large values of p result in an increase in the death rate and a decrease in the birth rate. If $p(0)$ equals p_0, find an expression for the population at any time t. Find the limiting population as $t \to \infty$. Compare these results with those of part (a). Note that, even if k is very small, the nature of the solution is radically changed (for large p) as soon as the quadratic term is introduced into $f(p)$.

8. It is known from experimental observations that, to an accuracy satisfactory in many circumstances, the surface temperature of an object changes at a rate proportional to the difference between the temperature of the object and that of the surroundings (the ambient temperature). This is sometimes known as Newton's law of cooling. Thus, if $u(t)$ is the temperature of the object at time t, and u_0 is the constant ambient temperature, we have the relation

$$\frac{du}{dt} = k(u - u_0),$$

where k is a constant proportionality factor.
  (a) Find the solution satisfying the initial condition $u(0) = u_1$.
  (b) Suppose the temperature of a cup of coffee is 200° F when freshly poured. One minute later it has cooled to 190° F in a room at 70° F. How long a period must elapse (assuming Newton's law of cooling to apply) before the coffee reaches a temperature of 150° F?

9. Assume that a spherical raindrop evaporates at a rate proportional to its surface area. If its radius originally is 3 mm, and 1 hour later has been reduced to 2 mm, find an expression for the radius of the raindrop at any time.

10. Consider a tank used in certain hydrodynamic experiments. After one experiment the tank contains 200 gal of a dye solution with a concentration of 1 gm/gal. To prepare for the next experiment the tank is to be rinsed with fresh water flowing in at a rate of 2 gal/min, the well-stirred solution flowing out at the same rate. Find the time which will elapse before the concentration of dye in the tank reaches 1% of its original value.

11. A tank originally contains 100 gal of fresh water. Then water containing $\frac{1}{2}$ lb of salt per gallon is poured into the tank at a rate of 2 gal/min, and the mixture is allowed to leave at the same rate. After 10 minutes the process is stopped, and fresh water is poured into the tank at a rate of 2 gal/min, with the mixture again leaving at the same rate. Find the amount of salt in the tank at the end of 20 minutes.

12. A tank with a capacity of 500 gal originally contains 200 gal of water with 100 lb of salt in solution. Water containing 1 lb of salt per gallon is entering at a rate of 3 gal/min, and the mixture is allowed to flow out of the tank at a rate of 2 gal/min. Find the amount of salt in the tank at any time prior to the instant when the solution begins to overflow. Find the concentration (in pounds per gallon) of salt in the tank when it is on the point of overflowing. Compare this concentration with the theoretical limiting concentration if the tank had infinite capacity.

13. A second order chemical reaction involves the interaction (collision) of one molecule of a substance P with one molecule of a substance Q in order to produce one molecule of a new substance X; $P + Q \to X$ is the usual notation.

Suppose that p and q are the initial concentrations of substances P and Q, respectively, and let $x(t)$ be the concentration of X at time t. Then $p - x(t)$ and $q - x(t)$ are the concentrations of P and Q at time t, and the rate at which the reaction occurs is described by the equation

$$\frac{dx}{dt} = \alpha(p - x)(q - x),$$

where α is a positive constant.

(a) If $x(0) = 0$, find $x(t)$.

(b) If the substances P and Q are the same, then

$$\frac{dx}{dt} = \alpha(p - x)^2.$$

If $x(0) = 0$, find $x(t)$.

14. Suppose that in a certain chemical reaction a substance P is transformed into a substance X. Let p be the initial concentration of P and let $x(t)$ be the concentration of X at time t. Then $p - x(t)$ is the concentration of P at t. Suppose further that the reaction is autocatalytic, that is, the reaction is stimulated by the substance being produced. Hence dx/dt is proportional both to x and $p - x$, and

$$\frac{dx}{dt} = \alpha x(p - x),$$

where α is a positive constant. If $x(0) = x_0$, find $x(t)$.

15. Suppose that a room containing 1200 cubic feet of air is originally free of carbon monoxide. Beginning at time $t = 0$ cigarette smoke, containing 4 percent carbon monoxide, is introduced into the room at a rate of 0.1 ft^3/min, and the well-circulated mixture is allowed to leave the room at the same rate.

(a) Find an expression for the concentration $x(t)$ of carbon monoxide in the room at any time $t > 0$.

(b) Extended exposure to a carbon monoxide concentration as low as 0.00012 is harmful to the human body. Find the time t^* at which this concentration is reached.

16. Consider a lake of constant volume V which contains at time t an amount $Q(t)$ of pollutant, evenly distributed throughout the lake with a concentration $c(t)$, where $c(t) = Q(t)/V$. Assume that water containing a concentration k of pollutant enters the lake at a rate r, and that water leaves the lake at the same rate. Suppose that pollutants are also added directly to the lake at a constant rate P. Note that the given assumptions neglect a number of factors which may, in some cases, be important; for example, the water added or lost by precipitation, absorption, and evaporation; the stratifying effect of temperature differences in a deep lake; the tendency of irregularities in the coastline to produce sheltered bays; and the fact that pollutants are not deposited evenly throughout the lake, but (usually) at isolated points around its periphery. The results below must be interpreted in the light of the neglect of such factors as these.

(a) If at time $t = 0$ the concentration of pollutant is c_0, find an expression for the concentration $c(t)$ at any time. What is the limiting concentration approached as $t \to \infty$?

(b) If the addition of pollutants to the lake is terminated ($k = 0$ and $P = 0$ for $t > 0$), determine the time interval T which must elapse before the concentration of pollutants is reduced to 50 percent of its original value; to 10 percent of its original value.

(c) Table 2.2 contains data† for several of the Great Lakes. Using these data determine from part (b) the time T necessary to reduce the contamination of each of these lakes to 10 percent of the original value.

TABLE 2.2

Lake	$V(\text{km}^3 \times 10^{-3})$	$r(\text{km}^3/\text{yr})$
Superior	12.2	65.2
Michigan	4.9	158
Erie	0.46	175
Ontario	1.6	209

17. In each of the following cases find the family of orthogonal trajectories of the given family of curves. Sketch both the given family and their orthogonal trajectories.

(a) $xy = c$

(b) $x^2 + y^2 = cx$

(c) $x^2 - xy + y^2 = c^2$

(d) $2cy + x^2 = c^2, \qquad c > 0$

18. If two straight lines in the xy plane, having slopes m_1 and m_2 respectively, intersect at an angle θ, show that

$$(\tan \theta)(1 + m_1 m_2) = m_2 - m_1.$$

Using this fact, find the family of curves that intersects each of the following families at an angle of 45°. In each case sketch both families of curves.

(a) $x - 2y = c$

(b) $x^2 + y^2 = c^2$

19. Find all plane curves such that the tangent line at each point (x, y) passes through the fixed point (a, b).

20. The line normal to a given curve at each point (x, y) on the curve passes through the point $(2, 0)$. If the curve contains the point $(2, 3)$, find its equation.

21. Find all plane curves for which the y axis bisects that part of the tangent line between the point of tangency and the x axis.

2.10   ELEMENTARY   MECHANICS

Some of the most important applications of first order differential equations are found in the realm of elementary mechanics. In this section

† This problem is based on R. H. Rainey, "Natural displacement of pollution from the Great Lakes," *Science*, **155** (1967) pp. 1242–1243; the information in the table was taken from that source.

we will consider some problems involving the motion of rigid bodies along a straight line. We will assume that such bodies obey Newton's (1642–1727) law of motion: *the product of the mass and the acceleration is equal to the external force.* In symbols,

$$F = ma, \tag{1}$$

where F is the external force, m is the mass of the body, and a is its acceleration in the direction of F. If the mass of the body is constant, then Eq. (1) can be put into the form

$$F = \frac{d}{dt}(mv) = \frac{dP}{dt}, \tag{2}$$

where v represents velocity, and $P = mv$ is the linear momentum.

Two systems of units are in common use. In the metric, or cgs system, the basic units are centimeters (length), grams (mass), and seconds (time). The unit of force, the dyne, is defined by Eq. (1) to be the force required to impart an acceleration of 1 cm/sec² to a mass of 1 gm. On the other hand, in the English system the basic units are feet (length), pounds (force), and seconds (time). The unit of mass, the slug, is defined by Eq. (1) to be that mass to which a force of 1 lb gives an acceleration of 1 ft/sec².

Now consider a body falling freely in a vacuum and close enough to the surface of the earth so that the only significant force acting on the body is its weight due to the earth's gravitational field. Equation (1) then takes the form

$$w = mg, \tag{3}$$

where w is the weight of the body and g denotes its acceleration due to gravity.

Even though the mass of the body remains constant, its weight and gravitational acceleration change with distance from the center of the earth's gravitational field. At sea level the value of g has been experimentally determined to be approximately 32 ft/sec² (English system), or 980 cm/sec² (metric system). It is customary to denote by g the gravitational acceleration at *sea level;* thus g is a constant. With this understanding Eq. (3) is exact only at sea level.

The general expression for the weight of a body of mass m is obtained from Newton's inverse-square law of gravitational attraction. If R is the radius of the earth, and x is the altitude above sea level, then

$$w(x) = \frac{K}{(x + R)^2},$$

where K is a constant. At $x = 0$ (sea level), $w = mg$; hence $K = mgR^2$, and

$$w(x) = \frac{mgR^2}{(x + R)^2}. \tag{4}$$

Expanding $(x + R)^{-2}$ in a Taylor series about $x = 0$ leads to

$$w(x) = mg\left(1 - 2\frac{x}{R} + \cdots\right). \tag{5}$$

It follows that if terms of the order of magnitude of x/R can be neglected in comparison with unity, then Eq. (4) can be replaced by the simpler approximation, Eq. (3). Thus, for motions in the vicinity of the earth's surface, or if extreme accuracy is not required, it is usually sufficient to use Eq. (3). In other cases, such as problems involving space flight, it may be necessary to use Eq. (4), or at least a better approximation to it than Eq. (3).

In many cases the external force F will include effects other than the weight of the body. For example, frictional forces due to the resistance offered by the air or other surrounding medium may need to be considered. Similarly, the effects of mass changes may be important, as in the case of a space vehicle which burns its fuel during flight.

In the problems we will consider here it is useful to describe the motion of the body with reference to some convenient coordinate system. We will always choose the x axis to be the line along which the motion takes place; the positive direction on the x axis can be chosen arbitrarily. Once the positive x direction is specified, a positive value of x indicates a displacement in this direction, a positive value of $v = dx/dt$ indicates the body is moving in the direction of the positive x axis, a positive value for a force F indicates it acts in the positive x direction, and so forth. The following examples are concerned with some typical problems.

Example 1. An object of mass m is dropped from rest in a medium which offers resistance proportional to $|v|$, the magnitude of the instantaneous velocity of the object.* Assuming the gravitational force to be constant, find the position and velocity of the object at any time t.

In this case it is convenient to draw the x axis positive downward with the origin at the initial position of the object; see Figure 2.8. The weight mg of the object then acts in the downward (positive) direction, but the resistance $k\,|v|$, where k is a positive constant, acts to impede the motion. When $v > 0$

FIGURE 2.8 $v > 0$.

---

* In general the resistance is a function of the speed, that is, the magnitude of the velocity. The assumption of a linear relation is reasonable only for comparatively low speeds. Where higher speeds are involved it may be necessary to assume that the resistance is proportional to some higher power of $|v|$, or even that it is given by some polynomial function of $|v|$.

the resistance is in the upward (negative) direction, and is thus given by $-kv$. When $v < 0$ the resistance acts downward and is still given by $-kv$. Thus in all cases Newton's law can be written as

$$m \frac{dv}{dt} = mg - kv$$

or

$$\frac{dv}{dt} + \frac{k}{m} v = g. \tag{6}$$

Equation (6) is a linear first order equation, and has the integrating factor $e^{kt/m}$. The solution of Eq. (6) is

$$v = \frac{mg}{k} + c_1 e^{-kt/m}. \tag{7}$$

The initial condition $v(0) = 0$ requires that $c_1 = -mg/k$; thus

$$v = \frac{mg}{k} (1 - e^{-kt/m}). \tag{8}$$

To obtain the position x of the body we replace v by dx/dt in Eq. (8); integration and use of the second initial condition $x(0) = 0$ gives

$$x = \frac{mg}{k} t - \frac{m^2 g}{k^2} (1 - e^{-kt/m}). \tag{9}$$

The position and velocity of the body at any time t are given by Eqs. (9) and (8) respectively.

It is worth noting that as $t \to \infty$ in Eq. (7) the velocity approaches the limiting value

$$v_l = \frac{mg}{k}. \tag{10}$$

The limiting velocity v_l does not depend on the initial conditions, but only on the mass of the object and the coefficient of resistance of the medium. Given either v_l or k, Eq. (10) provides a formula for calculating the other. As k approaches zero, that is, as the resistance diminishes, the limiting velocity increases without bound.

Example 2. A body of constant mass m is projected upward from the earth's surface with an initial velocity v_0. Assuming there is no air resistance, but taking into consideration the variation of the earth's gravitational field with altitude, find the smallest initial velocity for which the body will not return to the earth. This is the so-called "escape velocity."

Take the x axis positive upward, with the origin, on the surface of the earth; see Figure 2.9. The only force acting on the body is its weight, given by Eq. (4), which acts downward. Thus the equation of motion is

$$m\frac{dv}{dt} = -\frac{mgR^2}{(x+R)^2},\tag{11}$$

and the initial condition is

$$v(0) = v_0.\tag{12}$$

Since the force appearing on the right side of Eq. (11) is a function of x only, it is convenient to think of x, rather than t, as the independent variable. This requires that we express dv/dt in terms of dv/dx by the chain rule for differentiation; hence

$$\frac{dv}{dt} = \frac{dv}{dx}\frac{dx}{dt} = v\frac{dv}{dx},\tag{13}$$

and Eq. (11) is replaced by

$$v\frac{dv}{dx} = -\frac{gR^2}{(x+R)^2}.\tag{14}$$

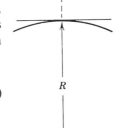

FIGURE 2.9

Separating the variables and integrating yields

$$\tfrac{1}{2}v^2 = \frac{gR^2}{x+R} + c.\tag{15}$$

Since $x = 0$ when $t = 0$, the initial condition (12) at $t = 0$ can be replaced by the condition that $v = v_0$ when $x = 0$. This requires that $c = \tfrac{1}{2}v_0^2 - gR$; therefore

$$v^2 = v_0^2 - 2gR + \frac{2gR^2}{x+R}.\tag{16}$$

The escape velocity is found by requiring that the velocity v given by Eq. (16) remain positive for all (positive) values of x. This condition will be met provided that $v_0^2 \geq 2gR$. Thus the escape velocity v_e is given by

$$v_e = (2gR)^{\frac{1}{2}};\tag{17}$$

the magnitude of v_e is approximately 6.9 miles/sec.

In calculating the escape velocity $v_e = (2gR)^{\frac{1}{2}}$, air resistance has been neglected. The actual escape velocity, including the effect of air resistance, is somewhat higher. On the other hand, the effective escape velocity can be significantly reduced if the body is transported a considerable distance above sea level before being fired. Both gravitational and frictional forces are thereby reduced; air resistance, in particular, diminishes quite rapidly with increasing altitude.

Bodies with Variable Mass. For a space vehicle whose initial mass m_0 contains a substantial supply of fuel which is burned in flight it is necessary to consider the change in the mass of the vehicle. In order to apply Eq. (2) to this situation we must take account not only of the momentum of the rocket, but also of that of the exhaust gases produced by the combustion of the fuel. We will assume that the exhaust gases are ejected from the vehicle at a constant velocity u relative to the vehicle, and that the total mass of the vehicle-fuel system (including the exhaust gases) remains constant. If $m(t)$ denotes the mass of the vehicle and its cargo at time t, and if $m_e(t)$ denotes the mass of the exhaust gases at this instant, then

$$m(t) + m_e(t) = m_0. \tag{18}$$

Applying Eq. (2) to the vehicle-gas system gives*

$$-mg = m\frac{dv}{dt} - u\frac{dm}{dt}, \tag{19}$$

where v is the velocity of the rocket. The second term on the right side of Eq. (19) results from a consideration of the contribution of the exhaust gases to the momentum of the system.

Example 3. Consider a space vehicle of initial mass m_0 projected upward from the surface of the earth with an initial velocity v_0. Assume that a part of the mass $m_f < m_0$ consists of fuel which is consumed at a constant rate β during the interval $(0, t_1)$. Assume that the exhaust speed $s = |u| = -u$ is also constant. Neglect air resistance and assume that the gravitational force is constant. Find an expression for the velocity of the vehicle as a function of time t.

The stated conditions imply that the mass of the vehicle is given by

$$m(t) = m_0 - \beta t, \qquad t < t_1. \tag{20}$$

At the time t_1 the mass of the vehicle has been reduced to the value $m_1 = m_0 - \beta t_1 = m_0 - m_f$. For $t < t_1$ the equation of motion (19) takes the form

$$-(m_0 - \beta t)g = (m_0 - \beta t)\frac{dv}{dt} - s\beta,$$

or

$$\frac{dv}{dt} = -g + \frac{s\beta}{m_0 - \beta t}. \tag{21}$$

---

* The details of the derivation are given in the Appendix beginning on page 82.

Integrating Eq. (21) gives

$$v = -gt - s \ln (m_0 - \beta t) + c.$$

The initial condition $v(0) = v_0$ requires that

$$c = v_0 + s \ln m_0,$$

and hence

$$v = v_0 - gt + s \ln \frac{m_0}{m_0 - \beta t}, \qquad t < t_1. \tag{22}$$

When the fuel is exhausted, at $t = t_1 = (m_0 - m_1)/\beta$, the vehicle has attained the velocity v_1,

$$v_1 = v_0 - \frac{gm_0}{\beta}\left(1 - \frac{m_1}{m_0}\right) + s \ln \frac{m_0}{m_1}. \tag{23}$$

If v_1 is at least as great as the escape velocity at the altitude attained at that instant, the vehicle will be able to leave the gravitational field of the earth. Otherwise, unless further stages are ignited, it will eventually return to the earth. It also follows from Eq. (22) that the velocity v increases with the exhaust speed s and the rate of burning β.

PROBLEMS

1. A body of constant mass m is projected vertically upward with an initial velocity v_0. Assuming the gravitational attraction of the earth to be constant, and neglecting all other forces acting on the body, find:
(a) the maximum height attained by the body;
(b) the time at which the maximum height is reached;
(c) the time at which the body returns to its starting point.

2. A body is thrown vertically downward with an initial velocity v_0 in a medium offering resistance proportional to the magnitude of the velocity. Find a relation between velocity v and time t. Find the limiting velocity v_l approached after a long time.

3. An object of mass m is dropped from rest in a medium offering resistance proportional to the magnitude of the velocity. Find the time interval which elapses before the velocity of the object reaches 90% of its limiting value.

4. A man and a motor boat together weigh 320 lbs. If the thrust of the motor is equivalent to a constant force of 10 lb in the direction of motion, and if the resistance of the water to the motion is equal numerically to twice the speed in feet/second, and if the boat is initially at rest, find:
(a) the velocity of the boat at time t;
(b) the limiting velocity.

5. A body with mass m is projected vertically downward with initial velocity v_0 in a medium offering resistance proportional to the square root of the magnitude of the velocity. Find the relation between the velocity v and the time t. Find the limiting velocity.

6. A body of mass m falls from rest in a medium offering resistance proportional to the square of the velocity. Find the relation between the velocity v and the time t. Find the limiting velocity.

7. A body of mass m falls in a medium offering resistance proportional to $|v|^r$, where r is a positive constant. Assuming the gravitational attraction to be constant, find the limiting velocity of the body.

8. A body of constant mass m is projected vertically upward with an initial velocity v_0 in a medium offering a resistance $k|v|$, where k is a constant. Neglecting changes in the gravitational force, find:
    (a) the maximum height x_m attained by the body;
    (b) the time t_m at which this maximum height is reached. Show also that t_m and x_m can be expressed as

$$t_m = \frac{v_0}{g}\left[1 - \frac{1}{2}\frac{kv_0}{mg} + \frac{1}{3}\left(\frac{kv_0}{mg}\right)^2 - \cdots\right],$$

$$x_m = \frac{v_0^2}{2g}\left[1 - \frac{2}{3}\frac{kv_0}{mg} + \frac{1}{2}\left(\frac{kv_0}{mg}\right)^2 - \cdots\right],$$

both series converging when $kv_0/mg < 1$.

9. A body falling in a relatively dense fluid, oil for example, is acted on by three forces (see Figure 2.10): a resistive force R, a buoyant force B, and its weight w due to gravity. The buoyant force is equal to the weight of the fluid displaced by the object. For a slowly moving spherical body of radius a, the resistive force is

FIGURE 2.10

given by Stokes' (1819–1903) law $R = 6\pi\mu a|v|$, where v is the velocity of the body, and μ is the coefficient of viscosity of the surrounding fluid. Find the limiting velocity of a solid sphere of radius a and density ρ falling freely in a medium of density ρ' and coefficient of viscosity μ.

10. (a) What is the weight of a body 1000 miles above the earth's surface if the body weighs 100 lb at sea level?

(b) The radius of the moon is approximately $\frac{27}{100}$ of the radius of the earth, and the average density of the moon is about $\frac{5}{8}$ of the average density of the earth. Find the apparent weight on the moon of an object weighing 100 lb on the surface of the earth.

11. A body of constant mass m is launched vertically upward from sea level with an initial velocity v_0 which does not exceed the escape velocity $v_e = (2gR)^{1/2}$. Neglecting air resistance, but considering the change of gravitational attraction with altitude, find the maximum altitude attained by the body. See Example 2.

12. Find the escape velocity for a body projected upward with an initial velocity v_0 from a point $x_0 = \xi R$ above the surface of the earth, where R is the radius of the earth and ξ is a constant. Neglect air resistance. Find the initial altitude from which the body must be launched in order to reduce the escape velocity to 85% of its value at the earth's surface.

13. Consider a rocket which, before launching, weighs 1200 lb, including 900 lb of fuel. Assume that the fuel burns evenly for a period of 60 sec, and that the exhaust speed of the rocket is 5000 ft/sec. If the rocket has no initial velocity, find its velocity at the end of 60 sec. Neglect air resistance and changes in the earth's gravitational field.

14. Consider a space vehicle of initial mass m_0 which starts from rest on the earth's surface. Assume that the rate of fuel consumption $\beta = -dm/dt$ is constant in the interval $0 < t < t_1$, and also that the exhaust speed s is constant. Assume further that the air resistance experienced by the vehicle is proportional to the magnitude of its velocity $v(t)$, but neglect the effect of air resistance on the exhaust gases, and also the change in the gravitational field with altitude. Show that the velocity of the vehicle satisfies the differential equation

$$m\frac{dv}{dt} + kv = -mg + s\beta, \qquad t < t_1$$

where $m(t) = m_0 - \beta t$. Solve this equation and obtain an expression for v at any time $t < t_1$.

*2.11   THE EXISTENCE AND UNIQUENESS THEOREM

In this section we will discuss the proof of Theorem 2.2, the fundamental existence and uniqueness theorem for first order initial value problems. This theorem states that under certain conditions on $f(x, y)$, the initial value problem

$$y' = f(x, y), \tag{1a}$$

$$y(x_0) = y_0 \tag{1b}$$

has a unique solution in some interval containing the point x_0.

In some cases (for example, if the differential equation is linear) the existence of a solution of the initial value problem (1) can be established directly by actually solving the problem and exhibiting a formula for the solution. However, in general this approach is not feasible because there is no method of solving Eq. (1a), which applies in all cases. Therefore, for the general case it is necessary to adopt an indirect approach that establishes the existence of a solution of Eqs. (1) but usually does not provide a means of finding it. The heart of this method is the construction of a sequence of functions which converges to a limit function that satisfies the initial value problem, although the members of the sequence individually do not. As a rule, it is impossible to compute explicitly more than a few members of the sequence; therefore the limit function can be found explicitly only in rare cases, and hence this method does not provide a useful way of actually solving initial value problems. Nevertheless, under the restrictions on $f(x, y)$ stated in Theorem 2.2, it is possible to show that the sequence in question converges and that the limit function has the desired properties. The argument is fairly intricate and depends, in part, on techniques and results that are usually encountered for the first time in a course on advanced calculus. Consequently, we will not go into all of the details of the proof here; we will, however, indicate its main features and point out some of the difficulties involved.

First of all, we note that it is sufficient to consider the problem in which the initial point (x_0, y_0) is the origin; that is, the problem

$$y' = f(x, y), \tag{2a}$$

$$y(0) = 0. \tag{2b}$$

If some other initial point is given, then we can always make a preliminary change of variables, corresponding to a translation of the coordinate axes, which will take the given point (x_0, y_0) into the origin. Specifically, we introduce new dependent and independent variables w and s, respectively, which are defined by the equations

$$w = y - y_0, \qquad s = x - x_0; \tag{3}$$

see also Figure 2.11. Thinking of w as a function of s, we have by the chain rule

$$\frac{dw}{ds} = \frac{dw}{dx}\frac{dx}{ds} = \frac{d}{dx}(y - y_0)\frac{dx}{ds} = \frac{dy}{dx}.$$

Denoting $f(x, y) = f(s + x_0, w + y_0)$ by $F(s, w)$, the initial value problem (1) is converted into the form

$$w'(s) = F[s, w(s)], \tag{4a}$$

$$w(0) = 0. \tag{4b}$$

Except for the names of the variables, Eqs. (4) are the same as Eqs. (2). Hereafter, we will consider the slightly simpler problem (2) rather than the original problem (1).

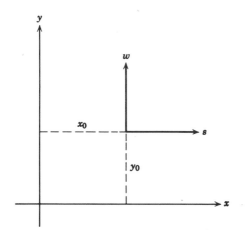

FIGURE 2.11

The existence and uniqueness theorem can now be stated in the following way.

Theorem 2.4.   *If f and $\partial f/\partial y$ are continuous in a rectangle R: $|x| \leq a$, $|y| \leq b$, then there is some interval $|x| \leq h \leq a$ in which there exists a unique solution $y = \phi(x)$ of the initial value problem (2)*

$$y' = f(x, y), \qquad y(0) = 0.$$

In order to prove this theorem it is necessary to transform the initial value problem (2) into a more convenient form. If we suppose temporarily that there is a function $y = \phi(x)$ which satisfies the initial value problem, then $f[x, \phi(x)]$ is a continuous function of x only. Hence we can integrate Eq. (2a) from the initial point $x = 0$ to an arbitrary value of x, obtaining

$$\phi(x) = \int_0^x f[t, \phi(t)] \, dt, \tag{5}$$

where Eq. (2b) has been used to eliminate $\phi(0)$.

Since Eq. (5) contains an integral of the unknown function ϕ, it is called an *integral equation*. This integral equation is not a formula for the solution of the initial value problem, but it does provide another relation which is satisfied by any solution of Eqs. (2). Conversely, suppose that there is a continuous function $y = \phi(x)$ that satisfies the integral equation (5); then this function also satisfies the initial value problem (2). To show this, we first substitute zero for x in Eq. (5), thus obtaining Eq. (2b). Further, since the integrand in Eq. (5) is continuous it follows from the fundamental theorem of calculus that $\phi'(x) = f[x, \phi(x)]$. Therefore the initial value problem and the integral equation are equivalent in the sense that any solution of one is also a solution of the other. It is more convenient to show that there is a unique solution of the integral equation in a certain interval $|x| \leq h$. The same conclusion will then also hold for the initial value problem.

One method of showing that the integral equation (5) has a unique solution is known as the *method of successive approximations*, or Picard's (1856–1941) method. In using this method we start by choosing an initial function ϕ_0, either arbitrarily or to approximate in some way the solution of the initial value problem. The simplest choice is to define ϕ_0 so that

$$\phi_0(x) = 0; \tag{6}$$

then ϕ_0 at least satisfies the initial condition (2b) although presumably not the differential equation (2a). The next approximation ϕ_1 is obtained by substituting $\phi_0(t)$ for $\phi(t)$ in the right side of Eq. (5), and calling the result of this operation $\phi_1(x)$. Thus

$$\phi_1(x) = \int_0^x f[t, \phi_0(t)] \, dt. \tag{7}$$

Similarly, ϕ_2 is obtained from ϕ_1:

$$\phi_2(x) = \int_0^x f[t, \phi_1(t)] \, dt, \tag{8}$$

and in general,

$$\phi_{n+1}(x) = \int_0^x f[t, \phi_n(t)] \, dt. \tag{9}$$

In this manner we generate the sequence of functions $\{\phi_n\} = \phi_0, \phi_1, \ldots, \phi_n, \ldots$. Each member of the sequence satisfies the initial condition (2b), but in general none satisfies the differential equation. However, if at some stage, say for $n = k$, we find that $\phi_{k+1}(x) = \phi_k(x)$, then it follows that ϕ_k is a solution of the integral equation (5). Hence ϕ_k is also a solution of the initial value problem (2), and the sequence is terminated at this point. In general, this will not occur, and it is necessary to consider the entire infinite sequence.

In order to establish Theorem 2.4 there are four principal questions which must be answered.

(i) Do all members of the sequence $\{\phi_n\}$ exist, or may the process break down at some stage?

(ii) Does the sequence converge?

(iii) What are the properties of the limit function; in particular, does it satisfy the integral equation (5), and hence the initial value problem (2)?

(iv) Is this the only solution, or may there be others?

We will first show how these questions can be answered in a specific and relatively simple example, and then comment on some of the difficulties that may be encountered in the general case.

Example.   Consider the initial value problem

$$y' = 2x(y + 1), \qquad y(0) = 0 \tag{10}$$

To solve this problem by the method of successive approximations we note first that if $y = \phi(x)$, then the corresponding integral equation is

$$\phi(x) = \int_0^x 2t[1 + \phi(t)] \, dt. \tag{11}$$

If the initial approximation is $\phi_0(x) = 0$, it follows that

$$\phi_1(x) = \int_0^x 2t[1 + \phi_0(t)] \, dt = \int_0^x 2t \, dt = x^2. \tag{12}$$

Similarly

$$\phi_2(x) = \int_0^x 2t[1 + \phi_1(t)] \, dt = \int_0^x 2t[1 + t^2] \, dt$$

$$= x^2 + \frac{x^4}{2}, \tag{13}$$

and

$$\phi_3(x) = \int_0^x 2t[1 + \phi_2(t)] \, dt = \int_0^x 2t\left[1 + t^2 + \frac{t^4}{2}\right] dt$$

$$= x^2 + \frac{x^4}{2} + \frac{x^6}{2 \cdot 3}. \tag{14}$$

Equations (12), (13), and (14) suggest that

$$\phi_n(x) = x^2 + \frac{x^4}{2!} + \frac{x^6}{3!} + \cdots + \frac{x^{2n}}{n!} \tag{15}$$

for each $n \geq 1$, and this result can be established by mathematical induction. Clearly Eq. (15) is true for $n = 1$, and we must show that if it is true for $n = k$, then it also holds for $n = k + 1$. We have

$$\phi_{k+1}(x) = \int_0^x 2t[1 + \phi_k(t)] \, dt$$

$$= \int_0^x 2t\left(1 + t^2 + \frac{t^4}{2!} + \cdots + \frac{t^{2k}}{k!}\right) dt$$

$$= x^2 + \frac{x^4}{2!} + \frac{x^6}{3!} + \cdots + \frac{x^{2k+2}}{(k + 1)!}, \tag{16}$$

and the inductive proof is complete.

It is clear from Eq. (15) that $\phi_n(x)$ is the nth partial sum in the infinite series

$$\sum_{k=1}^{\infty} x^{2k}/k! \, ; \tag{17}$$

hence $\lim_{n \to \infty} \phi_n(x)$ exists if and only if the series (17) converges. Applying the ratio test, we see that for each x

$$\left| \frac{x^{2k+2}}{(k+1)!} \frac{k!}{x^{2k}} \right| = \frac{x^2}{k+1} \to 0 \quad \text{as} \quad k \to \infty; \tag{18}$$

thus the series (17) converges for all x, and its sum $\phi(x)$ is the limit* of the sequence $\{\phi_n(x)\}$. Further, since the series (17) is a Taylor series, it can be differentiated or integrated term by term as long as x remains within the interval of convergence, which in this case is the whole x axis. Therefore we can verify by direct computation that $\phi(x) = \sum_{k=1}^{\infty} x^{2k}/k!$ is a solution of the integral equation (11). Alternatively, by substituting $\phi(x)$ for y in Eq. (10) we can verify that this function also satisfies the initial value problem.

Finally, to deal with the question of uniqueness, let us suppose that the initial value problem has another solution ψ, different from ϕ. We will show that this leads to a contradiction. Since ϕ and ψ both satisfy the integral equation (11), we have by subtraction that

$$\phi(x) - \psi(x) = \int_0^x 2t[\phi(t) - \psi(t)] \, dt.$$

Taking absolute values of both sides we have, if $x > 0$,

$$|\phi(x) - \psi(x)| \leq \int_0^x 2t \, |\phi(t) - \psi(t)| \, dt.$$

If we restrict x to lie in the interval $0 \leq x \leq A/2$, where A is arbitrary, then $2t \leq A$, and

$$|\phi(x) - \psi(x)| \leq A \int_0^x |\phi(t) - \psi(t)| \, dt. \tag{19}$$

It is convenient at this point to introduce the function U defined by

$$U(x) = \int_0^x |\phi(t) - \psi(t)| \, dt. \tag{20}$$

Then it follows at once that

$$U(0) = 0, \tag{21}$$

$$U(x) \geq 0, \quad \text{for} \quad x \geq 0. \tag{22}$$

Further, U is differentiable, and $U'(x) = |\phi(x) - \psi(x)|$. Hence, by Eq. (19),

$$U'(x) - AU(x) \leq 0. \tag{23}$$

---

* In this case it is possible to identify ϕ in terms of elementary functions, namely, $\phi(x) = e^{x^2} - 1$. However, this is irrelevant to the discussion of existence and uniqueness.

Multiplying Eq. (23) by the positive quantity e^{-Ax} gives

$$[e^{-Ax}U(x)]' \le 0. \tag{24}$$

Then, upon integrating Eq. (24) from zero to x and using Eq. (21), we obtain

$$e^{-Ax}U(x) \le 0 \qquad \text{for} \qquad x \ge 0.$$

Hence $U(x) \le 0$ for $x \ge 0$, and in conjunction with Eq. (22), this requires that $U(x) = 0$ for each $x \ge 0$. Thus $U'(x) \equiv 0$, and therefore $\psi(x) \equiv \phi(x)$, which contradicts the original hypothesis. Consequently, there cannot be two different solutions of the initial value problem for $x \ge 0$. A slight modification of this argument leads to the same conclusion for $x \le 0$.

Returning now to the general problem of solving the integral equation (5), let us consider briefly each of the questions raised earlier.

(i) Do all members of the sequence $\{\phi_n\}$ exist? In the example f and $\partial f/\partial y$ were continuous in the whole xy plane, and each member of the sequence could be explicitly calculated. In contrast, in the general case f and $\partial f/\partial y$ are assumed to be continuous only in the rectangle R: $|x| \le a$, $|y| \le b$; see Figure 2.12. Furthermore, the members of the sequence cannot as a rule be explicitly determined. The danger is that at some stage, say for $n = k$, the graph of $y = \phi_k(x)$ may contain points that lie outside of the rectangle R. Hence at the next stage—in the computation of $\phi_{k+1}(x)$—it would be necessary to evaluate $f(x, y)$ at points where it is not known to be continuous or even to exist. Thus the calculation of $\phi_{k+1}(x)$ might be impossible.

To avoid this danger it may be necessary to restrict x to a smaller interval than $|x| \le a$. To find such an interval it is necessary to make use of the fact

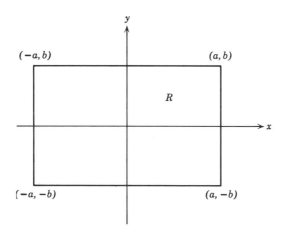

FIGURE 2.12

that a continuous function on a closed region is bounded. Hence f is bounded on R; thus there exists a positive number M such that

$$|f(x, y)| \leq M, \qquad (x, y) \text{ in } R. \tag{25}$$

We have mentioned before that

$$\phi_n(0) = 0$$

for each n. Since $f[x, \phi_k(x)]$ is equal to $\phi'_{k+1}(x)$ the maximum absolute slope of the graph of the equation $y = \phi_{k+1}(x)$ is M. Since this graph contains the point $(0, 0)$, it must lie in the wedge-shaped shaded region in Figure 2.13.

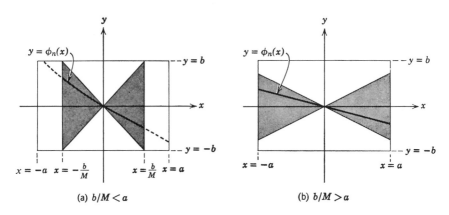

(a) $b/M < a$ (b) $b/M > a$

FIGURE 2.13

Hence the point $[x, \phi_{k+1}(x)]$ remains in R at least as long as R contains the wedge-shaped region, which is for $|x| \leq b/M$. We will hereafter consider only the rectangle D: $|x| \leq h$, $|y| \leq b$, where h is equal either to a or to b/M, whichever is smaller. With this restriction all members of the sequence $\{\phi_n(x)\}$ exist. Note that if $b/M < a$, then a larger value of h can be obtained by finding a better bound for $|f(x, y)|$, provided that M is not already equal to the maximum value of $|f(x, y)|$.

(ii) Does the sequence $\{\phi_n(x)\}$ converge? As in the example, we can identify $\phi_n(x) = \phi_1(x) + [\phi_2(x) - \phi_1(x)] + \cdots + [\phi_n(x) - \phi_{n-1}(x)]$ as the nth partial sum of the series

$$\phi_1(x) + \sum_{k=1}^{\infty} [\phi_{k+1}(x) - \phi_k(x)]. \tag{26}$$

The convergence of the sequence $\{\phi_n(x)\}$ is established by showing that the series (26) converges. To do this it is necessary to estimate the magnitude $|\phi_{k+1}(x) - \phi_k(x)|$ of the general term. The argument by which this is done is indicated in Problems 3 through 6, and will be omitted here. Assuming that the sequence converges, we will denote the limit function by ϕ, so that

$$\phi(x) = \lim_{n \to \infty} \phi_n(x). \tag{27}$$

(iii) What are the properties of the limit function ϕ? In the first place, we would like to know that ϕ is continuous. This is not, however, a necessary consequence of the convergence of the sequence $\{\phi_n(x)\}$, even though each member of the sequence is continuous itself. In Chapter 10 we will encounter some problems in which a sequence of continuous functions converges to a discontinuous limit. A simple example of this phenomenon is given in Problem 1. One way to show that ϕ is continuous is to show not only that the sequence $\{\phi_n\}$ converges but that it converges in a certain manner, known as uniform convergence. We will not take up this question here but will note only that the argument referred to in paragraph (ii) is sufficient to establish the uniform convergence of the sequence $\{\phi_n\}$ and hence the continuity of the limit function ϕ in the interval $|x| \leq h$.

Now let us return to Eq. (9),

$$\phi_{n+1}(x) = \int_0^x f[t, \phi_n(t)] \, dt. \tag{9}$$

Allowing n to approach ∞ on both sides, we obtain

$$\phi(x) = \lim_{n \to \infty} \int_0^x f[t, \phi_n(t)] \, dt. \tag{28}$$

We would like to interchange the operations of integration and taking the limit on the right side of Eq. (28), so as to obtain

$$\phi(x) = \int_0^x \lim_{n \to \infty} f[t, \phi_n(t)] \, dt. \tag{29}$$

In general, such an interchange is not permissible (see Problem 2, for example), but once again the fact that the sequence $\{\phi_n(x)\}$ not only converges but converges uniformly comes to the rescue and allows us to take the limiting operation inside the integral sign. Next we wish to take the limit inside the function f, which would give

$$\phi(x) = \int_0^x f\left[t, \lim_{n \to \infty} \phi_n(t)\right] dt \tag{30}$$

and hence

$$\phi(x) = \int_0^x f[t, \phi(t)] \, dt. \tag{31}$$

The statement that $\lim_{n \to \infty} f[t, \phi_n(t)] = f[t, \lim_{n \to \infty} \phi_n(t)]$ is equivalent to the statement that f is continuous in its second variable, which is known by hypothesis. Hence Eq. (31) is valid and the function ϕ satisfies the integral equation (5). Therefore ϕ is also a solution of the initial value problem (2).

(iv) May there be other solutions of the integral equation (5) besides $y = \phi(x)$? To show the uniqueness of the solution $y = \phi(x)$ we can proceed much as in the example. First assume the contrary, that is, the existence of another solution $y = \psi(x)$. It is then possible to show (see Problem 7) that the difference $\phi(x) - \psi(x)$ satisfies the inequality

$$|\phi(x) - \psi(x)| \leq A \int_0^x |\phi(t) - \psi(t)|\, dt \tag{32}$$

for $0 \leq x \leq h$ and for a suitable positive number A. From this point the argument is identical to that given in the example, and we conclude that there is no solution of the initial value problem (2) other than that obtained by the method of successive approximations.

PROBLEMS

1. Let $\phi_n(x) = x^n$ for $0 \leq x \leq 1$, and show that

$$\lim_{n \to \infty} \phi_n(x) = \begin{cases} 0, & 0 \leq x < 1, \\ 1, & x = 1. \end{cases}$$

This example shows that a sequence of continuous functions may converge to a limit function that is discontinuous.

2. Consider the sequence $\phi_n(x) = 2nxe^{-nx^2}$, $0 \leq x \leq 1$.
(a) Show that $\lim_{n \to \infty} \phi_n(x) = 0$ for each x in $0 \leq x \leq 1$ and hence that

$$\int_0^1 \lim_{n \to \infty} \phi_n(x)\, dx = 0.$$

(b) Show that $\int_0^1 2nxe^{-nx^2}\, dx = 1 - e^{-n}$ and hence that

$$\lim_{n \to \infty} \int_0^1 2nxe^{-nx^2}\, dx = 1.$$

This example shows that it is not necessarily true that

$$\lim_{n \to \infty} \int_a^b \phi_n(x)\, dx = \int_a^b \lim_{n \to \infty} \phi_n(x)\, dx$$

even though $\lim_{n \to \infty} \phi_n(x)$ exists and is continuous.

In Problems 3 through 6 we indicate how to prove that the sequence $\{\phi_n(x)\}$, defined by Eqs. (6) through (9), converges.

3. If $\partial f/\partial y$ is continuous in the rectangle D, show that there is a positive constant K such that

$$|f(x, y_1) - f(x, y_2)| \leq K|y_1 - y_2|$$

where (x, y_1) and (x, y_2) are any two points in D having the same x coordinate. *Hint:* Use the mean value theorem for partial derivatives, and choose K to be the maximum value of $|\partial f/\partial y|$ in D.

4. If $\phi_{n-1}(x)$ and $\phi_n(x)$ are members of the sequence $\{\phi_n(x)\}$, use the result of Problem 3 to show that

$$|f[x, \phi_n(x)] - f[x, \phi_{n-1}(x)]| \leq K|\phi_n(x) - \phi_{n-1}(x)|.$$

5. (a) Show that if $|x| \leq h$, then

$$|\phi_1(x)| \leq M|x|$$

where M is chosen so that $|f(x, y)| \leq M$ for (x, y) in D.

(b) Use the results of Problem 4 and part (a) of Problem 5 to show that

$$|\phi_2(x) - \phi_1(x)| \leq \frac{MK|x|^2}{2}.$$

(c) Show, by mathematical induction, that

$$|\phi_n(x) - \phi_{n-1}(x)| \leq \frac{MK^{n-1}|x|^n}{n!} \leq \frac{MK^{n-1}h^n}{n!}.$$

6. Note that

$$\phi_n(x) = \phi_1(x) + [\phi_2(x) - \phi_1(x)] + \cdots + [\phi_n(x) - \phi_{n-1}(x)].$$

(a) Show that

$$|\phi_n(x)| \leq |\phi_1(x)| + |\phi_2(x) - \phi_1(x)| + \cdots + |\phi_n(x) - \phi_{n-1}(x)|.$$

(b) Use the results of Problem 5 to show that

$$|\phi_n(x)| \leq \frac{M}{K}\left[Kh + \frac{(Kh)^2}{2!} + \cdots + \frac{(Kh)^n}{n!}\right].$$

(c) Show that the sum in part (b) converges as $n \to \infty$, and hence show that the sum in part (a) also converges as $n \to \infty$. Conclude therefore that the sequence $\{\phi_n(x)\}$ converges, since it is the sequence of partial sums of a convergent infinite series.

7. In this problem we deal with the question of uniqueness of the solution of the integral equation (5),

$$\phi(x) = \int_0^x f[t, \phi(t)]\, dt.$$

(a) Suppose that ϕ and ψ are two solutions of Eq. (5). Show that

$$\phi(x) - \psi(x) = \int_0^x \{f[t, \phi(t)] - f[t, \psi(t)]\}\, dt.$$

(b) Show that

$$|\phi(x) - \psi(x)| \leq \int_0^x |f[t, \phi(t)] - f[t, \psi(t)]|\, dt.$$

(c) Use the result of Problem 3 to show that

$$|\phi(x) - \psi(x)| \leq K \int_0^x |\phi(t) - \psi(t)|\, dt,$$

where K is an upper bound for $|\partial f/\partial y|$ in D. This is the same as Eq. (32), and the rest of the proof may be constructed as indicated in the text.

*2.12 THE EXISTENCE THEOREM FROM A MORE MODERN VIEWPOINT

The existence and uniqueness theorem and the method of proof discussed above go back to the nineteenth century. It may be worthwhile to consider this theorem briefly from a more modern point of view which has proved increasingly valuable in recent years. In order to introduce the main idea in a simpler and more familiar setting, we first recall certain properties of continuous functions.

Lemma (*Intermediate Value Property*). *If the function f is continuous for $a \leq x \leq b$, and $f(a) \geq 0$, $f(b) \leq 0$, then there is at least one point ξ in $a \leq x \leq b$ such that $f(\xi) = 0$.*

In other words, a continuous function cannot change sign without passing through zero at least once (see Figure 2.14). There may of course be more than one point ξ where $f(\xi)$ is zero. Stated in geometrical terms, the Lemma appears obvious, but its analytical proof ultimately rests on a profound property (the completeness property) of the real number system, and we will omit it. The following corollary is an immediate consequence of the intermediate value property.

Corollary 1. *If the function g is continuous for $a \leq x \leq b$ and if $a \leq g(x) \leq b$, then there is at least one point ξ in $a \leq x \leq b$ such that $g(\xi) = \xi$.*

To establish the Corollary let $f(x) = g(x) - x$; then f satisfies the conditions of the Lemma. Hence there is at least one point ξ where $f(\xi) = 0$, and hence $g(\xi) = \xi$ as well.

It is worthwhile to give a geometrical interpretation to this Corollary (see Figure 2.15). The graph of the equation $y = g(x)$ lies in the strip $a \leq y \leq b$, and must therefore pass from one side to the other of the line $y = x$. The coordinates of the point of intersection give the value ξ named

FIGURE 2.14

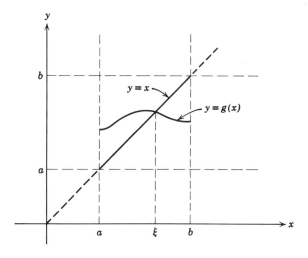

FIGURE 2.15

in the Corollary. If we think of the function g as a mapping or transformation of the interval $[a, b]$ on the x axis into the interval $[a, b]$ on the y axis, then the point ξ is left unchanged, or is mapped into itself. Consequently, ξ is called a *fixed point* of the transformation defined by g. In these terms the Corollary can be restated in the following way.

Corollary 2. *If g is a continuous function (transformation) and maps the closed interval $[a, b]$ into itself, then g has at least one fixed point.*

The idea of a fixed point of a transformation can be extended to transformations more general than continuous functions of a single real variable. Recall that in the last section we showed that the initial value problem

$$y' = f(x, y), \qquad y(0) = 0 \tag{1}$$

is equivalent to the integral equation

$$\phi(x) = \int_0^x f[t, \phi(t)]\, dt. \tag{2}$$

Now the operator indicated by the right side of Eq. (2) can be applied to any continuous function ϕ, whether it is a solution of the initial value problem (1) or not. Let us denote this operator by T; the result of this operation is a new function $T\phi$, whose value at a point x is given by

$$(T\phi)(x) = \int_0^x f[t, \phi(t)]\, dt. \tag{3}$$

We speak of T as an operator or transformation that acts over a certain set of functions as its domain and produces another set of functions as its range. To preserve the geometrical analogy we refer to such sets of functions as "spaces" of functions or "function spaces," and to individual functions as "points" in the "space."

The integral equation (2), when restated in terms of the operator T defined by Eq. (3), takes the form

$$\phi(x) = (T\phi)(x) \quad \text{or} \quad \phi = T\phi. \tag{4}$$

Hence the problem of solving the integral equation is exactly the same as that of finding fixed points of T.

Corollary 2 can be extended to deal with more general operators such as T. It is necessary first of all to develop the concept of continuity as it pertains to such operators. Then one must identify a suitable set of functions to serve as the domain of the operator. Once this has been done, it is possible to show that if a continuous transformation maps a suitable set of functions into itself, then there is at least one function that is left unchanged and is therefore a fixed point of the operator. If the operator is that defined by Eq. (3), then this fixed point constitutes a solution of the initial value problem (2). Thus an existence theorem for the initial value problem can be considered as a far-reaching generalization of the simple property of continuous functions stated in Corollary 1.

APPENDIX

Derivation of Equation of Motion of Body with Variable Mass.   To derive Eq. (19) of Section 2.10 we can proceed in the following way. Assuming that the total mass of the vehicle-fuel-exhaust system remains at the constant value m_0, we have

$$m(t) + m_e(t) = m_0, \tag{1}$$

where $m(t)$ and $m_e(t)$ are the mass of the vehicle (including fuel) and the mass of the exhaust gases respectively. Applying Newton's law to the total system gives

$$F = \frac{dP}{dt} = \frac{dP_r}{dt} + \frac{dP_e}{dt}, \tag{2}$$

where $P_r(t)$, $P_e(t)$, and $P(t)$ refer to the linear momenta of the vehicle, the exhaust gases, and the entire system respectively. In the present discussion we will assume that the only external force acting on the entire system is due to gravity. Neglecting resistive forces and variations in the gravitational field, it follows that

$$F = -m_0 g. \tag{3}$$

If $v(t)$ denotes the velocity of the vehicle at time t, then $P_r(t) = m(t)v(t)$, and

$$\frac{dP_r}{dt} = \frac{dm}{dt} v + m \frac{dv}{dt}. \tag{4}$$

On the other hand, the calculation of the momentum P_e of the exhaust gases is rendered more complicated by the fact that different portions of the exhaust gases have different velocities. Suppose that we think of the gas as being ejected continuously at a velocity u relative to the vehicle, and let $\Delta m_e(\tau)$ be the mass of gas ejected during the short time interval $(\tau, \tau + d\tau)$. The initial velocity of this mass element is approximately $v(\tau) + u$. Assuming that since its ejection it has been subject to the influence of gravitational forces only, the equation of motion of the mass element $\Delta m_e(\tau)$ is

$$\Delta m_e \frac{dv_e}{dt} = -g\,\Delta m_e,$$

where $v_e(t, \tau)$ is the velocity at time t of the gas element created at time τ. Hence $v_e(t, \tau) = -gt + c(\tau)$. The quantity $c(\tau)$ is determined from the condition that at time $t = \tau$ the velocity v_e is given by $v(\tau) + u$. Hence $c(\tau) = v(\tau) + u + g\tau$, and

$$v_e(t, \tau) = -(t - \tau)g + v(\tau) + u.$$

The momentum of the mass element Δm_e is thus equal to $v_e(t, \tau)\,\Delta m_e$; the total momentum $P_e(t)$ of all of the ejected gas is therefore given by the integral

$$P_e(t) = \int v_e(t, \tau)\,dm_e$$

taken over the entire gas. If the propulsion process originated at time $t = 0$, and has continued until the present time t, then $P_e(t)$ can also be represented by a time integral over the interval $(0, t)$. Thus

$$P_e(t) = \int_0^t v_e(t, \tau)\,\frac{dm_e}{d\tau}(\tau)\,d\tau$$

$$= \int_0^t [-(t - \tau)g + v(\tau) + u]\,\frac{dm_e}{d\tau}(\tau)\,d\tau,$$

or, since $dm_e/dt = -dm/dt$ from Eq. (1),

$$P_e(t) = \int_0^t [(t - \tau)g - v(\tau) - u]\,\frac{dm}{d\tau}(\tau)\,d\tau. \tag{5}$$

To compute dP_e/dt it is necessary to differentiate the integral in Eq. (5). Contributions to dP_e/dt result from the presence of the parameter t under the integral sign, as well as from its presence in the upper limit. We obtain

$$\frac{dP_e}{dt}(t) = g\int_0^t \frac{dm}{d\tau}(\tau)\,d\tau - [v(t) + u]\frac{dm}{dt}(t)$$

$$= g[m(t) - m(0)] - [v(t) + u]\frac{dm}{dt}(t)$$

$$= g[m(t) - m_0] - [v(t) + u]\frac{dm}{dt}(t), \tag{6}$$

where the fact that initially the mass of the vehicle comprises the total mass of the system has been used in the last step.

The equation of motion of the space vehicle of varying mass is obtained by substituting for F, dP_r/dt, and dP_e/dt in Eq. (2) the expressions found in Eqs. (3), (4), and (6) respectively. The result, after some obvious cancelations, is

$$-mg = m\frac{dv}{dt} - u\frac{dm}{dt}. \tag{7}$$

REFERENCES

A fuller discussion of the proof of the fundamental existence and uniqueness theorem can be found in many more advanced books on differential equations. Two that are reasonably accessible to elementary readers are:

Coddington, E. A., *An Introduction to Ordinary Differential Equations*, Prentice-Hall, Englewood Cliffs, N.J., 1961.
Brauer, F. and Nohel, J., *Ordinary Differential Equations*, Benjamin, New York, 1967.

A useful catalog of differential equations and their solutions is contained in the following book:

Kamke, E., *Differentialgleichungen Lösungsmethoden und Lösungen*, Chelsea, New York, 1948.

Although the text is in German, very little knowledge of German is required to consult the list of solved problems.

CHAPTER 3

Second Order Linear Equations

3.1 INTRODUCTION

The general second order differential equation is an equation of the form

$$F(x, y, y', y'') = 0. \tag{1}$$

The theory associated with such an equation is quite complicated. We will therefore begin by restricting our attention to equations which can be solved for y'', that is, equations which can be written in the form

$$y'' = f(x, y, y'). \tag{2}$$

For the first order differential equation $y' = f(x, y)$ we found that there is a solution containing one arbitrary constant. Since a second order equation involves a second derivative and hence, roughly speaking, two integrations are required to find a solution, it is natural to expect to find solutions of Eq. (2) containing two arbitrary constants. For example, the solution of

$$y'' = g(x) \tag{3}$$

is

$$y = \phi(x) = c_1 + c_2 x + \int^x \left[\int^t g(s) \, ds \right] dt, \tag{4}$$

where c_1 and c_2 are arbitrary constants. For a first order equation it was sufficient to specify the value of the solution at one point to determine a unique integral curve. Since we expect the solution of a second order equation to contain two arbitrary constants, in order to obtain a unique solution it will be necessary to specify two conditions, for example, the value of the solution y_0 and its derivative y_0' at a point x_0. These conditions are referred to as *initial conditions*. Thus to determine uniquely an integral curve of a second order equation it is necessary to specify not only a point through which it passes, but also the slope of the curve at the point.

To insure the existence of a solution of Eq. (2) satisfying prescribed initial conditions it is necessary to postulate certain properties for the function f. The situation is governed by the following existence and uniqueness theorem.

Theorem 3.1. *If the functions f, f_y, and f_v are continuous in an open region R of the three dimensional xyv space, and if the point (x_0, y_0, y_0') is in R, then in some interval about x_0 there exists a unique solution $y = \phi(x)$ of the differential equation (2),*

$$y'' = f(x, y, y'),$$

which satisfies the prescribed initial conditions

$$y(x_0) = y_0, \qquad y'(x_0) = y_0'. \tag{5}$$

The proof of this theorem is similar to that for the first order equation given in Section 2.11. Usually in carrying out the proof it is convenient to replace the second order equation by an equivalent system of two first order equations (see Chapter 7). Proofs can be found in many more advanced books, for example, Coddington [Chapter 6] or Ince [Chapter 3].

Even though the existence of a solution of Eq. (2) is guaranteed under the conditions of Theorem 3.1, it may not be possible to determine a convenient analytical expression for the solution unless f is a sufficiently simple function. Just as in the case of first order equations we distinguish between linear and nonlinear second order equations. The *general second order linear equation* is of the form

$$P(x)\frac{d^2y}{dx^2} + Q(x)\frac{dy}{dx} + R(x)y = G(x), \tag{6}$$

where P, Q, R, and G are given functions.

A simple but important example of a second order linear differential equation is the equation governing the motion of a mass on a spring:

$$m\frac{d^2u}{dt^2} + c\frac{du}{dt} + ku = F(t), \tag{7}$$

where m, c, and k are constants and F is a prescribed function. This equation is derived in Section 3.7. Other examples are Legendre's* equation

$$(1 - x^2)y'' - 2xy' + \alpha(\alpha + 1)y = 0, \tag{8}$$

of order α, and Bessel's† equation of order ν,

$$x^2y'' + xy' + (x^2 - \nu^2)y = 0, \tag{9}$$

---

* A. M. Legendre (1752–1833) was a distinguished French mathematician whose primary work was in the fields of elliptic functions and theory of numbers. The Legendre functions, which are solutions of the differential equation bearing his name, arose from his studies of the attraction of spheroids.

† F. W. Bessel (1784–1846) was a German mathematician who made fundamental contributions in the fields of astronomy, geodesy, and celestial mechanics. He was the first person to make a systematic analysis of the solutions (known as Bessel functions) of the equation that bears his name.

where α and ν are constants, often integers. Bessel's equation arises in many different physical situations, particularly in problems involving circular geometry, such as the determination of the temperature distribution in a circular plate. Legendre's equation often occurs in physical situations involving spherical geometry.

If Eq. (2) is not of the form (6) it is said to be nonlinear. Although the theory of nonlinear second order differential equations is fairly difficult, there are two special cases where it is possible to simplify the general second order nonlinear equation (2). These occur when either the variable x or the variable y is missing in $f(x, y, y')$; that is, when Eq. (2) is of the form

$$y'' = f(x, y') \tag{10}$$

or

$$y'' = f(y, y'). \tag{11}$$

In these cases it is always possible to reduce Eq. (10) or Eq. (11) to a first order equation for $v = y'$. Provided that the first order equation is of a type discussed in Chapter 2, we can solve that equation for v, and one more integration yields the solution of the original differential equation. This is discussed in Problems 1, 2, and 3 at the end of this section.

The rest of this chapter and the next chapter are devoted to methods of solving second order linear differential equations. Although there is no specific formula for the solution of Eq. (6), as was the case for the first order linear equation, there is an extensive mathematical theory for second order linear equations. In the following discussion we will assume, unless otherwise stated, that the functions P, Q, R, and G in Eq. (6) are continuous on some interval $\alpha < x < \beta$ (in some problems the interval may be unbounded, that is, α may be $-\infty$ and/or β may be $+\infty$), and that, further, the function P is nowhere zero in the interval. In this case we can divide Eq. (6) by $P(x)$ and obtain an equation of the form

$$\frac{d^2y}{dx^2} + p(x)\frac{dy}{dx} + q(x)y = g(x). \tag{12}$$

Notice that the above assumptions are fulfilled for Eq. (7) on $-\infty < x < \infty$; for Legendre's equation on the intervals, $-1 < x < 1$, or $x > 1$, or $x < -1$; and for Bessel's equation on any interval not including the origin.

If we write Eq. (12) in the form of Eq. (2), the function f is given by

$$f(x, y, y') = -p(x)y' - q(x)y + g(x). \tag{13}$$

Since $\partial f(x, y, y')/\partial y = -q(x)$ and $\partial f(x, y, y')/\partial y' = -p(x)$ are continuous, the existence and uniqueness of a solution of Eq. (12) satisfying the initial conditions $y(x_0) = y_0$, $y'(x_0) = y_0'$, $\alpha < x_0 < \beta$, in some interval about x_0 follows from Theorem 3.1. However, just as for first order equations, the existence and uniqueness theorem for second order equations can be stated in a stronger form for linear equations than for nonlinear ones.

Theorem 3.2.   *If the functions p, q, and g are continuous on the open interval $\alpha < x < \beta$, then there exists one and only one function $y = \phi(x)$ satisfying the differential equation (12),*

$$y'' + p(x)y' + q(x)y = g(x),$$

on the entire interval $\alpha < x < \beta$, and the prescribed initial conditions (5),

$$y(x_0) = y_0, \qquad y'(x_0) = y_0',$$

at a particular point x_0 in the interval.

To illustrate one use of this theorem consider the following simple examples.

Example 1.   Find the solution of the differential equation

$$y'' + y = 0,$$

which satisfies the initial conditions $y(0) = 0$, $y'(0) = 1$. It is easily verified that $\sin x$ and $\cos x$ are solutions of the differential equation. Further $y = \sin x$ satisfies $y(0) = 0$, $y'(0) = 1$; hence, according to Theorem 3.2, $y = \sin x$ is the unique solution of the problem.

Example 2.   What is the only solution of

$$y'' + p(x)y' + q(x)y = 0, \qquad \alpha < x < \beta,$$

satisfying the initial conditions $y(x_0) = 0$, $y'(x_0) = 0$, where x_0 is a point in the interval $\alpha < x < \beta$? Since $y = 0$ satisfies both the differential equation and the initial conditions, it is the unique solution.

In Theorems 3.1 and 3.2 it is important to note that the initial conditions which determine a unique solution of Eq. (2) or Eq. (12) are conditions on the value of the solution and its first derivative at a fixed point in the interval. In contrast, the question of finding a solution of, say, Eq. (12) satisfying conditions of the form $y(x_0) = A$, $y(x_1) = B$ where x_0 and x_1 are different points in the interval $\alpha < x < \beta$ is not covered by this theorem. Indeed, the latter problem may not always have a solution. Such problems are known as *boundary value problems* and will be discussed in Chapters 10 and 11.

In order to solve the second order differential equation (12),

$$y'' + p(x)y' + q(x)y = g(x),$$

we will find it is necessary only to solve the *homogeneous,** or *reduced*, or *complementary* equation

$$y'' + p(x)y' + q(x)y = 0 \tag{14}$$

---

* Note that the use of the word homogeneous here is not related to its use in the discussion of first order homogeneous differential equations in Section 2.7.

obtained from Eq. (12) by setting $g(x) = 0$. Once the solution of the homogeneous equation (14) is known we can, by a general method, solve the nonhomogeneous equation (12). The next section contains some general results about the homogeneous equation (14). Then in Section 3.5 we shall show how Eq. (14) can be solved in the particular case that the functions p and q are constants. Even this case is of considerable practical importance; for example, the equation for the motion of a mass on a spring has constant coefficients. In Section 3.6 we shall turn our attention to the nonhomogeneous equation (12). The rest of the chapter is devoted to applications in the areas of mechanical vibrations and electric networks.

PROBLEMS

1. For a second order differential equation of the form $y'' = f(x, y')$, the substitution $v = y'$, $v' = y''$ leads to a first order equation of the form $v' = f(x, v)$. Provided that this equation can be solved for v, y can be obtained by integrating $dy/dx = v(x)$. Notice that one arbitrary constant is obtained in solving the first order equation for v, and a second is obtained in the integration for y. Solve the following differential equations:

(a) $x^2 y'' + 2xy' - 1 = 0$, $\quad x > 0$ $\qquad$ (b) $xy'' + y' = 1$, $\quad x > 0$

(c) $y'' + x(y')^2 = 0$ $\qquad\qquad\qquad\qquad$ (d) $2x^2 y'' + (y')^3 = 2xy'$, $\quad x > 0$

2. Consider a second order differential equation of the form $y'' = f(y, y')$. If we let v equal y', we obtain $v' = f(y, v)$. This equation contains the variables v, x, and y and hence is not of the form of the first order equations discussed in Chapter 2. It is possible to eliminate the variable x by thinking of y as the independent variable; then by the chain rule

$$\frac{dv}{dx} = \frac{dv}{dy}\frac{dy}{dx} = v\frac{dv}{dy},$$

and hence the original differential equation can be written as

$$v\frac{dv}{dy} = f(y, v).$$

Provided that this first order equation can be solved, we obtain v as a function of y. A relation between y and x results from solving $dy/dx = v(y)$. Again there will be two arbitrary constants in the final result. Solve the following differential equations:

(a) $yy'' + (y')^2 = 0$ $\qquad\qquad\qquad\qquad$ (b) $y'' + y = 0$

(c) $y'' + y(y')^3 = 0$ $\qquad\qquad\qquad\qquad$ (d) $2y^2 y'' + 2y(y')^2 = 1$

3. Solve the following differential equations. If initial conditions are prescribed, find the solution satisfying the stated conditions.

(a) $y'y'' = 2$, $\qquad y(0) = 1$, $\qquad y'(0) = 2$

(b) $y'' - 3y^2 = 0$, $\qquad y(0) = 2$, $\qquad y'(0) = 4$

(c) $(1 + x^2)y'' + 2xy' + 3x^{-2} = 0$, $\qquad x > 0$

(d) $y'y'' - x = 0$, $\qquad y(1) = 2$, $\qquad y'(1) = 1$

4. Determine the intervals for which a unique solution of each of the following linear differential equations satisfying the initial conditions $y(x_0) = y_0$, $y'(x_0) = y_0'$, where x_0 is any point in the interval, is certain to exist.

(a) $xy'' + 3y = x$

(b) $y'' + 6y' + 7y = 2 \sin x$

(c) $x(x - 1)y'' + 3xy' + 4y = 2$

(d) $y'' + (\cos x)y' + 3(\ln |x|)y = 0$

(e) $(1 + x^2)y'' + 4y' = e^x$

(f) $e^x y'' + x^2 y' + y = \tan x$

5. Assuming that p and q are continuous on an open interval including the origin and that $y = \phi(x)$ is a solution of

$$y'' + p(x)y' + q(x)y = 0, \qquad y(0) = a_0, \qquad y'(0) = a_1,$$

determine $\phi''(0)$. If p and q are polynomials it can be shown that the solution $y = \phi(x)$ of the above differential equation can be differentiated infinitely many times. Assuming that p and q are polynomials, determine $\phi'''(0)$ in terms of a_0, a_1, $p(0)$, $q(0)$, $p'(0)$, and $q'(0)$. Can this process be continued indefinitely?

6. The solution of a second order equation of the form $y'' = f(x, y, y')$ will generally involve two arbitrary constants. Conversely, a given family of functions involving two arbitrary constants can be shown to be the solution of some second order differential equation. By eliminating the constants c_1 and c_2 among y, y', and y'', find the differential equation satisfied by each of the following families of functions.

(a) $y = c_1 e^x + c_2 e^{-x}$

(b) $y = c_1 \cos x + c_2 \sin x$

(c) $y = c_1 + c_2 x$

(d) $y = (c_1 + c_2 x)e^x$

(e) $y = c_1 x + c_2 x^2$

(f) $y = c_1 \cosh x + c_2 \sinh x$

(g) $y = c_1 x + c_2 \sin x$

(h) $y = c_1 + c_2 e^{-3x}$

3.2 FUNDAMENTAL SOLUTIONS OF THE HOMOGENEOUS EQUATION

In developing the theory of linear differential equations, it is helpful to introduce a differential operator notation. Let p and q be continuous functions on an open interval $\alpha < x < \beta$. Then for any twice differentiable function ϕ on $\alpha < x < \beta$, we define the *differential operator* L by the equation

$$L[\phi] = \phi'' + p\phi' + q\phi. \tag{1}$$

Note that $L[\phi]$ is also a function on $\alpha < x < \beta$; in fact L itself can be considered as a function whose domain and range are themselves functions of a single real variable. The operator L is often written as $L = D^2 + pD + q$, where D is the derivative operator. The value of the function $L[\phi]$ at the point x is

$$L[\phi](x) = \phi''(x) + p(x)\phi'(x) + q(x)\phi(x).$$

For example, if $p(x) = x^2$, $q(x) = 1 + x$, and $\phi(x) = \sin 3x$ then

$$L[\phi](x) = (\sin 3x)'' + x^2(\sin 3x)' + (1 + x) \sin 3x$$

$$= -9 \sin 3x + 3x^2 \cos 3x + (1 + x) \sin 3x.$$

In this section we will study the second order linear homogeneous equation

$$L[\phi](x) = \phi''(x) + p(x)\phi'(x) + q(x)\phi(x) = 0, \tag{2}$$

where it is understood that the functions p and q are continuous on an open interval $\alpha < x < \beta$. Recalling that it is customary to use the symbol y to indicate the value of the function under discussion, that is, for the function ϕ we let $y = \phi(x)$, we will often write in place of Eq. (2)

$$L[y] = y'' + p(x)y' + q(x)y = 0. \tag{3}$$

We emphasize that $L[\phi]$ as given in Eq. (1) is a function, while $L[y]$ as given in Eq. (3) is the value of the function $L[\phi]$ at the point x. Thus the symbol y is treated in a special way.

Using the fact that if u_1 and u_2 are differentiable functions, then

$$[c_1 u_1(x) + c_2 u_2(x)]' = c_1 u_1'(x) + c_2 u_2'(x),$$

where c_1 and c_2 are arbitrary constants, we can derive the following important theorem.

Theorem 3.3. *If $y = y_1(x)$ and $y = y_2(x)$ are solutions of the differential equation (3),*

$$L[y] = y'' + p(x)y' + q(x)y = 0,$$

then the linear combination $y = c_1 y_1(x) + c_2 y_2(x)$, where c_1 and c_2 are arbitrary constants, is also a solution of Eq. (3).

We must show that if $L[y_1] = y_1'' + py_1' + qy_1 = 0$, and $L[y_2] = y_2'' + py_2' + qy_2 = 0$,* then $L[c_1 y_1 + c_2 y_2] = 0$. But

$$\begin{aligned}
L[c_1 y_1 + c_2 y_2] &= (c_1 y_1 + c_2 y_2)'' + p(c_1 y_1 + c_2 y_2)' + q(c_1 y_1 + c_2 y_2) \\
&= c_1(y_1'' + py_1' + qy_1) + c_2(y_2'' + py_2' + qy_2) \\
&= c_1 L[y_1] + c_2 L[y_2] \\
&= 0,
\end{aligned}$$

which proves the theorem. If we set $c_2 = 0$ in the above proof we obtain the result that if the function y_1 is a solution of Eq. (3), then any constant multiple of y_1 is also a solution of Eq. (3).

In the process of proving Theorem 3.3, we have shown that for any two functions u_1 and u_2 possessing continuous second derivatives, and for any two arbitrary constants c_1 and c_2,

$$L[c_1 u_1 + c_2 u_2] = c_1 L[u_1] + c_2 L[u_2].$$

* Notice that since $L[y_1]$ is a function, the 0 on the right-hand side of the statement $L[y_1] = 0$ actually stands for the function which is identically zero on $\alpha < x < \beta$.

An operator with this property is known as a *linear operator* and, in particular, the differential operator L is a second order linear differential operator. Another example of a linear operator is given in Problem 10.

The fact that a linear combination of solutions of a *linear, homogeneous* equation is also a solution of the equation is of fundamental importance, and is often referred to as the *superposition principle*. The theory of linear homogeneous equations, including higher order ordinary differential equations and partial differential equations, depends strongly on the superposition principle. This principle is illustrated by the following simple examples.

Example 1. Verify by direct calculation that $\phi(x) = c_1 \cos x + c_2 \sin x$ is a solution of the differential equation $y'' + y = 0$.

Substituting $\phi(x)$ for y, we have

$$\phi''(x) + \phi(x) = (c_1 \cos x + c_2 \sin x)'' + (c_1 \cos x + c_2 \sin x)$$
$$= c_1[(\cos x)'' + \cos x] + c_2[(\sin x)'' + \sin x] = 0.$$

Example 2. Verify that $\phi(x) = x + 1$ is a solution of the differential equation $y'' + 3y' + y = x + 4$, but that $\psi(x) = 2\phi(x)$ is not a solution.

Since $\phi'(x) = 1$, $\phi''(x) = 0$ we have

$$\phi''(x) + 3\phi'(x) + \phi(x) = 0 + 3(1) + (x + 1) = x + 4.$$

However,

$$\psi''(x) + 3\psi'(x) + \psi(x) = 0 + 3(2) + 2(x + 1) \neq x + 4.$$

This is not a contradiction of Theorem 3.3, since the differential equation is not homogeneous.

Example 3. Show that if the functions y_1 and y_2 are solutions of the equation $L[y] = y'' + y^2 = 0$, it does *not* necessarily follow that the linear combination $c_1 y_1 + c_2 y_2$ is a solution.

Substituting, we have,

$$L[c_1 y_1 + c_2 y_2] = (c_1 y_1 + c_2 y_2)'' + (c_1 y_1 + c_2 y_2)^2$$
$$= c_1 y_1'' + c_2 y_2'' + c_1^2 y_1^2 + 2c_1 c_2 y_1 y_2 + c_2^2 y_2^2$$
$$\neq c_1 L[y_1] + c_2 L[y_2].$$

The superposition principle fails because the differential equation is nonlinear.

We have seen that if the functions y_1 and y_2 are solutions of Eq. (3), then the linear combination $c_1 y_1 + c_2 y_2$ is a solution of Eq. (3) and, corresponding to the infinity of values we can assign to c_1 and c_2, we can construct an infinity of solutions of Eq. (3). But does this infinity of solutions include all possible solutions of Eq. (3)?

Two solutions y_1 and y_2 of Eq. (3) are said to form a *fundamental set* of solutions of Eq. (3) if *every* solution of Eq. (3) can be expressed as a linear combination of y_1 and y_2. To prove then that two solutions, y_1 and y_2, of Eq. (3) form a fundamental set of solutions we must show that for every solution $y = \phi(x)$ of Eq. (3) we can find constants c_1 and c_2 such that $\phi(x) = c_1 y_1(x) + c_2 y_2(x)$.

Let $y = \phi(x)$ represent any solution of Eq. (3). Choose any point x_0 in the interval $\alpha < x < \beta$, and let y_0 and y_0' denote $\phi(x_0)$ and $\phi'(x_0)$, respectively. Now if we can choose c_1 and c_2 so that

$$
\begin{aligned}
c_1 y_1(x_0) + c_2 y_2(x_0) &= y_0, \\
c_1 y_1'(x_0) + c_2 y_2'(x_0) &= y_0',
\end{aligned}
\tag{4}
$$

then we will have $\phi(x) = c_1 y_1(x) + c_2 y_2(x)$ since, according to the uniqueness part of Theorem 3.2, there is only one solution of Eq. (3) satisfying the initial conditions

$$
y(x_0) = y_0, \qquad y'(x_0) = y_0'.
\tag{5}
$$

Equations (4) are two simultaneous linear algebraic equations and can always be solved uniquely for c_1 and c_2 provided that the determinant of the coefficients does not vanish. This requires that

$$
\begin{vmatrix} y_1(x_0) & y_2(x_0) \\ y_1'(x_0) & y_2'(x_0) \end{vmatrix} = y_1(x_0)y_2'(x_0) - y_1'(x_0)y_2(x_0) \neq 0.
$$

The choice of the point x_0 is completely arbitrary, and hence this equation must hold for all x_0 in the interval $\alpha < x < \beta$. In this case Eqs. (4) can always be solved regardless of the values of y_0, y_0', and x_0. Thus we have proved the following theorem.

Theorem 3.4. *If the functions p and q are continuous on the open interval $\alpha < x < \beta$ and if y_1 and y_2 are solutions of the differential equation (3),*

$$
L[y] = y'' + p(x)y' + q(x)y = 0,
$$

satisfying the condition

$$
y_1(x)y_2'(x) - y_1'(x)y_2(x) \neq 0
\tag{6}
$$

at every point in $\alpha < x < \beta$, then any solution of Eq. (3) on the interval $\alpha < x < \beta$ can be expressed as a linear combination of y_1 and y_2.

It is customary to call the linear combination $c_1 y_1 + c_2 y_2$ the *general solution* of Eq. (3).

Example 4. Find a fundamental set of solutions of the equation

$$
y'' + y = 0, \qquad -\infty < x < \infty.
\tag{7}
$$

By inspection we observe that $y_1(x) = \cos x$ and $y_2(x) = \sin x$ are solutions of Eq. (7). Further,

$$y_1(x)y_2'(x) - y_1'(x)y_2(x) = \cos x \cos x - (-\sin x) \sin x = 1.$$

Hence if $y = \phi(x)$ is a solution of Eq. (7), then there exist constants c_1 and c_2 such that $\phi(x) = c_1 \cos x + c_2 \sin x$.

Given two differentiable functions y_1 and y_2 on some open interval, the function $y_1 y_2' - y_1' y_2$ is referred to as the Wronskian* of y_1 and y_2, and is usually written as

$$W(y_1, y_2) = \begin{vmatrix} y_1 & y_2 \\ y_1' & y_2' \end{vmatrix} = y_1 y_2' - y_1' y_2. \tag{8}$$

The value of the Wronskian of y_1 and y_2 at the point x will be denoted by $W(y_1, y_2)(x)$ or simply $W(x)$ if it is clear what functions are being considered.

Now suppose we have found two solutions, y_1 and y_2, of Eq. (3). How do we decide whether the functions y_1 and y_2 form a fundamental set, that is, how do we decide whether $W(y_1, y_2)$ vanishes in the interval $\alpha < x < \beta$? In Example 4, $W(\cos x, \sin x) = 1$, and hence it is clear that $\cos x$ and $\sin x$ form a fundamental set for the differential equation $y'' + y = 0$ on any interval. However, in general, $W(y_1, y_2)$ will not be constant, and it may be difficult to determine whether this function vanishes at some point in an interval $\alpha < x < \beta$. Fortunately this question is answered by the following remarkable theorem.

Theorem 3.5. *If the functions p and q are continuous on the open interval $\alpha < x < \beta$, and if the functions y_1 and y_2 are solutions of the differential equation (3),*

$$L[y] = y'' + p(x)y' + q(x)y = 0,$$

on $\alpha < x < \beta$, then $W(y_1, y_2)$ either vanishes identically, or else is never zero in $\alpha < x < \beta$.

The proof of this theorem can be based on an argument similar to that used in proving Theorem 3.4; however, we will present an alternate proof in which we also will derive a formula for $W(y_1, y_2)$. We make use of the fact that the functions y_1 and y_2 satisfy

$$\begin{aligned} y_1'' + p y_1' + q y_1 &= 0, \\ y_2'' + p y_2' + q y_2 &= 0. \end{aligned} \tag{9}$$

Multiplying the first equation by $-y_2$, the second by y_1, and adding gives

$$(y_1 y_2'' - y_2 y_1'') + p(y_1 y_2' - y_1' y_2) = 0. \tag{10}$$

* In honor of the Polish mathematician Wronski (1778–1853).

Letting $W_{12}(x) = W(y_1, y_2)(x)$, and noting that

$$W'_{12} = y_1 y''_2 - y''_1 y_2, \tag{11}$$

allows us to write Eq. (10) in the form

$$W'_{12} + pW_{12} = 0. \tag{12}$$

This is a separable equation (Section 2.4) and also a first order linear equation (Section 2.1), and it can be integrated immediately to give

$$W_{12}(x) = c \exp\left[-\int^x p(t)\, dt\right], \tag{13}$$

where c is a constant.* Since the exponential function never vanishes, $W_{12}(x)$ will vanish only if c equals 0, and if c equals 0 then $W_{12}(x)$ is identically zero, thus proving the theorem. In addition, Eq. (13) gives a formula for determining the Wronskian of a fundamental set of solutions of Eq. (3) up to a multiplicative constant without solving the equation. Also note that the Wronskians of any two fundamental sets of solutions can differ only by a multiplicative constant.

Combining the results of Theorems 3.4 and 3.5 allows us to state the following theorem.

Theorem 3.6. *If the functions p and q are continuous on the open interval $\alpha < x < \beta$ and if the functions y_1 and y_2 are solutions of the differential equation (3),*

$$L[y] = y'' + p(x)y' + q(x)y = 0,$$

on the interval $\alpha < x < \beta$, and if there is at least one point in $\alpha < x < \beta$ where $W(y_1, y_2)$ is not zero, then any solution $y = \phi(x)$ of Eq. (3) can be expressed in the form

$$\phi(x) = c_1 y_1(x) + c_2 y_2(x).$$

Finally we must show that there actually does exist a fundamental set of solutions of Eq. (3). That is, we must prove the following theorem.

Theorem 3.7. *If the functions p and q are continuous on the open interval $\alpha < x < \beta$, then there exists a fundamental set of solutions of the differential equation (3),*

$$L[y] = y'' + p(x)y' + q(x)y = 0,$$

on the interval $\alpha < x < \beta$.

Let c be a point in $\alpha < x < \beta$. It follows from Theorem 3.2 that there exist unique solutions y_1 and y_2 of the initial value problems

$$y'' + p(x)y' + q(x)y = 0; \qquad y(c) = 1, \qquad y'(c) = 0$$
$$y'' + p(x)y' + q(x)y = 0; \qquad y(c) = 0, \qquad y'(c) = 1$$

* The result given in Eq. (13) was derived by the Norwegian mathematician N. H. Abel (1802–1829) in 1827, and is known as Abel's identity.

on the interval $\alpha < x < \beta$. It is readily seen that $W(y_1, y_2)(c) = 1 \neq 0$. Hence it follows from Theorem 3.6 that y_1 and y_2 form a fundamental set of solutions of Eq. (3).

We will conclude this section by giving an interesting alternative proof of Theorem 3.6, which does not require the use of the existence and uniqueness theorem. (Note the proof of Theorem 3.4.) Suppose that the functions y_1, y_2, and y_3 are solutions of Eq. (3), and that $W(y_1, y_2)(x)$ is never zero in $\alpha < x < \beta$. To show that $y_3 = c_1 y_1 + c_2 y_2$ consider

$$y_1'' + p y_1' + q y_1 = 0,$$
$$y_2'' + p y_2' + q y_2 = 0,$$
$$y_3'' + p y_3' + q y_3 = 0.$$

Multiplying the first equation by $-y_2$, the second by y_1, adding, and using Eq. (11) gives

$$W_{12}' + p W_{12} = 0, \tag{14}$$

where $W_{12}(x) = W(y_1, y_2)(x)$. Similar computations using the second and third equations, and the first and third equations, give

$$W_{23}' + p W_{23} = 0, \tag{15}$$

$$W_{13}' + p W_{13} = 0, \tag{16}$$

where the notation is clear. Equations (14), (15), and (16) are first order linear equations. Their solutions are

$$W_{12}(x) = y_1(x) y_2'(x) - y_1'(x) y_2(x) = k_{12} \exp\left[-\int^x p(t)\, dt\right], \tag{17}$$

$$W_{23}(x) = y_2(x) y_3'(x) - y_2'(x) y_3(x) = k_{23} \exp\left[-\int^x p(t)\, dt\right], \tag{18}$$

$$W_{13}(x) = y_1(x) y_3'(x) - y_1'(x) y_3(x) = k_{13} \exp\left[-\int^x p(t)\, dt\right], \tag{19}$$

where k_{12}, k_{23}, and k_{13} are constants; and in particular $k_{12} \neq 0$ since W_{12} is never zero by hypothesis. Multiplying Eq. (18) by $-y_1(x)$, Eq. (19) by $y_2(x)$, and adding gives

$$[y_1(x) y_2'(x) - y_1'(x) y_2(x)] y_3(x) = [-k_{23} y_1(x) + k_{13} y_2(x)] \exp\left[-\int^x p(t)\, dt\right]. \tag{20}$$

Finally substituting for $y_1(x) y_2'(x) - y_1'(x) y_2(x)$ from Eq. (17) and canceling the exponentials gives

$$y_3(x) = -\frac{k_{23}}{k_{12}} y_1(x) + \frac{k_{13}}{k_{12}} y_2(x).$$

Hence y_3 can be expressed as a linear combination of y_1 and y_2, as was to be proved.

PROBLEMS

1. Verify that e^x and e^{-2x} and the linear combination $c_1e^x + c_2e^{-2x}$, where c_1 and c_2 are arbitrary constants, are solutions of the differential equation

$$y'' + y' - 2y = 0.$$

2. In Problem 1 find the unique solution of the differential equation that satisfies the initial conditions $y(0) = 1$, $y'(0) = 0$. What is the unique solution of this problem if the initial conditions are $y(1) = 0$, $y'(1) = 0$?

3. Verify that e^x and e^{-x} are solutions of $y'' - y = 0$. Hence show that $\sinh x = (e^x - e^{-x})/2$ and $\cosh x = (e^x + e^{-x})/2$ are also solutions of this differential equation.

4. Verify that $\sin x$ and $\cos x$ are solutions of $y'' + y = 0$. Accepting for the moment that $(cf)' = cf'$ where f is a real-valued function and c is a complex number, show that the linear combination $(1 + i)\sin x + (2 - i)\cos x$ is also a solution of $y'' + y = 0$. Here i is the imaginary unit, $i^2 = -1$.

5. Verify that x^2 and x^{-1} and the linear combination $c_1x^2 + c_2x^{-1}$, where c_1 and c_2 are arbitrary constants, are solutions of the differential equation $x^2y'' - 2y = 0$, $x > 0$.

6. Verify that 1 and $x^{\frac{1}{2}}$ are solutions of the differential equation $yy'' + (y')^2 = 0$, $x > 0$; but that the linear combination $c_1 + c_2x^{\frac{1}{2}}$ is not, in general, a solution. Why?

7. Show that if $y = \phi(x)$ is a solution of the differential equation $y'' + p(x)y' + q(x)y = g(x)$, $g(x) \neq 0$, then $y = c\phi(x)$, where c is any constant other than one, is not a solution. Why?

8. If $L[y] = ay'' + by' + cy$, where a, b, and c are constants, compute

(a) $L[x]$ (b) $L[\sin x]$

(c) $L[e^{rx}]$, r a constant   (d) $L[x^r]$, r a constant

9. If $L[y] = ax^2y'' + bxy' + cy$, where a, b, and c are constants, compute

(a) $L[x^2]$ (b) $L[e^{rx}]$, r a constant

(c) $L[x^r]$, r a constant

10. Show that the operator M defined by

$$M[u](x) = \int_\alpha^\beta K(x - t)u(t)\, dt, \qquad \alpha < x < \beta,$$

where the function K is continuous on the interval $\alpha - \beta \leq s \leq \beta - \alpha$, is a linear operator; that is, show that

$$M[c_1u_1 + c_2u_2] = c_1M[u_1] + c_2M[u_2]$$

where c_1 and c_2 are constants.

11. Compute the Wronskians of the following pairs of functions:

(a) e^{mx}, e^{nx}, where m and n are integers, and $m \neq n$

(b) $\sinh x$, $\cosh x$ (c) x, xe^x

(d) $e^x \sin x$, $e^x \cos x$ (e) $\cos^2 x$, $1 + \cos 2x$

12. In the following problems verify that the functions y_1 and y_2 are solutions of the given differential equation and determine in what intervals they form a fundamental set of solutions by computing $W(y_1, y_2)$.

(a) $y'' + \lambda^2 y = 0$; $y_1(x) = \sin \lambda x$, $y_2(x) = \cos \lambda x$, where λ is a real number

(b) $y'' - y' - 2y = 0$; $y_1(x) = e^{-x}$, $y_2(x) = e^{2x}$

(c) $y'' - 2y' + y = 0$; $y_1(x) = e^x$, $y_2(x) = xe^x$

(d) $x^2 y'' - x(x + 2)y' + (x + 2)y = 0$; $y_1(x) = x$, $y_2(x) = xe^x$

Notice that if the equation of part (d) is put in the standard form $y'' + p(x)y' + q(x)y = 0$, the coefficients $p(x) = -(x + 2)/x$ and $q(x) = (x + 2)/x^2$ become unbounded as $x \to 0$, but the solutions x and xe^x are perfectly well behaved as $x \to 0$. Thus it does not necessarily follow that at a point where the coefficients are discontinuous the solution will be discontinuous—but this is often the case!

13. In the following problems verify that the functions y_1 and y_2 form a fundamental set of solutions of the given differential equations and determine the solution satisfying the prescribed initial conditions.

(a) $y'' - y = 0$, $y(0) = 0$, $y'(0) = 1$; $y_1(x) = e^x$, $y_2(x) = e^{-x}$

(b) $y'' - y = 0$, $y(0) = 0$, $y'(0) = 1$; $y_1(x) = \sinh x$, $y_2(x) = \cosh x$

Compare with the result for part (a).

(c) $y'' + 5y' + 6y = 0$, $y(0) = 1$, $y'(0) = 1$; $y_1(x) = e^{-2x}$,

$$y_2(x) = e^{-3x}$$

(d) $y'' + y' = 0$, $y(1) = 0$, $y'(1) = 1$; $y_1(x) = 2$, $y_2(x) = e^{-x}$

In Problems 14, 15, and 16 assume that p and q are continuous, and that the functions y_1 and y_2 are solutions of the differential equation $y'' + p(x)y' + q(x)y = 0$ on the interval $\alpha < x < \beta$.

14. Prove that if y_1 and y_2 vanish at the same point in $\alpha < x < \beta$, then they cannot form a fundamental set of solutions on that interval.

15. Prove that if y_1 and y_2 have maxima or minima at the same point in $\alpha < x < \beta$, then they cannot form a fundamental set of solutions on that interval.

*16. Prove that if y_1 and y_2 are a fundamental set of solutions, then they cannot have a common point of inflection in $\alpha < x < \beta$ unless p and q vanish simultaneously there.

*17. The concept of exactness which was discussed for first order differential equations can be extended to second order linear equations. The equation $P(x)y'' + Q(x)y' + R(x)y = 0$ is said to be exact if it can be written in the form $[P(x)y']' + [f(x)y]' = 0$, where $f(x)$ is to be determined in terms of $P(x)$, $Q(x)$, and $R(x)$. The latter equation can be integrated once immediately to give a first order linear equation for y which can be solved by the method of Section 2.1. Show by equating the coefficients of the above equations, and then eliminating $f(x)$, that a necessary condition for exactness is $P''(x) - Q'(x) + R(x) = 0$. It can also be shown that this is a sufficient condition for exactness. Determine whether the following equations are exact; if so, find their solution.

(a) $y'' + xy' + y = 0$

(b) $y'' + 3x^2y' + xy = 0$

(c) $xy'' - (\cos x)y' + (\sin x)y = 0, \qquad x > 0$

(d) $x^2y'' + xy' - y = 0, \qquad x > 0$

*18. If a second order linear homogeneous equation is not exact, it can be made exact by multiplying by an appropriate integrating factor $\mu(x)$. Thus we require that $\mu(x)$ be such that $\mu(x)P(x)y'' + \mu(x)Q(x)y' + \mu(x)R(x)y = 0$ can be written in the form $[\mu(x)P(x)y']' + [f(x)y]' = 0$. Show by equating coefficients in these two equations and then by eliminating $f(x)$ that the function μ must satisfy

$$P\mu'' + (2P' - Q)\mu' + (P'' - Q' + R)\mu = 0.$$

This equation is known as the *adjoint* equation. It plays a very important role in the advanced theory of differential equations. In general the problem of solving the adjoint differential equation is as difficult as that of solving the original equation. Determine the adjoint equation for each of the following differential equations.

(a) The Bessel equation of order v:

$$x^2y'' + xy' + (x^2 - v^2)y = 0$$

(b) The Legendre equation of order α:

$$(1 - x^2)y'' - 2xy' + \alpha(\alpha + 1)y = 0$$

(c) The Airy equation:

$$y'' - xy = 0$$

(d) The Whittaker equation:

$$x^2y'' + \left(-\frac{x^2}{4} + kx + \frac{1}{4} - m^2\right)y = 0,$$

where k and m are integers.

*19. Show for the second order linear equation $P(x)y'' + Q(x)y' + R(x)y = 0$ that the adjoint of the adjoint is the original equation.

*20. A second order linear equation $P(x)y'' + Q(x)y' + R(x)y = 0$ is said to be *self-adjoint* if its adjoint is identical with the original equation. Show that a necessary condition for this differential equation to be self-adjoint is $P'(x) = Q(x)$. Determine whether the equations of Problem 18 are self-adjoint.

3.3 LINEAR INDEPENDENCE

The concept of the general solution of a second order linear differential equation as a linear combination of two solutions whose Wronskian does not vanish is intimately related to the concept of linear independence of two functions. This is a very important concept and has significance far beyond the present problem; we will briefly discuss it in this section.

Two functions f and g are said to be *linearly dependent* on an interval $\alpha < x < \beta$ if there exist two constants c_1 and c_2, not both zero, such that

$$c_1 f(x) + c_2 g(x) = 0 \tag{1}$$

for all x in $\alpha < x < \beta$. Two functions f and g are said to be *linearly independent* on an interval $\alpha < x < \beta$ if they are not linearly dependent. The same definitions apply on any interval, open or not.

Example 1. The functions $\sin x$ and $\cos(x + \pi/2)$ are linearly dependent on any interval since

$$c_1 \sin x + c_2 \cos\left(x + \frac{\pi}{2}\right) = 0$$

for all x if we choose $c_1 = 1$, $c_2 = 1$.

Example 2. Show that the functions e^x and e^{2x} are linearly independent on any interval. We will show that the functions are linearly independent by showing that it is impossible to find constants c_1 and c_2, not both zero, such that

$$c_1 e^x + c_2 e^{2x} = 0$$

for all x in the given interval. Let x_0 and $x_1 \neq x_0$ be two points in the interval. From the above equation

$$c_1 e^{x_0} + c_2 e^{2x_0} = 0,$$
$$c_1 e^{x_1} + c_2 e^{2x_1} = 0.$$

Since the determinant of the coefficients is $e^{2x_1 + x_0} - e^{2x_0 + x_1} \neq 0$ it follows that the only solution of these equations is $c_1 = c_2 = 0$. Hence e^x and e^{2x} are linearly independent.

We can now restate Theorem 3.6 using the concept of linear independence.

Theorem 3.8. *If the functions p and q are continuous on the open interval $\alpha < x < \beta$, and if the functions y_1 and y_2 are linearly independent solutions of the differential equation*

$$L[y] = y'' + p(x)y' + q(x)y = 0, \tag{2}$$

then $W(y_1, y_2)$ is nonvanishing on $\alpha < x < \beta$, and hence any solution of Eq. (2) can be expressed as a linear combination of the solutions y_1 and y_2.

To prove this theorem we must show that if y_1 and y_2 are solutions of Eq. (2) and are linearly independent on $\alpha < x < \beta$, then $W(y_1, y_2)$ does not vanish on $\alpha < x < \beta$. Let us assume that there exists a point x_0, $\alpha < x_0 < \beta$, such that $W(y_1, y_2)(x_0) = 0$; we will show that this leads to a contradiction. If $W(y_1, y_2)(x_0) = 0$, then the system of equations

$$c_1 y_1(x_0) + c_2 y_2(x_0) = 0$$
$$c_1 y_1'(x_0) + c_2 y_2'(x_0) = 0 \tag{3}$$

for c_1 and c_2 has a nontrivial solution. Using these values of c_1 and c_2, let $\phi(x) = c_1 y_1(x) + c_2 y_2(x)$. Then ϕ is a solution of Eq. (2) and, further, by Eqs. (3) satisfies the initial conditions $\phi(x_0) = \phi'(x_0) = 0$. Therefore by the existence and uniqueness theorem (see Example 2 of Section 3.1) $\phi(x) = 0$ for all x in $\alpha < x < \beta$. Then $c_1 y_1(x) + c_2 y_2(x) = 0$ for all x in $\alpha < x < \beta$ which implies that y_1 and y_2 are linearly dependent, which is a contradiction.

The converse of Theorem 3.8 is also true, namely if $L[y_1] = 0$, $L[y_2] = 0$, and $W(y_1, y_2) \neq 0$ on $\alpha < x < \beta$ then the functions y_1 and y_2 are linearly independent on $\alpha < x < \beta$. To establish this fact, again assume the contrary: that y_1 and y_2 are linearly dependent on $\alpha < x < \beta$. Then there exist c_1 and c_2, not both zero, such that

$$c_1 y_1(x) + c_2 y_2(x) = 0 \tag{4}$$

for each x in $\alpha < x < \beta$. It follows that

$$c_1 y_1'(x) + c_2 y_2'(x) = 0 \tag{5}$$

on $\alpha < x < \beta$ as well. In order for nonzero values of c_1 and/or c_2 to satisfy Eqs. (4) and (5) it is necessary (and sufficient) for $W(y_1, y_2)$ to vanish for each x, which is a contradiction. Hence two solutions of Eq. (2) are linearly independent if and only if their Wronskian is nonzero at each point in the interval.

We emphasize that this relationship between the Wronskian and linear independence no longer holds if the functions are not solutions of Eq. (2). An example of two linearly independent functions whose Wronskian vanishes identically is given in Problem 10.

It is interesting to note the similarity of this result to several results in two dimensional vector algebra. Two vectors **a** and **b** are said to be linearly dependent if there are two scalars c_1 and c_2, not both zero, such that $c_1\mathbf{a} + c_2\mathbf{b} = \mathbf{0}$; otherwise they are said to be linearly independent. Let **i** and **j** be unit vectors directed along the positive x and y axes respectively. Since there are no scalars c_1 and c_2, not both zero, such that $c_1\mathbf{i} + c_2\mathbf{j} = \mathbf{0}$, the vectors **i** and **j** are linearly independent. Further we know that any vector with components a_1 and a_2 can be written as $a_1\mathbf{i} + a_2\mathbf{j}$, that is, as a linear combination of the two linearly independent vectors **i** and **j**. It is not difficult to show that any vector in two dimensions can be represented as a linear combination of any two linearly independent two dimensional vectors (see Problem 7). Such a pair of linearly independent vectors is said to form a basis for, or to span, the vector space of two dimensional vectors.

The term vector space is also applied to other collections of mathematical objects that satisfy the same laws of addition and multiplication by scalars that geometric vectors do. For example, it can be shown that the set of functions that are twice differentiable on $\alpha < x < \beta$ form a vector space. Similarly the set V of functions which satisfy Eq. (2) also form a vector space.

Since every member of V can be expressed as a linear combination of two linearly independent members y_1 and y_2, we say that such a pair spans V or forms a basis for V. This leads to the conclusion that V is two dimensional [Eq. (2) is second order], and analogous in many respects to the space of geometric vectors in a plane. Later we will find that the set of solutions of an nth order linear homogeneous differential equation forms a vector space of dimension n, which is spanned by any set of n linearly independent solutions of the differential equation.

PROBLEMS

In Problems 1 through 4 prove that the functions y_1 and y_2 are linearly independent solutions of the given differential equation.

1. $y'' - y = 0$; $y_1(x) = e^x$, $y_2(x) = e^{-x}$
2. $y'' - y = 0$; $y_1(x) = \cosh x$, $y_2(x) = \sinh x$
3. $y'' - y' - 6y = 0$; $y_1(x) = e^{-2x}$, $y_2(x) = e^{3x}$
4. $x^2 y'' + xy' - 4y = 0$, $x > 0$; $y_1(x) = x^2$, $y_2(x) = x^{-2}$

5. Prove that if the functions y_1 and y_2 are linearly independent solutions of $y'' + p(x)y' + q(x)y = 0$, then $c_1 y_1$ and $c_2 y_2$ are linearly independent solutions provided neither c_1 nor c_2 equals 0.

6. Prove that if the functions y_1 and y_2 are linearly independent solutions of the differential equation $y'' + p(x)y' + q(x)y = 0$, then $y_3 = y_1 + y_2$, and $y_4 = y_1 - y_2$ also form a fundamental set of solutions.

7. (a) Prove that any two dimensional vector can be written as a linear combination of the vectors $\mathbf{i} + \mathbf{j}$ and $\mathbf{i} - \mathbf{j}$.
Hint: Any vector $\mathbf{a}$ can be written as $a_1\mathbf{i} + a_2\mathbf{j}$. Show that it is possible to determine c_1 and c_2 such that $\mathbf{a} = c_1(\mathbf{i} + \mathbf{j}) + c_2(\mathbf{i} - \mathbf{j})$ by equating the two expressions for $\mathbf{a}$ and solving for c_1 and c_2 in terms of a_1 and a_2.
(b) Prove that if the vectors $\mathbf{x} = x_1\mathbf{i} + x_2\mathbf{j}$ and $\mathbf{y} = y_1\mathbf{i} + y_2\mathbf{j}$ are linearly independent, then any vector $\mathbf{z} = z_1\mathbf{i} + z_2\mathbf{j}$ can be expressed as a linear combination of $\mathbf{x}$ and $\mathbf{y}$. Note that if $\mathbf{x}$ and $\mathbf{y}$ are linearly independent then $x_1 y_2 - y_1 x_2 \neq 0$. Why?

*8. Verify that x and x^2 are linearly independent on $-1 < x < 1$, but that $W(x, x^2)$ vanishes at $x = 0$. From this what can you conclude about the possibility of x and x^2 being solutions of Eq. (2) of the text? Show that x and x^2 are solutions of $x^2 y'' - 2xy' + 2y = 0$. Does this contradict your conclusion? Does it contradict Theorem 3.5 of Section 3.2?

*9. If the functions y_1 and y_2 are linearly independent solutions of the differential equation $y'' + p(x)y' + q(x)y = 0$, show that between consecutive zeros of y_1 there is one and only one zero of y_2.

Hint: Use Rolle's (1652–1719) theorem and try to prove the conclusion by contradiction. This result is often referred to as Sturm's (1803–1855) theorem. As a particular example note that $\sin x$ and $\cos x$ are linearly independent solutions of $y'' + y = 0$.

10. Show that the functions $y_1(x) = x\,|x|$ and $y_2(x) = x^2$ are linearly dependent on $0 < x < 1$ and on $-1 < x < 0$ but are linearly independent on $-1 < x < 1$. Note that while y_1 and y_2 are linearly independent, $W(y_1, y_2)$ is identically zero on $-1 < x < 1$; hence y_1 and y_2 cannot be solutions of Eq. (2) of the text.

3.4 REDUCTION OF ORDER

A very important and useful fact is the following: If one solution of a second order linear homogeneous differential equation is known, a second linearly independent solution (and hence a fundamental set of solutions) can be determined. The procedure, which is due to D'Alembert,* is usually referred to as the method of reduction of order.

Suppose we know one solution y_1, not identically zero, of

$$y'' + p(x)y' + q(x)y = 0. \tag{1}$$

Then cy_1, where c is any constant, is also a solution of Eq. (1). This suggests the following question: Can we determine a function v, not a constant, such that $y = v(x)y_1(x)$ is a solution of Eq. (1)? The answer is yes, and further, we shall see that v can be determined in a straightforward manner. If we set

$$y = v(x)y_1(x), \tag{2}$$

then

$$y' = v(x)y_1'(x) + v'(x)y_1(x)$$

$$y'' = v(x)y_1''(x) + 2v'(x)y_1'(x) + v''(x)y_1(x).$$

Substituting for y, y', and y'' in Eq. (1) and collecting terms gives

$$v(y_1'' + py_1' + qy_1) + v'(2y_1' + py_1) + v''y_1 = 0. \tag{3}$$

Since y_1 is a solution of Eq. (1) the quantity in the first parenthesis is zero. In any interval in which y_1 does not vanish, we can divide by y_1 obtaining

$$v'' + \left(p + 2\frac{y_1'}{y_1}\right)v' = 0. \tag{4}$$

* Jean D'Alembert (1717–1783), a French mathematician, is particularly famous for his work in mechanics and hydrodynamics.

Equation (4) is a *first order linear equation* for v' and can be solved immediately (Section 2.1). The solution is

$$v'(x) = c \exp\left[-\int^x \left(p(s) + \frac{2y_1'(s)}{y_1(s)} \right) ds \right]$$

$$= cu(x),\tag{5}$$

where c is an arbitrary constant, and

$$u(x) = \frac{1}{[y_1(x)]^2} \exp\left[-\int^x p(s)\, ds \right].\tag{6}$$

Then

$$v(x) = c \int^x u(t)\, dt + k,\tag{7}$$

where k is also an arbitrary constant. However, we can omit the constant k since

$$y = y_1(x)v(x)$$

$$= cy_1(x) \int^x u(t)\, dt + ky_1(x),\tag{8}$$

and hence it only adds a multiple of $y_1(x)$ to the second solution. Thus two solutions of Eq. (1) are

$$y = y_1(x) \quad \text{and} \quad y = y_1(x) \int^x u(t)\, dt.\tag{9}$$

Since the antiderivative of the function u cannot be a constant the solutions are linearly independent. In using the method of reduction of order it is *not* important to try to memorize Eqs. (9) and (6); what is important to remember is that if one solution y_1 is known, a second solution of the form $y = v(x)y_1(x)$ can be found by the above procedure.

While the method of reduction of order does not tell us how to find the first solution of Eq. (1), it is encouraging to know that we have *reduced* the problem of solving Eq. (1) to that of finding just one solution.

It is also possible to derive the second linearly independent solution given in Eq. (9) by using Abel's formula for the Wronskian of two linearly independent solutions of Eq. (1). This is discussed in Problems 8 and 9.

Example.   Show that $y = x$ is a solution of the Legendre equation of order one,

$$(1 - x^2)y'' - 2xy' + 2y = 0, \quad -1 < x < 1,\tag{10}$$

and find a second linearly independent solution. First if $y = x$, then $y' = 1$ and $y'' = 0$. Substituting for y, y', and y'' in Eq. (10) gives

$$(1 - x^2) \cdot 0 - 2x + 2x = 0,$$

so indeed $y = x$ is a solution. To find a second solution let $y = xv(x)$; then

$$y' = xv' + v, \qquad y'' = xv'' + 2v'.$$

Substituting for y, y', and y'' in Eq. (10) gives

$$(1 - x^2)(xv'' + 2v') - 2x(xv' + v) + 2xv = 0.$$

Collecting terms and dividing by $x(1 - x^2)$ we obtain

$$v'' + \left(\frac{2}{x} - \frac{2x}{1 - x^2} \right) v' = 0. \tag{11}$$

Note that the coefficient of v' is not defined at $x = 0$, the zero of $y_1(x)$. However, this will not cause any difficulty in the final solution. First we will obtain a solution of Eq. (11) in the intervals $-1 < x < 0$ and $0 < x < 1$.

Equation (11) is a first order linear equation for v', and the integrating factor is $x^2(1 - x^2)$; hence

$$[x^2(1 - x^2)v']' = 0,$$
$$x^2(1 - x^2)v' = c,$$

so

$$v(x) = c \int^x \frac{dt}{t^2(1 - t^2)} = c \int^x \left(\frac{1}{t^2} + \frac{1}{1 - t^2} \right) dt$$

$$= c \left(-\frac{1}{x} + \frac{1}{2} \ln \frac{1 + x}{1 - x} \right).$$

Consequently a second solution (suppressing a constant multiplier without loss of generality) of Eq. (10) is

$$y_2(x) = xv(x) = 1 - \frac{x}{2} \ln \frac{1 + x}{1 - x}. \tag{12}$$

Although the function v is undefined at $x = 0$, clearly the limit of $y_2(x) = xv(x)$ as $x \to 0$ exists. The function y_2 defined by Eq. (12) on $-1 < x < 1$, actually satisfies the differential equation (10) on $-1 < x < 1$, not just on $-1 < x < 0$ and $0 < x < 1$. On the other hand, $y_2(x)$ becomes unbounded as $x \to \pm 1$; this is closely related to the fact that in Eq. (10) the coefficient of y'' vanishes at $x = \pm 1$, while the coefficients of y' and y are nonzero. This will be discussed further in Chapter 4.

PROBLEMS

In Problems 1 through 5 find a second solution of the given differential equation by the method of reduction of order.

1. $y'' - 4y' - 12y = 0$, $\qquad y_1(x) = e^{6x}$
2. $y'' + 2y' + y = 0$, $\qquad y_1(x) = e^{-x}$
3. $x^2y'' + 2xy' = 0$, $\qquad y_1(x) = 1$. For what range of x would you expect the solution to be valid?

4. $x^2y'' + 2xy' - 2y = 0$, $y_1(x) = x$. For what range of x would you expect the solution to be valid?

5. $(1 - x \cot x)y'' - xy' + y = 0, y_1(x) = x$. Consider the interval $0 < x < \pi$.

Hint: $\displaystyle\int \frac{x \, dx}{1 - x \cot x} = \ln (x \cos x - \sin x).$

6. Verify that $y_1(x) = 3x^2 - 1$ is one solution of Legendre's equation of order two,

$$(1 - x^2)y'' - 2xy' + 6y = 0,$$

and determine a second solution. Consider the intervals $-1 < x < -1/\sqrt{3}$, $-1/\sqrt{3} < x < 1/\sqrt{3}$, and $1/\sqrt{3} < x < 1$ separately, but observe that the final result for y_2 is valid on $-1 < x < 1$.

7. Verify that $y_1(x) = x^{-\frac{1}{2}} \sin x$ is one solution of Bessel's equation of order one-half,

$$x^2y'' + xy' + (x^2 - \tfrac{1}{4})y = 0,$$

and determine a second solution. Consider the interval $0 < x < \infty$.

8. Suppose that y_1 is a nonvanishing solution of $y'' + p(x)y' + q(x)y = 0$ and that we wish to find a second linearly independent solution y_2. Show that $(y_2/y_1)' = W(y_1, y_2)/y_1^2$ and then use Abel's formula for $W(y_1, y_2)$ to obtain y_2.

9. Verify that $y_1(x) = x$ is a solution of $x^2y'' + 2xy' - 2y = 0$, $x > 0$, and then, using the result of Problem 8, determine a second linearly independent solution.

3.5 HOMOGENEOUS EQUATIONS WITH CONSTANT COEFFICIENTS

We will now turn from the general theory of second order linear homogeneous equations to methods of actually solving such equations. In this section we will consider the problem of finding the general solution of a second order linear homogeneous differential equation with constant coefficients.* The corresponding problem with variable coefficients, which is much more difficult, will be considered in Chapter 4.†

Consider the equation

$$\begin{aligned} L[y] &= ay'' + by' + cy = 0 \\ &= (aD^2 + bD + c)y = 0, \end{aligned} \tag{1}$$

where $a \neq 0$, b, and c are real numbers. Since a, b, and c are constants it

* Both Daniel Bernoulli (1700–1782) and Euler (1707–1783) knew how to solve such equations before 1740. The first published account was given by Euler in 1743.
† In some cases it is possible to reduce a differential equation with variable coefficients to one with constant coefficients by a suitable change of variable. See Problems 16, 17, and 18 of Section 3.5.1.

follows immediately from the existence and uniqueness theorem 3.2 that the solutions of Eq. (1) will be valid on the interval $-\infty < x < \infty$.

A clue to the method of solving Eq. (1) can be found simply by reading the equation; that is, what function $y = \phi(x)$ satisfies the relationship that a times its second derivative plus b times its first derivative plus c times the function itself adds up to zero for all x? With only constant coefficients it is natural first to consider functions $y = \phi(x)$ such that y, y', y'' differ only by constant multiplicative factors.

One function that has been studied extensively in the elementary calculus has just the property we wish—the exponential function e^{rx}. Hence we will try to find solutions of Eq. (1) of the form e^{rx} for suitably chosen values of r. Substituting $y = e^{rx}$ in Eq. (1) leads to the equation

$$L[e^{rx}] = a(e^{rx})'' + b(e^{rx})' + ce^{rx} = 0 \tag{2}$$

or

$$e^{rx}(ar^2 + br + c) = 0. \tag{3}$$

Since e^{rx} never vanishes, we must have

$$ar^2 + br + c = 0. \tag{4}$$

Hence if r is a root of this quadratic equation, often called the *auxiliary* or *characteristic equation*, e^{rx} is a solution of Eq. (1). Notice that the coefficients in the auxiliary equation (4) are the same as those in the differential equation (1). The roots r_1 and r_2 of Eq. (4) are given by

$$r_1 = \frac{-b + (b^2 - 4ac)^{\frac{1}{2}}}{2a}, \qquad r_2 = \frac{-b - (b^2 - 4ac)^{\frac{1}{2}}}{2a}. \tag{5}$$

The nature of the solutions of Eq. (1) clearly depends on the values of r_1 and r_2 which in turn depend on the constant coefficients in the differential equation through the relations (5). Just as in elementary algebra we must examine separately the cases $b^2 - 4ac$ positive, zero, and negative.

Real and Unequal Roots.   For $b^2 - 4ac > 0$, Eqs. (5) give two real, unequal values for r_1 and r_2. Hence, $e^{r_1 x}$ and $e^{r_2 x}$ are solutions of Eq. (1). Further it is easy to verify that $W(e^{r_1 x}, e^{r_2 x})$ is nowhere zero; hence the general solution of Eq. (1) is

$$y = c_1 e^{r_1 x} + c_2 e^{r_2 x}. \tag{6}$$

Example 1.   Find the solution of the differential equation $y'' + 5y' + 6y = 0$ which satisfies the initial conditions $y(0) = 0$, $y'(0) = 1$.

Substituting $y = e^{rx}$ leads to

$$r^2 + 5r + 6 = 0,$$

$$(r + 3)(r + 2) = 0;$$

hence $r = -2, -3$. The general solution is

$$y = c_1 e^{-2x} + c_2 e^{-3x}.$$

To satisfy the initial conditions at $x = 0$ we must have

$$c_1 + c_2 = 0, \qquad -2c_1 - 3c_2 = 1.$$

Solving these equations gives

$$c_1 = 1, \qquad c_2 = -1.$$

Hence the solution of the differential equation satisfying the prescribed conditions is

$$y = e^{-2x} - e^{-3x}.$$

Real and Equal Roots. When $b^2 - 4ac = 0$, according to Eqs. (5), $r_1 = r_2 = -b/2a$ and we have only the one solution, $e^{-(b/2a)x}$. However, we can use the method of reduction of order (see Section 3.4) to reduce the order of the equation and find a second solution. Let

$$y = v(x)e^{-(b/2a)x};$$

then

$$y' = v'(x)e^{-(b/2a)x} - \frac{b}{2a} v(x)e^{-(b/2a)x},$$

$$y'' = \left[v''(x) - \frac{b}{a} v'(x) + \frac{b^2}{4a^2} v(x) \right] e^{-(b/2a)x}.$$

Substituting for y, y', and y'' in Eq. (1) and dividing out the common factor $e^{-(b/2a)x}$ gives the following equation for v:

$$a\left(v'' - \frac{b}{a} v' + \frac{b^2}{4a^2} v \right) + b\left(v' - \frac{b}{2a} v \right) + cv = 0.$$

After collecting terms we find that

$$av'' - \left(\frac{b^2}{4a} - c \right) v = 0.$$

Since $b^2 - 4ac = 0$ the last term drops out, and we obtain

$$v'' = 0.$$

Hence

$$v(x) = c_1 x + c_2,$$

where c_1 and c_2 are arbitrary constants. Consequently, a second solution of Eq. (1) is $(c_1 x + c_2)e^{-(b/2a)x}$. In particular, corresponding to $c_2 = 0$, $c_1 = 1$ we obtain $xe^{-(b/2a)x}$. Thus in the case $b^2 - 4ac = 0$, two linearly independent solutions of Eq. (1) are $e^{r_1 x}$ and $xe^{r_1 x}$ ($r_1 = -b/2a$), and the general solution is

$$y = c_1 e^{r_1 x} + c_2 x e^{r_1 x}. \tag{7}$$

Example 2.   Show that the general solution of

$$y'' + 4y' + 4y = 0$$

is $y = c_1 e^{-2x} + c_2 x e^{-2x}$. Substituting $y = e^{rx}$ leads to

$$r^2 + 4r + 4 = 0$$
$$(r + 2)(r + 2) = 0;$$

hence $r = -2$ is a repeated root of the auxiliary equation. One solution is e^{-2x} and a second linearly independent solution, according to the above theory, is xe^{-2x}. Thus the general solution is

$$y = c_1 e^{-2x} + c_2 x e^{-2x}.$$

There is an interesting alternative way of determining the second solution when the roots of the auxiliary equation are equal. Since r_1 is a repeated root of $ar^2 + br + c = 0$, it follows that $ar^2 + br + c = a(r - r_1)^2$. Then, for all r

$$L[e^{rx}] = a(e^{rx})'' + b(e^{rx})' + ce^{rx} = ae^{rx}(r - r_1)^2. \qquad (8)$$

The right-hand side of Eq. (8) vanishes when $r = r_1$, which shows that $e^{r_1 x}$ is a solution of Eq. (1) as we already know. Differentiating both sides of Eq. (8) with respect to r, and interchanging differentiation with respect to r and x gives

$$L[xe^{rx}] = axe^{rx}(r - r_1)^2 + 2ae^{rx}(r - r_1). \qquad (9)$$

When $r = r_1$ the right side of Eq. (9) vanishes and hence $L[xe^{r_1 x}] = 0$; thus $xe^{r_1 x}$ is also a solution of Eq. (1).

PROBLEMS

In each of Problems 1 through 13 determine the general solution of the given differential equation. If initial conditions are given, find the solution satisfying the stated conditions.

1. $y'' + 2y' - 3y = 0$
2. $4y'' + 4y' + y = 0$
3. $6y'' - y' - y = 0$
4. $2y'' - 3y' + y = 0$
5. $y'' - y = 0$
6. $y'' - 2y' + y = 0$
7. $y'' + 5y' = 0$
8. $y'' - 9y' + 9y = 0$
9. $y'' - 2y' - 2y = 0$
10. $y'' + 2y' + y = 0$
11. $y'' + y' - 2y = 0$, $\quad y(0) = 1$, $\quad y'(0) = 1$
12. $y'' - 6y' + 9y = 0$, $\quad y(0) = 0$, $\quad y'(0) = 2$
13. $y'' + 8y' - 9y = 0$, $\quad y(1) = 1$, $\quad y'(1) = 0$
14. Show that the general solution of $y'' - 4y = 0$ is

$$y = c_1 \sinh 2x + c_2 \cosh 2x.$$

15. Show that if $r_1 \neq r_2$ then the functions $e^{r_1 x}$ and $e^{r_2 x}$ are linearly independent on $-\infty < x < \infty$. This completes the proof of the result given in Eq. (6) of the text.

3.5.1 COMPLEX ROOTS

To complete our discussion of the equation

$$ay'' + by' + cy = 0 \tag{1}$$

we consider the case where the roots of the auxiliary equation

$$ar^2 + br + c = 0 \tag{2}$$

are complex numbers of the form $\lambda + i\mu$. This immediately raises the question of what we mean by expressions of the form $e^{(\lambda+i\mu)x}$.

First recall that in elementary calculus it was shown that the Taylor (1685–1731) series for e^x about $x = 0$ is

$$e^x = \sum_{n=0}^{\infty} \frac{x^n}{n!}, \qquad -\infty < x < \infty. \tag{3}$$

If we substitute ix for x in Eq. (3) and take the result as the definition of e^{ix} we find that

$$
\begin{aligned}
e^{ix} &= \sum_{n=0}^{\infty} \frac{(ix)^n}{n!} \\
&= \sum_{n=0}^{\infty} \frac{(-1)^n x^{2n}}{(2n)!} + i\sum_{n=1}^{\infty} \frac{(-1)^{n-1} x^{2n-1}}{(2n-1)!},
\end{aligned}
\tag{4}
$$

where we have made use of the fact that $i^2 = -1$, $i^3 = -i$, $i^4 = 1$, etc. The first series in Eq. (4) is precisely the Taylor series for $\cos x$, and the second is the Taylor series for $\sin x$. Hence we *define*

$$e^{ix} = \cos x + i \sin x. \tag{5}$$

This relationship is referred to as Euler's formula. Substituting $-x$ for x in Eq. (5) and making use of the relations $\cos(-x) = \cos x$, $\sin(-x) = -\sin x$ gives

$$e^{-ix} = \cos x - i \sin x. \tag{6}$$

The functions $\cos x$ and $\sin x$ can be expressed in terms of e^{ix} and e^{-ix} by respectively adding and subtracting Eqs. (5) and (6). We obtain

$$\cos x = \frac{e^{ix} + e^{-ix}}{2}, \qquad \sin x = \frac{e^{ix} - e^{-ix}}{2i}.$$

Next we *define*

$$e^{(\lambda+i\mu)x} = e^{\lambda x} e^{i\mu x} = e^{\lambda x}(\cos \mu x + i \sin \mu x). \tag{7}$$

With this definition it can be shown that the usual laws of algebra hold. For example,

$$
\begin{aligned}
\frac{e^{(\lambda+i\mu)x}}{e^{(\alpha+i\beta)x}} &= e^{(\lambda+i\mu)x-(\alpha+i\beta)x} \\
&= e^{(\lambda-\alpha)x+i(\mu-\beta)x},
\end{aligned}
$$

and

$$[e^{(\lambda+i\mu)x}]^n = e^{n(\lambda+i\mu)x}$$
$$= e^{n\lambda x + in\mu x},$$

where λ and μ are real numbers and n is a positive or negative integer. Actually the last result is also valid for nonintegral values of n.

Finally we must consider the question of differentiating $e^{(\lambda+i\mu)x}$ with respect to x. While we know that

$$\frac{d}{dx}(e^{rx}) = re^{rx} \tag{8}$$

for r a real number we do not know that this is true if r is complex. However, it can be shown by direct computation using the definition given by Eq. (7) that Eq. (8) is true for r complex. Indeed the usual laws of the elementary calculus are valid for complex exponentials with the understanding that e^{rx} is defined by Eq. (7) for r complex. More generally for a complex-valued function $f(x) = u(x) + iv(x)$, where u and v are real-valued functions, and for a complex constant c we have $f'(x) = u'(x) + iv'(x)$ and $(cf)' = cf'$.

Now we can return to the problem of solving Eq. (1) when the roots of the auxiliary equation are complex. Since a, b, and c are real, the roots occur in conjugate pairs $r_1 = \lambda + i\mu$ and $r_2 = \lambda - i\mu$; hence the general solution of Eq. (1) is

$$y = c_1 e^{(\lambda+i\mu)x} + c_2 e^{(\lambda-i\mu)x}. \tag{9}$$

The general solution (9) has the disadvantage that the functions $e^{(\lambda+i\mu)x}$ and $e^{(\lambda-i\mu)x}$ are complex-valued. Since the differential equation is real it would seem desirable, if possible, to express the general solution of Eq. (1) as a linear combination of real-valued solutions. This can be done as follows. Since $e^{(\lambda+i\mu)x}$ and $e^{(\lambda-i\mu)x}$ are solutions of Eq. (1), their sums and differences are also solutions; thus

$$e^{(\lambda+i\mu)x} + e^{(\lambda-i\mu)x} = e^{\lambda x}(\cos \mu x + i \sin \mu x) + e^{\lambda x}(\cos \mu x - i \sin \mu x)$$
$$= 2e^{\lambda x} \cos \mu x$$

and

$$e^{(\lambda+i\mu)x} - e^{(\lambda-i\mu)x} = e^{\lambda x}(\cos \mu x + i \sin \mu x) - e^{\lambda x}(\cos \mu x - i \sin \mu x)$$
$$= 2ie^{\lambda x} \sin \mu x$$

are solutions of Eq. (1). Hence, neglecting the constant multipliers 2 and $2i$, respectively, the functions

$$e^{\lambda x} \cos \mu x, \qquad e^{\lambda x} \sin \mu x \tag{10}$$

are real-valued solutions of Eq. (1). It can easily be shown that

$$W(e^{\lambda x} \cos \mu x, e^{\lambda x} \sin \mu x) = \mu e^{2\lambda x},$$

and since this never vanishes these two functions form a fundamental set of real-valued solutions. Hence we can express the general solution of Eq. (1) in the form

$$y = c_1 e^{\lambda x} \cos \mu x + c_2 e^{\lambda x} \sin \mu x$$

where c_1 and c_2 are arbitrary constants.

Example.   Find the general solution of

$$y'' + y' + y = 0. \tag{11}$$

The auxiliary equation is

$$r^2 + r + 1 = 0,$$

and the roots are

$$r = \frac{-1 \pm (1 - 4)^{1/2}}{2} = -\frac{1}{2} \pm i \frac{\sqrt{3}}{2} \, ;$$

hence the general solution of Eq. (11) is

$$y = e^{-x/2} \left(c_1 \cos \frac{\sqrt{3}}{2} x + c_2 \sin \frac{\sqrt{3}}{2} x \right).$$

Let us consider again the real-valued solutions $e^{\lambda x} \cos \mu x$ and $e^{\lambda x} \sin \mu x$ of Eq. (1). Notice that these functions are the real and imaginary parts, respectively, of the complex-valued solution $e^{(\lambda + i\mu)x}$. This is just a special case of a general result that depends only on the fact that the coefficients in the differential equation are real-valued, whether or not they are constants. We state this result as a theorem.

Theorem 3.9.   *Let the real-valued functions p and q be continuous on the open interval $\alpha < x < \beta$. Let $y = \phi(x) = u(x) + iv(x)$ be a complex-valued solution of the differential equation*

$$L[y] = y'' + p(x)y' + q(x)y = 0, \tag{12}$$

where u and v are real-valued functions. Then u and v are also solutions of the differential equation (12).

To prove this theorem, observe that

$$
\begin{aligned}
L[u + iv] &= (u + iv)'' + p(u + iv)' + q(u + iv) \\
&= (u'' + pu' + qu) + i(v'' + pv' + qv) \\
&= L[u] + iL[v] = 0.
\end{aligned}
$$

But a complex number is zero if, and only if, both its real and imaginary parts are zero; thus $L[u] = 0$ and $L[v] = 0$.

If the constants a, b, and c in Eq. (1) are complex numbers, it is still possible to find solutions of the form e^{rx} where r must satisfy

$$ar^2 + br + c = 0.$$

However, in general the roots of the auxiliary equation will be complex numbers but not complex conjugates, and the corresponding solutions of Eq. (1) will be complex-valued. This is briefly discussed in Problems 13, 14, and 15.

PROBLEMS

In each of Problems 1 through 8 determine the general solution of the given differential equation. If initial conditions are given, find the solution satisfying the stated conditions.

1. $y'' - 2y' + 2y = 0$ 2. $y'' - 2y' + 6y = 0$

3. $y'' + 2y' - 8y = 0$ 4. $y'' + 2y' + 2y = 0$

5. $9y'' - 6y' + y = 0$ 6. $y'' + 6y' + 13y = 0$

7. $y'' + 4y = 0$, $y(0) = 0$, $y'(0) = 1$

8. $y'' + 4y' + 5y = 0$, $y(0) = 1$, $y'(0) = 0$

9. Verify that $W(e^{\lambda x} \cos \mu x, e^{\lambda x} \sin \mu x) = \mu e^{2\lambda x}$.

10. Show that if a, b, and c are positive then all solutions of $ay'' + by' + cy = 0$ approach zero as $x \to \infty$.

11. Show that the general solution of

$$y'' + y = 0$$

can be expressed as $y = A_1 \cos (x + \delta_1)$ or as $y = A_2 \sin (x + \delta_2)$, where A_1, δ_1 and A_2, δ_2 are constants.

12. For r a real number show that

$$(\cos x + i \sin x)^r = \cos rx + i \sin rx.$$

For r a positive integer this is known as De Moivre's (1667–1754) formula. Use this result to obtain the double angle formulas $\sin 2x = 2 \sin x \cos x$ and $\cos 2x = \cos^2 x - \sin^2 x$.

*13. Show that any complex number $a + ib$ can be written in the form $Ae^{i\theta}$, where A and θ are positive real numbers, and $0 \le \theta < 2\pi$.
Hint: Expand $Ae^{i\theta}$ using Euler's formula and solve for A and θ in terms of a and b.

*14. Defining the two possible square roots of a complex number $Ae^{i\theta}$ as $\pm A^{1/2} e^{i\theta/2}$, compute the square roots of $1 + i$, $1 - i$, i.

*15. Solve

(a) $y'' + iy' + 2y = 0$ (b) $y'' + 2y' + iy = 0$

Note that the roots of the auxiliary equations are not complex conjugates. Does the real or imaginary part of either of the solutions satisfy the differential equation?

*16. Now that we know how to solve second order equations with constant coefficients, let us determine the conditions under which the equation $y'' + p(x)y' + q(x)y = 0$ can be transformed into one having constant coefficients by a suitable change of independent variable. Let z be the new independent variable, $z = u(x)$, where for the moment the relationship between z and x is unspecified. Show that

(a) $\dfrac{dy}{dx} = \dfrac{dz}{dx}\dfrac{dy}{dz}$

$$\frac{d^2y}{dx^2} = \left(\frac{dz}{dx}\right)^2 \frac{d^2y}{dz^2} + \frac{d^2z}{dx^2}\frac{dy}{dz}$$

(b) The differential equation becomes

$$\left(\frac{dz}{dx}\right)^2 \frac{d^2y}{dz^2} + \left(\frac{d^2z}{dx^2} + p(x)\frac{dz}{dx}\right)\frac{dy}{dz} + q(x)y = 0$$

(c) The equation of part (b) will have constant coefficients if we choose

$$z = u(x) = \int^x [q(t)]^{1/2}\,dt,$$

provided that

$$\frac{z'' + p(x)z'}{q(x)} = \frac{q'(x) + 2p(x)q(x)}{2[q(x)]^{3/2}}$$

is a constant.

Hence conclude that a necessary and sufficient condition for transforming $y'' + p(x)y' + q(x)y = 0$ into an equation with constant coefficients by a change of the independent variable is that the function $(q' + 2pq)/q^{3/2}$ be a constant.

*17. Using the result of Problem 16, determine whether each of the following equations can be transformed into equations with constant coefficients by a change of the independent variable. If so, find the general solution of the given equation.

(a) $y'' + xy' + e^{-x^2}y = 0,$ $-\infty < x < \infty$

(b) $y'' + 3xy' + x^2y = 0,$ $-\infty < x < \infty$

(c) $xy'' + (x^2 - 1)y' + x^3y = 0,$ $0 < x < \infty$

*18. Show, using the result of Problem 16, that it is always possible to transform an equation of the form

$$x^2y'' + \alpha xy' + \beta y = 0, \qquad x > 0,$$

where α and β are real constants, to an equation with constant coefficients by letting $z = e^x$. An equation of this type is called an Euler equation; it is discussed in Section 4.4. Find the general solution of $x^2y'' + xy' + y = 0, x > 0$.

3.6 THE NONHOMOGENEOUS PROBLEM

In the previous sections of this chapter we have discussed the general theory of second order linear homogeneous differential equations, and in the case of constant coefficients have shown how to construct solutions. We will now turn our attention to solving the nonhomogeneous differential equation

$$L[y] = y'' + p(x)y' + q(x)y = g(x). \tag{1}$$

Throughout the discussion we will assume that the functions p, q, and g are continuous on the interval of interest.

In modern engineering the problem of solving Eq. (1) is often referred to as an input-output problem. Supposing for the moment that the differential equation (1) represents a certain mechanical or electrical system, it is natural to refer to the solution $y = \phi(x)$ as the output of the system. The coefficients p and q are determined by the physical mechanism. The problem of solving Eq. (1) for different nonhomogeneous terms g, input functions, corresponds to determining the output of the system for different input functions.

Before considering particular cases of Eq. (1), we will prove several simple but very useful general results which will simplify our succeeding work.

Theorem 3.10. *The difference of any two solutions of the differential equation* (1),

$$L[y] = y'' + p(x)y' + q(x)y = g(x),$$

is a solution of the corresponding homogeneous differential equation

$$L[y] = y'' + p(x)y' + q(x)y = 0. \tag{2}$$

To prove this theorem suppose that the functions u_1 and u_2 are solutions of Eq. (1). Then

$$L[u_1] = g,$$

and

$$L[u_2] = g.$$

Subtracting the second equation from the first equation gives

$$L[u_1] - L[u_2] = 0,$$

or, since L is a linear operator,

$$L[u_1 - u_2] = 0,$$

which is the desired result. With the aid of this theorem we can prove the following important theorem.

Theorem 3.11. *Any solution $y = \phi(x)$ of the nonhomogeneous linear differential equation* (1)

$$L[y] = y'' + p(x)y' + q(x)y = g(x)$$

can be expressed as

$$\phi(x) = y_p(x) + c_1 y_1(x) + c_2 y_2(x) \tag{3}$$

where y_p is any solution of the nonhomogeneous equation and y_1 and y_2 are linearly independent solutions of the corresponding homogeneous equation.

To prove this theorem, observe that according to Theorem 3.10 $\phi - y_p$ is a solution of the homogeneous equation. Thus, according to Theorem 3.4 of Section 3.2, $\phi - y_p$ can be expressed as a linear combination of y_1 and y_2, which establishes the theorem.

It is customary to refer to the linear combination (3) as the *general solution* of Eq. (1).

Consequently, to find the general solution of Eq. (1) we must find the general solution of the homogeneous equation (2) and then find *any* solution of the nonhomogeneous equation. As we could have anticipated (see Section 3.1) the general solution of Eq. (1) involves two arbitrary constants, and hence to specify a unique solution of Eq. (1) it is necessary to specify two additional conditions, namely, the initial conditions $y(x_0) = y_0$ and $y'(x_0) = y_0'$.

The general solution of the homogeneous equation (2) is often referred to as the *complementary solution* and denoted by y_c. Thus $y_c(x) = c_1 y_1(x) + c_2 y_2(x)$. A solution of the nonhomogeneous equation y_p is usually called a *particular solution.** Notice that y_p is not uniquely determined since if Y is a solution of the nonhomogeneous equation then Y plus any multiple of y_1 or y_2 is still a solution of the nonhomogeneous equation. It follows from Theorem 3.11 that the general solution of the nonhomogeneous equation (1) is

$$y = y_c(x) + y_p(x). \tag{4}$$

In many problems the nonhomogeneous term g may be very complicated; however, if g can be expressed as the sum of a finite number of functions we can make use of the linearity of the differential equation to replace the original problem by several simpler ones. For example, suppose it is possible to write $g(x)$ as $g_1(x) + g_2(x) + \cdots + g_m(x)$; then Eq. (1) becomes

$$L[y] = y'' + p(x)y' + q(x)y = g_1(x) + g_2(x) + \cdots + g_m(x). \tag{5}$$

If we can find particular solutions y_{p_i} of the differential equations

$$L[y] = g_i(x), \quad i = 1, 2, \ldots, m, \tag{6}$$

then it follows by direct substitution that

$$y_p(x) = y_{p_1}(x) + y_{p_2}(x) + \cdots + y_{p_m}(x) \tag{7}$$

is a particular solution of Eq. (5). Hence the general solution of Eq. (5) is of the form

$$y = y_c(x) + y_{p_1}(x) + \cdots + y_{p_m}(x). \tag{8}$$

In general it is easier to find solutions of Eqs. (6) and to add the results than to try to solve Eq. (5) as it stands. This method of constructing the solution

---

* This is rather an unfortunate usage, since the term particular solution may also refer to a solution satisfying prescribed initial conditions. The meaning is usually clear from the context.

of a complicated problem by adding solutions of simpler problems is known as the method of superposition.

Example. Find the general solution of

$$y'' + 4y = 1 + x + \sin x. \tag{9}$$

First consider the corresponding homogeneous equation, $y'' + 4y = 0$. Substituting $y = e^{rx}$ yields the auxiliary equation $r^2 + 4 = 0$. Thus the complementary solution is

$$y_c(x) = c_1 \cos 2x + c_2 \sin 2x.$$

To determine a particular solution of Eq. (9) we superimpose particular solutions of $y'' + 4y = 1$, $y'' + 4y = x$, and $y'' + 4y = \sin x$. It can be readily verified that $\frac{1}{4}$, $\frac{1}{4}x$, and $\frac{1}{3} \sin x$ are particular solutions of these equations, respectively. Thus the general solution of Eq. (9) is

$$y = c_1 \cos 2x + c_2 \sin 2x + \tfrac{1}{4} + \tfrac{1}{4}x + \tfrac{1}{3} \sin x.$$

3.6.1 THE METHOD OF UNDETERMINED COEFFICIENTS

A number of methods can be used to obtain particular solutions of second order nonhomogeneous differential equations. When applicable, the method of undetermined coefficients is one of the simplest. Basically, the method consists in making an intelligent guess as to the form of the particular solution and then substituting this function, which in general will involve one or more unknown coefficients, into the differential equation. For this method to be successful we must be able to determine the unknown coefficients so that the function actually does satisfy the differential equation.

Clearly such a method depends to a considerable extent on the ability to discover in advance the general form of a particular solution. For a completely arbitrary differential equation very little can be said. However, if the equation is of the form

$$a\frac{d^2y}{dx^2} + b\frac{dy}{dx} + cy = g(x), \tag{1}$$

where a, b, and c are real constants, and the nonhomogeneous term $g(x)$ is an exponential function ($e^{\alpha x}$), or a polynomial ($a_0 x^n + \cdots + a_n$), or sinusoidal in character ($\sin \beta x$ or $\cos \beta x$), then definite rules can be given for the determination of a particular solution by the method of undetermined coefficients. These rules also cover the more general case in which $g(x)$ is a product of terms of the above types, such as

$$g(x) = e^{\alpha x}(a_0 x^n + a_1 x^{n-1} + \cdots + a_n)\begin{cases} \cos \beta x \\ \sin \beta x. \end{cases} \tag{2}$$

Notice that any other product of exponentials, polynomials, and sines and cosines is equivalent to a sum of terms of the type (2). In particular, the product of two or more sinusoidal terms can always be reduced to a sum of individual sinusoidal terms by the use of trigonometric identities. We can treat the case in which $g(x)$ is a sum of terms of type (2) by using the method of superposition which was discussed in the last section. For more general nonhomogeneous terms than (2) or for equations with variable coefficients the method of undetermined coefficients is rarely useful.

Before discussing the general procedure let us consider a few simple examples which will illustrate the method.

Example 1. Find a particular solution of the differential equation

$$y'' - 3y' - 4y = 2 \sin x. \tag{3}$$

We want to find a function y_p such that the sum of its second derivative minus three times its first derivative minus four times the function itself adds up to $2 \sin x$. There is little hope in trying such functions as $\ln x$, e^x, or x^2 for $y_p(x)$ since no matter how we combine such functions and their derivatives it is impossible to obtain $\sin x$. The obvious functions to consider for $y_p(x)$ are $\sin x$ and $\cos x$. So we *assume* that $y_p(x)$ is of the form

$$y_p(x) = A \cos x + B \sin x,$$

where A and B are, for the moment, unknown constants. Then

$$y_p'(x) = -A \sin x + B \cos x,$$
$$y_p''(x) = -A \cos x - B \sin x.$$

Substituting for y, y', and y'' in Eq. (3) and collecting terms gives

$$(-A - 3B - 4A) \cos x + (-B + 3A - 4B) \sin x = 2 \sin x.$$

This equation will be satisfied identically if and only if

$$-5A - 3B = 0, \qquad 3A - 5B = 2.$$

Hence $A = \frac{3}{17}$, $B = -\frac{5}{17}$, and a particular solution of Eq. (3) is

$$y_p(x) = \tfrac{1}{17}(3 \cos x - 5 \sin x).$$

Example 2. Find a particular solution of the differential equation

$$y'' - 3y' - 4y = 4x^2. \tag{4}$$

It is natural to try $y_p(x) = Ax^2$ where A is a constant to be determined. Then $y_p'(x) = 2Ax$, $y_p''(x) = 2A$, and substituting in Eq. (4) gives

$$2A - 6Ax - 4Ax^2 = 4x^2.$$

If this equation is to be satisfied for all x the coefficients of like powers of

x on each side of the equation must be identical. This leads to three equations and there is no choice of A that will satisfy all three. Hence it is impossible to find a particular solution of Eq. (4) of the form Ax^2.

However, if we think of the nonhomogeneous term $4x^2$ in Eq. (4) as the polynomial $4x^2 + 0x + 0$ it now appears reasonable to assume that the form of $y_p(x)$ is $Ax^2 + Bx + C$, where A, B, and C are constants to be determined. Substituting for y, y', and y'' in Eq. (4) and equating like powers of x on both sides of the equation gives three simultaneous linear algebraic nonhomogeneous equations for A, B, and C. The solution is $A = -1$, $B = \frac{3}{2}$, and $C = -\frac{13}{8}$; hence a particular solution of Eq. (4) is

$$y_p(x) = -x^2 + \tfrac{3}{2}x - \tfrac{13}{8}.$$

The student may wonder what would happen if a higher degree polynomial, such as $Ax^4 + Bx^3 + Cx^2 + Dx + E$, were assumed for $y_p(x)$. The answer is that all coefficients beyond the quadratic term would turn out to be zero. Thus with certain exceptions to be noted later, it is unnecessary to assume for $y_p(x)$ a polynomial of higher degree than the degree of the polynomial in the nonhomogeneous term.

Example 3.   Find a particular solution of the equation

$$y'' - 3y' - 4y = e^{-x}. \tag{5}$$

Following the reasoning used before we assume $y_p(x) = Ae^{-x}$. Substituting in Eq. (5) gives

$$(A + 3A - 4A)e^{-x} = e^{-x},$$

or

$$0 \cdot Ae^{-x} = e^{-x},$$

which does not permit the determination of A. Hence the particular solution is not of the form Ae^{-x}. The difficulty in this case stems from the fact that e^{-x} is a solution of the homogeneous differential equation; hence the operations of the left-hand side of Eq. (5), when applied to any constant multiple of e^{-x}, yield zero. This raises the general question of whether the method of undetermined coefficients can still be used when the nonhomogeneous term is a solution of the homogeneous equation. We shall soon see that the answer to this question is yes.

Let us now turn to the general cases in which $g(x)$ is of the form

$$g(x) = \begin{cases} P_n(x) = a_0 x^n + a_1 x^{n-1} + \cdots + a_n \\ e^{\alpha x} P_n(x) \\ e^{\alpha x} P_n(x) \sin \beta x \\ e^{\alpha x} P_n(x) \cos \beta x. \end{cases}$$

If $g(x) = P_n(x)$, then Eq. (1) becomes

$$ay'' + by' + cy = a_0x^n + a_1x^{n-1} + \cdots + a_n. \qquad (6)$$

To obtain a particular solution we assume

$$y_p(x) = A_0x^n + A_1x^{n-1} + \cdots + A_{n-2}x^2 + A_{n-1}x + A_n. \qquad (7)$$

Substituting in Eq. (6) we obtain

$$a[n(n-1)A_0x^{n-2} + \cdots + 2A_{n-2}] + b(nA_0x^{n-1} + \cdots + A_{n-1})$$
$$+ c(A_0x^n + \cdots + A_n) = a_0x^n + \cdots + a_n. \qquad (8)$$

Equating the coefficients of like powers of x gives

$$cA_0 = a_0,$$
$$cA_1 + nbA_0 = a_1,$$
$$\cdot$$
$$\cdot$$
$$\cdot$$
$$cA_n + bA_{n-1} + 2aA_{n-2} = a_n.$$

Provided $c \neq 0$ the solution of the first equation is $A_0 = a_0/c$, and the remaining equations determine $A_1, A_2, \ldots, A_n$ successively. If $c = 0$, but $b \neq 0$, the polynomial on the left-hand side of Eq. (8) is of degree $n - 1$, and we cannot satisfy Eq. (8). In order to insure that $ay_p''(x) + by_p'(x)$ will be a polynomial of degree n we must choose $y_p(x)$ to be a polynomial of degree $n + 1$. Hence we assume

$$y_p(x) = x(A_0x^n + \cdots + A_n).$$

There is no constant term in this expression for $y_p(x)$, but there is no need to include such a term since when $c = 0$ a constant is a solution of the homogeneous differential equation. Since $b \neq 0$ we have $A_0 = a_0/b(n + 1)$, and the coefficients $A_1, \ldots, A_n$ can be determined similarly. If both c and b vanish, we would assume

$$y_p(x) = x^2(A_0x^n + \cdots + A_n).$$

The term $ay_p''(x)$ gives rise to a term of degree n, and we can proceed as before.* Again the constant and linear terms in $y_p(x)$ are omitted since in this case they are both solutions of the homogeneous equation.

If $g(x)$ is of the form $e^{\alpha x}P_n(x)$ the problem of determining a particular solution of

$$ay'' + by' + cy = e^{\alpha x}P_n(x) \qquad (9)$$

* The student should note that in the case $c = 0$, $b \neq 0$, Eq. (6) can be integrated once giving a first order linear equation whose nonhomogeneous term is a polynomial of degree $n + 1$. A particular solution of this equation could then be found by the method of undetermined coefficients with $y_p(x)$ a polynomial of degree $n + 1$. If both c and b vanish, then Eq. (6) can be integrated immediately, the solution being a polynomial of degree $n + 2$.

can be reduced to the one just solved.* Let

$$y_p(x) = e^{\alpha x}u(x);$$

then

$$y_p'(x) = e^{\alpha x}[u'(x) + \alpha u(x)]$$

and

$$y_p''(x) = e^{\alpha x}[u''(x) + 2\alpha u'(x) + \alpha^2 u(x)].$$

Substituting for y, y', and y'' in Eq. (9), canceling the factor $e^{\alpha x}$, and collecting terms give

$$au''(x) + (2a\alpha + b)u'(x) + (a\alpha^2 + b\alpha + c)u(x) = P_n(x). \qquad (10)$$

The determination of a particular solution of Eq. (10) is precisely the problem that we just solved. If $a\alpha^2 + b\alpha + c$ does not vanish we assume $u(x) = (A_0 x^n + \cdots + A_n)$, and hence a particular solution of Eq. (9) is of the form

$$y_p(x) = e^{\alpha x}(A_0 x^n + A_1 x^{n-1} + \cdots + A_n). \qquad (11)$$

On the other hand, if $a\alpha^2 + b\alpha + c$ vanishes but $(2a\alpha + b)$ does not, we must take $u(x)$ to be of the form $x(A_0 x^n + \cdots + A_n)$. The corresponding form for $y_p(x)$ is x times the expression in the right member of Eq. (11). It should be noted that the vanishing of $a\alpha^2 + b\alpha + c$ implies that $e^{\alpha x}$ is a solution of the homogeneous equation. If both $a\alpha^2 + b\alpha + c$ and $2a\alpha + b$ vanish (and this implies that both $e^{\alpha x}$ and $xe^{\alpha x}$ are solutions of the homogeneous equation) then the correct form for $u(x)$ is $x^2(A_0 x^n + \cdots + A_n)$; and hence $y_p(x)$ is x^2 times the expression in the right member of Eq. (11).

If $g(x)$ is of the form $e^{\alpha x}P_n(x) \sin \beta x$ we can reduce this problem to the previous one by recalling that $\sin \beta x = (e^{i\beta x} - e^{-i\beta x})/2i$. Hence $g(x)$ is of the form

$$g(x) = P_n(x)\frac{e^{(\alpha+i\beta)x} - e^{(\alpha-i\beta)x}}{2i}$$

and we should choose

$$y_p(x) = e^{(\alpha+i\beta)x}(A_0 x^n + \cdots + A_n) + e^{(\alpha-i\beta)x}(B_0 x^n + \cdots + B_n),$$

or equivalently

$$y_p(x) = e^{\alpha x}(A_0 x^n + \cdots + A_n) \cos \beta x + e^{\alpha x}(B_0 x^n + \cdots + B_n) \sin \beta x.$$

Usually the latter form is preferred. If $\alpha \pm i\beta$ satisfy the auxiliary equation corresponding to the homogeneous equation we must, of course, multiply each of the polynomials by x to increase their degree by one.

If the nonhomogeneous term involves expressions such as $e^{\alpha x} \cos \beta x$ and $e^{\alpha x} \sin \beta x$ it is convenient to treat these together, since each one individually gives rise to the same form for a particular solution. For example,

* One of a mathematician's favorite devices is to reduce a new problem to one which he already knows how to solve.

if $g(x) = x \sin x + 2 \cos x$, the form for $y_p(x)$ would be

$$(A_0 x + A_1) \sin x + (B_0 x + B_1) \cos x$$

provided that $\sin x$ and $\cos x$ were not solutions of the homogeneous equation. We can summarize the preceding results in Table 3.1.

TABLE 3.1   The Particular Solution of $ay'' + by' + cy = g(x)$

$g(x)$	$y_p(x)$
$P_n(x) = a_0 x^n + a_1 x^{n-1} + \cdots + a_n$	$x^s(A_0 x^n + A_1 x^{n-1} + \cdots + A_n)$
$P_n(x)e^{\alpha x}$	$x^s(A_0 x^n + A_1 x^{n-1} + \cdots + A_n)e^{\alpha x}$
$P_n(x)e^{\alpha x}\begin{cases} \sin \beta x \\ \cos \beta x \end{cases}$	$x^s[(A_0 x^n + A_1 x^{n-1} + \cdots + A_n)e^{\alpha x} \cos \beta x$ $+ (B_0 x^n + B_1 x^{n-1} + \cdots + B_n)e^{\alpha x} \sin \beta x]$

Here s is the smallest nonnegative integer ($s = 0, 1,$ or 2) which will insure that no term in $y_p(x)$ is a solution of the corresponding homogeneous equation.

These results, coupled with the fact that the principle of superposition can be used to find the corresponding particular solution when the non-homogeneous term consists of the sum of several functions, allow us to solve fairly rapidly a wide class of linear constant coefficient nonhomogeneous differential equations.

If the differential equation has variable coefficients or the nonhomogeneous term is more complicated than Eq. (2), it is usually better to use the method of variation of parameters, which is discussed in the next section.

Example 4.   Using the method of undetermined coefficients, determine the correct form for $y_p(x)$ for the differential equation

$$y'' + 4y = xe^x + x \sin 2x. \tag{12}$$

We use the superposition principle, and consider the problems

$$y'' + 4y = xe^x \tag{13}$$

and

$$y'' + 4y = x \sin 2x \tag{14}$$

separately. For the first problem we assume $y_p(x) = (A_0 x + A_1)e^x$. Since e^x is not a solution of the homogeneous equation it is not necessary to do anything more. For the second problem we assume $y_p(x) = (B_0 x + B_1) \cos 2x + (C_0 x + C_1) \sin 2x$, but since $\cos 2x$ and $\sin 2x$ are solutions of the homogeneous equation it is necessary to multiply their polynomial coefficients by x. Hence the correct form for $y_p(x)$ for Eq. (12) is

$$y_p(x) = (A_0 x + A_1)e^x + (B_0 x^2 + B_1 x) \cos 2x + (C_0 x^2 + C_1 x) \sin 2x.$$

In determining the coefficients in this expression it is easier to compute the particular solution corresponding to xe^x, Eq. (13), and $x \sin 2x$, Eq. (14), separately than to try to do all the algebra at one time.

PROBLEMS

Using the method of undetermined coefficients to find a particular solution of the nonhomogeneous equation, find the general solution of the following differential equations. Where specified find the solution satisfying the given initial conditions.

1. $y'' + y' - 2y = 2x$, $y(0) = 0$, $y'(0) = 1$

2. $2y'' - 4y' - 6y = 3e^{2x}$

3. $y'' + 4y = x^2 + 3e^x$, $y(0) = 0$, $y'(0) = 2$

4. $y'' + 2y' = 3 + 4 \sin 2x$

5. $y'' + 9y = x^2 e^{3x} + 6$

6. $y'' - 2y' + y = xe^x + 4$, $y(0) = 1$, $y'(0) = 1$

7. $2y'' + 3y' + y = x^2 + 3 \sin x$

8. $y'' + y = 3 \sin 2x + x \cos 2x$

9. $y'' + 2y' + y = e^x \cos x$

10. $u'' + \omega_0^2 u = \cos \omega t$, $\omega \neq \omega_0$

11. $u'' + \omega_0^2 u = \cos \omega_0 t$,

12. $u'' + \mu u' + \omega_0^2 u = \cos \omega t$ $\mu^2 - 4\omega_0^2 < 0$

13. $y'' + y' + y = \sin^2 x$

14. $y'' + y' + 4y = 2 \sinh x$.   Hint: $\sinh x = (e^x - e^{-x})/2$

15. $y'' - y' - 2y = \cosh 2x$.   Hint: $\cosh x = (e^x + e^{-x})/2$

In Problems 16 through 22 determine a suitable form for $y_p(x)$ if the method of undetermined coefficients is to be used. Do not evaluate the constants.

16. $y'' + 3y' = 2x^4 + x^2 e^{-3x} + \sin 3x$

17. $y'' + y = x(1 + \sin x)$

18. $y'' - 5y' + 6y = e^x \cos 2x + e^{2x}(3x + 4) \sin x$

19. $y'' + 2y' + 2y = 3e^{-x} + 2e^{-x} \cos x + 4e^{-x}x^2 \sin x$

20. $y'' - 4y' + 4y = 2x^2 + 4xe^{2x} + x \sin 2x$

21. $y'' + 4y = x^2 \sin 2x + (6x + 7) \cos 2x$

22. $y'' + 3y' + 2y = e^x(x^2 + 1) \sin 2x + 3e^x \cos x + 4e^x$

23. Determine the general solution of

$$y'' + \lambda^2 y = \sum_{m=1}^{N} a_m \sin m\pi x$$

where $\lambda > 0$ and $\lambda \neq m\pi$, $m = 1, 2, \ldots, N$.

24. If a, b, and c are positive and Y_1 and Y_2 are solutions of

$$ay'' + by' + cy = g(x),$$

show that $Y_1(x) - Y_2(x) \to 0$ as $x \to \infty$. What is the behavior of the solution of Problem 10 for large t? Of Problem 11?

25. In many physical problems the input function, i.e., the nonhomogeneous term, may be specified by different formulas in different time periods. As a simple example of such a problem determine the solution $y = \phi(t)$ of

$$y'' + y = \begin{cases} t, & 0 \le t \le \pi, \\ \pi e^{\pi - t}, & t > \pi, \end{cases}$$

satisfying the initial conditions $y(0) = 0$ and $y'(0) = 1$, and the requirement that y and y' be continuous for all t. Plot the nonhomogeneous term and the solution $y = \phi(t)$ as a function of time.

Hint: First solve the initial value problem for $t \le \pi$, then solve for $t > \pi$ determining the arbitrary constants so that y and y' are continuous at $t = \pi$.

26. Determine a suitable form for $y_p(x)$ for the differential equation

$$ay'' + by' + cy = e^{\alpha x}(a_0 x^n + a_1 x^{n-1} + \cdots + a_n) \sinh \beta x, \qquad \beta \ne 0,$$

(i) If neither $e^{(\alpha + \beta)x}$ nor $e^{(\alpha - \beta)x}$ is a solution of the homogeneous equation.

(ii) If $e^{(\alpha + \beta)x}$ but not $e^{(\alpha - \beta)x}$ is a solution of the homogeneous equation.

(iii) If both $e^{(\alpha + \beta)x}$ and $e^{(\alpha - \beta)x}$ are solutions of the homogeneous equation.

(iv) In each of cases (i)–(iii) find suitable expressions for $y_p(x)$ which only involve products of $e^{\alpha x}$, $\cosh \beta x$, $\sinh \beta x$, and polynomials.

3.6.2 THE METHOD OF VARIATION OF PARAMETERS

In Section 3.6.1 we discussed a simple method of determining particular solutions of nonhomogeneous differential equations with constant coefficients provided the nonhomogeneous term is of a suitable form. In this section we will consider a *general method* of determining a particular solution of the equation

$$y'' + p(x)y' + q(x)y = g(x) \tag{1}$$

where the functions p, q, and g are continuous on the interval of interest. In order to use this method, known as the method of variation of parameters,* it is necessary to know a fundamental set of solutions of the corresponding homogeneous equation

$$y'' + p(x)y' + q(x)y = 0. \tag{2}$$

Suppose y_1 and y_2 are linearly independent solutions of the homogeneous equation (2). Then the general solution of Eq. (2) is

$$y_c(x) = c_1 y_1(x) + c_2 y_2(x).$$

The method of variation of parameters involves the replacement of the constants c_1 and c_2 by functions u_1 and u_2. We then seek to determine the

---

* The method is also referred to a Lagrange's method in honor of the French mathematician, J. L. Lagrange (1736–1813), who used it in 1774. Lagrange is famous for his work in celestial mechanics, analytical mechanics, and mathematical analysis. By the age of twenty-five he was recognized as one of the greatest living mathematicians.

two functions u_1 and u_2 so that

$$y_p(x) = u_1(x)y_1(x) + u_2(x)y_2(x) \tag{3}$$

satisfies the nonhomogeneous differential equation (1). The importance of this method is due to the fact that it is possible to determine the functions u_1 and u_2 in a simple manner. In order to determine u_1 and u_2 two conditions are required. One condition on u_1 and u_2 stems from the fact that y_p must satisfy Eq. (1). A second condition can be imposed arbitrarily, and will be selected so as to facilitate the calculations. Differentiating Eq. (3) gives

$$y_p' = (u_1'y_1 + u_2'y_2) + (u_1y_1' + u_2y_2'). \tag{4}$$

As just indicated we will simplify this by requiring that u_1 and u_2 satisfy

$$u_1'y_1 + u_2'y_2 = 0. \tag{5}$$

With this condition on u_1' and u_2', y_p'' is given by

$$y_p'' = u_1'y_1' + u_2'y_2' + u_1y_1'' + u_2y_2''. \tag{6}$$

Notice that only *first derivatives* of u_1 and u_2 appear in the expression for y_p''. Substituting for y_p' and y_p'' in Eq. (1) gives

$$u_1(y_1'' + py_1' + qy_1) + u_2(y_2'' + py_2' + qy_2) + u_1'y_1' + u_2'y_2' = g.$$

The terms in parentheses vanish since y_1 and y_2 are solutions of the homogeneous equation (2); hence the condition that y_p satisfy Eq. (1) leads to the requirement

$$u_1'y_1' + u_2'y_2' = g. \tag{7}$$

Rewriting Eqs. (5) and (7), we have the following system of two equations

$$u_1'y_1 + u_2'y_2 = 0$$
$$u_1'y_1' + u_2'y_2' = g$$

for the two unknown functions u_1' and u_2'. Solving this system of equations gives

$$u_1' = \frac{-y_2 g}{W(y_1, y_2)}, \qquad u_2' = \frac{y_1 g}{W(y_1, y_2)}, \tag{8}$$

where $W(y_1, y_2) = y_1y_2' - y_1'y_2$. Division by $W(y_1, y_2)$ is permissible since y_1 and y_2 are linearly independent solutions of the homogeneous equation and hence $W(y_1, y_2)$ cannot vanish in the interval. Integrating Eqs. (8) and substituting in Eq. (3) gives a particular solution of the nonhomogeneous equation (1). We state this result in a theorem.

Theorem 3.12. *If the functions p, q, and g are continuous on $\alpha < x < \beta$, and if the functions y_1 and y_2 are linearly independent solutions of the* *homogeneous equation associated with the differential equation* (1),

$$y'' + p(x)y' + q(x)y = g(x),$$

then a particular solution of Eq. (1) *is given by*

$$y_p(x) = -y_1(x) \int^x \frac{y_2(t)g(t)}{W(y_1, y_2)(t)} dt + y_2(x) \int^x \frac{y_1(t)g(t)}{W(y_1, y_2)(t)} dt. \qquad (9)$$

Equation (9) can also be written as

$$y_p(x) = \int^x \frac{y_1(t)y_2(x) - y_1(x)y_2(t)}{y_1(t)y_2'(t) - y_1'(t)y_2(t)} g(t) \, dt. \qquad (10)$$

Note that in Eq. (10) t is a dummy variable of integration and x is the independent variable.

In using the method of variation of parameters for a particular problem it is usually safer to substitute $y_p(x) = u_1(x)y_1(x) + u_2(x)y_2(x)$ and proceed as above rather than to try to remember either formula (9) or (10). It should be mentioned that while Eqs. (9) and (10) provide formulas for computing $y_p(x)$, it may not always be easy or even possible to evaluate these integrals in closed form. Nevertheless, even in these cases the formulas for $y_p(x)$ will provide a starting point for the numerical evaluation of $y_p(x)$, and that may be the best that can be done. From a numerical point of view it is usually advantageous to have an integral form of the solution, since numerical evaluation of an integral is usually, but not always, considerably easier than direct numerical integration of a differential equation.

Again we emphasize that in computing a particular solution by the method of variation of parameters it is not necessary that the coefficients in the differential equation be constants; all that is required is that we know two linearly independent solutions of the homogeneous equation.

Example. Determine the general solution of the differential equation

$$y'' + y = \sec x, \qquad 0 < x < \pi/2. \qquad (11)$$

Two linearly independent solutions of the homogeneous equation are $y_1(x) = \cos x$, $y_2(x) = \sin x$. For a particular solution we try

$$y_p(x) = u_1(x) \cos x + u_2(x) \sin x.$$

Then

$$y_p'(x) = [-u_1(x) \sin x + u_2(x) \cos x] + [u_1'(x) \cos x + u_2'(x) \sin x].$$

Setting the second parenthesis equal to zero, differentiating again, and substituting in Eq. (11) gives

$$u_1'(x) \cos x + u_2'(x) \sin x = 0,$$
$$-u_1'(x) \sin x + u_2'(x) \cos x = \sec x.$$

Solving we obtain

$$u_1'(x) = -\tan x, \qquad u_2'(x) = 1,$$
$$u_1(x) = \ln \cos x, \qquad u_2(x) = x.$$

Hence a particular solution of Eq. (11) is

$$y_p(x) = x \sin x + (\cos x) \ln \cos x,$$

and the general solution is

$$y = c_1 \cos x + c_2 \sin x + x \sin x + (\cos x) \ln \cos x.$$

We can summarize the results of the preceding sections of this chapter, which are concerned with methods of solving the differential equation (1)

$$y'' + p(x)y' + q(x)y = g(x),$$

where the functions p, q, and g are continuous on $\alpha < x < \beta$, as follows.

1. If p and q are constants it is always possible to find two linearly independent solutions of the homogeneous equation. A particular solution can then be obtained by the method of variation of parameters, and hence the complete solution is known. If g is of the appropriate form it will probably be easier to use the method of undetermined coefficients rather than the method of variation of parameters to determine the particular solution.

2. If p and q are not constants, there is no general way to solve Eq. (1) in terms of a finite number of elementary functions.* However, if one solution of the homogeneous equation can be found, a second solution can be obtained in principle by reducing the order of the equation. Then a particular solution can be obtained by the method of variation of parameters, and hence the complete solution is known. Actually both calculations can be done together. If we know one solution of the homogeneous equation, we can solve the nonhomogeneous equation by the method of reduction of order and obtain both a particular solution and a second linearly independent solution of the homogeneous equation. This is illustrated in Problems 13 and 14. Thus, in general, the problem of solving Eq. (1) rests on the possibility of finding *one* solution of the corresponding homogeneous equation.

PROBLEMS

Determine a particular solution, using the method of variation of parameters, of each of the following differential equations.

1. $y'' - 5y' + 6y = 2e^x$ 2. $y'' - y' - 2y = 2e^{-x}$

3. $y'' + 2y' + y = 3e^{-x}$ 4. $y'' + y = \tan x, \qquad 0 < x < \pi/2$

---

* Methods involving infinite series, which are useful for a large class of problems involving variable coefficients, are discussed in Chapter 4. Numerical methods are discussed in Chapter 8.

5. $y'' + 9y = 9 \sec^2 3x$, $0 < x < \pi/6$

6. $y'' + 4y' + 4y = e^{-2x}/x^2$, $x > 0$

7. $y'' + 4y = 3 \csc 2x$, $0 < x < \pi/2$

8. Two linearly independent solutions of Bessel's equation of order one-half,

$$x^2 y'' + xy' + (x^2 - \tfrac{1}{4})y = 0, \qquad x > 0,$$

are $x^{-\frac{1}{2}} \sin x$ and $x^{-\frac{1}{2}} \cos x$. Find the general solution of

$$x^2 y'' + xy' + (x^2 - \tfrac{1}{4})y = 3x^{\frac{3}{2}} \sin x, \qquad x > 0.$$

9. Verify that e^x and x are solutions of the homogeneous equation corresponding to

$$(1 - x)y'' + xy' - y = 2(x - 1)^2 e^{-x}, \qquad 0 < x < 1,$$

and find the general solution.

10. Find a formula for a particular solution of the differential equation

$$y'' - 5y' + 6y = g(x).$$

11. Find a formula for a particular solution of the differential equation

$$x^2 y'' + xy' + (x^2 - \tfrac{1}{4})y = g(x), \qquad x > 0.$$

(See Problem 8.)

*12. Consider the problem of solving the intial value problem

$$y'' + y = g(x), \qquad y(0) = 0, \qquad y'(0) = 0.$$

(i) Show that the general solution of $y'' + y = g(x)$ is

$$y = \phi(x) = \left(c_1 - \int_\alpha^x g(t) \sin t \, dt \right) \cos x + \left(c_2 + \int_\beta^x g(t) \cos t \, dt \right) \sin x$$

where c_1 and c_2 are arbitrary constants and α and β are any conveniently chosen points.

(ii) Using (i) show that $y(0) = 0$ and $y'(0) = 0$ if

$$c_1 = \int_\alpha^0 g(t) \sin t \, dt, \qquad c_2 = -\int_\beta^0 g(t) \cos t \, dt;$$

and hence the solution of the above initial value problem for arbitrary $g(x)$ can be written as

$$y = \phi(x) = \int_0^x g(t) \sin (x - t) \, dt.$$

Notice that this equation gives a formula for computing the solution of the original initial value problem for any given nonhomogeneous term, $g(x)$. The function ϕ will not only satisfy the differential equation but will also *automatically* satisfy the initial conditions. If we think of x as time, the formula also shows the relation between the input $g(x)$ and the output $\phi(x)$. Further, we see that the output at time x_0 depends only on the behavior of the input from the initial time 0 to the time of interest x_0. This integral is often referred to as the *convolution* of $\sin x$ and $g(x)$.

(iii) Now that we have the solution of the linear nonhomogeneous differential equation satisfying homogeneous initial conditions we can solve the same problem with nonhomogeneous initial conditions by superimposing a solution of the homogeneous equation satisfying the nonhomogeneous initial conditions. Show that the solution of $y'' + y = g(x)$ with $y(x_0) = y_0$, $y'(x_0) = y_0'$ is

$$y = \phi(x) = \int_0^x g(t) \sin (x - t) \, dt + y_0 \cos x + y_0' \sin x.$$

13. Provided that one solution of the homogeneous equation is known, the nonhomogeneous equation

$$y'' + p(x)y' + q(x)y = g(x) \tag{i}$$

can also be solved by the method of reduction of order (see Section 3.4). Suppose that y_1 is a known solution of the homogeneous equation.

(a) Show that $y = y_1(x)v(x)$ is a solution of Eq. (i) provided that v satisfies

$$y_1 v'' + (2y_1' + py_1)v' = g. \tag{ii}$$

(b) Equation (ii) is a first order linear equation for v'. Show that the solution is

$$y_1^2(x)h(x)v'(x) = \int^x y_1(s)h(s)g(s) \, ds + k,$$

where $h(x) = \exp\left[\int^x p(s) \, ds\right]$ and k is a constant.

(c) Using part (b) show that the general solution of Eq. (i) is

$$y = c_1 y_1(x) + c_2 y_1(x) \int^x \frac{ds}{y_1^2(s)h(s)} + y_1(x) \int^x \frac{1}{y_1^2(s)h(s)} \left[\int^s y_1(t)h(t)g(t) \, dt\right] ds.$$

14. Using the procedure developed in Problem 13 solve the following differential equations

(a) $x^2 y'' - 2xy' + 2y = 4x^2$, $x > 0$; $y_1(x) = x$
(b) $x^2 y'' + 7xy' + 5y = x$, $x > 0$; $y_1(x) = x^{-1}$

3.7 MECHANICAL VIBRATIONS

In Sections 3.1 through 3.6.2 of this chapter methods of solving second order linear ordinary differential equations have been developed. We found that when the differential equation has constant coefficients it can be solved in a straightforward manner. Two important areas of application of this theory are in the fields of mechanical and electrical oscillations where a large number of phenomena are governed by equations of the form

$$m \frac{d^2u}{dt^2} + c \frac{du}{dt} + ku = F(t). \tag{1}$$

Here m, c, and k are constants, F is a given function, and $u = \phi(t)$ represents the response of a certain physical system as a function of the time t. In particular, this equation governs the motion of a vibrating mass at the end of a vertical spring. The derivation of Eq. (1) for this problem is worth considering in detail since the principles are common to many problems.

First consider the case of the static elongation of a spring of natural length l due to the addition of a mass m. Let Δl denote the elongation; see Figure 3.1. The forces acting on the mass are the force of gravity acting downward, $mg = w$, where g is the acceleration due to gravity and w is the weight of the mass; and the spring force acting upward. Since the mass is in equilibrium in this position these forces are numerically equal. If the displacement Δl is small compared to the length l, the spring force, according

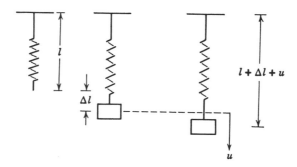

FIGURE 3.1

to Hooke's law,* will be proportional to Δl and hence will have magnitude $k\Delta l$. The constant k depends on the spring and is called the spring constant. For a known weight w it can be computed by measuring Δl and using

$$k\Delta l = mg. \tag{2}$$

Notice that k has the dimensions of $mg/\Delta l$, that is, force/length.

In the corresponding dynamic problem we are interested in studying the motion of the mass when it is acted on by an external force or is initially displaced. Let u, measured positive downward, denote the displacement of the mass from the equilibrium position. The displacement u depends on t and is related to the forces acting on the mass through Newton's law, which states that md^2u/dt^2 must have the same magnitude and be in the same direction as the net resultant force acting on the mass m. In deriving the equation governing the motion of the mass, care must be exercised to determine the correct signs of the various forces that act on the mass. In the derivation below we adopt the convention that a force in the downward

---

* Hooke (1635–1703) first published his law in 1676 as an anagram: *ceiiinosssttuv*; and in 1678 gave the solution *ut tensio sic vis* which means, roughly, "as the force so is the displacement."

direction is positive, while a force in the upward direction is negative. There are four forces acting on the mass. They are:

1. Its weight, $w = mg$, which always acts downward.
2. The force due to the spring, F_s, which is proportional to the elongation, $\Delta l + u$, and always acts to restore the spring to its natural position. If $\Delta l + u > 0$, the spring is extended and the force, which is directed upward, is given by $F_s(t) = -k(\Delta l + u)$. Note that the magnitude of the force on the mass due to the spring is $k(\Delta l + u)$; the minus sign tells us that this force is directed upward in this particular case. If $u + \Delta l < 0$, that is, $-u > \Delta l$, the spring is compressed a distance* $(-u) - (\Delta l)$ and the force, which is directed downward, is $k[(-u) - (\Delta l)]$; hence for all u

$$F_s(t) = -k(\Delta l + u). \tag{3}$$

We emphasize again that Eq. (3) gives not only the magnitude but also the direction of the force exerted on the mass by the spring at any position u.

3. The damping or resisting force, $F_d(t)$. This force may be due to the viscous properties of the fluid in which the mass is moving (air resistance, for instance); or the moving mass may be attached to an oil or dashpot mechanism (see Figure 3.2). In either case the damping force will act in a direction opposite to the direction of motion of the mass. We know from experimental evidence that as long as the speed of the mass is not too large the resistance may be taken to be proportional to the speed, $|du/dt|$. If the mass is moving downward, u is increasing and hence du/dt is positive, so $F_d(t)$, which is directed upward, is given by $-c(du/dt)$. The positive constant c is referred to as the damping constant; it has the units of force/velocity. If the mass is moving upward, u is decreasing, du/dt is negative, and $F_d(t)$, which is now directed downward, is again given by $-c(du/dt)$. Hence for all u

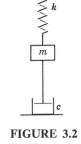

$$F_d(t) = -c\frac{du}{dt}. \tag{4}$$

FIGURE 3.2

4. An applied force $F(t)$ which is directed downward or upward as $F(t)$ is positive or negative. This could be a force due to the motion of the mount to which the spring is attached, or it could be a force applied directly to the mass.

According to Newton's law

$$mg + F_s(t) + F_d(t) + F(t) = m\frac{d^2u}{dt^2}.$$

* Remember that if the mass is above the equilibrium position its *distance* above the equilibrium position is $-u$, not u.

Substituting for $F_s(t)$ and $F_d(t)$ gives

$$mg - k(\Delta l + u) - c\frac{du}{dt} + F(t) = m\frac{d^2u}{dt^2}. \tag{5}$$

Since $k\Delta l = mg$, Eq. (5) reduces to the differential equation (1),

$$m\ddot{u} + c\dot{u} + ku = F(t).$$

In writing this equation we have followed the common convention of indicating time derivatives by dots.

It is important to remember that in Eq. (1), the mass m, the damping constant c, and the spring constant k are all *positive* constants. It is also important to recognize that Eq. (1) represents only an approximate equation for the determination of u. In reality the relationship between $F_s(t)$ and $\Delta l + u$ is not linear; however, for most of the usual materials, such as steel, and for $(\Delta l + u)/l \ll 1$, the relationship is, to a high degree of accuracy, approximately linear. Similarly, the expression for the damping force is an approximate one. Also we have neglected the mass of the spring compared to the mass of the attached body in deriving Eq. (1). Fortunately, for a wide variety of applications, Eq. (1) is a satisfactory mathematical model of the physical system.

The complete formulation of the vibration problem requires the specification of two initial conditions—the initial displacement u_0, and the initial velocity $\dot{u}_0$. It may not be obvious from physical reasoning that we can only specify two initial conditions, or that these are the two that should be specified. However, it does follow from the existence and uniqueness theorem 3.2 that these conditions give a mathematical problem which has a unique solution. The solution of Eq. (1) satisfying these initial conditions gives the position of the mass as a function of time.

Example. Derive the initial value problem for the following spring-dashpot-mass system. It is known that a 5-lb weight stretches the spring 1 in. The dashpot mechanism exerts a force of 0.02 lb for a velocity of 2 in./sec. A 2-lb weight is attached to the spring and released from a position 2 in. below equilibrium.

We have

$$m = \frac{w}{g} = \frac{2\text{ lb}}{32\text{ ft/sec}^2} = \frac{1}{16}\frac{\text{lb-sec}^2}{\text{ft}},$$

$$c = \frac{0.02\text{ lb}}{2\text{ in./sec}} = \frac{0.02\text{ lb}}{(1/6)\text{ ft/sec}} = 0.12\frac{\text{lb-sec}}{\text{ft}},$$

$$k = \frac{5\text{ lb}}{1\text{ in.}} = \frac{5\text{ lb}}{(1/12)\text{ ft}} = 60\frac{\text{lb}}{\text{ft}};$$

and hence

$$\tfrac{1}{16}\ddot{u} + 0.12\dot{u} + 60u = 0,$$

or

$$\ddot{u} + 1.92\dot{u} + 960u = 0,$$

where u is measured in feet and t in seconds. The initial conditions are $u(0) = \frac{1}{6}$, $\dot{u}(0) = 0$.

3.7.1 FREE VIBRATIONS

If there is no external force and no damping, Eq. (1) from the previous section reduces to

$$m\ddot{u} + ku = 0. \tag{1}$$

The solution of this equation is

$$u = A \cos \omega_0 t + B \sin \omega_0 t, \tag{2}$$

where

$$\omega_0{}^2 = k/m, \tag{3}$$

and ω_0, called the circular frequency, clearly has the units of 1/time. For a particular problem, the constants A and B are determined by the prescribed initial conditions.

In discussing the solution of Eq. (1) it is convenient to write Eq. (2) in the form

$$u = R \cos (\omega_0 t - \delta). \tag{4}$$

Regardless of the values of A and B this can always be done by taking $R = (A^2 + B^2)^{1/2}$ and solving the equations $A = R \cos \delta$ and $B = R \sin \delta$ for δ.

Because of the periodic character of the cosine function, Eq. (4) represents a periodic motion, or simple harmonic motion, of period

$$T = \frac{2\pi}{\omega_0} = 2\pi \left(\frac{m}{k}\right)^{1/2}. \tag{5}$$

To distinguish between problems of free vibrations without damping and problems of damped vibrations or forced vibrations, the circular frequency, ω_0, and period, $2\pi/\omega_0$, of the undamped, unforced motion are usually referred to as the *natural* circular frequency and *natural* period of the vibration.

Since $|\cos (\omega_0 t - \delta)| \leq 1$, u always lies between the lines $u = \pm R$. The maximum displacement occurs at the times $\omega_0 t - \delta = 0, \pm \pi, \pm 2\pi, \ldots$. The constants R and δ are referred to as the amplitude and phase angle, respectively, of the motion. A sketch of the motion represented by Eq. (4) is shown in Figure 3.3. Notice that this periodic motion does not die out with increasing time. This is a consequence of neglecting the damping force, which would allow a means of dissipating the energy supplied to the system by the original displacement and velocity.

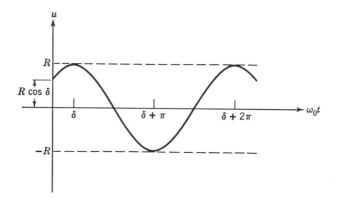

FIGURE 3.3 Simple harmonic motion.

Example. Find the natural period of a spring-mass system if the mass weighs 10 lb and stretches a steel spring 2 in. If the spring is stretched an additional 2 in. and then released, determine the subsequent motion.

The spring constant is $k = 10$ lb/2 in. $= 60$ lb/ft. The mass $m = w/g = \frac{10}{32}$ lb/(ft/sec^2). Hence

$$T = 2\pi \left(\frac{m}{k}\right)^{\frac{1}{2}} = 2\pi \left[\frac{10}{(32)60}\right]^{\frac{1}{2}} = \frac{\pi\sqrt{3}}{12} \text{ sec.}$$

The equation of motion is

$$\tfrac{10}{32}\ddot{u} + 60u = 0;$$

hence

$$u = A \cos (8\sqrt{3}t) + B \sin (8\sqrt{3}t).$$

The solution satisfying the initial conditions $u(0) = \frac{1}{6}$ ft and $\dot{u}(0) = 0$ is

$$u = \tfrac{1}{6} \cos (8\sqrt{3}t),$$

where t is measured in seconds and u is measured in feet.

Damped Free Vibrations. If we include the effect of damping, the differential equation governing the motion of the mass is

$$m\ddot{u} + c\dot{u} + ku = 0. \tag{6}$$

The roots of the corresponding auxiliary equation are

$$r_1, r_2 = \frac{-c \pm \sqrt{c^2 - 4km}}{2m} = -\frac{c}{2m} \pm \left(\frac{c^2}{4m^2} - \frac{k}{m}\right)^{\frac{1}{2}}. \tag{7}$$

Since c, k, and m are positive, $c^2 - 4km$ is always less than c^2; hence if $c^2 - 4km \geq 0$ the values of r_1 and r_2 given by Eq. (7) are *negative*. If $c^2 - 4km < 0$ the values of r_1 and r_2 given by Eq. (7) are complex, but with *negative* real part. In tabular form the solution of Eq. (6) is

$$c^2 - 4km > 0, \qquad u = Ae^{r_1t} + Be^{r_2t}, \qquad r_1 \text{ and } r_2 < 0; \tag{8}$$

$$c^2 - 4km = 0, \qquad u = (A + Bt)e^{-(c/2m)t}; \tag{9}$$

$$c^2 - 4km < 0, \qquad u = e^{-(c/2m)t}(A \cos \mu t + B \sin \mu t),$$

$$\mu = \sqrt{4km - c^2}/2m > 0. \tag{10}$$

In all three cases, regardless of the initial conditions, that is, regardless of the values of A and B, $u \to 0$ as $t \to \infty$, and hence the motion dies out with increasing time. Thus the solutions of Eqs. (1) and (6) confirm what we would intuitively expect—without damping the motion always continues unabated and with damping the motion must decay to zero with increasing time.

The first two cases, Eqs. (8) and (9), which are referred to as *overdamped* and *critically damped* respectively, represent motions in which the originally displaced mass "creeps" back to its equilibrium position. Depending on the initial conditions, it may be possible to overshoot the equilibrium position once, but this is not a "vibratory motion." Two typical examples of such a motion are sketched in Figure 3.4. The theory is discussed further in Problems 14 and 15.

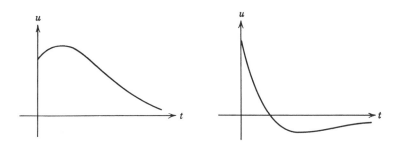

FIGURE 3.4   Overdamped motions.

The third case, which is referred to as an *underdamped motion*, often occurs in mechanical systems and represents a "damped vibration." To see this, again letting $A = R \cos \delta$ and $B = R \sin \delta$ in Eq. (10), we obtain

$$u = Re^{-(c/2m)t} \cos (\mu t - \delta). \tag{11}$$

The displacement u must lie between the curves $u = \pm Re^{-(c/2m)t}$, and hence resembles a cosine curve with decreasing amplitude. A typical example is sketched in Figure 3.5.

While the motion is not truly periodic, we can define a quasi-period, $T_d = 2\pi/\mu$, as the time between successive maxima of the displacement.

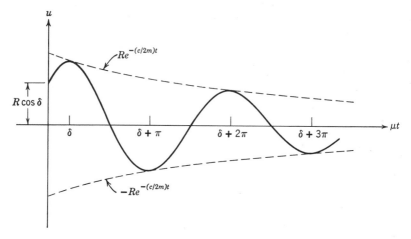

FIGURE 3.5 Damped vibration.

It is interesting to note the relation between T_d and T. We have

$$T_d = \frac{2\pi}{\mu} = 2\pi\left(\frac{k}{m} - \frac{c^2}{4m^2}\right)^{-\frac{1}{2}} = 2\pi\left(\frac{k}{m}\right)^{-\frac{1}{2}}\left(1 - \frac{c^2}{4km}\right)^{-\frac{1}{2}}$$

$$= T\left(1 - \frac{c^2}{4km}\right)^{-\frac{1}{2}}.$$

Hence if $c^2/4km$ is small,

$$T_d \cong T\left(1 + \frac{c^2}{8km}\right).$$

Consequently when the damping is very small, that is, when the dimensionless quantity $c^2/4km \ll 1$, we can neglect damping in computing the quasi-period of vibration. In many physical problems this is precisely the situation. On the other hand, if we want to study the detailed motion of the mass for all time, we can *never* neglect the damping force, no matter how small. The importance of the damping force will be seen even more emphatically in the next section where we discuss forced vibrations.

PROBLEMS

1. A 2-lb weight stretches a 2-ft spring 6 in. If the weight is pulled down an additional 3 in. and released, determine the subsequent motion neglecting air resistance. What are the amplitude, circular frequency, and period of the motion?

2. A mass of 100 gm is attached to a steel spring of natural length 50 cm. The spring is stretched 5 cm by the addition of this mass. If the mass is started in motion with a velocity of 10 cm/sec in the downward direction, determine the subsequent motion. Neglect air resistance.

3. A 3-lb weight stretches a spiral spring 3 in. If the weight is pushed upward, contracting the spring a distance 1 in., and then released with a velocity in the downward direction of 2 ft/sec, determine the subsequent motion. Neglect air resistance. What are the amplitude, circular frequency, and period of the motion?

4. Show that the period of motion of an undamped vibration of a mass hanging from a vertical spring is $2\pi \sqrt{\Delta l/g}$ where Δl is the elongation due to the weight w.

5. In Problem 3 suppose air resistance exerts a damping force which is given by $0.3\dot{u}$ lb. Compare the "quasi-period" of the damped motion with the natural period of the undamped motion. What is the percentage change based on the natural period?

6. In Problem 5, how large would the damping coefficient have to be in order to cause a 50% change in the period of the motion?

7. Show that $A \cos \omega_0 t + B \sin \omega_0 t$ can be written in the form $r \sin (\omega_0 t - \theta)$. Determine r and θ in terms of A and B. What is the relationship between r, R, θ, and δ if $R \cos (\omega_0 t - \delta) = r \sin (\omega_0 t - \theta)$?

8. Determine the solution of the differential equation $m\ddot{u} + ku = 0$ satisfying the following initial conditions. Express your answer in the form $R \cos (\omega_0 t - \delta)$.

(a) $u(0) = u_0$, $\dot{u}(0) = 0$ (b) $u(0) = 0$, $\dot{u}(0) = \dot{u}_0$ (c) $u(0) = u_0$, $\dot{u}(0) = \dot{u}_0$

9. Determine the natural period of oscillation of the pendulum of length l shown in Figure 3.6. Neglect air resistance and the weight of the string compared to the weight of the mass. Assume that θ is small enough that $\sin \theta \cong \theta$.

10. A mass of 20 gm stretches a spiral spring a distance of 5 cm. If the spring is attached to an oil dashpot damper which has a damping constant of 400 dyne sec/cm, determine the subsequent motion if the mass is pulled down an additional 2 cm and released.

FIGURE 3.6

11. A 16-lb weight stretches a spring 3 in. The weight is attached to a dashpot mechanism which has a damping constant of 2 lb sec/ft. Determine the subsequent motion if the weight is released from its equilibrium position with a velocity of 3 in./sec in the downward direction.

12. A weight of 8 lb is attached to a steel spring of length 15 in. The weight extends the spring a distance of $\frac{1}{8}$ ft. If the weight is also attached to an oil dashpot damper which has a damping constant c, determine the values of c for which the motion will be overdamped, critically damped, and underdamped. Be sure to give the correct units for c.

13. Determine a solution of the differential equation $m\ddot{u} + c\dot{u} + ku = 0$ in the case $c^2 - 4km < 0$ satisfying the following initial conditions. Express your answer in the form $Re^{-(c/2m)t} \cos (\mu t - \delta)$.

(a) $u(0) = u_0$, $\dot{u}(0) = 0$ (b) $u(0) = 0$, $\dot{u}(0) = \dot{u}_0$ (c) $u(0) = u_0$, $\dot{u}(0) = \dot{u}_0$

14. Show that if the damping constant c in the equation $m\ddot{u} + c\dot{u} + ku = 0$ is such that the motion is overdamped or critically damped, then the mass can pass through its zero displacement position at most once, regardless of the initial conditions.

Hint: Determine all possible values of t such that $u = 0$.

15. For the case of critical damping, find the general solution of Eq. (6) satisfying the initial conditions $u(0) = u_0$, $\dot{u}(0) = \dot{u}_0$. If $\dot{u}_0 = 0$, show that $u \to 0$ as $t \to \infty$, but $u \neq 0$ for any finite value of t. Assuming u_0 is positive, determine a condition on $\dot{u}_0$ that will insure that the mass passes through the zero displacement position after it is released.

*16. For the damped oscillation given by Eq. (11) the time between successive maxima is $T_d = 2\pi/\mu$. The ratio of the displacement at two successive maxima (time t and time $t + T_d$) is given by $e^{(c/2m)T_d}$. Thus successive displacements at time intervals T_d form a geometric progression with ratio $e^{(c/2m)T_d}$. The natural logarithm of this ratio, denoted by $\Delta = (c/2m)T_d = (\pi c/m\mu)$, is referred to as the *logarithmic decrement*. Since m, μ, and Δ are quantities which can easily be measured for a mechanical system, this equation provides a convenient and *practical* method of computing the damping constant of the system. In particular, for the motion of a vibrating mass in a viscous fluid the damping constant depends on the viscosity of the fluid; for simple geometric shapes the form of this dependence is known, and the above relation allows the determination of the viscosity experimentally. This is one of the most accurate ways of determining the viscosity of a gas at high pressure.

(a) In Problem 11, what is the logarithmic decrement?

(b) In Problem 12 if the measured logarithmic decrement is 3, and $T_d = 0.3$ sec, determine the damping constant c.

3.7.2 FORCED VIBRATIONS

Consider now the case in which a periodic external force, say $F_0 \cos \omega t$, is applied to a spring-mass system. In this case the equation of motion is

$$m\ddot{u} + c\dot{u} + ku = F_0 \cos \omega t. \tag{1}$$

First suppose there is no damping; then Eq. (1) reduces to

$$m\ddot{u} + ku = F_0 \cos \omega t. \tag{2}$$

Provided $\omega_0 = \sqrt{k/m} \neq \omega$, the general solution of Eq. (2) is

$$u = c_1 \cos \omega_0 t + c_2 \sin \omega_0 t + \frac{F_0}{m(\omega_0^2 - \omega^2)} \cos \omega t. \tag{3}$$

The constants c_1 and c_2 are determined by the initial conditions. The resultant motion is, in general, the sum of two periodic motions of different frequencies (ω_0 and ω) and amplitudes. We consider two examples.

Beats.   Suppose the mass is initially at rest, that is, $u(0) = 0$, $\dot{u}(0) = 0$. Then it turns out that the constants c_1 and c_2 in Eq. (3) are given by

$$c_1 = \frac{-F_0}{m(\omega_0{}^2 - \omega^2)}, \qquad c_2 = 0, \tag{4}$$

and the solution of Eq. (2) is

$$u = \frac{F_0}{m(\omega_0{}^2 - \omega^2)}(\cos \omega t - \cos \omega_0 t). \tag{5}$$

This is the sum of two periodic functions of different periods but the same amplitude. Making use of the trigonometric identities $\cos (A \pm B) = \cos A \cos B \mp \sin A \sin B$ with $A = (\omega_0 + \omega)t/2$ and $B = (\omega_0 - \omega)t/2$, we can write Eq. (5) in the form

$$u = \frac{2F_0}{m(\omega_0{}^2 - \omega^2)} \sin \frac{(\omega_0 - \omega)t}{2} \sin \frac{(\omega_0 + \omega)t}{2}. \tag{6}$$

If $|\omega_0 - \omega|$ is small, $\omega_0 + \omega \gg |\omega_0 - \omega|$, and consequently $\sin (\omega_0 + \omega)t/2$ will be a rapidly oscillating function compared to $\sin (\omega_0 - \omega)t/2$. Then the motion is a rapid oscillation with circular frequency $(\omega_0 + \omega)/2$, but with a slowly varying sinusoidal amplitude. This type of motion, possessing a periodic variation of amplitude, exhibits what is called a *beat*. Such a phenomenon occurs in acoustics when two tuning forks of nearly equal frequency are sounded simultaneously. In this case the periodic variation of amplitude is quite apparent to the unaided ear. In electronics the variation of the amplitude with time is called *amplitude modulation*. The function $u = \phi(t)$ given in Eq. (6) is sketched in Figure 3.7.

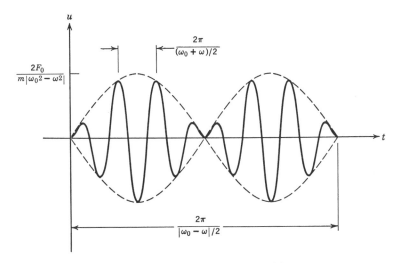

FIGURE 3.7   The phenomenon of beats.

Resonance. As a second example, consider the case $\omega = \omega_0$; that is, the period of the forcing function is the same as the natural period of the system. Then the nonhomogeneous term $F_0 \cos \omega t$ is a solution of the homogeneous equation. In this case, the solution of Eq. (2) is

$$u = c_1 \cos \omega_0 t + c_2 \sin \omega_0 t + \frac{F_0}{2m\omega_0} t \sin \omega_0 t. \tag{7}$$

Because of the presence of the term $t \sin \omega_0 t$ in Eq. (7) it is clear regardless of the values of c_1 and c_2 that the motion will become unbounded as $t \to \infty$. (See Figure 3.8.) This is the phenomenon known as *resonance*. In actual practice, however, the spring would probably break. Of course as soon as u becomes large, our theory is no longer valid since we have assumed that u is small when we used a linear relation to determine the spring constant. If damping is included in the system the motion will remain bounded; however, there may still be a large response to the input function $F_0 \cos \omega t$ if the damping is small and ω is close to ω_0.

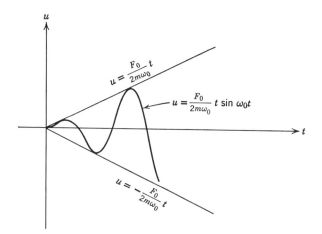

FIGURE 3.8   The phenomenon of resonance.

Damped Forced Vibrations. The motion of the spring-mass system with damping and the forcing function $F_0 \cos \omega t$ can be determined in a straightforward manner. Although the computations are rather lengthy they are not difficult. The solution of Eq. (1) is

$$u = c_1 e^{r_1 t} + c_2 e^{r_2 t} + \frac{F_0}{\sqrt{m^2(\omega_0^2 - \omega^2)^2 + c^2\omega^2}} \cos(\omega t - \delta), \tag{8}$$

where δ is given by $\cos \delta = m(\omega_0^2 - \omega^2)/\Delta$ and $\sin \delta = c\omega/\Delta$ with $\Delta = \sqrt{m^2(\omega_0^2 - \omega^2)^2 + c^2\omega^2}$. Here r_1 and r_2 are the roots of the auxiliary equation associated with Eq. (1). As was shown in the last section both $e^{r_1 t}$ and $e^{r_2 t}$ approach zero as $t \to \infty$. Hence as $t \to \infty$,

$$u \to u_p(t) = \frac{F_0}{\sqrt{m^2(\omega_0^2 - \omega^2)^2 + c^2 \omega^2}} \cos(\omega t - \delta). \tag{9}$$

For this reason $u_c(t) = c_1 e^{r_1 t} + c_2 e^{r_2 t}$ is often called the *transient solution* and $u_p(t)$ is called the *steady state solution*. To speak roughly, the transient solution allows us to satisfy the imposed initial conditions; with increasing time the energy put into the system by the initial displacement and velocity is dissipated through the damping force, and the motion then represents the response of the system to the external force $F(t)$. Without damping (which, of course, is impossible in any physical system) the effect of the initial conditions would persist for all time.

Notice that $m^2(\omega_0^2 - \omega^2)^2 + c^2 \omega^2$ is never zero, even for $\omega = \omega_0$; hence with damping the motion is always bounded. For fixed values of m, c, and k the amplitude of the steady state solution will be a maximum when $m^2(\omega_0^2 - \omega^2)^2 + c^2 \omega^2$ is a minimum; this corresponds to choosing

$$\omega^2 = \omega_0^2 - \frac{1}{2}\left(\frac{c}{m}\right)^2. \tag{10}$$

In designing a spring-mass system* to detect periodic forces in a narrow frequency range around ω it is clear that we would want to choose k, c, and m in such a way that Eq. (10) is satisfied or nearly satisfied. In this way we obtain the maximum response of the system to such forces thus making their detection easier. A similar situation occurs in problems involving the detection of electrical signals in electrical networks.

PROBLEMS

1. Express $\cos 9t - \cos 7t$ in the form $A \sin \alpha t \sin \beta t$.

2. Express $\sin 7t - \sin 6t$ in the form $A \sin \alpha t \cos \beta t$.

3. A spiral spring is stretched $\frac{1}{8}$ ft by a weight of 4 lb. The spring is acted on by an external force $2 \cos 3t$ lb. If the weight is displaced a distance 2 in. from its position of equilibrium and then released, determine the subsequent motion. Neglect damping. If the external force is $4 \sin \omega t$ lb, for what value of ω will resonance occur?

4. If an undamped spring-mass system with weight 6 lb and spring constant 1 lb/in. is suddenly set in motion at $t = 0$ by an external force of $4 \cos 7t$ lb, determine the subsequent motion and draw a graph of the displacement versus t.

* Such instruments are usually referred to as seismic instruments since they are similar in principle to the seismograph which is used to detect motions of the earth's surface. The periodic motion of the mount to which the spring is attached is equivalent to a problem in which a periodic force acts on the mass.

5. Determine the solution of the differential equation $m\ddot{u} + ku = F_0 \cos \omega t$, $\omega \neq \sqrt{k/m}$, satisfying the following initial conditions:

(a) $u(0) = u_0$, $\dot{u}(0) = 0$ (b) $u(0) = 0$, $\dot{u}(0) = \dot{u}_0$ (c) $u(0) = u_0$, $\dot{u}(0) = \dot{u}_0$

6. A generalization of the phenomenon of beats occurs when the motion is the sum of two periodic functions of different amplitudes $A \cos \omega t$ and $B \cos \omega_0 t$. Show that such a motion can be expressed as

$$R(t) \cos \left[\frac{\omega_0 + \omega}{2} t - \delta(t) \right].$$

If $|A - B| \ll 1$ and $|\omega - \omega_0| \ll 1$, show that R is a slowly varying function. The variation of the phase angle δ with t is referred to as *frequency modulation*.

*7. Determine the motion $u = \phi(t)$ of a mass m hanging on a spring with spring constant k if the mass is acted on by a force

$$F(t) = F_0 \begin{cases} 0, & t \leq 0 \\ t, & 0 < t \leq \pi \\ 2\pi - t, & \pi < t \leq 2\pi \\ 0, & 2\pi < t \end{cases}$$

where t is measured in seconds. For convenience assume $\omega_0^2 = k/m = 1$. Neglect air resistance.
Hint: Treat each time interval separately, and match the solutions in the different intervals by requiring that ϕ and $\dot{\phi}$ be continuous functions of t.

8. A spiral spring is stretched 6 in. by a weight of 8 lb. The mass is attached to a dashpot mechanism which has a damping constant of 0.25 lb sec/ft. If the mass is subjected to an external force of the form $4 \cos 2t$ lb, determine the steady state response of the system. What is the optimum choice of the mass m in order to maximize the response of the system to this external force?

9. Determine the solution of the differential equation $m\ddot{u} + c\dot{u} + ku = F_0 \sin \omega t$ satisfying the following initial conditions. Assume $c^2 - 4km < 0$.

(a) $u(0) = u_0$, $\dot{u}(0) = 0$ (b) $u(0) = 0$, $\dot{u}(0) = \dot{u}_0$ (c) $u(0) = u_0$, $\dot{u}(0) = \dot{u}_0$

3.8 ELECTRICAL NETWORKS

As a second example of the application of the theory of linear second order differential equations with constant coefficients, we consider the flow of electric current in a simple series circuit. The circuit is depicted in Figure 3.9. The current $I = \phi(t)$ (measured in amperes) will be a function of the time t. The resistance R (ohms), the capacitance C (farads), and the inductance L (henrys) are all positive, and in general may depend on the time t and the current I. For a wide variety of applications this dependence can be neglected, and we will assume that R, C, and L are known constants. The

FIGURE 3.9

impressed voltage E (volts) will be a given function of time—often of the form $E_0 \cos \omega t$. Another physical quantity that will appear in our discussion is the total charge $Q = \psi(t)$ (coulombs) on the capacitor at the time t. The charge Q is related to the current I by $I = dQ/dt$.

The flow of current in the circuit under consideration is governed by Kirchhoff's* second law: *In a closed circuit the impressed voltage is equal to the sum of the voltage drops in the rest of the circuit.*

According to the elementary laws of electricity we know that

$$\text{The voltage drop across the resistance} = IR,$$

$$\text{The voltage drop across the capacitor} = \frac{1}{C}Q,$$

$$\text{The voltage drop across the inductance} = L\frac{dI}{dt}.$$

Hence

$$L\frac{dI}{dt} + RI + \frac{1}{C}Q = E(t). \tag{1}$$

The units have been chosen so that 1 volt = 1 ohm · 1 ampere = 1 coulomb/ 1 farad = 1 henry · 1 ampere/1 second.

Since I equals dQ/dt we can substitute for I in Eq. (1), obtaining the following second order linear nonhomogeneous equation for Q,

$$L\ddot{Q} + R\dot{Q} + \frac{1}{C}Q = E(t), \tag{2}$$

where dots denote differentiation with respect to t. The initial conditions that must be specified, say at time $t = 0$, are

$$Q(0) = Q_0, \qquad \dot{Q}(0) = I(0) = I_0. \tag{3}$$

Thus we must know the initial charge on the capacitor, and the initial current in the circuit.

---

* Gustav Kirchhoff (1824–1887), a German physicist, is famous for his contributions in electricity (the theorems that bear his name) and for his work in spectroscopy.

Alternatively we can obtain a second order differential equation for the current I by differentiating Eq. (1) with respect to t, and then substituting for dQ/dt. This gives

$$L\ddot{I} + R\dot{I} + \frac{1}{C} I = \dot{E}(t). \tag{4}$$

The initial conditions that must be specified are

$$I(0) = I_0, \qquad \dot{I}(0) = \dot{I}_0. \tag{5}$$

Notice from Eq. (1) that

$$\dot{I}_0 = \frac{1}{L}\left[E(0) - RI_0 - \frac{1}{C} Q_0 \right]. \tag{6}$$

Hence $\dot{I}_0$ is known if we specify $I(0)$ and $Q(0)$. The initial charge and current are physically measurable quantities and a knowledge of these quantities allows us to determine the initial conditions (3) corresponding to Eq. (2) or the initial conditions (5) corresponding to Eq. (4).

TABLE 3.2

Mechanical System		Electric Circuit	
$m\ddot{u} + c\dot{u} + ku = F(t)$		$L\ddot{Q} + R\dot{Q} + \dfrac{1}{C} Q = E(t)$	
Displacement	u	Charge	Q
Velocity	$\dot{u}$	Current	$I = \dot{Q}$
Mass	m	Inductance	L
Damping	c	Resistance	R
Spring constant	k	Elastance	$1/C$
Impressed force	$F(t)$	Impressed voltage	$E(t)$

It is interesting to note the analogy between the mechanical vibration problem discussed earlier and the present electric circuit problem. This is clearly shown in Table 3.2. This analogy between the two systems allows us to solve problems in mechanical vibrations by building the corresponding electrical circuit and then measuring the charge Q. This is one of the basic ideas in the large and important field of analog computers.*

It is apparent that the general initial value problem

$$a\ddot{y} + b\dot{y} + cy = g(t); \qquad y(0) = y_0, \qquad \dot{y}(0) = \dot{y}_0 \tag{7}$$

for a linear second order equation with constant coefficients corresponds to at least two physical problems: the motion of a mass on a vibrating spring, and the flow of electric current in a simple series circuit. Actually, other

---

* For a particularly simple introduction to the theory of analog computers, see T. D. Truitt and A. E. Rogers.

physical problems, such as the torsional oscillation of a shaft with a flywheel, also lead to the initial value problem (7). This situation illustrates a fundamental relationship between mathematics and physics: *many physical problems, when formulated mathematically, are identical.* Thus the solution of several physical problems can be obtained from the solution of a single mathematical problem by an appropriate interpretation of the symbols.

Let us now consider Eq. (2) when the impressed voltage is a periodic function, $E_0 \cos \omega t$. Just as for the spring-mass system discussed in Sections 3.7.1 and 3.7.2 we can develop the concepts of a natural frequency, critical damping, resonance, beats, transient solution, and steady state solution for the series circuit. This is done in the following example and in the problems.

Example. Determine the behavior of the solution of Eq. (2) as $t \to \infty$ if $E(t) = E_0 \cos \omega t$ and $R \neq 0$. First, since L, R, and C are positive it follows that all solutions of the homogeneous equation corresponding to Eq. (2) approach zero as $t \to \infty$. (See Section 3.7.1.)

To find a particular solution of

$$L\ddot{Q} + R\dot{Q} + \frac{1}{C}Q = E_0 \cos \omega t \qquad (8)$$

we use the method of undetermined coefficients. Substituting

$$Q_p(t) = A \cos \omega t + B \sin \omega t \qquad (9)$$

we find that A and B must satisfy

$$\left(\frac{1}{C} - L\omega^2\right) A + \omega R B = E_0$$

$$-\omega R A + \left(\frac{1}{C} - L\omega^2\right) B = 0.$$

Solving for A and B and substituting for them in Eq. (9) gives

$$Q_p(t) = \frac{E_0(1/C - L\omega^2) \cos \omega t + \omega R E_0 \sin \omega t}{(1/C - L\omega^2)^2 + \omega^2 R^2}. \qquad (10)$$

Equation (10) can also be written as

$$Q_p(t) = \frac{E_0 \sin(\omega t + \delta)}{\sqrt{(1/C - L\omega^2)^2 + \omega^2 R^2}}, \qquad (11)$$

where δ is given by $\sin \delta = (1/C - L\omega^2)/\Delta$, $\cos \delta = \omega R/\Delta$ and $\Delta = \sqrt{(1/C - L\omega^2)^2 + \omega^2 R^2}$. Since $Q = Q_c(t) + Q_p(t)$ and $Q_c(t) \to 0$ as $t \to \infty$, it follows that $Q \to Q_p(t)$ as $t \to \infty$. For this reason $Q_p(t)$ is often referred to as the steady state solution of Eq. (8).

Generally we wish to know the steady state current in the circuit, and this can be found by differentiating $Q_p(t)$. We obtain

$$I_p(t) = \frac{E_0 \cos(\omega t + \delta)}{\sqrt{R^2 + [\omega L - 1/(\omega C)]^2}}. \tag{12}$$

Notice that the steady state current has the same frequency as the impressed voltage. The term $\omega L - 1/(\omega C)$ that appears in Eq. (12) is known as the *reactance* of the circuit, and the expression $\sqrt{R^2 + [\omega L - 1/(\omega C)]^2}$ is called the *impedance* of the circuit.

PROBLEMS

1. If there is no resistance present in a simple series circuit, show that in the absence of an impressed voltage the charge Q on the capacitor is periodic in time with frequency $\omega_0 = \sqrt{1/LC}$. The quantity $\sqrt{1/LC}$ is referred to as the natural frequency of the circuit.

2. Show that if there is no resistance in the circuit and the impressed voltage is of the form $E_0 \cos \omega t$, then the charge on the capacitor will become unbounded as $t \to \infty$ if $\omega = \sqrt{1/LC}$. This is the phenomenon of resonance. Show that the charge will always be bounded, no matter what the choice of ω, provided that there is some resistance, no matter how small, in the circuit.

3. Show that the solution of $L\ddot{I} + R\dot{I} + (1/C)I = 0$ is of the form

$$I = Ae^{r_1 t} + Be^{r_2 t}, \qquad \text{for } R^2 - 4L/C > 0;$$
$$= (A + Bt)e^{r_1 t}, \qquad \text{for } R^2 - 4L/C = 0;$$
$$= e^{\lambda t}(A \cos \mu t + B \sin \mu t) \quad \text{for } R^2 - 4L/C < 0.$$

The circuit is said to be overdamped, critically damped, or underdamped corresponding to these three cases respectively.

4. Suppose that a series circuit consisting of an inductor, a resistor, and a capacitor is open, and that there is an initial charge $Q_0 = 10^{-6}$ on the capacitor. Determine the variation of the charge and the current after the switch is closed for the following cases:

(a) $L = 0.2$, $C = 10^{-5}$, $R = 3 \times 10^2$
(b) $L = 1$, $C = 4 \times 10^{-6}$, $R = 10^3$
(c) $L = 2$, $C = 10^{-5}$, $R = 4 \times 10^2$

5. If $L = 0.2$ henry and $C = 0.8 \times 10^{-6}$ farads, determine the resistance R so that the circuit is critically damped.

6. A series circuit has a capacitor of 0.25×10^{-6} farad, a resistor of 5×10^3 ohms, and an inductor of 1 henry. The initial charge on the capacitor is zero. If a 12-volt battery is connected to the circuit and the circuit is closed at $t = 0$, determine the charge on the capacitor at $t = 0.001$ sec, at $t = 0.01$ sec, and the steady state charge.

7. Determine the steady state current in a series circuit if the impressed voltage is $E(t) = 110 \cos 120\pi t$ volts, and $L = 10$ henrys, $R = 3 \times 10^3$ ohms, and $C = 0.25 \times 10^{-5}$ farad.

8. For a series circuit with given values of L, R, and C and an impressed voltage $E_0 \cos \omega t$, for what value of ω will the steady state current be a maximum?

*9. In electrical engineering practice it is often convenient to think of $E_0 \cos \omega t$ as the real part of $E_0 e^{j\omega t}(j = \sqrt{-1}$, which is standard notation in electrical engineering). Then corresponding to Eq. (8) of the text we would consider

$$L\ddot{Q} + R\dot{Q} + \frac{1}{C}Q = E_0 e^{j\omega t}, \tag{i}$$

where it is understood that when we finish our computations we must take the real part of the solution.† Assume that $R \neq 0$.

(a) Show that the steady state solution of Eq. (i) is

$$Q = \frac{E_0}{j\omega R - \omega^2 L + 1/C} e^{j\omega t}.$$

Hint: Substitute $Q = Ae^{j\omega t}$.

(b) Hence show that the steady state current is

$$I = \frac{E_0}{R + j(\omega L - 1/\omega C)} e^{j\omega t}.$$

(c) Using the fact that $(\alpha + i\beta) = \sqrt{\alpha^2 + \beta^2} e^{j\gamma}$ where $\gamma = \tan^{-1}(\beta/\alpha)$ show that

$$I = \frac{E_0}{\sqrt{R^2 + (\omega L - 1/\omega C)^2}} e^{j(\omega t - \delta)},$$

where $\delta = \tan^{-1}[(\omega L - 1/\omega C)/R]$. Finally show that the real part of this expression is identical with that derived in the example of this section.

(d) What is the steady state current if the impressed voltage is $E(t) = E_0 \sin \omega t$.

(e) If we let $Z = R + j(\omega L - 1/\omega C)$, Z is known as the *complex impedance*. The reciprocal of Z is called the *admittance*, and the real and imaginary parts of $1/Z$ are called the *conductance* and *susceptance*. Determine the admittance, conductance, and susceptance.

REFERENCES

Coddington, E. A., *An Introduction to Ordinary Differential Equations*, Prentice-Hall, Englewood Cliffs, N.J., 1961.

Ince, E. L., *Ordinary Differential Equations*, Longmans, Green, London, 1927.

Truitt, T. D. and Rogers, A. E., *Basics of Analog Computers*, Rider, New York, 1960.

† The use of the complex notation for electrical circuit problems was pioneered by the American mathematician and inventor Charles P. Steinmetz (1865–1923).

CHAPTER 4

Series Solutions of Second Order Linear Equations

4.1 INTRODUCTION. REVIEW OF POWER SERIES

In Chapter 3 we described methods of solving linear second order differential equations with constant coefficients. We will now consider methods of solving linear second order equations when the coefficients are functions of the independent variable. It is sufficient to consider the homogeneous equation

$$P(x) \frac{d^2y}{dx^2} + Q(x) \frac{dy}{dx} + R(x)y = 0, \tag{1}$$

since the procedure for the corresponding nonhomogeneous equation is similar.

A wide class of problems in mathematical physics leads to equations of the form (1) having polynomial coefficients; for example, Bessel's equation

$$x^2y'' + xy' + (x^2 - \nu^2)y = 0,$$

where ν is a constant, and Legendre's equation

$$(1 - x^2)y'' - 2xy' + \alpha(\alpha + 1)y = 0,$$

where α is a constant. For this reason, as well as to simplify the algebraic computations, we will primarily consider the case in which the functions P, Q, and R are polynomials. However, as we will see, the method of solution is applicable for a class of functions more general than polynomials.

Although we will consider generalizations later, suppose for the present that P, Q, and R are polynomials. Suppose also that we are interested in solving Eq. (1) in the neighborhood of a point x_0, which is often, but not always, a point where initial conditions are specified. If the functions P, Q, and R have $x - x_0$ as a common factor we will assume that this common factor has been canceled from Eq. (1). Hence if $P(x_0) = 0$, then at least one of $Q(x_0)$ and $R(x_0)$ is not equal to zero. The solution of Eq. (1) in an interval containing x_0 is closely associated with the behavior of P in that interval. In particular, if P does not vanish in the interval, the existence of a

148

solution is guaranteed by Theorem 3.2. In Sections 4.2 and 4.2.1 we will consider the solution of Eq. (1) in the neighborhood of a point x_0 where $P(x_0) \neq 0$. Such a point is called an *ordinary point* of Eq. (1). On the other hand, if $P(x_0) = 0$, Theorem 3.2 does not apply. Such a point is called a *singular point* of Eq. (1). Sections 4.3 through 4.7 deal with the determination of solutions of Eq. (1) in the neighborhood of a singular point.

In either case the method of solution is based on the idea of expressing y as an infinite series in powers of $x - x_0$, where x_0 is some specified point. While at first sight it may appear discouraging to think of finding solutions of differential equations in the form of infinite series, from a computational point of view this may be the most convenient way of solving the differential equation. Indeed, tables of $\sin x$ and $\cos x$ (the solutions of $y'' + y = 0$) have been computed from their Taylor series about $x = 0$:

$$\sin x = x - \frac{x^3}{3!} + \frac{x^5}{5!} + \cdots + (-1)^n \frac{x^{2n+1}}{(2n+1)!} + \cdots = \sum_{n=0}^{\infty} \frac{(-1)^n x^{2n+1}}{(2n+1)!}, \quad (2)$$

$$\cos x = 1 - \frac{x^2}{2!} + \frac{x^4}{4!} + \cdots + (-1)^n \frac{x^{2n}}{(2n)!} + \cdots = \sum_{n=0}^{\infty} \frac{(-1)^n x^{2n}}{(2n)!}, \quad (3)$$

$$(0! = 1)$$

or similar series. In carrying out a computation on a high-speed electronic computer which requires the values of $\sin x$ at a large number of points, it is much more practical and quicker to use a series representation for $\sin x$, such as that given by Eq. (2), actually computing the values of $\sin x$ as part of the problem, than to look up the values of $\sin x$ in a table and read this information into the computer.

Since we will be using infinite series a great deal in this chapter, it is worthwhile to summarize without proof some of the pertinent results concerning infinite series, and in particular, power series.

1. A power series $\sum_{n=0}^{\infty} a_n(x - x_0)^n$ is said to converge at a point x if

$$\lim_{m \to \infty} \sum_{n=0}^{m} a_n(x - x_0)^n$$

exists. It is clear that the series converges for $x = x_0$; it may converge for all x, or it may converge for some values of x and not for others.

2. The series $\sum_{n=0}^{\infty} a_n(x - x_0)^n$ is said to converge absolutely at a point x if the series

$$\sum_{n=0}^{\infty} |a_n(x - x_0)^n|$$

converges. It can be shown that if the series converges absolutely, then the series also converges; however, the converse is not necessarily true.

3. One of the most useful tests for the absolute convergence of a power series is the ratio test. If for a fixed value of x

$$\lim_{n \to \infty} \left| \frac{a_{n+1}(x - x_0)^{n+1}}{a_n(x - x_0)^n} \right| = l,$$

the power series converges absolutely at that value of x if $l < 1$, and diverges if $l > 1$. If $l = 1$ the test is inconclusive.

4. If the power series $\sum_{n=0}^{\infty} a_n(x - x_0)^n$ converges at $x = x_1$, it converges absolutely for $|x - x_0| < |x_1 - x_0|$; and if it diverges at $x = x_1$, it diverges for $|x - x_0| > |x_1 - x_0|$.

5. There is a number ρ, called the *radius of convergence*, such that $\sum_{n=0}^{\infty} a_n(x - x_0)^n$ converges absolutely for $|x - x_0| < \rho$ and diverges for $|x - x_0| > \rho$. For a series that converges nowhere except at x_0, we define ρ to be zero; for a series that converges for all x, we say that ρ is infinite. The interval of convergence is depicted by the hatched lines in Figure 4.1.

FIGURE 4.1

If $\sum_{n=0}^{\infty} a_n(x - x_0)^n$ and $\sum_{n=0}^{\infty} b_n(x - x_0)^n$ converge to $f(x)$ and $g(x)$, respectively, for $|x - x_0| < \rho$, $\rho > 0$, then the following are true for $|x - x_0| < \rho$.

6. The series can be added or subtracted termwise, and

$$f(x) \pm g(x) = \sum_{n=0}^{\infty} (a_n \pm b_n)(x - x_0)^n.$$

7. The series can be formally multiplied, and

$$f(x)g(x) = \left[\sum_{n=0}^{\infty} a_n(x - x_0)^n \right] \cdot \left[\sum_{n=0}^{\infty} b_n(x - x_0)^n \right] = \sum_{n=0}^{\infty} c_n(x - x_0)^n$$

where $c_n = a_0 b_n + a_1 b_{n-1} + \cdots + a_n b_0$. Further, if $g(x_0) \neq 0$, the series can be formally divided and

$$\frac{f(x)}{g(x)} = \sum_{n=0}^{\infty} d_n(x - x_0)^n,$$

although the formula for d_n is complicated. Also in the case of division the radius of convergence of the resulting power series may be less than ρ.

8. The function f is continuous and has derivatives of all orders for $|x - x_0| < \rho$. Further, $f', f'', \ldots$ can be computed by differentiating the series termwise; that is,

$$f'(x) = a_1 + 2a_2(x - x_0) + \cdots + na_n(x - x_0)^{n-1} + \cdots$$

$$= \sum_{n=1}^{\infty} na_n(x - x_0)^{n-1},$$

etc., and each of the series converges absolutely for $|x - x_0| < \rho$.

9. The value of a_n is given by

$$a_n = \frac{f^{(n)}(x_0)}{n!}.$$

The series is called the Taylor series for the function f about $x = x_0$.

10. If $\sum_{n=0}^{\infty} a_n(x - x_0)^n = \sum_{n=0}^{\infty} b_n(x - x_0)^n$ for each x, then $a_n = b_n$, $n = 0$, 1, 2, ... In particular, if $\sum_{n=0}^{\infty} a_n(x - x_0)^n = 0$ for each x, then $a_0 = a_1 = \cdots = a_n = \cdots = 0$.

A function f that has a Taylor series expansion about $x = x_0$,

$$f(x) = \sum_{n=0}^{\infty} \frac{f^{(n)}(x_0)}{n!}(x - x_0)^n,$$

with a radius of convergence $\rho > 0$ is said to be *analytic* at $x = x_0$. According to the above statements, if f and g are analytic at x_0 then $f \pm g, f \cdot g$, and f/g (provided $g(x_0) \neq 0$) are analytic at $x = x_0$. The result that will be used most often in the following sections is that a polynomial is analytic at every point; thus sums, differences, products, and quotients (except at zeros of the denominator) of polynomials are analytic at every point.

PROBLEMS

1. Determine the radius of convergence of each of the following power series.

(a) $\sum_{n=0}^{\infty} (x - 3)^n$

(b) $\sum_{n=0}^{\infty} \frac{n}{2^n} x^n$

(c) $\sum_{n=0}^{\infty} \frac{x^{2n}}{n!}$

(d) $\sum_{n=0}^{\infty} 2^n x^n$

(e) $\sum_{n=1}^{\infty} \frac{(2x + 1)^n}{n^2}$

(f) $\sum_{n=1}^{\infty} \frac{(x - x_0)^n}{n}$

2. Determine the Taylor series about the point x_0 for each of the following functions. Also determine the radius of convergence of the series.

(a) $\sin x$, $x_0 = 0$ (b) e^x, $x_0 = 0$

(c) x, $x_0 = 1$ (d) x^2, $x_0 = -1$

(e) $\ln x$, $x_0 = 1$ (f) $\dfrac{1}{1+x}$, $x_0 = 0$

(g) $\dfrac{1}{1-x}$, $x_0 = 0$ (h) $\dfrac{1}{1-x}$, $x_0 = 2$

3. Given that $y = \sum\limits_{n=0}^{\infty} n x^n$, compute y' and y'' and write out the first four terms of each series as well as the coefficient of x^n in the general term.

4. Given that $y = \sum\limits_{n=0}^{\infty} a_n x^n$, compute y' and y'' and write out the first four terms of each series as well as the coefficient of x^n in the general term. Show that if $y'' = y$ the coefficients a_0 and a_1 are arbitrary, and determine a_2 and a_3 in terms of a_0 and a_1. Show that $a_{n+2} = a_n/(n+2)(n+1)$, $n = 0, 1, 2, 3, \ldots$.

5. It is often convenient to transform an infinite series by making a change in the index of summation. The index of summation is a dummy parameter just as the integration variable is a dummy variable for a definite integral. Verify the following:

(a) $\sum\limits_{n=2}^{\infty} a_n x^n = \sum\limits_{n=0}^{\infty} a_{n+2} x^{n+2} = \sum\limits_{k=0}^{\infty} a_{k+2} x^{k+2}$

(b) $\sum\limits_{n=2}^{\infty} n(n-1) a_n x^{n-2} = \sum\limits_{n=0}^{\infty} (n+2)(n+1) a_{n+2} x^n$

(c) $\sum\limits_{n=0}^{\infty} a_n x^{n+2} = \sum\limits_{n=2}^{\infty} a_{n-2} x^n$

(d) $\sum\limits_{n=k}^{\infty} a_{n+m} x^{n+p} = \sum\limits_{n=0}^{\infty} a_{n+m+k} x^{n+p+k}$

where k and m are given integers and p is a constant, $x > 0$.

(e) $x^2 \sum\limits_{n=0}^{\infty} (n+r)(n+r-1) a_n x^{n+r-2} + \alpha x \sum\limits_{n=0}^{\infty} (n+r) a_n x^{n+r-1} + \beta x^2 \sum\limits_{n=0}^{\infty} a_n x^{n+r}$

$= [r(r-1) + \alpha r] a_0 x^r + [(r+1)r + \alpha(r+1)] a_1 x^{r+1}$

$+ \sum\limits_{n=2}^{\infty} [(n+r)(n+r-1) a_n + \alpha(n+r) a_n + \beta a_{n-2}] x^{n+r}$, $x > 0$,

where r is a constant.

4.2   SERIES SOLUTIONS NEAR
AN ORDINARY POINT, PART I

In this section we will illustrate the method of solving

$$P(x)y'' + Q(x)y' + R(x)y = 0 \tag{1}$$

when the functions P, Q, and R are polynomials, by considering several specific examples. We are interested in solving Eq. (1) in the neighborhood of a point x_0 at which $P(x_0) \neq 0$; that is, x_0 is an ordinary point. Since $P(x_0) \neq 0$ and P is continuous, it follows that there is some interval about the point x_0 in which P is never zero;* in this interval Q/P and R/P are continuous functions. Hence, according to the existence and uniqueness theorem 3.2 there exists a unique solution of Eq. (1) which satisfies the initial conditions $y(x_0) = y_0$, $y'(x_0) = y_0'$ for an arbitrary choice of y_0 and y_0'.

We will look for solutions of Eq. (1) of the form

$$y = a_0 + a_1(x - x_0) + \cdots + a_n(x - x_0)^n + \cdots = \sum_{n=0}^{\infty} a_n(x - x_0)^n. \quad (2)$$

We must consider two questions. The first is whether we can formally determine† the a_n so that y as given by Eq. (2) satisfies Eq. (1). The second is whether the series thus determined actually converges, and if so, for what values of $x - x_0$. If we can show that the series does converge for $|x - x_0| < \rho$, $\rho > 0$, then all the formal procedures such as termwise differentiation can be justified, and we will have constructed a solution of Eq. (1) that is valid for $|x - x_0| < \rho$.

We will postpone until Section 4.2.1 all consideration of more theoretical matters such as the radius of convergence of the series (2). For the present we will simply assume that such a solution exists, and show how to determine the a_n. The most practical way to do this is simply to substitute the series (2) and its derivatives for y, y', and y'' in Eq. (1); the a_n are then determined so that the differential equation is formally satisfied. The following examples will illustrate the procedure. The differential equations involved are also of considerable importance in their own right.

Example 1.   Find a series solution in powers of x of Airy's‡ equation

$$y'' = xy, \qquad -\infty < x < \infty. \quad (3)$$

For this equation $P(x) = 1$, $Q(x) = 0$, and $R(x) = -x$; hence, $x = 0$ is an ordinary point and we assume that

$$y = a_0 + a_1 x + a_2 x^2 + \cdots + a_n x^n + \cdots = \sum_{n=0}^{\infty} a_n x^n. \quad (4)$$

---

* Geometrically this is plausible, and it can be proven rigorously.
† By "formally determine" we mean "carry out all the algebraic computations necessary for the determination of a solution without justifying at each step that it is permissible to perform the computation."
‡ Sir George Airy (1801–1892), a famous English astronomer and mathematician, was made the Lucasian Professor of Mathematics at Cambridge at the age of 25, and was director of the Greenwich Observatory from 1835 to 1881. One reason Airy's equation is of interest is that for x negative the solutions are oscillatory, similar to trigonometric functions, and for x positive one solution grows exponentially and the other decays exponentially. Can you explain why it is reasonable to expect such behavior?

Differentiating Eq. (4) term by term yields

$$y' = a_1 + 2a_2x + \cdots + na_nx^{n-1} + (n+1)a_{n+1}x^n + \cdots$$

$$= \sum_{n=0}^{\infty}(n+1)a_{n+1}x^n, \tag{5}$$

$$y'' = 2a_2 + \cdots + (n+1)na_{n+1}x^{n-1} + (n+2)(n+1)a_{n+2}x^n + \cdots$$

$$= \sum_{n=0}^{\infty}(n+2)(n+1)a_{n+2}x^n. \tag{6}$$

Substituting the series (4) and (6) for y and y'' in Eq. (3) gives

$$[2a_2 + (3 \cdot 2)a_3x + \cdots + (n+2)(n+1)a_{n+2}x^n + \cdots]$$
$$= x(a_0 + a_1x + \cdots + a_{n-1}x^{n-1} + a_nx^n + \cdots),$$

or

$$\sum_{n=0}^{\infty}(n+2)(n+1)a_{n+2}x^n = x\sum_{n=0}^{\infty}a_nx^n$$

$$= \sum_{n=0}^{\infty}a_nx^{n+1} = \sum_{n=1}^{\infty}a_{n-1}x^n.$$

For this equation to be satisfied it is necessary that the coefficients of like powers of x be equal; hence we have

$$2a_2 = 0,$$
$$(3 \cdot 2)a_3 = a_0,$$
$$(4 \cdot 3)a_4 = a_1,$$
$$(5 \cdot 4)a_5 = a_2,$$

and in general

$$(n+2)(n+1)a_{n+2} = a_{n-1} \quad \text{for} \quad n \geq 1. \tag{7}$$

Note that there are no conditions on a_0 and a_1; hence they are arbitrary. Upon reflection this is not surprising. Notice from Eq. (2) that y and y' evaluated at x_0 are a_0 and a_1, respectively, and since the initial conditions $y(x_0)$ and $y'(x_0)$ can be chosen arbitrarily, it follows that a_0 and a_1 should be arbitrary until specific initial conditions are stated.

Equation (7) is referred to as a *recurrence relation*. According to this relation a_0 determines a_3, which in turn determines a_6, etc. For example,

$$a_9 = \frac{a_6}{9 \cdot 8} = \frac{a_3}{9 \cdot 8 \cdot 6 \cdot 5} = \frac{a_0}{9 \cdot 8 \cdot 6 \cdot 5 \cdot 3 \cdot 2},$$

or

$$a_{3n} = \frac{a_0}{(3n)(3n-1)(3n-3)(3n-4)\cdots 6 \cdot 5 \cdot 3 \cdot 2}, \quad \text{for} \quad n = 1, 2, \ldots.$$

Similarly a_1 determines a_4, a_7, a_{10}, etc.; and a_2 determines a_5, a_8, a_{11}, etc. Since $a_2 = 0$, we conclude that $a_5 = a_8 = a_{11} = \cdots = 0$. The solution of

Airy's equation is

$$y = a_0 \left[1 + \frac{x^3}{3 \cdot 2} + \frac{x^6}{6 \cdot 5 \cdot 3 \cdot 2} + \cdots + \frac{x^{3n}}{(3n)(3n-1) \cdots 3 \cdot 2} + \cdots \right]$$

$$+ a_1 \left[x + \frac{x^4}{4 \cdot 3} + \frac{x^7}{7 \cdot 6 \cdot 4 \cdot 3} + \cdots \right.$$

$$\left. + \frac{x^{3n+1}}{(3n+1)(3n)(3n-2)(3n-3) \cdots 4 \cdot 3} + \cdots \right]$$

$$= a_0 \left[1 + \sum_{n=1}^{\infty} \frac{x^{3n}}{(3n)(3n-1)(3n-3)(3n-4) \cdots 3 \cdot 2} \right]$$

$$+ a_1 \left[x + \sum_{n=1}^{\infty} \frac{x^{3n+1}}{(3n+1)(3n)(3n-2)(3n-3) \cdots 4 \cdot 3} \right]. \quad (8)$$

Because of the rapid growth of the denominators of the terms in the series (8) we might expect these series to have a large radius of convergence. Indeed as we shall see in the next section both of these series converge for all x. Also see Problem 4.

Assume for the moment that the series do converge for all x, and let y_1 and y_2 denote the functions defined by the first and second sets of brackets, respectively, in Eq. (8). Then, by first choosing $a_0 = 1$, $a_1 = 0$ and then $a_0 = 0$, $a_1 = 1$, it is clear that y_1 and y_2 are individually solutions of Eq. (3). Notice that y_1 satisfies the initial conditions $y_1(0) = 1$, $y_1'(0) = 0$ and y_2 satisfies the initial conditions $y_2(0) = 0$, $y_2'(0) = 1$. Thus $W(y_1, y_2)(0) = 1 \neq 0$; and consequently y_1 and y_2 are linearly independent. Hence the general solution of Airy's equation is

$$y = a_0 y_1(x) + a_1 y_2(x), \qquad -\infty < x < \infty.$$

Example 2. Find a solution of Airy's equation in powers of $x - 1$.

The point $x = 1$ is an ordinary point of Eq. (3), and thus we look for a solution of the form

$$y = \sum_{n=0}^{\infty} a_n (x - 1)^n.$$

Then

$$y' = \sum_{n=1}^{\infty} n a_n (x - 1)^{n-1} = \sum_{n=0}^{\infty} (n + 1) a_{n+1} (x - 1)^n,$$

and

$$y'' = \sum_{n=2}^{\infty} n(n - 1) a_n (x - 1)^{n-2} = \sum_{n=0}^{\infty} (n + 2)(n + 1) a_{n+2} (x - 1)^n.$$

Substituting for y and y'' in Eq. (3) gives

$$\sum_{n=0}^{\infty} (n + 2)(n + 1) a_{n+2} (x - 1)^n = x \sum_{n=0}^{\infty} a_n (x - 1)^n. \quad (9)$$

Now in order to equate the coefficients of like powers of $(x - 1)$ we must express x, the coefficient of y in Eq. (3), in powers of $x - 1$; that is, we write $x = 1 + (x - 1)$. Note that this is precisely the Taylor series for x about $x = 1$. Then Eq. (9) takes the form

$$\sum_{n=0}^{\infty} (n + 2)(n + 1)a_{n+2}(x - 1)^n = [1 + (x - 1)] \sum_{n=0}^{\infty} a_n(x - 1)^n$$

$$= \sum_{n=0}^{\infty} a_n(x - 1)^n + \sum_{n=0}^{\infty} a_n(x - 1)^{n+1}.$$

Shifting the index of summation in the second series on the right gives

$$\sum_{n=0}^{\infty} (n + 2)(n + 1)a_{n+2}(x - 1)^n = \sum_{n=0}^{\infty} a_n(x - 1)^n + \sum_{n=1}^{\infty} a_{n-1}(x - 1)^n.$$

Equating coefficients of like powers of $x - 1$ we obtain

$$2a_2 = a_0,$$
$$(3 \cdot 2)a_3 = a_1 + a_0,$$
$$(4 \cdot 3)a_4 = a_2 + a_1,$$
$$(5 \cdot 4)a_5 = a_3 + a_2,$$
$$\cdot$$
$$\cdot$$
$$\cdot$$

The general recurrence relation is

$$n(n - 1)a_n = a_{n-2} + a_{n-3} \qquad \text{for} \qquad n \geq 3. \tag{10}$$

Solving for the first few a_n in terms of a_0 and a_1 gives

$$a_2 = \frac{a_0}{2^1}, \qquad a_3 = \frac{a_1}{6} + \frac{a_0}{6},$$

$$a_4 = \frac{a_2}{12} + \frac{a_1}{12} = \frac{a_0}{24} + \frac{a_1}{12},$$

$$a_5 = \frac{a_3}{20} + \frac{a_2}{20} = \frac{a_0}{30} + \frac{a_1}{120},$$

$$\cdot$$
$$\cdot$$
$$\cdot$$

Hence

$$y = a_0 \left[1 + \frac{(x - 1)^2}{2} + \frac{(x - 1)^3}{6} + \frac{(x - 1)^4}{24} + \frac{(x - 1)^5}{30} + \cdots \right]$$

$$+ a_1 \left[(x - 1) + \frac{(x - 1)^3}{6} + \frac{(x - 1)^4}{12} + \frac{(x - 1)^5}{120} + \cdots \right]. \tag{11}$$

In general when the recurrence relation has three terms, such as the one given in Eq. (10), the determination of the coefficients in the series solution will be fairly complicated. In this example the formula for a_n in terms of a_0 and a_1 is not readily apparent. However, even without knowing the formula for a_n, we shall see in Section 4.2.1 that it is possible to establish that the series in Eq. (11) converge for all x, and further define functions y_1 and y_2, which are linearly independent solutions of the Airy equation (3). Thus

$$y = a_0 y_1(x) + a_1 y_2(x)$$

is the general solution of Airy's equation for $-\infty < x < \infty$.

It is worth emphasizing, as we saw in Example 2, that if we look for a solution of Eq. (1) of the form $y = \sum_{n=0}^{\infty} a_n(x - x_0)^n$, then the coefficients $P(x)$, $Q(x)$, and $R(x)$ in Eq. (1) must also be expressed in powers of $(x - x_0)$. Alternatively we can make the change of variable $x - x_0 = t$, obtaining a new differential equation for y as a function of t and then look for solutions of this new equation of the form $\sum_{n=0}^{\infty} a_n t^n$. When we have finished the calculations we replace t by $x - x_0$; see Problem 3.

Another point of interest is the following. The functions y_1 and y_2 defined by the series in Eq. (8) are linearly independent solutions of Eq. (3) for all x, and this is similarly true for the functions y_1 and y_2 defined by the series in Eq. (11). According to the general theory of second order linear equations each of the first two functions can be expressed as a linear combination of the latter two functions and vice versa—a result that is certainly not obvious.

Example 3.   The Hermite* equation is

$$y'' - 2xy' + \lambda y = 0, \qquad -\infty < x < \infty, \tag{12}$$

where λ is a constant. This equation is important in many branches of mathematical physics; for example, in quantum mechanics the Hermite equation arises in the investigation of the Schrödinger (1887–1961) equation for a harmonic oscillator.

To find a solution of Eq. (12) in the neighborhood of the ordinary point $x = 0$, we substitute the series (4), (5), and (6) for y, y', and y'' in Eq. (12) obtaining

$$\sum_{n=0}^{\infty} (n + 2)(n + 1)a_{n+2}x^n - \sum_{n=0}^{\infty} 2(n + 1)a_{n+1}x^{n+1} + \sum_{n=0}^{\infty} \lambda a_n x^n = 0.$$

* Charles Hermite (1822–1901) was a distinguished French mathematician whose work in the field of algebra was particularly elegant.

Shifting the index of summation in the second series so that it becomes $\sum\limits_{n=1}^{\infty} 2na_n x^n$ and collecting terms gives

$$(2a_2 + \lambda a_0) + \sum_{n=1}^{\infty} [(n + 2)(n + 1)a_{n+2} - 2na_n + \lambda a_n]x^n = 0.$$

Hence a_0 and a_1 are arbitrary, and the general recurrence relation is

$$a_{n+2} = \frac{2n - \lambda}{(n + 2)(n + 1)} a_n, \qquad n \geq 0. \tag{13}$$

Thus a_0 determines a_2, which in turn determines a_4, which in turn determines a_6, and so on. Similarly, the coefficients of the odd powers of x are determined by the recurrence relation (13). The formal series solution for the Hermite equation is

$$y = a_0\left[1 - \frac{\lambda}{2!} x^2 - \frac{(4 - \lambda)\lambda}{4!} x^4 - \frac{(8 - \lambda)(4 - \lambda)\lambda}{6!} x^6 - \cdots\right]$$

$$+ a_1\left[x + \frac{(2 - \lambda)}{3!} x^3 + \frac{(6 - \lambda)(2 - \lambda)}{5!} x^5\right.$$

$$\left. + \frac{(10 - \lambda)(6 - \lambda)(2 - \lambda)}{7!} x^7 + \cdots\right]$$

$$= a_0 y_1(x) + a_1 y_2(x). \tag{14}$$

Again the results of Section 4.2.1 will establish the convergence of these series for all x. If λ is a nonnegative even integer, one or the other of the above series terminates. In particular for $\lambda = 0, 2, 4, 6$, respectively, one solution of the Hermite equation is 1, x, $1 - 2x^2$, and $x - 2x^3/3$. The polynomial solution corresponding to $\lambda = 2n$, after being multiplied by a proper constant,* is known as the Hermite polynomial $H_n(x)$.

PROBLEMS

1. Proceeding formally, find two linearly independent power series solutions in powers of $x - x_0$ for each of the following differential equations. What is the recurrence relation?

(a) $y'' - y = 0$, $x_0 = 0$

(b) $y'' - xy' - y = 0$, $x_0 = 0$

---

* This process is usually referred to as normalization. The constant is often chosen so that the solution has a specified value at a particular point, or so that a certain integral of the solution over a prescribed range has a definite value. For example, the Hermite polynomial of order n is uniquely specified by the statement that it is a polynomial solution of degree n of the Hermite equation with $\lambda = 2n$, and with the coefficient of x^n equal to 2^n.

(c) $y'' - xy' - y = 0$, $x_0 = 1$

(d) $y'' + k^2x^2y = 0$; $x_0 = 0$, k a constant

(e) $(1 - x)y'' + y = 0$, $x_0 = 0$

(f) $(2 + x^2)y'' - xy' + 4y = 0$, $x_0 = 0$

2. Find the solution of Problem 1(b) that satisfies the initial conditions $y(0) = 0$, $y'(0) = 1$.

3. By making the change of variable $x - 1 = t$, find two linearly independent series solutions of

$$y'' + (x - 1)^2y' + (x^2 - 1)y = 0$$

in powers of $x - 1$. Show that you can obtain the same result by expanding $x^2 - 1$ in a Taylor series about $x = 1$, and then substituting

$$y = \sum_{n=0}^{\infty} a_n(x - 1)^n.$$

4. Show directly, using the ratio test, that the series solutions of Airy's equation about $x = 0$ converge for all x. See Eq. (8) of the text.

4.2.1 SERIES SOLUTIONS NEAR AN ORDINARY POINT, PART II

In the previous section we considered the problem of finding solutions of

$$P(x)y'' + Q(x)y' + R(x)y = 0, \tag{1}$$

where P, Q, and R are polynomials, in the neighborhood of an ordinary point x_0. Assuming that Eq. (1) does have a solution $y = \phi(x)$, and that ϕ has a Taylor series

$$y = \phi(x) = \sum_{n=0}^{\infty} a_n(x - x_0)^n \tag{2}$$

which converges for $|x - x_0| < \rho$, $\rho > 0$, we found that the a_n can be determined by directly substituting the series (2) for y in Eq. (1).

Let us now consider how we might justify the statement that if x_0 is an ordinary point of Eq. (1), then there will exist solutions of the form (2). We will also consider the question of the radius of convergence of such a series. In doing this we will be led to a generalization of the definition of an ordinary point.

Suppose, then, that there is a solution of Eq. (1) of the form (2). It is clear on differentiating Eq. (2) m times and setting x equal to x_0 that

$$m! \, a_m = \phi^{(m)}(x_0).$$

Hence, in order to compute the a_n in the series (2), we must show that we can determine $\phi^{(n)}(x_0)$ for $n = 0, 1, 2, \ldots$ from the differential equation (1). Suppose that $y = \phi(x)$ is a solution of Eq. (1) satisfying the initial conditions $y(x_0) = y_0$, $y'(x_0) = y_0'$. Then $a_0 = y_0$ and $a_1 = y_0'$.

If we are solely interested in finding a solution of Eq. (1) without specifying any initial conditions, then a_0 and a_1 will be arbitrary. To determine $\phi^{(n)}(x_0)$ and the corresponding a_n for $n = 2, 3, \ldots$, we turn to Eq. (1). Since ϕ is a solution of Eq. (1) we have

$$P(x)\phi''(x) + Q(x)\phi'(x) + R(x)\phi(x) = 0.$$

For the interval about x_0 for which P is nonvanishing we can write this equation in the form

$$\phi''(x) = -p(x)\phi'(x) - q(x)\phi(x) \tag{3}$$

where $p(x) = Q(x)/P(x)$ and $q(x) = R(x)/P(x)$. Setting x equal to x_0 in Eq. (3) gives

$$\phi''(x_0) = -p(x_0)\phi'(x_0) - q(x_0)\phi(x_0).$$

Hence a_2 is given by

$$2! \, a_2 = -p(x_0)a_1 - q(x_0)a_0. \tag{4}$$

To determine a_3 we differentiate Eq. (3) and then set x equal to x_0, obtaining

$$\phi'''(x_0) = 3! \, a_3 = -[p\phi'' + (p' + q)\phi' + q'\phi]_{x=x_0}$$
$$= -2! \, p(x_0)a_2 - [p'(x_0) + q(x_0)]a_1 - q'(x_0)a_0. \tag{5}$$

Substituting for a_2 from Eq. (4) gives a_3 in terms of a_1 and a_0. Since P, Q, and R are polynomials and $P(x_0) \neq 0$, all of the derivatives of p and q exist at x_0. Hence we can continue to differentiate Eq. (3) indefinitely, determining after each differentiation the successive coefficients $a_4, \ldots$, etc., by setting x equal to x_0.

Notice that the important property that we used in determining the a_n was that we could compute infinitely many derivatives of the functions p and q. It might seem reasonable to relax our assumption that the functions p and q are ratios of polynomials, and simply require that they be infinitely differentiable in the neighborhood of x_0. Unfortunately, this condition is too weak to insure that we can prove the convergence of the resulting series expansion for $y = \phi(x)$. However, there is a more general condition which we can require of p and q. It allows us to carry out the above computations for the a_n, and also to prove the convergence of the series solution. This condition is that the functions p and q be *analytic* at x_0, that is, that they have *Taylor series* expansions that converge in some interval about the point x_0:

$$p(x) = p_0 + p_1(x - x_0) + \cdots + p_n(x - x_0)^n + \cdots = \sum_{n=0}^{\infty} p_n(x - x_0)^n, \tag{6}$$

$$q(x) = q_0 + q_1(x - x_0) + \cdots + q_n(x - x_0)^n + \cdots = \sum_{n=0}^{\infty} q_n(x - x_0)^n. \tag{7}$$

As mentioned in Section 4.1 if each of the functions p and q is the quotient of polynomials, then they have series expansions* of the form (6) and (7). With this idea in mind we can generalize the definition of an ordinary point and a singular point of Eq. (1) as follows: If the functions $p = Q/P$ and $q = R/P$ are analytic at x_0, then the point x_0 is said to be an *ordinary point* of the differential equation (1); otherwise it is a *singular point*.

Now let us turn to the question of the interval of convergence of the series solution. One possibility is actually to compute the series solution for each problem and then to apply one of the tests for convergence of an infinite series to determine the radius of convergence of the series solution. Fortunately the question can be answered at once for a wide class of problems by the following theorem.

Theorem 4.1.   *If x_0 is an ordinary point of the differential equation* (1)

$$P(x)y'' + Q(x)y' + R(x)y = 0;$$

that is, if $p = Q/P$ and $q = R/P$ are analytic at x_0, then the general solution of Eq. (1) *is*

$$y = \sum_{n=0}^{\infty} a_n(x - x_0)^n = a_0 y_1(x) + a_1 y_2(x),$$

where a_0 and a_1 are arbitrary, and y_1 and y_2 are linearly independent series solutions which are analytic at x_0. Further the radius of convergence for each of the series solutions y_1 and y_2 is at least as large as the minimum of the radii of convergence for the series for p and q. The coefficients in the series solutions are determined by substituting the series (2) *for y in Eq.* (1).

Notice from the form of the series solution that $y_1(x) = 1 + b_2(x - x_0)^2 + \cdots$, and $y_2(x) = (x - x_0) + c_2(x - x_0)^2 + \cdots$. Hence y_1 is a solution satisfying the initial conditions $y_1(x_0) = 1$, $y_1'(x_0) = 0$, and y_2 is a solution satisfying the initial conditions $y_2(x_0) = 0$, $y_2'(x_0) = 1$.

While this theorem, which in a slightly more general form is due to Fuchs (1833–1902), is not too difficult to prove, it is beyond the scope and intent of this book to do so. What is important for our purposes is that the radius of convergence of the series solution cannot be less than the smaller of the radii of convergence of the series for p and q; hence we need only determine these.

This can be done in one of two ways. Again one possibility is simply to compute the power series for p and q, and then determine the radii of convergence by using one of the convergence tests for infinite series. However, there is an easier way when P, Q, and R are polynomials. It is shown in the

---

* The careful reader has probably reached the conclusion (which is correct) that if p is of the form (6) then p has infinitely many derivatives at x_0, but that the converse does not follow. An example of a function with infinitely many derivatives at $x = 0$, but which does not have a Taylor series expansion, is given in Problem 8.

theory of functions of a complex variable that the ratio of two polynomials, say Q/P, will have a convergent power series expansion about a point $x = x_0$ if $P(x_0) \neq 0$. Further, assuming that any factors common to Q and P have been canceled, the radius of convergence of the power series for Q/P about the point x_0 is precisely the distance from x_0 to the nearest zero of P. In determining this distance we must remember that $P(x) = 0$ may have complex roots, and these must also be considered.

Example 1. What is the radius of convergence of the Taylor series for $(1 + x^2)^{-1}$ about $x = 0$?

For $x^2 < 1$ we know that a convergent power series expansion for $(1 + x^2)^{-1}$ is

$$\frac{1}{1 + x^2} = 1 - x^2 + x^4 - x^6 + \cdots + (-1)^n x^{2n} + \cdots.$$

Clearly this series diverges for $x^2 > 1$ since then the nth term does not approach zero as $n \to \infty$. Hence the radius of convergence is $\rho = 1$. (This can be verified by the ratio test.)

To determine the radius of convergence using the theory that was just discussed, we note that the polynomial $1 + x^2$ has zeros at $x = \pm i$; since the distance from 0 to i in the complex plane is 1, the radius of convergence of the power series about $x = 0$ is 1.

Example 2. What is the radius of convergence of the Taylor series for $(x^2 - 2x + 2)^{-1}$ about $x = 0$? About $x = 1$?

First notice that

$$x^2 - 2x + 2 = 0$$

has solutions $x = 1 \pm i$. The distance from $x = 0$ to either $x = 1 + i$ or $x = 1 - i$ in the complex plane is $\sqrt{2}$; hence the radius of convergence of the Taylor series expansion, $\sum\limits_{n=0}^{\infty} a_n x^n$, about $x = 0$ is $\sqrt{2}$. The distance from $x = 1$ to either $x = 1 + i$ or $x = 1 - i$ is 1; hence the radius of convergence of the Taylor series expansion, $\sum\limits_{n=0}^{\infty} b_n (x - 1)^n$, about $x = 1$ is 1.

According to Theorem 4.1 the series solutions of Airy's equation in Examples 1 and 2, and of the Hermite equation in Example 3 of the previous section converge for all values of x, $x - 1$, and x respectively, since in each problem $P(x) = 1$ and hence never vanishes.

It should be emphasized that a series solution may converge for a wider range of x than indicated by Theorem 4.1, so the theorem actually gives only a lower bound on the radius of convergence of the series solution. This is illustrated in the following example.

Example 3. Determine a lower bound for the radius of convergence of series solutions about $x = 0$ for the Legendre equation

$$(1 - x^2)y'' - 2xy' + \alpha(\alpha + 1)y = 0,$$

where α is a constant.

Since $P(x) = 1 - x^2$, $Q(x) = -2x$, and $R(x) = \alpha(\alpha + 1)$ are polynomials, and the zeros of P, $x = \pm 1$, are a distance 1 from $x = 0$, a series solution of the form $\sum_{n=0}^{\infty} a_k x^k$ will converge for $|x| < 1$ at least, and possibly for larger values of x. Indeed, it can be shown that if α is a positive integer, one of the series solutions will terminate after a finite number of terms and hence will converge not just for $|x| < 1$ but for all x. For example, if $\alpha = 1$ the polynomial solution is $y = x$. See Problems 10 through 16 at the end of this section for a more complete discussion of the Legendre equation.

Example 4. Determine a lower bound for the radius of convergence of series solutions of the differential equation

$$(1 + x^2)y'' + 2xy' + 4x^2y = 0$$

about the point $x = 0$; about the point $x = -\frac{1}{2}$.

Again P, Q, and R are polynomials, and P has zeros at $x = \pm i$. The distance in the complex plane from 0 to $\pm i$ is 1, and from $-\frac{1}{2}$ to $\pm i$ is $\sqrt{1 + \frac{1}{4}} = \sqrt{5}/2$. Hence in the first case the series $\sum_{n=0}^{\infty} a_n x^n$ will converge at least for $|x| < 1$, and in the second case the series $\sum_{n=0}^{\infty} b_n(x + \frac{1}{2})^n$ will converge at least for $|x + \frac{1}{2}| < \sqrt{5}/2$.

Example 5. Can we determine a series solution about $x = 0$ for the differential equation

$$y'' + (\sin x)y' + (1 + x^2)y = 0,$$

and if so what is the radius of convergence?

For this differential equation, $p(x) = \sin x$ and $q(x) = 1 + x^2$. Recall from Section 4.1 that $\sin x$ has a Taylor series expansion about $x = 0$, which converges for all x. Further, q also has a Taylor series expansion about $x = 0$, namely $q(x) = 1 + x^2$, which converges for all x. Thus there is a series solution of the form $y = \sum_{n=0}^{\infty} a_n x^n$ with a_0 and a_1 arbitrary, and the series converges for all x.

PROBLEMS

1. Determine $\phi''(x_0)$, $\phi'''(x_0)$, and $\phi^{iv}(x_0)$ for the given point x_0 if $y = \phi(x)$ is a solution of the given initial value problem.

(a) $y'' + xy' + y = 0$; $y(0) = 1$, $y'(0) = 0$
(b) $y'' + (\sin x)y' + (\cos x)y = 0$; $y(0) = 0$, $y'(0) = 1$
(c) $x^2y'' + (1 + x)y' + 3(\ln x)y = 0$; $y(1) = 2$, $y'(1) = 0$
(d) $y'' + x^2y' + (\sin x)y = 0$; $y(0) = a_0$, $y'(0) = a_1$

In part (d) express $\phi''(0)$, $\phi'''(0)$, and $\phi^{iv}(0)$ in terms of a_0 and a_1.

2. Determine a lower bound for the radius of convergence of series solutions about each given point x_0 for each of the following differential equations.

(a) $y'' + 4y' + 6xy = 0$; $x_0 = 0$, $x_0 = 4$
(b) $(x^2 - 2x - 3)y'' + xy' + 4y = 0$; $x_0 = 4$, $x_0 = -4$, $x_0 = 0$
(c) $(1 + x^3)y'' + 4xy' + y = 0$; $x_0 = 0$, $x_0 = 2$
(d) $xy'' + y = 0$; $x_0 = 1$

3. Determine a lower bound for the radius of convergence of series solutions for each of the differential equations in Problem 1 of Section 4.2.

4. The Tchebycheff (1821–1894) differential equation is

$$(1 - x^2)y'' - xy' + \alpha^2 y = 0,$$

where α is a constant.

(a) Determine two linearly independent solutions in powers of x for $|x| < 1$.
(b) Show that if α is a nonnegative integer n, then there is a polynomial solution of degree n. These polynomials, when properly normalized, are called the Tchebycheff polynomials. They are very useful in problems requiring a polynomial approximation to a function defined on $-1 \leq x \leq 1$.
(c) Find a polynomial solution for each of the cases $n = 0, 1, 2$, and 3.

5. Find the first three terms in each of two linearly independent power series solutions in powers of x of

$$y'' + (\sin x)y = 0.$$

Hint: Expand $\sin x$ in a Taylor series about $x = 0$, and retain a sufficient number of terms to compute the necessary coefficients in $y = \sum\limits_{n=0}^{\infty} a_n x^n$.

6. Find the first three terms in each of two linearly independent power series solutions in powers of x of

$$e^x y'' + xy = 0.$$

What is the radius of convergence of each series solution?
Hint: Expand e^x or xe^{-x} in a power series about $x = 0$.

7. Suppose that you are told that x and x^2 are solutions of a differential equation $P(x)y'' + Q(x)y' + R(x)y = 0$. What can you say about the point $x = 0$: Is it an ordinary point or a singular point?
Hint: Use the existence and uniqueness theorem 3.2, and note the value of x and x^2 at $x = 0$.

*8. To show that it is possible to have a function that is infinitely differentiable at a point but does not have a Taylor series expansion about the point, consider the function

$$f(x) = \begin{cases} e^{-1/x^2}, & x \neq 0, \\ 0, & x = 0. \end{cases}$$

Show, using the definition of a derivative as the limit of a difference quotient, that f is infinitely differentiable at the origin, and that $f^{(n)}(0) = 0$ for all n. Hence the series

$$\sum_{n=0}^{\infty} \frac{f^{(n)}(0)}{n!} x^n$$

vanishes for all x, and converges to $f(x)$ only at $x = 0$.

9. The series methods discussed in this section are directly applicable to the first order linear differential equation $P(x)y' + Q(x)y = 0$ at a point x_0, if the function $p = Q/P$ has a Taylor series expansion about that point. Such a point is called an ordinary point, and further, the radius of convergence of the series $y = \sum_{n=0}^{\infty} a_n(x - x_0)^n$ will be at least as large as the radius of convergence of the series for Q/P. Solve the following differential equations by series in powers of x and verify that a_0 is arbitrary in each case. Problems (e) and (f) involve non-homogeneous differential equations to which the series methods can be easily extended.

(a) $y' - y = 0$ (b) $y' - xy = 0$

(c) $y' = e^{x^2}y$, three terms (d) $(1 - x)y' = y$

*(e) $y' - y = x^2$ *(f) $y' + xy = 1 + x$

Where possible, compare the series solution with the solution obtained by using the methods of Chapter 2.

Legendre Equation.   Problems 10 through 16 deal with the Legendre equation

$$(1 - x^2)y'' - 2xy' + \alpha(\alpha + 1)y = 0.$$

As indicated in Example 3, the point $x = 0$ is an ordinary point of this equation, and the distance from the origin to the nearest zero of $P(x) = 1 - x^2$ is 1. Hence the radius of convergence of series solutions about $x = 0$ will be at least 1.

10. Show that two linearly independent solutions of the Legendre equation for $|x| < 1$ are

$$y_1(x) = 1 + \sum_{m=1}^{\infty} (-1)^m$$

$$\times \frac{\alpha(\alpha - 2)(\alpha - 4) \cdots (\alpha - 2m + 2)(\alpha + 1)(\alpha + 3) \cdots (\alpha + 2m - 1)}{(2m)!} x^{2m},$$

$$y_2(x) = x + \sum_{m=1}^{\infty} (-1)^m$$

$$\times \frac{(\alpha - 1)(\alpha - 3) \cdots (\alpha - 2m + 1)(\alpha + 2)(\alpha + 4) \cdots (\alpha + 2m)}{(2m + 1)!} x^{2m+1}.$$

11. Show that if α is zero or a positive even integer $2n$ the series solution for y_1 reduces to a polynomial of degree $2n$ containing only even powers of x. Show that corresponding to $\alpha = 0$, 2, and 4 these polynomials are

$$1, 1 - 3x^2, 1 - 10x^2 + \tfrac{3}{3}\tfrac{5}{3}x^4.$$

Show that if α is a positive odd integer $2n + 1$ then the series solution for y_2 reduces to a polynomial of degree $2n + 1$ containing only odd powers of x and that corresponding to $\alpha = 1$, 3, 5 these polynomials are

$$x, x - \tfrac{5}{3}x^3, x - \tfrac{14}{3}x^3 + \tfrac{21}{5}x^5.$$

12. The Legendre polynomial P_n is defined as the polynomial solution of the Legendre equation with $\alpha = n$ which satisfies the condition $P_n(1) = 1$. Show using the results of Problem 11 that

$$P_0(x) = 1, \quad P_1(x) = x, \quad P_2(x) = \tfrac{1}{2}(3x^2 - 1), \quad P_3(x) = \tfrac{1}{2}(5x^3 - 3x).$$

It can be shown that the general formula is

$$P_n(x) = \frac{1}{2^n} \sum_{k=0}^{[n/2]} \frac{(-1)^k (2n - 2k)!}{k!\,(n - k)!\,(n - 2k)!} x^{n-2k},$$

where $[n/2]$ denotes the greatest integer less than or equal to $n/2$. Show that $P_n(-1) = (-1)^n$.

13. The Legendre polynomials play an important role in mathematical physics. For example, in solving Laplace's equation (the potential equation) in spherical coordinates we encounter the equation

$$\frac{d^2F(\varphi)}{d\varphi^2} + \cot \varphi \, \frac{dF(\varphi)}{d\varphi} + n(n + 1)F(\varphi) = 0, \qquad 0 < \varphi < \pi,$$

where n is a positive integer. Show that the change of variable $x = \cos \varphi$ leads to the Legendre equation with $\alpha = n$ for $y = f(x) = F(\cos^{-1} x)$.

14. Show that for $n = 0$, 1, 2, 3 the corresponding Legendre polynomial is given by

$$P_n(x) = \frac{1}{2^n n!} \frac{d^n}{dx^n} (x^2 - 1)^n.$$

This formula, known as Rodrigues' (1794–1851) formula, is true for all n.

15. Show that the Legendre equation can also be written as

$$[(1 - x^2)y']' = -\alpha(\alpha + 1)y.$$

Then it follows that $[(1 - x^2)P_n'(x)]' = -n(n + 1)P_n(x)$ and $[(1 - x^2)P_m'(x)]' = -m(m + 1)P_m(x)$. Show, by multiplying the first equation by $P_m(x)$ and the second equation by $P_n(x)$, and then integrating by parts that

$$\int_{-1}^{1} P_n(x)P_m(x)\, dx = 0 \qquad \text{if} \qquad n \neq m.$$

This property of the Legendre polynomials is known as the orthogonality property. If $m = n$, it can be shown that the value of the above integral is $2/(2n + 1)$.

16. Given a polynomial f of degree n, it is possible to express f as a linear combination of $P_0, P_1, P_2, \ldots, P_n$:

$$f(x) = \sum_{k=0}^{n} a_k P_k(x).$$

Show, using the result of Problem 15, that

$$a_k = \frac{2k + 1}{2} \int_{-1}^{1} f(x) P_k(x) \, dx.$$

4.3   REGULAR SINGULAR POINTS

In this section we will consider the equation

$$P(x)y'' + Q(x)y' + R(x)y = 0 \tag{1}$$

in the neighborhood of a singular point x_0. Recall that if the functions P, Q, and R are polynomials having no common factors, the singular points of Eq. (1) are the points for which $P(x) = 0$.

Example 1.   The Bessel equation of order ν is

$$x^2 y'' + xy' + (x^2 - \nu^2)y = 0. \tag{2}$$

The point $x = 0$ is clearly a singular point since $P(x) = x^2$ vanishes there. Furthermore, if we divide Eq. (2) by x^2, the coefficients of y' and y will be undefined at $x = 0$. All other points are ordinary points of Eq. (2).

Example 2.   Determine the singular points and ordinary points of the Legendre equation

$$(1 - x^2)y'' - 2xy' + \alpha(\alpha + 1)y = 0, \tag{3}$$

where α is a constant.

The singular points are the zeros of $P(x) = 1 - x^2$, namely the points $x = \pm 1$. All other points are ordinary points.

The solution of Eq. (1) in the neighborhood of a singular point x_0 frequently becomes large in magnitude, experiences rapid changes in magnitude, or is peculiar in some manner. Thus, the behavior of a physical system governed by such an equation is frequently most interesting in the neighborhood of a singular point. Often geometrical singularities in a physical problem, such as corners or sharp edges, lead to singular points in the corresponding differential equation. Mathematically, the singular points of a differential equation, while usually few in number, determine the principal features of the solution to a much larger extent than one might at first suspect. Thus, while we might want to avoid the few points where a differential equation is singular, it is precisely at these points that it is necessary to study the solution most carefully.

Unfortunately, if x_0 is a singular point the methods of the previous section fail, and it is necessary to consider a more general type of series expansion than a Taylor series. This is illustrated by the differential equation in Example 3 below, for which one of the solutions does not have a Taylor series expansion about $x = 0$. Without any additional information about the behavior of Q/P and R/P in the neighborhood of the singular point, it is impossible to describe the behavior of the solutions of Eq. (1) near $x = x_0$. It may be that there are two linearly independent solutions of Eq. (1) that remain bounded as $x \to x_0$, or there may be only one with the other becoming unbounded as $x \to x_0$, or they may both become unbounded as $x \to x_0$. To illustrate this consider the following examples.

Example 3.   The differential equation

$$x^2 y'' - 2y = 0 \tag{4}$$

has a singular point at $x = 0$. It can be easily verified by direct substitution that for $x > 0$ or $x < 0$, $y = x^2$ and $y = 1/x$ are linearly independent solutions of Eq. (4). Thus in any interval not containing the origin the general solution of Eq. (4) is $y = c_1 x^2 + c_2 x^{-1}$. The only solution of Eq. (4) that is bounded as $x \to 0$ is $y = c_1 x^2$. Indeed this solution is analytic at the origin even though if Eq. (2) is put in the standard form, $y'' - (2/x^2)y = 0$, the function $q(x) = -2/x^2$ is not analytic at $x = 0$, and Theorem 4.1 is not applicable. On the other hand notice that the solution $y = x^{-1}$ does not have a Taylor series expansion about the origin (is not analytic at $x = 0$); therefore, the method of Section 4.2 would fail in this case.

Example 4.   The differential equation

$$x^2 y'' - 2xy' + 2y = 0 \tag{5}$$

also has a singular point at $x = 0$. It can be verified that $y_1(x) = x$ and $y_2(x) = x^2$ are linearly independent solutions of Eq. (5), and both are analytic at $x = 0$. Nevertheless, it is still not proper to pose an initial value problem with initial conditions at $x = 0$. It is impossible to prescribe arbitrary initial conditions at $x = 0$, since any linear combination of x and x^2 is zero at $x = 0$.

It is also possible to construct a differential equation with a singular point x_0, such that every solution of the differential equation becomes unbounded as $x \to x_0$. Even if Eq. (1) does not have a solution that remains bounded as $x \to x_0$, it is often important to determine how the solutions of Eq. (1) behave as $x \to x_0$; for example, does $y \to \infty$ in the same manner as $(x - x_0)^{-1}$ or $|x - x_0|^{-\frac{1}{2}}$, or in some other manner?

In order to develop a reasonably simple mathematical theory for solving Eq. (1) in the neighborhood of a singular point x_0, it is necessary to restrict ourselves to cases in which the singularities in the functions Q/P and R/P at

$x = x_0$ are not too severe, that is, to so-called "weak singularities." A priori, it is not clear exactly what is an acceptable singularity. However, we will show later (see Section 4.5.1, Problems 5 and 6) that if P, Q, and R are polynomials, the conditions that distinguish "weak singularities" are

$$\lim_{x \to x_0} (x - x_0) \frac{Q(x)}{P(x)} \quad \text{is finite} \tag{6}$$

and

$$\lim_{x \to x_0} (x - x_0)^2 \frac{R(x)}{P(x)} \quad \text{is finite.} \tag{7}$$

This means that the singularity in Q/P can be no worse than $(x - x_0)^{-1}$ and the singularity in R/P can be no worse than $(x - x_0)^{-2}$. Such a point is called a *regular singular point* of Eq. (1). For more general functions than polynomials, x_0 is a *regular singular point* of Eq. (1) if it is a singular point, and if both*

$$(x - x_0) \frac{Q(x)}{P(x)} \quad \text{and} \quad (x - x_0)^2 \frac{R(x)}{P(x)} \tag{8}$$

have convergent Taylor series about x_0, that is, if the functions in Eq. (8) are analytic at $x = x_0$. Equations (6) and (7) imply that this will be the case when P, Q, and R are polynomials. Any singular point of Eq. (1) that is not a regular singular point is called an *irregular singular point* of Eq. (1).

In the following sections we will discuss how to solve Eq. (1) in the neighborhood of a regular singular point. A discussion of the solutions of differential equations in the neighborhood of irregular singular points is beyond the scope of an elementary text.

Example 5.   Determine the singular points of the differential equation

$$2(x - 2)^2 x y'' + 3xy' + (x - 2)y = 0,$$

and classify them as regular or irregular.

Dividing by $2(x - 2)^2 x$ we have

$$y'' + \frac{3}{2(x - 2)^2} y' + \frac{1}{2(x - 2)x} y = 0,$$

so $p(x) = 3/2(x - 2)^2$ and $q(x) = 1/2x(x - 2)$. The singular points are $x = 0$ and $x = 2$. Consider $x = 0$. We have

$$\lim_{x \to 0} xp(x) = \lim_{x \to 0} x \frac{3}{2(x - 2)^2} = 0$$

$$\lim_{x \to 0} x^2 q(x) = \lim_{x \to 0} x^2 \frac{1}{2x(x - 2)} = 0;$$

---

* The functions given in Eq. (8) may not be defined at x_0, in which case their values at x_0 are to be taken equal to their limits as $x \to x_0$.

hence $x = 0$ is a regular singular point. For $x = 2$ we have

$$\lim_{x \to 2} (x - 2)p(x) = \lim_{x \to 2} (x - 2) \frac{3}{2(x - 2)^2}$$

does not exist; hence $x = 2$ is an irregular singular point.

PROBLEMS

In Problems 1 through 8 determine whether each of the points -1, 0, and 1 is an ordinary point, a regular singular point, or an irregular singular point for the given differential equation.

1. $xy'' + (1 - x)y' + xy = 0$

2. $x^2(1 - x^2)y'' + 2xy' + 4y = 0$

3. $2x^4(1 - x^2)y'' + 2xy' + 3x^2y = 0$

4. $x^2(1 - x^2)y'' + \dfrac{2}{x}y' + 4y = 0$

5. $(1 - x^2)^2y'' + x(1 - x)y' + (1 + x)y = 0$

6. $y'' + \left(\dfrac{x}{1 - x}\right)^2 y' + 3(1 + x)^2y = 0$

7. $(x + 3)y'' - 2xy' + (1 - x^2)y = 0$

8. $x(1 - x^2)^3y'' + (1 - x^2)^2y' + 2(1 + x)y = 0$

9. Assuming that the function f defined by $f(x) = x^{-1} \sin x$ for $x \neq 0$ and $f(0) = 1$ is analytic at $x = 0$, show that $x = 0$ is a regular singular point of the differential equation

$$(\sin x)y'' + xy' + 4y = 0,$$

and an irregular singular point of the differential equation

$$(x \sin x)y'' + 3y' + xy = 0.$$

*10. The definitions of an ordinary point and a regular singular point given in the preceding sections apply only if the point x_0 is finite. In more advanced work in differential equations it is often necessary to discuss the point at infinity. This is done by making the change of variable $\xi = 1/x$ and studying the resulting equation at $\xi = 0$. Show that for the differential equation $P(x)y'' + Q(x)y' + R(x)y = 0$ the point at infinity is an ordinary point if

$$\frac{1}{P(1/\xi)} \left[\frac{2P(1/\xi)}{\xi} - \frac{Q(1/\xi)}{\xi^2} \right] \quad \text{and} \quad \frac{R(1/\xi)}{\xi^4 P(1/\xi)}$$

have Taylor series expansions about $\xi = 0$. Show also that the point at infinity is a regular singular point if one or the other of the above functions does not have a Taylor series expansion, but both

$$\frac{\xi}{P(1/\xi)} \left[\frac{2P(1/\xi)}{\xi} - \frac{Q(1/\xi)}{\xi^2} \right] \quad \text{and} \quad \frac{R(1/\xi)}{\xi^2 P(1/\xi)}$$

do have such expansions.

*11. For the following differential equations determine whether the point at infinity is an ordinary point, a regular singular point, or an irregular singular point.
   (a) The Legendre equation

$$(1 - x^2)y'' - 2xy' + \alpha(\alpha + 1)y = 0$$

   (b) The Bessel equation

$$x^2y'' + xy' + (x^2 - v^2)y = 0$$

   (c) The Hermite equation

$$y'' - 2xy' + \lambda y = 0$$

   (d) The Airy equation

$$y'' - xy = 0$$

4.4 EULER EQUATIONS

One of the simplest examples of a differential equation having a regular singular point is the Euler equation or equidimensional equation

$$L[y] = x^2 \frac{d^2y}{dx^2} + \alpha x \frac{dy}{dx} + \beta y = 0, \tag{1}$$

where α and β are constants. Unless otherwise stated we shall consider α and β to be real. It is easy to see that $x = 0$ is a regular singular point of Eq. (1). Because the solution of the Euler equation is typical of the solution of all differential equations with a regular singular point, it is worthwhile considering this equation in detail before discussing the more general problem.

In any interval not including the origin, Eq. (1) has a general solution of the form $y = c_1y_1(x) + c_2y_2(x)$ where y_1 and y_2 are linearly independent. For convenience we will first consider the interval $x > 0$, extending our results later to the interval $x < 0$. First, we note that $(x^r)' = rx^{r-1}$ and $(x^r)'' = r(r - 1)x^{r-2}$. Hence, if we assume that Eq. (1) has a solution of the form*

$$y = x^r, \tag{2}$$

we obtain

$$L[x^r] = x^2(x^r)'' + \alpha x(x^r)' + \beta x^r$$

$$= x^r F(r), \tag{3}$$

where

$$F(r) = r(r - 1) + \alpha r + \beta. \tag{4}$$

If r is a root of the quadratic equation $F(r) = 0$, then $L[x^r]$ is zero, and

---

* This assumption is also suggested by the fact that the first order Euler equation $xy' + ky = 0$ has the solution $y = x^{-k}$.

$y = x^r$ is a solution of Eq. (1). The roots of $F(r) = 0$ are

$$r_1 = \frac{-(\alpha - 1) + \sqrt{(\alpha - 1)^2 - 4\beta}}{2},$$

$$r_2 = \frac{-(\alpha - 1) - \sqrt{(\alpha - 1)^2 - 4\beta}}{2}, \qquad (5)$$

and $F(r) = (r - r_1)(r - r_2)$. Just as in the case of the second order linear differential equation with constant coefficients (see Section 3.5), we must examine separately the cases $(\alpha - 1)^2 - 4\beta$ positive, zero, and negative. Indeed the entire theory presented in this section is similar to the theory for second order linear equations with constant coefficients, e^{rx} being replaced by x^r. See Problems 4 and 5.

Case 1. $(\alpha - 1)^2 - 4\beta > 0$. In this case Eq. (5) gives two real unequal roots r_1 and r_2. Since $W(x^{r_1}, x^{r_2})$ is nonvanishing for $r_1 \neq r_2$ and $x > 0$ it follows that the general solution of Eq. (1) is

$$y = c_1 x^{r_1} + c_2 x^{r_2}, \qquad x > 0. \qquad (6)$$

Note that if r_1 is not a rational number, then x^{r_1} is defined by $x^{r_1} = e^{r_1 \ln x}$.

Example 1. Solve

$$2x^2 y'' + 3xy' - y = 0, \qquad x > 0. \qquad (7)$$

Substituting $y = x^r$ gives

$$x^r(2r^2 + r - 1) = 0,$$

$$x^r(2r - 1)(r + 1) = 0.$$

Hence

$$r_1 = \tfrac{1}{2}, \qquad r_2 = -1,$$

and

$$y = c_1 x^{1/2} + c_2 x^{-1}, \qquad x > 0. \qquad (8)$$

Case 2. $(\alpha - 1)^2 - 4\beta = 0$. In this case, according to Eq. (5), $r_1 = r_2 = -(\alpha - 1)/2$, and we have only one solution, $y_1(x) = x^{r_1}$, of the differential equation. A second solution can be obtained by the method of reduction of order, but for the purpose of our future discussion we will consider an alternative method. Since $r_1 = r_2$, it follows that $F(r) = (r - r_1)^2$. Thus in this case not only does $F(r_1) = 0$, but also $F'(r_1) = 0$. This suggests differentiating Eq. (3) with respect to r and then setting r equal to r_1. Differentiating Eq. (3) with respect to r gives

$$\frac{\partial}{\partial r} L[x^r] = \frac{\partial}{\partial r} [x^r F(r)].$$

Substituting for $F(r)$, interchanging differentiation with respect to x and r, and noting that $\partial(x^r)/\partial r = x^r \ln x$, we obtain

$$L[x^r \ln x] = (r - r_1)^2 x^r \ln x + 2(r - r_1)x^r. \tag{9}$$

The right-hand side of Eq. (9) vanishes for $r = r_1$; consequently,

$$y_2(x) = x^{r_1} \ln x, \qquad x > 0, \tag{10}$$

is a second solution of Eq. (1). Since x^{r_1} and $x^{r_1} \ln x$ are linearly independent for $x > 0$, the general solution of Eq. (1) is

$$y = (c_1 + c_2 \ln x)x^{r_1}, \qquad x > 0. \tag{11}$$

Example 2. Solve

$$x^2 y'' + 5xy' + 4y = 0, \qquad x > 0. \tag{12}$$

Substituting $y = x^r$ gives $x^r(r^2 + 4r + 4) = 0$. Hence $r_1 = r_2 = -2$, and

$$y = x^{-2}(c_1 + c_2 \ln x), \qquad x > 0. \tag{13}$$

Case 3. $(\alpha - 1)^2 - 4\beta < 0$. In this case the roots r_1 and r_2 are complex conjugates, say $r_1 = \lambda + i\mu$ and $r_2 = \lambda - i\mu$. We must now explain what is meant by x^r when r is complex. Remembering that when $x > 0$ and r is real we can write

$$x^r = e^{r \ln x}, \tag{14}$$

we can use this equation to *define* x^r when r is complex. Then

$$
\begin{aligned}
x^{(\lambda + i\mu)} = e^{(\lambda + i\mu) \ln x} &= e^{\lambda \ln x} e^{i\mu \ln x} \\
&= x^\lambda e^{i\mu \ln x} \\
&= x^\lambda \{\cos(\mu \ln x) + i \sin(\mu \ln x)\}, \qquad x > 0. \tag{15}
\end{aligned}
$$

With this definition of x^r for complex values of r, it can be verified that the usual laws of algebra and the differential calculus hold, and hence x^{r_1} and x^{r_2} are indeed solutions of Eq. (1). The general solution of Eq. (1) is

$$y = c_1 x^{\lambda + i\mu} + c_2 x^{\lambda - i\mu}. \tag{16}$$

The disadvantage of this expression is that the functions $x^{\lambda + i\mu}$ and $x^{\lambda - i\mu}$ are complex-valued. Recall that we had a similar situation for the second order differential equation with constant coefficients when the roots of the auxiliary equation were complex. In the same way as we did then we observe that the real and imaginary parts of $x^{\lambda + i\mu}$,

$$x^\lambda \cos(\mu \ln x) \qquad \text{and} \qquad x^\lambda \sin(\mu \ln x) \tag{17}$$

are linearly independent solutions of Eq. (1). Hence for the case of complex roots, the general solution of Eq. (1) is

$$y = c_1 x^\lambda \cos(\mu \ln x) + c_2 x^\lambda \sin(\mu \ln x), \qquad x > 0. \tag{18}$$

Example 3. Solve

$$x^2 y'' + xy' + y = 0. \tag{19}$$

Substituting $y = x^r$ gives

$$x^r[r(r-1) + r + 1] = 0.$$

Hence $r = \pm i$, and the general solution is

$$y = c_1 \cos(\ln x) + c_2 \sin(\ln x), \qquad x > 0. \tag{20}$$

Now let us consider the interval $x < 0$. The difficulty here is in explaining what is meant by x^r when x is negative, and r is not an integer; similarly $\ln x$ is not defined for $x < 0$. The solutions of the Euler equation that we have given for $x > 0$ can be shown to be valid for $x < 0$ but they will in general be complex-valued. Thus in Example 1 the solution $x^{\frac{1}{2}}$ is imaginary for $x < 0$.

It is always possible to obtain real-valued solutions of the Euler equation (1) in the interval $x < 0$ by making the following change of variable. Let $x = -\xi$; then $x < 0$ implies $\xi > 0$; further,

$$\frac{d}{dx} = (-1)\frac{d}{d\xi}, \qquad \frac{d^2}{dx^2} = \frac{d^2}{d\xi^2}. \tag{21}$$

With this change of variable Eq. (1) takes the form

$$\xi^2 \frac{d^2 u}{d\xi^2} + \alpha\xi \frac{du}{d\xi} + \beta u = 0, \qquad \xi > 0, \tag{22}$$

where, to avoid confusion, we have introduced a new dependent variable u. But we have solved Eq. (22) for $\xi > 0$; hence u is given by Eq. (6), (11), or (18) as $(\alpha - 1)^2 - 4\beta$ is greater than, equal to, or less than zero, respectively, with x replaced by ξ. Now since $\xi = -x$, and

$$|x| = \begin{cases} x & \text{for} & x > 0, \\ -x = \xi & \text{for} & x < 0, \end{cases} \tag{23}$$

it follows that we need only replace x by $|x|$ in Eqs. (6), (11), and (18) to obtain real-valued solutions valid in any interval not containing the origin. (Also see Problems 6 and 7.) These results are summarized in the following theorem.

Theorem 4.2. *To solve the Euler equation* (1)

$$x^2 y'' + \alpha xy' + \beta y = 0$$

in any interval not containing the origin, substitute $y = x^r$, *and compute the roots* r_1 *and* r_2 *of the equation*

$$F(r) = r^2 + (\alpha - 1)r + \beta = 0.$$

If the roots are real and unequal,

$$y = c_1 |x|^{r_1} + c_2 |x|^{r_2}. \tag{24}$$

If the roots are real and equal,

$$y = (c_1 + c_2 \ln |x|) |x|^{r_1}. \tag{25}$$

If the roots are complex,

$$y = |x|^{\lambda} [c_1 \cos (\mu \ln |x|) + c_2 \sin (\mu \ln |x|)] \tag{26}$$

where $r_1, r_2 = \lambda \pm i\mu.$

For an Euler equation of the form

$$(x - x_0)^2 y'' + \alpha(x - x_0)y' + \beta y = 0, \tag{27}$$

the situation is exactly the same. One looks for solutions of the form $y = (x - x_0)^r$. The general solution is given by either Eq. (24), (25), or (26) with x replaced by $(x - x_0)$. Alternatively we can reduce Eq. (27) to the form of Eq. (1) by making the change of independent variable $t = x - x_0$.

The situation for a general second order differential equation with a regular singular point is similar to that for an Euler equation. We will consider that problem in the next section.

PROBLEMS

1. Determine the general solution of each of the following second order differential equations that is valid in any interval not including the singular point.

(a) $x^2 y'' + 4xy' + 2y = 0$ (b) $x^2 y'' + 3xy' + \frac{3}{4} y = 0$

(c) $x^2 y'' - 3xy' + 4y = 0$ (d) $x^2 y'' + 3xy' + 5y = 0$

(e) $x^2 y'' - xy' + y = 0$ (f) $(x - 1)^2 y'' + 8(x - 1)y' + 12y = 0$

(g) $x^2 y'' + 6xy' - y = 0$ (h) $2x^2 y'' - 4xy' + 6y = 0$

(i) $x^2 y'' - 5xy' + 9y = 0$ (j) $(x - 2)^2 y'' + 5(x - 2)y' + 8y = 0$

(k) $x^2 y'' + 2xy' + 4y = 0$ (l) $x^2 y'' - 4xy' + 4y = 0$

2. Using the method of reduction of order, show that if r_1 is a repeated root of $r(r - 1) + \alpha r + \beta = 0$, then x^{r_1} and $x^{r_1} \ln x$ are solutions of

$$x^2 y'' + \alpha xy' + \beta y = 0, \qquad x > 0.$$

3. Find all values of α for which all solutions of $x^2 y'' + \alpha xy' + \frac{5}{2} y = 0$ approach zero as $x \to 0$.

4. The second order Euler equation $x^2 y'' + \alpha xy' + \beta y = 0$ can be reduced to a second order linear equation with constant coefficients by an appropriate change of the independent variable. Remembering that x^r plays the same role for the Euler equation as $e^{rx} = (e^x)^r$ plays for the equation with constant coefficients, it would appear reasonable to make the change of variable $x = e^z$, or $z = \ln x$. Consider only the interval $x > 0$.

(a) Show that

$$\frac{dy}{dx} = \frac{1}{x}\frac{dy}{dz} \quad \text{and} \quad \frac{d^2y}{dx^2} = \frac{1}{x^2}\frac{d^2y}{dz^2} - \frac{1}{x^2}\frac{dy}{dz}$$

(b) Show that the Euler equation becomes

$$\frac{d^2y}{dz^2} + (\alpha - 1)\frac{dy}{dz} + \beta y = 0.$$

Letting r_1 and r_2 denote the roots of $r^2 + (\alpha - 1)r + \beta = 0$, show that

(c) if r_1 and r_2 are real and unequal, then

$$y = c_1 e^{r_1 z} + c_2 e^{r_2 z} = c_1 x^{r_1} + c_2 x^{r_2},$$

(d) if r_1 and r_2 are equal, then

$$y = (c_1 + c_2 z)e^{r_1 z} = (c_1 + c_2 \ln x)x^{r_1},$$

(e) if r_1 and r_2 are complex conjugates, $r_1 = \lambda + i\mu$, then

$$y = e^{\lambda z}(c_1 \cos \mu z + c_2 \sin \mu z) = x^\lambda[c_1 \cos (\mu \ln x) + c_2 \sin (\mu \ln x)].$$

5. Using the method of Problem 4, solve the following differential equations for $x > 0$.

(a) $x^2 y'' - 2y = 0$ (b) $x^2 y'' - 3xy' + 4y = \ln x$

(c) $x^2 y'' + 7xy' + 5y = x$ (d) $x^2 y'' - 2xy' + 2y = 3x^2 + 2\ln x$

(e) $x^2 y'' + xy' + 4y = \sin (\ln x)$ (f) $3x^2 y'' + 12xy' + 9y = 0$

6. Show that if $L[y] = x^2 y'' + \alpha xy' + \beta y$, then

$$L[(-x)^r] = (-x)^r F(r)$$

for $x < 0$, where $F(r) = r(r - 1) + \alpha r + \beta$. Hence conclude that if $r_1 \neq r_2$ are roots of $F(r) = 0$, then linearly independent solutions of $L[y] = 0$ for $x < 0$ are $(-x)^{r_1}$ and $(-x)^{r_2}$.

7. Suppose that x^{r_1} and x^{r_2} are solutions of an Euler equation, where $r_1 \neq r_2$, and r_1 is an integer. According to Eq. (24) the general solution in any interval not containing the origin is $y = c_1 |x|^{r_1} + c_2 |x|^{r_2}$. Show that the general solution can also be written as $y = k_1 x^{r_1} + k_2 |x|^{r_2}$.
Hint: Show by a proper choice of constants that the expressions are identical for $x > 0$; and by a different choice of constants that they are identical for $x < 0$.

8. If the constants α and β in the Euler equation $x^2 y'' + \alpha xy' + \beta y = 0$ are complex numbers, it is still possible to obtain solutions of the form x^r. However, in general, the solutions will no longer be real-valued. Determine the general solution of each of the following equations for the interval $x > 0$.

(a) $x^2 y'' + 2ixy' - iy = 0$

(b) $x^2 y'' + (1 - i)xy' + 2y = 0$

(c) $x^2 y'' + xy' - 2iy = 0$

Hint: See Problems 13, 14, and 15 of Section 3.5.1.

4.5 SERIES SOLUTIONS NEAR A REGULAR
SINGULAR POINT, PART I

We will now consider the question of solving the general linear second order equation

$$P(x)y'' + Q(x)y' + R(x)y = 0 \tag{1}$$

in the neighborhood of a regular singular point $x = x_0$. For convenience we will assume that $x_0 = 0$. If $x_0 \neq 0$ the equation can be transformed into one for which the regular singular point is at the origin by letting $x - x_0$ equal z.

The fact that $x = 0$ is a regular singular point of Eq. (1) means that $xQ(x)/P(x) = xp(x)$ and $x^2R(x)/P(x) = x^2q(x)$ have finite limits as $x \to 0$, and are analytic at $x = 0$ having power series expansions of the form

$$xp(x) = \sum_{n=0}^{\infty} p_n x^n, \qquad x^2q(x) = \sum_{n=0}^{\infty} q_n x^n, \tag{2}$$

which are convergent for some interval $|x| < \rho$, $\rho > 0$, about the origin. It is convenient for theoretical purposes to divide Eq. (1) by $P(x)$ and then multiply by x^2, obtaining

$$x^2y'' + x[xp(x)]y' + [x^2q(x)]y = 0, \tag{3a}$$

or

$$x^2y'' + x(p_0 + p_1x + \cdots + p_nx^n + \cdots)y'$$
$$+ (q_0 + q_1x + \cdots + q_nx^n + \cdots)y = 0. \tag{3b}$$

If all of the p_n and q_n are zero except

$$p_0 = \lim_{x \to 0} \frac{xQ(x)}{P(x)}, \qquad q_0 = \lim_{x \to 0} \frac{x^2R(x)}{P(x)},$$

then Eq. (3) reduces to the Euler equation

$$x^2y'' + p_0xy' + q_0y = 0,$$

which was discussed in the previous section. In general, of course, some of the p_n and q_n, $n \geq 1$, will not be zero. However, the essential character of solutions of Eq. (3) is identical to that of solutions of the Euler equation. The presence of the variable terms $xp(x)$ and $x^2q(x)$ merely complicates the calculations.

We shall primarily restrict our discussion to the interval $x > 0$. The interval $x < 0$ can be treated, just as for the Euler equation, by making the change of variable $x = -\xi$ and then solving the resulting equation for $\xi > 0$.

Since the coefficients in Eq. (3) are "Euler coefficients" times power series, it is natural to seek solutions of the form of "Euler solutions" times power series:

$$y = x^r(a_0 + a_1x + \cdots + a_nx^n + \cdots) = x^r \sum_{n=0}^{\infty} a_n x^n. \tag{4}$$

As part of our problem we have to determine:

1. The values of r for which Eq. (1) has a solution of the form (4).

2. The recurrence relation for the a_n.

3. The radius of convergence of the series $\sum\limits_{n=0}^{\infty} a_n x^n$.

We shall find that Eq. (1) will always have at least one solution of the form (4) with a_0 arbitrary, and possibly a second solution corresponding to a second value of r. If there is not a second solution of the form (4), the second solution will involve a logarithmic term just as did the second solution of the Euler equation when the roots were equal. In theory, of course, once we obtain the first solution, which will be of the form (4), a second solution can be obtained by the method of reduction of order. Unfortunately, this is not always a convenient method for obtaining a second solution; we will give an alternate method in Sections 4.6 and 4.7.

The general theory is due to the German mathematician Frobenius (1849–1917) and is fairly complicated. Rather than trying to present this theory we shall simply assume in this and the next three sections that there does exist a solution of the stated form. In particular we assume that any power series in an expression for a solution has a nonzero radius of convergence, and shall concentrate on showing how to determine the coefficients in such a series.

Let us first illustrate the method of Frobenius for a specific differential equation which has two solutions of the form (4). Consider the equation

$$2x^2 y'' - xy' + (1 + x)y = 0. \tag{5}$$

By comparison with Eq. (3), it is clear that $x = 0$ is a regular singular point of Eq. (5). We will formally try to find a solution of Eq. (5) of the form (4) for $x > 0$. Then y' and y'' are given by

$$y' = \sum_{n=0}^{\infty} a_n (r + n) x^{r+n-1}, \tag{6}$$

and

$$y'' = \sum_{n=0}^{\infty} a_n (r + n)(r + n - 1) x^{r+n-2}. \tag{7}$$

Hence

$$2x^2 y'' - xy' + (1 + x)y = \sum_{n=0}^{\infty} 2a_n (r + n)(r + n - 1) x^{r+n}$$

$$- \sum_{n=0}^{\infty} a_n (r + n) x^{r+n} + \sum_{n=0}^{\infty} a_n x^{r+n} + \sum_{n=0}^{\infty} a_n x^{r+n+1}.$$

Noting that the last sum can be written in the form $\sum\limits_{n=1}^{\infty} a_{n-1} x^{r+n}$ and combining terms gives

$$2x^2y'' - xy' + (1 + x)y = a_0[2r(r - 1) - r + 1]x^r$$
$$+ \sum_{n=1}^{\infty} \{[2(r + n)(r + n - 1) - (r + n) + 1]a_n + a_{n-1}\}x^{r+n} = 0. \quad (8)$$

If Eq. (8) is to be identically satisfied, the coefficient of each power of x in Eq. (8) must be zero. Corresponding to x^r we obtain, since $a_0 \neq 0$,*

$$2r(r - 1) - r + 1 = 0; \quad (9)$$

and from the coefficient of x^{r+n} we have

$$[2(r + n)(r + n - 1) - (r + n) + 1]a_n + a_{n-1} = 0, \quad n \geq 1. \quad (10)$$

Equation (9) is called the *indicial equation* for Eq. (5). It is a quadratic equation in r, and its roots determine the two possible values of r for which there may be solutions of Eq. (5) of the form (4). Factoring Eq. (9) gives $(2r - 1)(r - 1) = 0$; hence the roots of the indicial equation are

$$r_1 = 1, \quad r_2 = \tfrac{1}{2}. \quad (11)$$

In the following, whenever the roots of the indicial equation are real and unequal, the larger one will be denoted by r_1. The roots of the indicial equation are often referred to as the *exponents of the singularity* at the regular singular point.

Equation (10) gives a recurrence relation for the coefficients a_n. Corresponding to $r = r_1 = 1$, we have, on transposing a_{n-1} and dividing by the coefficient of a_n,

$$a_n = \frac{-1}{2(n + 1)n - (n + 1) + 1} a_{n-1}, \quad n \geq 1$$

$$= \frac{-1}{(2n + 1)n} a_{n-1}.$$

Thus

$$a_n = \frac{-1}{(2n + 1)n} \cdot \frac{-1}{(2n - 1)(n - 1)} a_{n-2}$$

$$\vdots$$

$$= \frac{(-1)^n}{(2n + 1)n(2n - 1)(n - 1) \cdots (5 \cdot 2)(3 \cdot 1)} a_0. \quad (12)$$

* Nothing is gained by taking $a_0 = 0$, as this would simply mean that the series would start with the term a_1x^{r+1} or, if $a_1 = 0$, the term a_2x^{r+2}, and so on. Suppose the first nonzero term is a_mx^{r+m}; this is equivalent to using the series (4) with r replaced by $r + m$ and a_m replaced by a_0. Indeed r is chosen to be the lowest power of x appearing in the series and we take $a_0 \neq 0$ as its coefficient.

Hence one solution of Eq. (5), omitting the constant multiplier a_0, is

$$y_1(x) = x\left[1 + \sum_{n=1}^{\infty} \frac{(-1)^n x^n}{(2n + 1)n(2n - 1)(n - 1) \cdots (5 \cdot 2)(3 \cdot 1)}\right], \qquad x > 0.$$

(13)

To determine the radius of convergence of the series in Eq. (13) we use the ratio test:

$$\lim_{n \to \infty} \left| \frac{a_{n+1} x^{n+1}}{a_n x^n} \right| = \lim_{n \to \infty} \frac{|x|}{(2n + 3)(n + 1)} = 0$$

for all x. Thus the series converges for all x.

Corresponding to the second root $r = r_2 = \frac{1}{2}$, we proceed similarly:

$$a_n = \frac{-1}{2(n + \frac{1}{2})(n - \frac{1}{2}) - (n + \frac{1}{2}) + 1} a_{n-1}$$

$$= \frac{-1}{2n(n - \frac{1}{2})} a_{n-1}$$

$$= \frac{-1}{2n(n - \frac{1}{2})} \frac{-1}{(2n - 2)(n - \frac{3}{2})} a_{n-2}$$

.

.

.

$$= \frac{(-1)^n}{2n(n - \frac{1}{2})(2n - 2)(n - \frac{3}{2}) \cdots (4 \cdot \frac{3}{2})(2 \cdot \frac{1}{2})} a_0, \qquad n \geq 1. \quad (14)$$

Again omitting the constant multiplier a_0, we obtain a second solution

$$y_2(x) = x^{1/2}\left[1 + \sum_{n=1}^{\infty} \frac{(-1)^n x^n}{2n(n - \frac{1}{2})(2n - 2)(n - \frac{3}{2}) \cdots (4 \cdot \frac{3}{2})(2 \cdot \frac{1}{2})}\right], \qquad x > 0.$$

(15)

As before, we can show that the series in Eq. (15) converges for all x. Since the leading terms in the series solutions y_1 and y_2 are x and $x^{1/2}$, respectively, it is clear that the solutions are linearly independent. Hence the general solution of Eq. (5) is

$$y = c_1 y_1(x) + c_2 y_2(x), \qquad x > 0.$$

The preceding example is illuminating in several respects. Let us reconsider our calculations from a more general viewpoint. Let

$$F(r) = 2r(r - 1) - r + 1$$

$$= (2r - 1)(r - 1); \qquad (16)$$

then the indicial equation is $F(r) = 0$, and the recurrence relation (10) becomes

$$F(r + n)a_n + a_{n-1} = 0, \qquad n \geq 1. \tag{17}$$

There are two possible sources of trouble. First, if the two roots r_1 and r_2 of the indicial equation are equal, then we will obtain only one series solution of the form (4). Second, there is the possibility that for a given root r_1 or r_2 we may not be able to solve for one of the a_n from Eq. (17) because $F(r + n)$ may be zero. When can this happen? The only zeros of $F(r)$ are r_1 and r_2, and if $r_1 > r_2$, then clearly $r_1 + n > r_1 > r_2$ for all n and $F(r_1 + n) \neq 0$ for all n. Thus there will never be any difficulty in computing the series solution corresponding to the larger of the roots of the indicial equation. On the other hand consider $F(r_2 + n)$, and suppose that $r_1 - r_2 = N$, a positive integer. Then for $n = N$ we have

$$F(r_2 + N)a_N + a_{N-1} = 0;$$

but $F(r_2 + N) = F(r_1) = 0$ and we cannot solve for a_N, and hence cannot obtain a second series solution. In more general problems, as we shall see in the next section, the recurrence relation will be more complicated and even though $F(r_2 + N)$ may vanish, it may be possible to determine a second solution of the form (4) corresponding to $r = r_2$. In any event the cases $r_1 = r_2$ and $r_1 - r_2 = N$, a positive integer, require special attention.

Finally, we note that if the roots of the indicial equation are complex, then this type of difficulty cannot occur; on the other hand the solutions corresponding to r_1 and r_2 will be complex-valued functions of x. However, just as for the Euler equation, it is possible to obtain real-valued solutions by taking suitable linear combinations of the original solutions.

Before turning to a general discussion and the special cases $r_1 = r_2$ and $r_1 - r_2 = N$, a positive integer, there is a practical point that should be mentioned. If P, Q, and R are polynomials, it is much better to work directly with Eq. (1) than with Eq. (3). This avoids the necessity of expressing $xQ(x)/P(x)$ and $x^2R(x)/P(x)$ as power series. For example, it is more convenient to consider the equation

$$x(1 + x)y'' + 2y' + xy = 0$$

than to write it in the form

$$x^2y'' + x\,\frac{2}{1 + x}\,y' + \frac{x^2}{1 + x}\,y = 0,$$

and then to expand $2/(1 + x)$ and $x^2/(1 + x)$, which gives

$$x^2y'' + x[2(1 - x + x^2 - \cdots)]y' + (x^2 - x^3 + x^4 - \cdots)y = 0.$$

PROBLEMS

1. Show that each of the following differential equations has a regular singular point at $x = 0$. Determine the indicial equation, the recurrence relation, and the roots of the indicial equation. Find the series solution ($x > 0$) corresponding to the larger root. If the roots are unequal and do not differ by an integer, find the series solution corresponding to the smaller root.

(a) $2xy'' + y' + xy = 0$ (b) $x^2y'' + xy' + (x^2 - \frac{1}{9})y = 0$

(c) $xy'' + y = 0$ (d) $xy'' + y' - y = 0$

(e) $3x^2y'' + 2xy' + x^2y = 0$ (f) $x^2y'' + xy' + (x - 2)y = 0$

2. The Legendre equation of order α is

$$(1 - x^2)y'' - 2xy' + \alpha(\alpha + 1)y = 0.$$

The solution of this equation near the ordinary point $x = 0$ was discussed in Problems 10 and 11 of Section 4.2.1. Show that $x = \pm 1$ are regular singular points. Determine the indicial equation and its roots for the point $x = 1$. Find a series solution in powers of $x - 1$ for $x - 1 > 0$.

Hint: Write $1 + x = 2 + (x - 1)$, and $x = 1 + (x - 1)$. Alternatively, make the change of variable $x - 1 = z$ and determine a series solution in powers of z.

3. The Laguerre (1834–1886) differential equation is

$$xy'' + (1 - x)y' + \lambda y = 0.$$

Show that $x = 0$ is a regular singular point. Determine the indicial equation, its roots, the recurrence relation, and one solution ($x > 0$). Show that if $\lambda = m$, a positive integer, this solution reduces to a polynomial. When properly normalized this polynomial is known as the Laguerre polynomial, $L_m(x)$.

4. The Bessel equation of order zero is

$$x^2y'' + xy' + x^2y = 0.$$

Show that $x = 0$ is a regular singular point; that the roots of the indicial equation are $r_1 = r_2 = 0$; and that one solution for $x > 0$ is

$$J_0(x) = 1 + \sum_{n=1}^{\infty} \frac{(-1)^n x^{2n}}{2^{2n}(n!)^2}.$$

Notice that the series converges for all x, not just $x > 0$. The function J_0 is known as the Bessel function of the first kind of order zero.

5. Referring to Problem 4 show, using the method of reduction of order, that the second solution of the Bessel equation of order zero will contain a logarithmic term.

Hint: If $y_2(x) = J_0(x)v(x)$, then

$$y_2(x) = J_0(x) \int^x \frac{\exp\left(-\int^s dt/t\right)}{[J_0(s)]^2} \, ds = J_0(x) \int^x \frac{ds}{s[J_0(s)]^2}.$$

Find the first term in the series expansion for $1/s[J_0(s)]^2$.

6. The Bessel equation of order one is

$$x^2y'' + xy' + (x^2 - 1)y = 0.$$

(a) Show that $x = 0$ is a regular singular point; that the roots of the indicial equation are $r_1 = 1$ and $r_2 = -1$; and that one solution for $x > 0$ is

$$J_1(x) = \frac{x}{2} \sum_{n=0}^{\infty} \frac{(-1)^n x^{2n}}{(n + 1)! \, n! \, 2^{2n}}.$$

Notice as in Problem 4 that the series actually converges for all x. The function J_1 is known as the Bessel function of the first kind of order one.

(b) Show that it is impossible to determine a second solution of the form

$$x^{-1} \sum_{n=0}^{\infty} b_n x^n, \qquad x > 0.$$

4.5.1 SERIES SOLUTIONS NEAR A REGULAR SINGULAR POINT, PART II

Now let us consider the general problem of determining a solution of the equation

$$x^2y'' + x[xp(x)]y' + [x^2q(x)]y = 0 \tag{1}$$

where

$$xp(x) = \sum_{n=0}^{\infty} p_n x^n \quad \text{and} \quad x^2q(x) = \sum_{n=0}^{\infty} q_n x^n,$$

and both series have nonzero radii of convergence [see Eq. (3) of Section 4.5]. The point $x = 0$ is a regular singular point. For convenience, we first suppose $x > 0$, and look for a solution of the form

$$y = \sum_{n=0}^{\infty} a_n x^{r+n}. \tag{2}$$

Substituting in Eq. (1) gives

$$a_0 r(r - 1)x^r + a_1(r + 1)rx^{r+1} + \cdots + a_n(r + n)(r + n - 1)x^{r+n} + \cdots$$
$$+ (p_0 + p_1 x + \cdots + p_n x^n + \cdots)$$
$$\times [a_0 r x^r + a_1(r + 1)x^{r+1} + \cdots + a_n(r + n)x^{r+n} + \cdots]$$
$$+ (q_0 + q_1 x + \cdots + q_n x^n + \cdots)$$
$$\times (a_0 x^r + a_1 x^{r+1} + \cdots + a_n x^{r+n} + \cdots) = 0. \tag{3}$$

Multiplying the infinite series together and then collecting terms, we obtain

$$a_0 F(r)x^r + [a_1 F(r + 1) + a_0(p_1 r + q_1)]x^{r+1}$$
$$+ \{a_2 F(r + 2) + a_0(p_2 r + q_2) + a_1[p_1(r + 1) + q_1]\}x^{r+2}$$
$$+ \cdots + \{a_n F(r + n) + a_0(p_n r + q_n) + a_1[p_{n-1}(r + 1) + q_{n-1}]$$
$$+ \cdots + a_{n-1}[p_1(r + n - 1) + q_1]\}x^{r+n} \cdots = 0,$$

or in a more compact form

$$a_0 F(r)x^r + \sum_{n=1}^{\infty}\left\{F(r + n)a_n + \sum_{k=0}^{n-1}a_k[(r + k)p_{n-k} + q_{n-k}]\right\}x^{r+n} = 0, \quad (4)$$

where

$$F(r) = r(r - 1) + p_0 r + q_0. \quad (5)$$

If Eq. (4) is to be satisfied identically, the coefficient of each power of x must be zero. Since $a_0 \neq 0$, the term involving x^r yields the indicial equation $F(r) = 0$. Let us denote the roots of the indicial equation by r_1 and r_2 with $r_1 \geq r_2$ if the roots are real. If the roots are complex the ordering is immaterial. Only for these values of r can we expect to find solutions of Eq. (1) of the form (2).

Setting the coefficient of x^{r+n} in Eq. (4) equal to zero gives the recurrence relation

$$F(r + n)a_n + \sum_{k=0}^{n-1}a_k[(r + k)p_{n-k} + q_{n-k}] = 0. \quad (6)$$

Equation (6) shows that, in general, a_n depends upon all of the preceding coefficients $a_0, a_1, \ldots, a_{n-1}$. It also shows that we can successively compute $a_1, a_2, \ldots, a_n$ in terms of the coefficients in the series for $xp(x)$ and $x^2 q(x)$ provided that $F(r + 1), F(r + 2), \ldots, F(r + n)$ do not vanish. The only values of r for which $F(r)$ vanishes are $r = r_1$ and $r = r_2$; since $r_1 + n$ is not equal to r_1 or r_2 for $n \geq 1$, it follows that $F(r_1 + n) \neq 0$ for $n \geq 1$. Hence we can always determine one solution

$$y_1(x) = x^{r_1}\sum_{n=0}^{\infty}a_n(r_1)x^n. \quad (7)$$

Here we have introduced the notation $a_n(r_1)$ to indicate that the a_n have been determined from Eq. (6) with $r = r_1$. Also for definiteness we have taken a_0 to be one.

If r_2 is not equal to r_1, and $r_1 - r_2$ is not a positive integer, then $r_2 + n$ is not equal to r_1 for any value of $n \geq 1$; hence $F(r_2 + n) \neq 0$, and we can obtain a second solution

$$y_2(x) = x^{r_2}\sum_{n=0}^{\infty}a_n(r_2)x^n. \quad (8)$$

Before continuing we will make several remarks about the series solutions (7) and (8). Within their radii of convergence, the power series $\sum_{n=0}^{\infty}a_n(r_1)x^n$ and $\sum_{n=0}^{\infty}a_n(r_2)x^n$ define functions that are analytic at $x = 0$. Thus the singular behavior, if there is any, of the solutions y_1 and y_2 is determined by the terms x^{r_1} and x^{r_2} which multiply these two analytic functions respectively. To obtain real-valued solutions for $x < 0$, we can make the substitution $x = -\xi$ with $\xi > 0$. As we might expect from our discussion of the

Euler equation it turns out that we need only replace x^{r_1} in Eq. (7) and x^{r_2} in Eq. (8) by $|x|^{r_1}$ and $|x|^{r_2}$, respectively. Finally we note that if r_1 and r_2 are complex numbers, then they are necessarily complex conjugates and $r_2 \neq r_1 + N$. Thus we will be able to compute two series solutions of the form (2); however, they will be complex-valued functions of x. Real-valued solutions can be obtained by taking suitable linear combinations of y_1 and y_2.

If $r_2 = r_1$, we obtain only one solution of the form (2). A procedure for determining a second solution is discussed in Section 4.6.

If $r_1 - r_2 = N$, where N is a positive integer, then $F(r_2 + N) = F(r_1) = 0$, and we will not be able to determine a_N from Eq. (6) unless it happens that the sum in Eq. (6) also vanishes for $n = N$. If this is so, it can be shown (see Section 4.7) that a_N will be arbitrary and we can obtain a second series solution; if not, there is only one series solution of the form (2).

The next question to consider is the convergence of the infinite series in the formal solution. As we might expect this is related to the radii of convergence of the power series for $xp(x)$ and $x^2q(x)$. We summarize the results of our discussion and the additional conclusions about the convergence of the series solution in the following theorem.

Theorem 4.3.   *Consider the differential equation* (1)

$$x^2y'' + x[xp(x)]y' + [x^2q(x)]y = 0,$$

where $x = 0$ is a regular singular point. Then $xp(x)$ and $x^2q(x)$ are analytic at $x = 0$ with convergent power series expansion

$$xp(x) = \sum_{n=0}^{\infty} p_n x^n, \qquad x^2q(x) = \sum_{n=0}^{\infty} q_n x^n$$

for $|x| < \rho$ where ρ is some positive number. Let r_1 and r_2 be the roots of the indicial equation

$$F(r) = r(r - 1) + p_0 r + q_0 = 0,$$

with $r_1 \geq r_2$ if r_1 and r_2 are real. Then in either of the intervals $-\rho < x < 0$ or $0 < x < \rho$, there exists a solution of the form

$$y_1(x) = |x|^{r_1}\left[1 + \sum_{n=1}^{\infty} a_n(r_1)x^n \right] \qquad (9)$$

where the $a_n(r_1)$ are given by the recurrence relation (6) *with $a_0 = 1$ and $r = r_1$. If $r_1 - r_2$ is not zero or a positive integer, then in either of the intervals $-\rho < x < 0$ or $0 < x < \rho$, there exists a second linearly independent solution of the form*

$$y_2(x) = |x|^{r_2}\left[1 + \sum_{n=1}^{\infty} a_n(r_2)x^n \right]. \qquad (10)$$

The $a_n(r_2)$ are also determined by the recurrence relation (6) *with $a_0 = 1$ and $r = r_2$. The power series in Eqs.* (9) *and* (10) *converge for $|x| < \rho$.*

While it is beyond the scope of this text to prove this theorem, we can make several observations. To determine the roots r_1 and r_2 of the indicial equation, which play such an important role in the present theory, we need only determine p_0 and q_0 and then solve Eq. (5). These coefficients are given by

$$p_0 = \lim_{x \to 0} xp(x), \qquad q_0 = \lim_{x \to 0} x^2 q(x). \tag{11}$$

In practice, rather than remember the recurrence formula (6) for the a_n, we usually substitute the series (2) for y in Eq. (1), determine the values of r, and then explicitly calculate the a_n.

If $x = 0$ is a regular singular point of the equation

$$P(x)y'' + Q(x)y' + R(x)y = 0, \tag{12}$$

where the functions P, Q, and R are polynomials, then $xp(x) = xQ(x)/P(x)$ and $x^2 q(x) = x^2 R(x)/P(x)$. Thus

$$p_0 = \lim_{x \to 0} x \frac{Q(x)}{P(x)}, \qquad q_0 = \lim_{x \to 0} x^2 \frac{R(x)}{P(x)}. \tag{13}$$

Further, the radius of convergence ρ for the series in Eqs. (9) and (10) is at least equal to the distance from the origin to the nearest zero of P.

Example. Discuss the nature of the solutions of the equation

$$2x(1 + x)y'' + (3 + x)y' - xy = 0$$

in the neighborhood of the origin.

This equation is of the form (12) with $P(x) = 2x(1 + x)$, $Q(x) = 3 + x$, and $R(x) = -x$. The point $x = 0$ is a regular singular point, since

$$\lim_{x \to 0} x \frac{Q(x)}{P(x)} = \lim_{x \to 0} x \frac{3 + x}{2x(1 + x)} = \frac{3}{2},$$

$$\lim_{x \to 0} x^2 \frac{R(x)}{P(x)} = \lim_{x \to 0} x^2 \frac{-x}{2x(1 + x)} = 0.$$

Further from Eq. (13), $p_0 = 3/2$ and $q_0 = 0$. Thus the indicial equation is $r(r - 1) + (3/2)r = 0$, and the roots are $r_1 = 0$, $r_2 = -\frac{1}{2}$. Since these roots are not equal and do not differ by an integer there will be linearly independent solutions of the form

$$y_1(x) = 1 + \sum_{n=1}^{\infty} a_n(0)x^n \qquad \text{and} \qquad y_2(x) = |x|^{-1/2}\left[1 + \sum_{n=1}^{\infty} a_n(-\tfrac{1}{2})x^n\right],$$

for $0 < |x| < \rho$. A lower bound for the radius of convergence of the series is 1, the distance from $x = 0$ to $x = -1$, the other zero of $P(x)$. Notice that the solution y_1 is bounded as $x \to 0$, indeed is analytic there. On the other hand the second solution y_2 is unbounded as $x \to 0$.

PROBLEMS

1. Find all the regular singular points of each of the following differential equations. Determine the indicial equation and the exponents of the singularity at each regular singular point.

(a) $xy'' + 2xy' + 6e^x y = 0$

(b) $x^2 y'' - x(2 + x)y' + (2 + x^2)y = 0$

(c) $x(x - 1)y'' + 6x^2 y' + 3y = 0$

(d) $y'' + 4xy' + 6y = 0$

(e) $x^2 y'' + 3(\sin x)y' - 2y = 0$

(f) $2x(x + 2)y'' + y' - xy = 0$

(g) $x^2 y'' + \frac{1}{2}(x + \sin x)y' + y = 0$

(h) $(x + 1)^2 y'' + 3(x^2 - 1)y' + 3y = 0$

2. Show that

$$x^2 y'' + (\sin x)y' - (\cos x)y = 0$$

has a regular singular point at $x = 0$, and that the roots of the indicial equation are ± 1. Determine the first three nonzero terms in the series corresponding to the larger root.

3. Show that

$$(\ln x)y'' + \frac{1}{2}y' + y = 0$$

has a regular singular point at $x = 1$. Determine the roots of the indicial equation at $x = 1$. Determine the first three nonzero terms in the series $\sum_{n=0}^{\infty} a_n(x - 1)^{r+n}$ corresponding to the larger root. Take $x - 1 > 0$. What would you expect the radius of convergence of the series to be?

4. In several problems in mathematical physics (for example, the Schrödinger equation for a hydrogen atom) it is necessary to study the differential equation

$$x(1 - x)y'' + [\gamma - (1 + \alpha + \beta)x]y' - \alpha\beta y = 0, \qquad (i)$$

where α, β, and γ are constants. This equation is known as the *hypergeometric equation*.

(a) Show that $x = 0$ is a regular singular point, and that the roots of the indicial equation are 0 and $1 - \gamma$.

(b) Show that $x = 1$ is a regular singular point, and that the roots of the indicial equation are 0 and $\gamma - \alpha - \beta$.

(c) Assuming that $1 - \gamma$ is not a positive integer, show that in the neighborhood of $x = 0$ one solution of (i) is

$$y_1(x) = 1 + \frac{\alpha\beta}{\gamma \cdot 1!}x + \frac{\alpha(\alpha + 1)\beta(\beta + 1)}{\gamma(\gamma + 1)2!}x^2 + \cdots.$$

What would you expect the radius of convergence of this series to be?

(d) Assuming that $1 - \gamma$ is not an integer or zero, show that a second solution for $0 < x < 1$ is

$$y_2(x) = x^{(1-\gamma)}\left[1 + \frac{(\alpha - \gamma + 1)(\beta - \gamma + 1)}{(2 - \gamma)1!}x\right.$$

$$\left. + \frac{(\alpha - \gamma + 1)(\alpha - \gamma + 2)(\beta - \gamma + 1)(\beta - \gamma + 2)}{(2 - \gamma)(3 - \gamma)2!}x^2 + \cdots\right].$$

*(e) Show that the point at infinity is a regular singular point, and that the roots of the indicial equation are α and β. See Problem 10 of Section 4.3.

5. Consider the differential equation

$$x^3 y'' + \alpha x y' + \beta y = 0$$

where $\alpha \neq 0$ and β are real constants.

(a) Show that $x = 0$ is an irregular singular point.

(b) Show that if we attempt to determine a solution of the form $x^r \sum_{n=0}^{\infty} a_n x^n$, the indicial equation for r will be linear, and as a consequence there will be only one formal solution of this form.

6. Consider the differential equation

$$y'' + \frac{\alpha}{x^s} y' + \frac{\beta}{x^t} y = 0, \tag{i}$$

where $\alpha \neq 0$ and $\beta \neq 0$ are real numbers, and s and t are positive integers which for the moment are arbitrary.

(a) Show that if $s > 1$ or $t > 2$ the point $x = 0$ is an irregular singular point.

(b) Suppose we try to find a solution of Eq. (i) of the form

$$y = \sum_{n=0}^{\infty} a_n x^{r+n}, \qquad x > 0. \tag{ii}$$

Show that if $s = 2$ and $t = 2$ there is only one possible value of r for which there is a formal solution of Eq. (i) of the form (ii).

(c) Show that if $s = 1$ and $t = 3$ there are no solutions of Eq. (i) of the form (ii).

(d) Show that the maximum values of s and t for which the indicial equation is quadratic in r (and hence we can hope to find two solutions of the form (ii)) are $s = 1$ and $t = 2$. These are precisely the conditions that distinguish a "weak singularity," or a regular singular point from an irregular singular point, as we defined them in Section 4.3.

As a note of caution we should point out that while it is sometimes possible to obtain a formal series solution of the form (ii) at an irregular singular point, the series may not converge.

*4.6 SERIES SOLUTIONS NEAR A REGULAR SINGULAR POINT; $r_1 = r_2$ AND $r_1 - r_2 = N$

We now consider the cases in which the roots r_1 and r_2 of the indicial equation are equal or differ by a positive integer, $r_1 - r_2 = N$. If $r_1 = r_2$, we would expect by analogy with the Euler equation that the second solution will contain a logarithmic term. This may also be the case when the roots differ by an integer. The general situation, including the case in which r_1 and r_2 do not differ by an integer, is summarized in the following theorem.

Theorem 4.4.   *Consider the differential equation*

$$L[y] = x^2 y'' + x[xp(x)]y' + [x^2 q(x)]y = 0, \tag{1}$$

*where $x = 0$ is a regular singular point.   Then the functions $xp(x)$ and $x^2q(x)$
are analytic at $x = 0$ with power series representations*

$$xp(x) = \sum_{n=0}^{\infty} p_n x^n, \qquad x^2 q(x) = \sum_{n=0}^{\infty} q_n x^n, \tag{2}$$

*which converge for $|x| < \rho$, $\rho > 0$.   Let r_1 and r_2, where $r_1 \geq r_2$ if they are
real, be the roots of the indicial equation*

$$F(r) = r(r - 1) + p_0 r + q_0 = 0. \tag{3}$$

*Then in either of the intervals $-\rho < x < 0$ or $0 < x < \rho$, Eq. (1) has two
linearly independent solutions y_1 and y_2 of the following form.*

1. *If $r_1 - r_2$ is not an integer, then*

$$y_1(x) = |x|^{r_1} \left[1 + \sum_{n=1}^{\infty} a_n(r_1) x^n \right], \tag{4a}$$

$$y_2(x) = |x|^{r_2} \left[1 + \sum_{n=1}^{\infty} a_n(r_2) x^n \right]. \tag{4b}$$

2. *If $r_1 = r_2$, then*

$$y_1(x) = |x|^{r_1} \left[1 + \sum_{n=1}^{\infty} a_n(r_1) x^n \right], \tag{5a}$$

$$y_2(x) = y_1(x) \ln |x| + |x|^{r_1} \sum_{n=1}^{\infty} b_n(r_1) x^n. \tag{5b}$$

3. *If $r_1 - r_2 = N$, a positive integer, then*

$$y_1(x) = |x|^{r_1} \left[1 + \sum_{n=1}^{\infty} a_n(r_1) x^n \right], \tag{6a}$$

$$y_2(x) = a y_1(x) \ln |x| + |x|^{r_2} \left[1 + \sum_{n=1}^{\infty} c_n(r_2) x^n \right]. \tag{6b}$$

*The coefficients $a_n(r_1)$, $a_n(r_2)$, $b_n(r_1)$, $c_n(r_2)$, and the constant a can be de-
termined by substituting the form of the series solution for y in Eq. (1).   The
constant a may turn out to be zero.   Each of the series in Eqs. (4), (5), and (6)
converges for $|x| < \rho$ and defines a function that is analytic at $x = 0$.*

   The case in which $r_1 - r_2$ is not an integer was discussed in Section
4.5.1.   We turn now to the case $r_1 = r_2$, and assume that $x > 0$.   The case
$x < 0$ can be treated, as before, by letting $x = -\xi$.

   The method of finding the second solution is essentially the same as that
which we used in finding the second solution of the Euler equation (see
Section 4.4) when the roots of the indicial equation were equal.   We seek a
solution of Eq. (1) of the form

$$y = \phi(r, x) = x^r \sum_{n=0}^{\infty} a_n x^n = x^r \left(a_0 + \sum_{n=1}^{\infty} a_n x^n \right), \tag{7}$$

where we have written $y = \phi(r, x)$ to emphasize the fact that ϕ depends on the choice of r. If we substitute the series (2) for $xp(x)$ and $x^2q(x)$, compute and substitute for y' and y'' from Eq. (7), and finally collect terms, we obtain (see Eqs. (3) and (4) of Section 4.5.1)

$$L[\phi](r, x) = x^r a_0 F(r) + \sum_{n=1}^{\infty} \left\{ a_n F(r + n) + \sum_{k=0}^{n-1} a_k[(r + k)p_{n-k} + q_{n-k}] \right\} x^{r+n},$$

(8)

where

$$F(r) = r(r - 1) + p_0 r + q_0.$$

(9)

If the roots of the indicial equation are both equal to r_1, we can obtain one solution by setting r equal to r_1 and choosing the a_n so that each term of the series in Eq. (8) is zero.

To determine a second solution we will think of r as a continuous variable, and determine a_n as a function of r by requiring that the coefficient of x^{r+n}, $n \geq 1$, in Eq. (8) be zero. Then assuming $F(r + n) \neq 0$ we have

$$a_n(r) = - \frac{\sum_{k=0}^{n-1} a_k[(r + k)p_{n-k} + q_{n-k}]}{F(r + n)}, \qquad n \geq 1.$$

(10)

With this choice for $a_n(r)$ for $n \geq 1$, Eq. (8) reduces to

$$L[\phi](r, x) = a_0 x^r F(r).$$

(11)

Since r_1 is a repeated root of $F(r)$, it follows from Eq. (9) that $F(r) = (r - r_1)^2$. Setting $r = r_1$ in Eq. (11) we find that $L[\phi](r_1, x) = 0$; hence—as we already know—

$$y_1(x) = \phi(r_1, x) = x^{r_1} \left[a_0 + \sum_{n=1}^{\infty} a_n(r_1)x^n \right], \qquad x > 0,$$

(12)

is one solution of Eq. (1). But more important, it also follows from Eq. (11), just as for the Euler equation, that

$$L\left[\frac{\partial \phi}{\partial r} \right](r_1, x) = a_0 \frac{\partial}{\partial r} [x^r(r - r_1)^2] \Big|_{r=r_1}$$

$$= a_0[(r - r_1)^2 x^r \ln x + 2(r - r_1)x^r]|_{r=r_1}$$

$$= 0.$$

(13)

Hence, a second solution of Eq. (1) is

$$y_2(x) = \frac{\partial \phi(r, x)}{\partial r} \Big|_{r=r_1} = \frac{\partial}{\partial r} \left\{ x^r \left[a_0 + \sum_{n=1}^{\infty} a_n(r)x^n \right] \right\} \Big|_{r=r_1}$$

$$= x^{r_1} \ln x \left[a_0 + \sum_{n=1}^{\infty} a_n(r_1)x^n \right] + x^{r_1} \sum_{n=1}^{\infty} a_n'(r_1)x^n$$

$$= y_1(x) \ln x + x^{r_1} \sum_{n=1}^{\infty} a_n'(r_1)x^n, \qquad x > 0,$$

(14)

where $a_n'(r_1)$ denotes da_n/dr evaluated at $r = r_1$.

Note that in addition to the assumptions we have already made, we have also assumed that it is permissible to differentiate the series $\sum\limits_{n=1}^{\infty} a_n(r)x^n$ term by term with respect to r. It is certainly not a trivial matter to determine $a_n(r_1)$ and $a_n'(r_1)$; however, the determination of two solutions of a second order differential equation with a regular singular point is not a trivial problem.

Also notice that the $b_n(r_1)$ of Eq. (5b) are given by $b_n(r_1) = a_n'(r_1)$. Thus the b_n can be determined either directly by substituting the expression (5b) for y in Eq. (1) or by determining $a_n(r)$ and then computing $a_n'(r_1)$. In some cases the former may be more convenient, particularly if the formula for $a_n(r)$ is complicated, or if only the first few terms in the series for $y_2(x)$ are needed. In other cases it may be more convenient to compute $a_n'(r_1)$. As a third alternative the method of reduction of order can be used.

For the case $r_1 - r_2 = N$, a positive integer, the necessary arguments to derive the form (6b) of the second solution are considerably more complicated and will not be given. However, we note that if we assume $y_2(x) = \sum\limits_{n=0}^{\infty} a_n x^{r_2+n}$, then there may be difficulty in computing $a_N(r_2)$ from Eq. (10) since $F(r_2 + N) = F(r_1) = 0$. This difficulty is circumvented by choosing a_0, which can be chosen arbitrarily, to be $r - r_2$. Following an analysis similar to that for the case $r_1 = r_2$, it turns out that the solution is of the form (6b) with

$$c_n(r_2) = \frac{d}{dr}[(r - r_2)a_n(r)]\Big|_{r=r_2}, \qquad n = 1, 2, \ldots \qquad (15)$$

where $a_n(r)$ is given by Eq. (10), and

$$a = \lim_{r \to r_2}(r - r_2)a_N(r). \qquad (16)$$

If $a_N(r_2)$ is finite then $a = 0$, and there is no logarithmic term in y_2. This procedure is discussed in Coddington [Chapter 4].

In practice the best way to determine whether a will be zero in the second solution is simply to try to compute the a_n corresponding to the root r_2 and to see whether it is possible to determine $a_N(r_2)$. If so, there is no further problem. If not, we must use the form (6b) with $a \neq 0$.

In the next section we will give three examples that illustrate the cases $r_1 = r_2$, $r_1 - r_2 = N$ with a zero, and $r_1 - r_2 = N$ with a nonzero.

*4.7 BESSEL'S EQUATION

In this section we consider three special cases of Bessel's equation,

$$x^2y'' + xy' + (x^2 - v^2)y = 0, \qquad (1)$$

where v is a constant, which illustrate the theory discussed in Section 4.6. Clearly $x = 0$ is a regular singular point. For simplicity we consider only the case $x > 0$.

Bessel Equation of Order Zero. This example illustrates the situation in which the roots of the indicial equation are equal. Setting $v = 0$ in Eq. (1) gives

$$L[y] = x^2 y'' + xy' + x^2 y = 0. \tag{2}$$

Substituting

$$y = \phi(r, x) = a_0 x^r + \sum_{n=1}^{\infty} a_n x^{r+n}, \tag{3}$$

we obtain

$$L[\phi](r, x) = \sum_{n=0}^{\infty} a_n[(n + r)(n + r - 1) + (n + r)]x^{r+n} + \sum_{n=0}^{\infty} a_n x^{r+n+2}$$

$$= a_0[r(r - 1) + r]x^r + a_1[(r + 1)r + (r + 1)]x^{r+1}$$

$$+ \sum_{n=2}^{\infty} \{a_n[(n + r)(n + r - 1) + (n + r)] + a_{n-2}\}x^{r+n} = 0. \tag{4}$$

The roots of the indicial equation $F(r) = r(r - 1) + r = 0$ are $r_1 = 0$ and $r_2 = 0$; hence we have the case of equal roots. The recurrence relation is

$$a_n(r) = \frac{-a_{n-2}(r)}{(n + r)(n + r - 1) + (n + r)} = -\frac{a_{n-2}(r)}{(n + r)^2}, \qquad n \geq 2. \tag{5}$$

To determine $y_1(x)$ we set r equal to 0. Then from Eq. (4) it follows that $a_1 = 0$. Hence from Eq. (5), $a_3 = a_5 = a_7 = \cdots = a_{2n+1} = \cdots = 0$. Further

$$a_n(0) = -a_{n-2}(0)/n^2, \qquad n = 2, 4, 6, 8, \ldots,$$

or letting $n = 2m$,

$$a_{2m}(0) = -\frac{a_{2m-2}(0)}{(2m)^2}$$

$$= +\frac{a_{2m-4}(0)}{(2m)^2(2m - 2)^2} = \frac{(-1)a_{2m-6}(0)}{(2m)^2(2m - 2)^2(2m - 4)^2}$$

$$\vdots$$

$$= \frac{(-1)^m a_0}{(2m)^2(2m - 2)^2(2m - 4)^2 \cdots 2^2}$$

$$= \frac{(-1)^m a_0}{2^{2m}(m!)^2}, \qquad m = 1, 2, 3, \ldots. \tag{6}$$

Hence

$$y_1(x) = a_0 \left[1 + \sum_{m=1}^{\infty} \frac{(-1)^m x^{2m}}{2^{2m}(m!)^2}\right], \qquad x > 0. \tag{7}$$

The function in brackets is known as the *Bessel function of the first kind of order zero*, and is denoted by $J_0(x)$. It follows from Theorem 4.4 that the series converges for all x, and that J_0 is analytic at $x = 0$. Some of the important properties of J_0 are discussed in the problems.

In this example we will determine $y_2(x)$ by computing $a_n'(0)$. The alternate procedure in which we simply substitute the form (5b) of Section 4.6 in Eq. (2), and then determine the b_n is discussed in Problem 7. First we note from Eq. (4) that since $(r + 1)^2 a_1(r) = 0$ it follows that not only does $a_1(0) = 0$, but also $a_1'(0) = 0$. It is easy to deduce from the recurrence relation (5) that $a_3'(0) = a_5'(0) = \cdots = a_{2n+1}'(0) = \cdots = 0$; hence we need only compute $a_{2m}'(0)$, $m = 1, 2, 3, \ldots$. From Eq. (5)

$$a_{2m}(r) = -\frac{a_{2m-2}(r)}{(2m + r)^2} = +\frac{a_{2m-4}(r)}{(2m + r)^2(2m - 2 + r)^2}$$

$$\vdots$$

$$= \frac{(-1)^m a_0}{(2m + r)^2(2m - 2 + r)^2(2m - 4 + r)^2 \cdots (2 + r)^2},$$
$$m = 1, 2, 3, \ldots. \quad (8)$$

The computation of $a_{2m}'(r)$ can be carried out most conveniently by noting that if

$$f(x) = (x - \alpha_1)^{\beta_1}(x - \alpha_2)^{\beta_2}(x - \alpha_3)^{\beta_3} \cdots (x - \alpha_n)^{\beta_n}$$

then

$$f'(x) = \beta_1(x - \alpha_1)^{\beta_1 - 1}[(x - \alpha_2)^{\beta_2} \cdots (x - \alpha_n)^{\beta_n}]$$
$$+ \beta_2(x - \alpha_2)^{\beta_2 - 1}[(x - \alpha_1)^{\beta_1}(x - \alpha_3)^{\beta_3} \cdots (x - \alpha_n)^{\beta_n}] + \cdots;$$

and hence for x not equal to $\alpha_1, \alpha_2, \ldots, \alpha_n$

$$\frac{f'(x)}{f(x)} = \frac{\beta_1}{x - \alpha_1} + \frac{\beta_2}{x - \alpha_2} + \cdots + \frac{\beta_n}{x - \alpha_n}.$$

Thus, from Eq. (8)

$$\frac{a_{2m}'(r)}{a_{2m}(r)} = -2\left(\frac{1}{2m + r} + \frac{1}{2m - 2 + r} + \cdots + \frac{1}{2 + r}\right),$$

and setting r equal to 0 we obtain

$$a_{2m}'(0) = -2\left[\frac{1}{2m} + \frac{1}{2(m - 1)} + \frac{1}{2(m - 2)} + \cdots + \frac{1}{2}\right]a_{2m}(0).$$

Substituting for $a_{2m}(0)$ from Eq. (6), and letting

$$H_m = \frac{1}{m} + \frac{1}{m - 1} + \cdots + \frac{1}{2} + 1, \quad (9)$$

we obtain finally

$$a_{2m}'(0) = -H_m \frac{(-1)^m a_0}{2^{2m}(m!)^2}, \quad m = 1, 2, 3, \ldots. \quad (10)$$

The second solution of the Bessel equation of order zero is obtained by setting $a_0 = 1$, and substituting for $y_1(x)$ and $a_{2m}'(0) = b_{2m}(0)$ in Eq. (5b) of

Section 4.6. We obtain

$$y_2(x) = J_0(x) \ln x + \sum_{m=1}^{\infty} \frac{(-1)^{m+1} H_m}{2^{2m}(m!)^2} x^{2m}, \qquad x > 0. \qquad (11)$$

In place of y_2, the second solution is usually taken to be a certain linear combination of J_0 and y_2. It is known as the Bessel function of the second kind of order zero, and is denoted by Y_0. Following Copson [Chapter 12], we define*

$$Y_0(x) = \frac{2}{\pi} [y_2(x) + (\gamma - \ln 2) J_0(x)]. \qquad (12)$$

Here γ is a constant, known as the Euler-Máscheroni (1750–1800) constant; it is defined by the equation

$$\gamma = \lim_{n \to \infty} (H_n - \ln n) \cong 0.5772. \qquad (13)$$

Substituting for $y_2(x)$ in Eq. (12) we obtain

$$Y_0(x) = \frac{2}{\pi} \left[\left(\gamma + \ln \frac{x}{2} \right) J_0(x) + \sum_{m=1}^{\infty} \frac{(-1)^{m+1} H_m}{2^{2m}(m!)^2} x^{2m} \right], \qquad x > 0. \qquad (14)$$

The general solution of the Bessel equation of order zero for $x > 0$ is

$$y = c_1 J_0(x) + c_2 Y_0(x).$$

Notice that since $J_0(x) \to 1$ as $x \to 0$, $Y_0(x)$ has a logarithmic singularity at $x = 0$; that is, $Y_0(x)$ behaves as $(2/\pi) \ln x$ when $x \to 0$ through positive values. Thus if we are interested in solutions of Bessel's equation of order zero which are finite at the origin, which is often the case, we must discard Y_0. The graphs of the functions J_0 and Y_0 are shown in Figure 4.2.

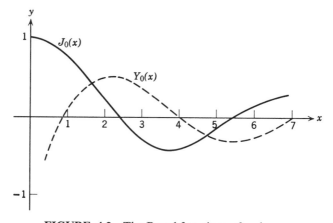

FIGURE 4.2   The Bessel functions of order zero.

* Other authors use other definitions for Y_0. The present choice for Y_0 is also known as the Weber (1842–1913) function.

Bessel Equation of Order One-Half. This example illustrates the situation in which the roots of the indicial equation differ by a positive integer, but there is no logarithmic term in the second solution. Setting $v = \frac{1}{2}$ in Eq. (1) gives

$$L[y] = x^2 y'' + x y' + (x^2 - \tfrac{1}{4})y = 0. \tag{15}$$

If we substitute the series (3) for $y = \phi(r, x)$, we obtain

$$L[\phi](r, x) = \sum_{n=0}^{\infty} [(r+n)(r+n-1) + (r+n) - \tfrac{1}{4}]a_n x^{r+n} + \sum_{n=0}^{\infty} a_n x^{r+n+2}$$

$$= (r^2 - \tfrac{1}{4})a_0 x^r + [(r+1)^2 - \tfrac{1}{4}]a_1 x^{r+1}$$

$$+ \sum_{n=2}^{\infty} \{[(r+n)^2 - \tfrac{1}{4}]a_n + a_{n-2}\}x^{r+n} = 0. \tag{16}$$

The roots of the indicial equation are $r_1 = \frac{1}{2}$, $r_2 = -\frac{1}{2}$; hence the roots differ by an integer. The recurrence relation is

$$[(r+n)^2 - \tfrac{1}{4}]a_n = -a_{n-2}, \qquad n \geq 2. \tag{17}$$

Corresponding to the larger root $r_1 = \frac{1}{2}$ we find from Eq. (16) that $a_1 = 0$, and hence from Eq. (17) that $a_3 = a_5 = \cdots = a_{2n+1} = \cdots = 0$. Further, for $r = \frac{1}{2}$

$$a_n = -\frac{a_{n-2}}{n(n+1)}, \qquad n = 2, 4, 6, \ldots,$$

or letting $n = 2m$,

$$a_{2m} = -\frac{a_{2m-2}}{(2m+1)2m} = \frac{a_{2m-4}}{(2m+1)(2m)(2m-1)(2m-2)}$$

$$\cdot$$
$$\cdot$$
$$\cdot$$

$$= \frac{(-1)^m a_0}{(2m+1)!}, \qquad m = 1, 2, 3, \ldots. \tag{18}$$

Hence

$$y_1(x) = x^{1/2}\left[1 + \sum_{m=1}^{\infty} \frac{(-1)^m x^{2m}}{(2m+1)!}\right]$$

$$= x^{-1/2} \sum_{m=0}^{\infty} \frac{(-1)^m x^{2m+1}}{(2m+1)!}, \qquad x > 0. \tag{19}$$

The infinite series in Eq. (19) is precisely the Taylor series for $\sin x$; hence one solution of the Bessel equation of order one-half is $x^{-\frac{1}{2}} \sin x$. The Bessel function of the first kind of order one-half, $J_{\frac{1}{2}}$, is defined as $(2/\pi)^{\frac{1}{2}}y_1$. Thus

$$J_{\frac{1}{2}}(x) = \left(\frac{2}{\pi x}\right)^{\frac{1}{2}} \sin x, \qquad x > 0. \tag{20}$$

Corresponding to the root $r_2 = -\frac{1}{2}$ it is possible that we may have difficulty in computing a_1 since $N = r_1 - r_2 = 1$. However, it is clear from Eq. (16) that for $r = -\frac{1}{2}$ the coefficients of a_0 and a_1 are zero, and hence a_0 and a_1 can be chosen arbitrarily. Then corresponding to a_0 we obtain $a_2, a_4, \ldots$ from the recurrence relation (17); and corresponding to a_1 we obtain $a_3, a_5, a_7, \ldots$. Hence the second solution will not involve a logarithmic term. It is left as an exercise for the student to show from Eq. (17) that for $r = -\frac{1}{2}$,

$$a_{2n} = \frac{(-1)^n a_0}{(2n)!}, \qquad n = 1, 2, \ldots,$$

and

$$a_{2n+1} = \frac{(-1)^n a_1}{(2n+1)!}, \qquad n = 1, 2, \ldots.$$

Hence

$$y_2(x) = x^{-\frac{1}{2}} \left[a_0 \sum_{n=0}^{\infty} \frac{(-1)^n x^{2n}}{(2n)!} + a_1 \sum_{n=0}^{\infty} \frac{(-1)^n x^{2n+1}}{(2n+1)!} \right]$$

$$= a_0 \frac{\cos x}{x^{\frac{1}{2}}} + a_1 \frac{\sin x}{x^{\frac{1}{2}}}, \qquad x > 0. \tag{21}$$

The constant a_1 simply introduces a multiple of $y_1(x)$. The second linearly independent solution of the Bessel equation of order one-half is usually taken to be the solution generated by a_0 with $a_0 = (2/\pi)^{\frac{1}{2}}$. It is denoted by $J_{-\frac{1}{2}}$. Then

$$J_{-\frac{1}{2}}(x) = \left(\frac{2}{\pi x} \right)^{\frac{1}{2}} \cos x, \qquad x > 0. \tag{22}$$

The general solution of Eq. (15) is $y = c_1 J_{\frac{1}{2}}(x) + c_2 J_{-\frac{1}{2}}(x)$.

Bessel Equation of Order One. This example illustrates the situation in which the roots of the indicial equation differ by a positive integer and the second solution involves a logarithmic term. Setting $\nu = 1$ in Eq. (1) gives

$$L[y] = x^2 y'' + x y' + (x^2 - 1)y = 0. \tag{23}$$

If we substitute for $y = \phi(r, x)$ the series (3), and collect terms as in the previous examples, we obtain

$$L[\phi](r, x) = a_0(r^2 - 1)x^r + a_1[(r+1)^2 - 1]x^{r+1}$$

$$+ \sum_{n=2}^{\infty} \{[(r+n)^2 - 1]a_n + a_{n-2}\}x^{r+n} = 0. \tag{24}$$

The roots of the indicial equation are $r_1 = 1$ and $r_2 = -1$. The recurrence relation is

$$[(r+n)^2 - 1]a_n(r) = -a_{n-2}(r), \qquad n \geq 2. \tag{25}$$

Corresponding to the larger root $r = 1$ the recurrence relation is

$$a_n = -\frac{a_{n-2}}{(n+2)n}, \qquad n = 2, 4, 6, \ldots.$$

We also find from Eq. (24) that $a_1 = 0$, and hence from the recurrence relation $a_3 = a_5 = \cdots = 0$. For even values of n, let $n = 2m$; then

$$a_{2m} = -\frac{a_{2m-2}}{2^2(m+1)m} = +\frac{a_{2m-4}}{2^4(m+1)m \cdot m(m-1)}$$

$$\cdot$$
$$\cdot$$
$$\cdot$$

$$= \frac{(-1)^m a_0}{2^{2m}(m+1)! \, m!}, \qquad m = 1, 2, 3, \ldots. \tag{26}$$

With $a_0 = 1$ we have

$$y_1(x) = x \sum_{m=0}^{\infty} \frac{(-1)^m x^{2m}}{2^{2m}(m+1)! \, m!}. \tag{27}$$

The Bessel function of the first kind of order one is usually taken to be $\frac{1}{2}y_1$ and is denoted by J_1:

$$J_1(x) = \frac{1}{2}y_1(x) = \frac{x}{2} \sum_{m=0}^{\infty} \frac{(-1)^m x^{2m}}{2^{2m}(m+1)! \, m!}. \tag{28}$$

The series converges absolutely for all x; hence the function J_1 is defined for all x.

In determining a second solution of Bessel's equation of order one, we will illustrate the method of direct substitution. According to Theorem 4.4 we assume that

$$y_2(x) = aJ_1(x) \ln x + x^{-1}\left[1 + \sum_{n=1}^{\infty} b_n x^n\right], \qquad x > 0. \tag{29}$$

Computing $y_2'(x)$, $y_2''(x)$, substituting in Eq. (23), and making use of the fact that J_1 is a solution of Eq. (23) gives

$$2axJ_1'(x) + \sum_{n=0}^{\infty} [(n-1)(n-2)b_n + (n-1)b_n - b_n]x^{n-1} + \sum_{n=0}^{\infty} b_n x^{n+1} = 0 \tag{30}$$

where $b_0 = 1$. Substituting for $J_1(x)$ from Eq. (28), shifting the indices of summation in the two series, and carrying out several steps of algebra gives

$$-b_1 + [0 \cdot b_2 + b_0]x + \sum_{n=2}^{\infty} [(n^2-1)b_{n+1} + b_{n-1}]x^n$$

$$= -a\left[x + \sum_{m=1}^{\infty} \frac{(-1)^m(2m+1)x^{2m+1}}{2^{2m}(m+1)! \, m!}\right]. \tag{31}$$

From Eq. (31) we observe first that $b_1 = 0$, and $a = -b_0 = -1$. Next since there are only odd powers of x on the right, the coefficient of each even power of x on the left must be zero. Thus, since $b_1 = 0$, we have $b_3 = b_5 = \cdots = 0$. Corresponding to the odd powers of x we obtain the recurrence relation (let $n = 2m + 1$)

$$[(2m + 1)^2 - 1]b_{2m+2} + b_{2m} = \frac{(-1)(-1)^m(2m + 1)}{2^{2m}(m + 1)!\, m!}, \qquad m = 1, 2, 3, \ldots.$$

$$(32)$$

When we set $m = 1$ in Eq. (32) we obtain

$$(3^2 - 1)b_4 + b_2 = (-1)3/(2^2 \cdot 2!).$$

Notice that b_2 can be selected *arbitrarily*, and then this equation determines b_4. Also notice that in the equation for the coefficient of x, b_2 appeared multiplied by 0, and that equation was used to determine a. That b_2 is arbitrary is not surprising, since b_2 is the coefficient of x in the expression $x^{-1}\left[1 + \sum_{n=1}^{\infty} b_n x^n\right]$. Consequently, b_2 simply generates a multiple of J_1, and y_2 is only determined up to an additive multiple of J_1. In accord with the usual practice we choose $b_2 = 1/2^2$. Then we obtain

$$b_4 = \frac{-1}{2^4 \cdot 2}\left[\tfrac{3}{2} + 1\right] = \frac{-1}{2^4 2!}\left[(1 + \tfrac{1}{2}) + 1\right]$$

$$= \frac{(-1)}{2^4 \cdot 2!}(H_2 + H_1).$$

Although it is not an easy task to show, the solution of the recurrence relation (32) is

$$b_{2m} = \frac{(-1)(-1)^m(H_m + H_{m-1})}{2^{2m}m!\,(m - 1)!}, \qquad m = 1, 2, \ldots$$

with the understanding that $H_0 = 1$. Thus

$$y_2(x) = -J_1(x)\ln x + \frac{1}{x}\left[1 - \sum_{m=1}^{\infty}\frac{(-1)^m(H_m + H_{m-1})}{2^{2m}m!\,(m - 1)!}x^{2m}\right], \qquad x > 0.$$

$$(33)$$

The calculation of $y_2(x)$ using the alternate procedure [see Eqs. (15) and (16) of Section 4.6] in which we determine the $c_n'(r_2)$ is also fairly complicated. However, the latter procedure does yield the general formula for the b_{2m} without the necessity of solving a recurrence relation of the form (32). In this regard the reader may wish to compare the calculations of the second solution of Bessel's equation of order zero in the text and in Problem 7.

The second solution of Eq. (23), the Bessel function of the second kind of order one, Y_1, is usually taken to be a certain linear combination of J_1

and y_2. Following Copson [Chapter 12], Y_1 is defined as

$$Y_1(x) = \frac{2}{\pi}[-y_2(x) + (\gamma - \ln 2)J_1(x)], \tag{34}$$

where γ, the Euler-Máscheroni constant, is defined in Eq. (13). The general solution of Eq. (23) for $x > 0$ is

$$y = c_1 J_1(x) + c_2 Y_1(x).$$

Notice that while J_1 is analytic at $x = 0$, the second solution Y_1 becomes unbounded in the same manner as $1/x$ as $x \to 0$.

PROBLEMS

1. Show that each of the following differential equations has a regular singular point at $x = 0$, and determine two linearly independent solutions for $x > 0$.

(a) $x^2 y'' + 2xy' + xy = 0$ (b) $x^2 y'' + 3xy' + (1 + x)y = 0$

(c) $x^2 y'' + xy' + 2xy = 0$ (d) $x^2 y'' + 4xy' + (2 + x)y = 0$

2. Find two linearly independent solutions of the Bessel equation of order $\frac{3}{2}$,

$$x^2 y'' + xy' + (x^2 - \tfrac{9}{4})y = 0,$$

for $x > 0$.

3. Show that the Bessel equation of order one-half,

$$x^2 y'' + xy' + (x^2 - \tfrac{1}{4})y = 0, \qquad x > 0,$$

can be reduced to the equation

$$v'' + v = 0$$

by the change of dependent variable $y = x^{-1/2}v(x)$. From this conclude that $y_1(x) = x^{-1/2} \cos x$ and $y_2(x) = x^{-1/2} \sin x$ are solutions of the Bessel equation of order one-half.

4. Show directly that the series for $J_0(x)$, Eq. (7), converges absolutely for all x.

5. Show directly that the series for $J_1(x)$, Eq. (28), converges absolutely for all x and that $J_0'(x) = -J_1(x)$.

6. Consider the Bessel equation of order ν

$$x^2 y'' + xy' + (x^2 - \nu^2)y = 0, \qquad x > 0.$$

Take ν real and greater than zero.

(a) Show that $x = 0$ is a regular singular point, and that the roots of the indicial equation are ν and $-\nu$.

(b) Corresponding to the larger root ν, show that one solution is

$$y_1(x) = x^\nu \left[1 + \sum_{m=1}^{\infty} \frac{(-1)^m}{m!\,(m+\nu)(m+\nu-1)\cdots(2+\nu)(1+\nu)} \left(\frac{x}{2}\right)^{2m} \right].$$

(c) If 2ν is not an integer show that a second solution is

$$y_2(x) = x^{-\nu}\left[1 + \sum_{m=1}^{\infty} \frac{(-1)^m}{m!\,(m-\nu)(m-\nu-1)\cdots(2-\nu)(1-\nu)} \left(\frac{x}{2}\right)^{2m}\right].$$

Note that $y_1(x)$ is analytic at $x = 0$, and that $y_2(x)$ is unbounded as $x \to 0$.

(d) Verify by direct methods that the power series in the expressions for $y_1(x)$ and $y_2(x)$ converge absolutely for all x. Also verify that y_2 is a solution provided only that ν is not an integer.

7. In this section we showed that one solution of Bessel's equation of order zero,

$$L[y] = x^2y'' + xy' + x^2y = 0$$

is J_0, where $J_0(x)$ is given by Eq. (7) with $a_0 = 1$. According to Theorem 4.4 a second solution will have the form $(x > 0)$

$$y_2(x) = J_0(x)\ln x + \sum_{n=1}^{\infty} b_nx^n.$$

(a) Show that

$$L[y_2](x) = \sum_{n=2}^{\infty} n(n-1)b_nx^n + \sum_{n=1}^{\infty} nb_nx^n + \sum_{n=1}^{\infty} b_nx^{n+2} + 2xJ_0'(x). \qquad \text{(i)}$$

(b) Substituting the series representation for $J_0(x)$ in Eq. (i), show that

$$b_1x + 2^2b_2x^2 + \sum_{n=3}^{\infty} (n^2b_n + b_{n-2})x^n = -2\sum_{n=1}^{\infty} \frac{(-1)^n2nx^{2n}}{2^{2n}(n!)^2}. \qquad \text{(ii)}$$

(c) Note that only even powers of x appear on the right-hand side of Eq. (ii). Show that $b_1 = b_3 = b_5 = \cdots = 0$, $b_2 = 1/2^2(1!)^2$, and that

$$(2n)^2b_{2n} + b_{2n-2} = -2(-1)^n(2n)/2^{2n}(n!)^2, \qquad n = 2, 3, 4, \ldots.$$

Deduce that

$$b_4 = \frac{-1}{2^24^2}\left(1 + \tfrac{1}{2}\right) \qquad \text{and} \qquad b_6 = \frac{1}{2^24^26^2}\left(1 + \tfrac{1}{2} + \tfrac{1}{3}\right).$$

The general solution of the recurrence relation is $b_{2n} = (-1)^{n+1}H_n/2^{2n}(n!)^2$, and substituting in the expression for $y_2(x)$ we obtain the solution given in Eq. (11).

8. By a suitable change of variables it is often possible to transform a differential equation with variable coefficients into a Bessel equation of a certain order. For example, show that a solution of

$$x^2y'' + (\alpha^2\beta^2x^{2\beta} + \tfrac{1}{4} - \nu^2\beta^2)y = 0, \qquad x > 0$$

is given by $y = x^{1/2}f(\alpha x^\beta)$ where $f(\xi)$ is a solution of the Bessel equation of order ν.

9. Using the result of Problem 8 show that the general solution of the Airy equation

$$y'' - xy = 0, \qquad x > 0$$

is $y = x^{1/2}[c_1f_1(\tfrac{2}{3}x^{3/2}) + c_2f_2(\tfrac{2}{3}x^{3/2})]$ where $f_1(\xi)$ and $f_2(\xi)$ are linearly independent solutions of the Bessel equation of order one-third.

10. It can be shown that J_0 has infinitely many zeros for $x > 0$. In particular the first three zeros are approximately 2.405, 5.520, and 8.653 (see Figure 4.2, page 194). Letting $\lambda_j, j = 1, 2, \ldots$, denote the zeros of J_0, it follows that

$$J_0(\lambda_j x) = \begin{cases} 1, & x = 0, \\ 0, & x = 1. \end{cases}$$

Verify that $y = J_0(\lambda_j x)$ satisfies the differential equation

$$y'' + \frac{1}{x}y' + \lambda_j^2 y = 0, \qquad x > 0.$$

Hence show that

$$\int_0^1 xJ_0(\lambda_i x)J_0(\lambda_j x)\, dx = 0 \qquad \text{if} \qquad \lambda_i \neq \lambda_j.$$

This important property of $J_0(\lambda_i x)$, known as the orthogonality property, is useful in solving boundary value problems. See Sections 11.3 and 11.6.
Hint: Write the differential equation for $J_0(\lambda_i x)$. Multiply it by $xJ_0(\lambda_j x)$ and subtract it from $xJ_0(\lambda_i x)$ times the differential equation for $J_0(\lambda_j x)$. Then integrate from 0 to 1.

REFERENCES

Coddington, E. A., *An Introduction to Ordinary Differential Equations*, Prentice-Hall, Englewood Cliffs, N.J., 1961.

Copson, E. T., *An Introduction to the Theory of Functions of a Complex Variable*, Oxford University, Oxford, 1935.

Proofs of Theorems 4.1, 4.3, and 4.4 can be found in intermediate or advanced books; for example, see Chapters 3 and 4 of Coddington, or Chapters 3 and 4 of

Rainville, E. D., *Intermediate Differential Equations*, 2nd ed., Macmillan, New York, 1964.

Also see these texts for a discussion of the point at infinity, which was mentioned in Problem 10 of Section 4.3. The behavior of solutions near an irregular singular point is an even more advanced topic; a brief discussion can be found in Chapter 5 of

Coddington, E. A. and Levinson, N., *Theory of Ordinary Differential Equations*, McGraw-Hill, New York, 1955.

More complete discussions of the Bessel equation, the Legendre equation, and many of the other named equations can be found in advanced books on differential equations, methods of applied mathematics, and special functions. A text dealing with special functions such as the Legendre polynomials, the Bessel functions, etc., is

Hochstadt, H., *Special Functions of Mathematical Physics*, Holt, Rinehart & Winston, New York, 1961.

Higher Order Linear Equations

5.1 INTRODUCTION

In this chapter we will extend the theory of second order linear equations developed in Chapter 3 to higher order linear equations. An nth order linear differential equation is an equation of the form

$$P_0(x)\frac{d^n y}{dx^n} + P_1(x)\frac{d^{n-1}y}{dx^{n-1}} + \cdots + P_{n-1}(x)\frac{dy}{dx} + P_n(x)y = G(x). \quad (1)$$

We will assume, unless otherwise stated, that the functions $P_0, \ldots, P_n$, and G are continuous real-valued functions on some interval $\alpha < x < \beta$, and that P_0 is nowhere zero in the interval. Then dividing Eq. (1) by $P_0(x)$ we obtain

$$L[y] = \frac{d^n y}{dx^n} + p_1(x)\frac{d^{n-1}y}{dx^{n-1}} + \cdots + p_{n-1}(x)\frac{dy}{dx} + p_n(x)y = g(x), \quad (2)$$

where, using the same notation as in Chapter 3, we have introduced the linear differential operator L. The mathematical theory associated with Eq. (2) is completely analogous to that for the second order linear equation; for this reason we shall, for the most part, simply state the results for the nth order linear equation. The proofs of most of the results are also similar to those for the second order linear equation and are usually left as exercises.

First we note that since Eq. (2) involves the nth derivative of y with respect to x, it will, so to speak, require n integrations to solve Eq. (2). Each of these integrations introduces an arbitrary constant. Hence we can expect that to obtain a unique solution it is necessary to specify n initial conditions, say

$$y(x_0) = y_0, \, y'(x_0) = y_0', \, \ldots, y^{(n-1)}(x_0) = y_0^{(n-1)}, \quad (3)$$

where x_0 may be any point in the interval $\alpha < x < \beta$ and $y_0, y_0', \ldots, y_0^{(n-1)}$ is any set of prescribed real constants. That there does exist such a solution and that it is unique is assured by the following existence and uniqueness theorem.

Theorem 5.1. *If the functions $p_1, p_2, \ldots, p_n$, and g are continuous on the open interval $\alpha < x < \beta$, then there exists one and only one function $y = \phi(x)$ satisfying Eq. (2) on the interval $\alpha < x < \beta$ and the prescribed initial conditions (3).*

The proof of this theorem will not be given here; however, we note that if the functions $p_1, p_2, \ldots, p_n$ are constants we will actually construct the solution of Eq. (2) satisfying the initial conditions (3), (see Sections 5.3 and 5.5). Even though we know a solution in this case, we do not know it is unique without the use of Theorem 5.1. A proof of the complete theorem can be found in Ince [Section 3.32] or Coddington [Chapter 6].

As in the corresponding second order problem, we will first discuss the problem of solving the homogeneous or complementary equation

$$y^{(n)} + p_1(x)y^{(n-1)} + \cdots + p_{n-1}(x)y' + p_n(x)y = 0. \tag{4}$$

The general theory of the homogeneous equation (4) is discussed in Section 5.2, and a method of solving Eq. (4) when the p_j are constants is given in Section 5.3. Next we will consider the problem of finding a particular solution y_p of the nonhomogeneous equation (2). The method of undetermined coefficients and the method of variation of parameters for determining a particular solution of Eq. (2) are discussed in Sections 5.4 and 5.5, respectively.

PROBLEMS

1. Assuming that the functions $p_1, \ldots, p_n$ are continuous on an interval including the origin, and that $y = \phi(x)$ is a solution of the initial value problem

$$y^{(n)} + p_1(x)y^{(n-1)} + \cdots + p_n(x)y = 0, \qquad y(0) = y_0, \ldots, y^{(n-1)}(0) = y_0^{(n-1)},$$

determine $\phi^{(n)}(0)$. Show that if $p_1, \ldots, p_n$ are differentiable at $x = 0$, then $\phi^{(n+1)}(0)$ can be determined in terms of the initial data.

2. We can expect by analogy with the first order and second order differential equations that under suitable conditions on f the nth order differential equation $y^{(n)} = f(x, y, y', y'', \ldots, y^{(n-1)})$ will have a solution involving n arbitray constants. Conversely, a family of functions involving n arbitrary constants can be shown to be the solution of an nth order differential equation. By eliminating the constants $c_1, \ldots, c_n$, determine the differential equation satisfied by each of the following functions.

(a) $y = c_1 + c_2 x + c_3 x^2 + \sin x$

(b) $y = c_1 + c_2 \cos x + c_3 \sin x$

(c) $y = c_1 e^x + c_2 e^{-x} + c_3 e^{2x}$

(d) $y = c_1 x + c_2 x^2 + c_3 x^3$

(e) $y = x + c_1 + c_2 \cos x + c_3 \sin x$

(f) $y = c_1 + c_2 x + c_3 \sinh x + c_4 \cosh x$

3. Determine the intervals in which solutions of each of the following linear equations are sure to exist.

(a) $y^{iv} + 4y''' + 3y = x$

(b) $xy''' + (\sin x)y'' + 3y = \cos x$

(c) $x(x - 1)y^{iv} + e^x y'' + 4x^2 y = 0$

(d) $y''' + xy'' + x^2 y' + x^3 y = \ln x$

5.2 GENERAL THEORY OF nth ORDER LINEAR EQUATIONS

If the functions $y_1, y_2, \ldots, y_n$ are solutions of the nth order linear homogeneous differential equation

$$L[y] = y^{(n)} + p_1(x)y^{(n-1)} + \cdots + p_n(x)y = 0, \tag{1}$$

it follows by direct computation that the linear combination

$$y = c_1 y_1(x) + c_2 y_2(x) + \cdots + c_n y_n(x), \tag{2}$$

where $c_1, \ldots, c_n$ are arbitrary constants, is also a solution of Eq. (1). It is natural to ask whether every solution of Eq. (1) can be expressed as a linear combination of $y_1, y_2, \ldots, y_n$. This will be true if, regardless of the initial conditions

$$y(x_0) = y_0, y'(x_0) = y_0', \ldots, y^{(n-1)}(x_0) = y_0^{(n-1)} \tag{3}$$

that are specified, it is possible to choose the constants $c_1, \ldots, c_n$ so that the linear combination (2) will satisfy the initial conditions. Specifically, for any choice of the point x_0 in $\alpha < x < \beta$, and for any choice of $y_0, y_0', y_0'', \ldots, y_0^{(n-1)}$, we must be able to determine $c_1, \ldots, c_n$ so that the equations

$$
\begin{aligned}
c_1 y_1(x_0) &+ \cdots + c_n y_n(x_0) &= y_0 \\
c_1 y_1'(x_0) &+ \cdots + c_n y_n'(x_0) &= y_0'
\end{aligned}
$$

$$
\vdots
\tag{4}
$$

$$c_1 y_1^{(n-1)}(x_0) + \cdots + c_n y_n^{(n-1)}(x_0) = y_0^{(n-1)}$$

are satisfied. Equations (4) can always be solved for the constants $c_1, \ldots, c_n$, provided that the determinant of the coefficients does not vanish. On the other hand, if the determinant of the coefficients does vanish, it is always possible to choose values of $y_0, y_0', \ldots, y_0^{(n-1)}$ such that Eqs. (4) do not have a solution. Hence a necessary and sufficient condition for the existence of a solution of Eqs. (4) for arbitrary values of $y_0, y_0', \ldots, y_0^{(n-1)}$ is that the Wronskian

$$W(y_1, y_2, \ldots, y_n) = \begin{vmatrix} y_1 & y_2 & \cdots & y_n \\ y_1' & y_2' & \cdots & y_n' \\ \vdots & \vdots & & \vdots \\ y_1^{(n-1)} & y_2^{(n-1)} & \cdots & y_n^{(n-1)} \end{vmatrix} \tag{5}$$

does not vanish at $x = x_0$. Since x_0 can be any point in the interval $\alpha < x < \beta$ it is necessary and sufficient that $W(y_1, y_2, \ldots, y_n)$ be nonvanishing at every point in the interval. Just as for the second order linear equation, it can be shown that if $y_1, y_2, \ldots, y_n$ are solutions of Eq. (1), then $W(y_1, y_2, \ldots, y_n)$ is either identically zero on the interval $\alpha < x < \beta$ or else never vanishes (see Problem 2). Hence we have the following theorem.

Theorem 5.2.   *If the functions $p_1, p_2, \ldots, p_n$ are continuous on the open interval $\alpha < x < \beta$, if the functions $y_1, y_2, \ldots, y_n$ are solutions of Eq. (1), and if $W(y_1, \ldots, y_n)(x) \neq 0$ at least at one point in $\alpha < x < \beta$, then any solution of Eq. (1) can be expressed as a linear combination of the solutions $y_1, y_2, \ldots, y_n$.*

Such a set of solutions $y_1, y_2, \ldots, y_n$ of Eq. (1) is referred to as a *fundamental set of solutions* of Eq. (1). That a fundamental set of solutions exists can be shown in precisely the same way as for the second order linear equation. See Theorem 3.7. Since all solutions of Eq. (1) are of the form (2), it is customary to use the term *general solution* to refer to an arbitrary linear combination of any fundamental set of solutions of Eq. (1).

The discussion of linear independence given in Section 3.3 can also be generalized. The functions $y_1, \ldots, y_n$ are said to be *linearly independent* on $\alpha < x < \beta$ if there is no set of constants $c_1, c_2, \ldots, c_n$ (except $c_1 = c_2 = \cdots = c_n = 0$) such that

$$c_1 y_1(x) + c_2 y_2(x) + \cdots + c_n y_n(x) = 0 \tag{6}$$

for all x in $\alpha < x < \beta$. If $y_1, \ldots, y_n$ are solutions of Eq. (1), it can be shown that a necessary and sufficient condition for them to be linearly independent is that $W(y_1, \ldots, y_n)$ be nonvanishing on $\alpha < x < \beta$. See Problem 3. Hence the functions forming a fundamental set of solutions of Eq. (1) are linearly independent, and a linearly independent set of n solutions of Eq. (1) forms a fundamental set of solutions of Eq. (1).

Nonhomogeneous Problem.   Now consider the nonhomogeneous equation

$$L[y] = y^{(n)} + p_1(x)y^{(n-1)} + \cdots + p_n(x)y = g(x). \tag{7}$$

If y_{p_1} and y_{p_2} are any two particular solutions of Eq. (7), it follows immediately from the linearity of the operator L that $L[y_{p_1} - y_{p_2}] = g - g = 0$, and hence the difference of any two solutions of the nonhomogeneous equation (7) is a solution of the homogeneous equation (1). Since any solution of the homogeneous equation can be expressed as a linear combination of a fundamental set of solutions $y_1, y_2, \ldots, y_n$, it follows that any solution of Eq. (7) can be written as

$$y = y_c(x) + y_p(x)$$

$$= c_1 y_1(x) + c_2 y_2(x) + \cdots + c_n y_n(x) + y_p(x), \tag{8}$$

where y_p is any solution of the nonhomogeneous equation (7). The linear combination (8) is usually referred to as the *general solution* of the non-homogeneous equation (7).

The primary problem is to determine a fundamental set of solutions $y_1, y_2, \ldots, y_n$. If the coefficients in the differential equation are constants this is a fairly simple problem; it is discussed in the next section. If the coefficients are not constants, it is usually necessary to use numerical methods (Chapter 8) or series methods similar to those used for the second order linear differential equation with variable coefficients.*

In conclusion, it can be shown that the method of reduction of order also applies to nth order linear differential equations. Thus if y_1 is one solution of Eq. (1), the substitution $y = y_1(x)v(x)$ leads to a linear differential equation of order $n - 1$ for v'. See Problems 7 and 8. Corresponding to y_1 and the $n - 1$ linearly independent solutions $v_1, \ldots, v_{n-1}$ of the reduced equation we obtain the fundamental set of solutions $y_1, y_1v_1, \ldots, y_1v_{n-1}$ of Eq. (1). If one solution of the equation for v' is known, the method of reduction of order can again be used to obtain a linear differential equation of order $n - 2$ and so on until a first order equation is obtained. However, in practice the method of reduction of order is seldom useful for equations of higher than second order. If $n \geq 3$ the reduced equation is itself at least of second order, and only rarely will it be simpler to solve than the original equation. On the other hand, as we have seen in Section 3.4, if $n = 2$ the reduced equation is of first order and hence considerable simplification may be achieved.

PROBLEMS

1. Verify that the differential operator L defined by $L[y] = y^{(n)} + p_1(x)y^{(n-1)} + \cdots + p_n(x)y$ is a linear differential operator. That is, show that

$$L[c_1y_1 + c_2y_2] = c_1L[y_1] + c_2L[y_2],$$

where y_1 and y_2 are n times differentiable functions and c_1 and c_2 are arbitrary constants. Hence, show that if $y_1, y_2, \ldots, y_n$ are solutions of $L[y] = 0$, then the linear combination $c_1y_1 + \cdots + c_ny_n$ is also a solution of $L[y] = 0$.

2. In Section 3.2 it was shown that the Wronskian $W(y_1, y_2)$ of two solutions of $y'' + p_1(x)y' + p_2(x)y = 0$ can be written as $W(y_1, y_2)(x) = c \exp\left[-\int^x p_1(t)\,dt\right]$, where c is a constant. It can be shown more generally that if $y_1, y_2, \ldots, y_n$ are solutions of $y^{(n)} + p_1(x)y^{(n-1)} + \cdots + p_n(x)y = 0$ for $\alpha < x < \beta$, then

$$W(y_1, y_2, \ldots, y_n)(x) = c \exp\left[-\int^x p_1(t)\,dt\right].$$

* A discussion of series methods for higher order equations can be found in Ince [Chapter 16] or Coddington and Levinson [Chapter 4].

This is known as Abel's identity. To show this result for $n = 3$ we can proceed as follows.

(a) Show that

$$W' = \begin{vmatrix} y_1 & y_2 & y_3 \\ y_1' & y_2' & y_3' \\ y_1''' & y_2''' & y_3''' \end{vmatrix},$$

where $W(y_1, y_2, y_3) = W$.

Hint: The derivative of a 3 by 3 determinant is the sum of three 3 by 3 determinants with the first, second, and third rows differentiated respectively.

(b) Substitute for y_1''', y_2''', and y_3''' from the differential equation; multiply the first row by p_3, the second by p_2, and add these to the last row to obtain

$$W' = -p_1 W.$$

The desired result follows from this equation. The proof for the general case is similar. Since the exponential function never vanishes this result shows that $W(y_1, y_2, \ldots, y_n)$ either is identically zero or else is nowhere zero on $\alpha < x < \beta$.

3. The purpose of this problem is to show that if $W(y_1, y_2, \ldots, y_n)$ is not identically zero on $\alpha < x < \beta$, then $y_1, y_2, \ldots, y_n$ are linearly independent; and if they are linearly independent and solutions of

$$L[y] = y^{(n)} + p_1(x)y^{(n-1)} + \cdots + p_n(x)y = 0, \qquad \alpha < x < \beta, \tag{i}$$

then $W(y_1, y_2, \ldots, y_n)$ is nowhere zero on $\alpha < x < \beta$.

(a) Suppose $W(y_1, y_2, \ldots, y_n)$ is not identically zero on $\alpha < x < \beta$. To show that $y_1, y_2, \ldots, y_n$ are linearly independent we must show that it is impossible to find constants $c_1, c_2, \ldots, c_n$ (not all zero) such that

$$c_1 y_1(x) + c_2 y_2(x) + \cdots + c_n y_n(x) = 0, \tag{ii}$$

for all x in $\alpha < x < \beta$. By writing the equations for the first, second, . . . , and $(n-1)$st derivatives of Eq. (ii) at a point at which $W(y_1, y_2, \ldots, y_n) \neq 0$, show that the c's must all be zero if Eq. (ii) is true. Hence the $y_1, y_2, \ldots, y_n$ are linearly independent.

(b) Suppose that $y_1, y_2, \ldots, y_n$ are linearly independent solutions of Eq. (i). To show that $W(y_1, y_2, \ldots, y_n)$ is nowhere zero on $\alpha < x < \beta$, assume that $W(y_1, y_2, \ldots, y_n)(x_0) = 0$ and show that this leads to a contradiction.

Hint: If $W(y_1, y_2, \ldots, y_n)(x_0) = 0$, there exists a nonzero solution of Eq. (i) satisfying the initial conditions $y = y' = y'' = \cdots = y^{(n-1)} = 0$ at x_0; then use the existence and uniqueness theorem.

4. Verify that the given functions are solutions of the differential equation, and compute the Wronskian of the solutions.

(a) $y''' + y' = 0$; 1, $\cos x$, $\sin x$

(b) $y^{iv} + y'' = 0$; 1, x, $\cos x$, $\sin x$

(c) $y''' + 2y'' - y' - 2y = 0$; e^x, e^{-x}, e^{-2x}

(d) $y^{iv} + 2y''' + y'' = 0$; 1, x, e^{-x}, xe^{-x}

(e) $xy''' - y'' = 0$; 1, x, x^3

5. Show that $W(5, \sin^2 x, \cos 2x) = 0$. Can you establish this result without directly evaluating the Wronskian?

6. Let the linear differential operator L be defined by

$$L[y] = a_0 y^{(n)} + a_1 y^{(n-1)} + a_2 y^{(n-2)} + \cdots + a_n y,$$

where $a_0, a_1, \ldots, a_n$ are real constants. Compute (a) $L[x^n]$; (b) $L[e^{rx}]$.
   (c) Determine four solutions of the equation $y^{iv} - 5y'' + 4y = 0$. Do you think the four solutions form a fundamental set of solutions? Why?

7. Show that if y_1 is a solution of

$$y''' + p_1(x)y'' + p_2(x)y' + p_3(x)y = 0,$$

then the substitution $y = y_1(x)v(x)$ leads to the following second order linear equation for v':

$$y_1 v''' + (3y_1' + p_1 y_1)v'' + (3y_1'' + 2p_1 y_1' + p_2 y_1)v' = 0.$$

8. Using the method of reduction of order, solve the following differential equations.

(a) $x^3 y''' - 3x^2 y'' + 6xy' - 6y = 0,$ $x > 0;$ $y_1(x) = x$
(b) $x^2(x + 3)y''' - 3x(x + 2)y'' + 6(1 + x)y' - 6y = 0,$ $x > 0;$
   $y_1(x) = x^2,$ $y_2(x) = x^3$

5.3   THE HOMOGENEOUS EQUATION WITH CONSTANT COEFFICIENTS

Consider the nth order linear homogeneous differential equation

$$L[y] = a_0 y^{(n)} + a_1 y^{(n-1)} + \cdots + a_{n-1} y' + a_n y = 0, \tag{1}$$

where $a_0, a_1, \ldots, a_n$ are real constants. It is natural to anticipate from our knowledge of second order linear equations with constant coefficients that for suitable values of r, $y = e^{rx}$ will be a solution of Eq. (1). Indeed,

$$L[e^{rx}] = e^{rx}(a_0 r^n + a_1 r^{n-1} + \cdots + a_{n-1} r + a_n)$$
$$= e^{rx} Z(r) \tag{2}$$

for all r. For those values of r for which $Z(r) = 0$, it follows that $L[e^{rx}] = 0$ and $y = e^{rx}$ is a solution of Eq. (1). The polynomial $Z(r)$ is referred to as the *auxiliary polynomial* or *characteristic polynomial* and the equation $Z(r) = 0$ as the *auxiliary equation* or *characteristic equation* of the differential equation (1). A polynomial of degree n has n zeros, say $r_1, r_2, \ldots, r_n$; hence we can write the auxiliary polynomial in the form

$$Z(r) = a_0(r - r_1)(r - r_2) \cdots (r - r_n). \tag{3}$$

Real Unequal Roots.   If the roots of the auxiliary equation are real and no two are equal, then we have n distinct solutions $e^{r_1 x}, e^{r_2 x}, \ldots, e^{r_n x}$ of Eq.

(1). To show in this case that the general solution of Eq. (1) is of the form

$$y = c_1 e^{r_1 x} + c_2 e^{r_2 x} + \cdots + c_n e^{r_n x}, \tag{4}$$

we must show that the functions $e^{r_1 x}, \ldots, e^{r_n x}$ are linearly independent on the interval $-\infty < x < \infty$. Let us assume that they are linearly dependent and show that this leads to a contradiction. Then there exist constants c_1, $c_2, \ldots, c_n$, not all zero, such that $c_1 e^{r_1 x} + c_2 e^{r_2 x} + \cdots + c_n e^{r_n x} = 0$ for all x in $-\infty < x < \infty$. Multiplying by $e^{-r_1 x}$ gives $c_1 + c_2 e^{(r_2 - r_1)x} + \cdots + c_n e^{(r_n - r_1)x} = 0$ for $-\infty < x < \infty$ and, differentiating, we obtain

$$(r_2 - r_1)c_2 e^{(r_2 - r_1)x} + (r_3 - r_1)c_3 e^{(r_3 - r_1)x} + \cdots + (r_n - r_1)c_n e^{(r_n - r_1)x} = 0$$

for $-\infty < x < \infty$. Multiplying this last result by $e^{-(r_2 - r_1)x}$ and then differentiating gives

$$(r_3 - r_2)(r_3 - r_1)c_3 e^{(r_3 - r_2)x} + \cdots + (r_n - r_2)(r_n - r_1)c_n e^{(r_n - r_2)x} = 0$$

for $-\infty < x < \infty$. Continuing in this manner, we finally obtain

$$(r_n - r_{n-1})(r_n - r_{n-2}) \cdots (r_n - r_2)(r_n - r_1)c_n e^{(r_n - r_{n-1})x} = 0 \tag{5}$$

for $-\infty < x < \infty$. Since the exponential function does not vanish and the r_i are unequal, we have $c_n = 0$. Thus $c_1 e^{r_1 x} + c_2 e^{r_2 x} + \cdots + c_{n-1} e^{r_{n-1} x} = 0$ and, proceeding as above, we obtain $c_{n-1} = 0$. Similarly $c_{n-2}, \ldots, c_1 = 0$, and this is a contradiction of the assumption that $e^{r_1 x}, \ldots, e^{r_n x}$ are linearly dependent.

Complex Roots.   If the auxiliary equation has complex roots, they must occur in conjugate pairs, $\lambda \pm i\mu$, since the coefficients $a_0, \ldots, a_n$ are real numbers. Provided that none of the roots are repeated, the general solution of Eq. (1) will still be of the form* (4). However, following the same procedure as for the second order equation (Section 3.5.1) in place of the complex-valued solutions $e^{(\lambda + i\mu)x}$ and $e^{(\lambda - i\mu)x}$ we will normally use the real-valued solutions

$$e^{\lambda x} \cos \mu x, \qquad e^{\lambda x} \sin \mu x \tag{6}$$

obtained as the real and imaginary parts of $e^{(\lambda + i\mu)x}$. Thus even though some of the roots of the auxiliary equation are complex, it is still possible to express the general solution of Eq. (1) as a linear combination of real-valued solutions.

Example 1.   Find the general solution of

$$y^{\text{iv}} - y = 0. \tag{7}$$

* The linear independence of the solutions $e^{r_1 x}, \ldots, e^{r_n x}$, in the case that some of the r's are complex numbers, follows by a generalization of the argument just given for the case of the r's real.

Substituting e^{rx} for y, we find that the auxiliary equation is

$$r^4 - 1 = (r^2 - 1)(r^2 + 1) = 0.$$

The roots are $r = 1, -1, i, -i$; hence the general solution of Eq. (7) is

$$y = c_1 e^x + c_2 e^{-x} + c_3 \cos x + c_4 \sin x.$$

Repeated Roots.   If the roots of the auxiliary equation are not distinct, that is, if some of the roots are repeated, then the solution (4) is clearly not the general solution of Eq. (1). Recalling that if r_1 was a repeated root for the second order linear equation $a_0 y'' + a_1 y' + a_2 y = 0$, then the two linearly independent solutions were $e^{r_1 x}$ and $xe^{r_1 x}$, it seems reasonable to expect that if a root of $Z(r) = 0$, say $r = r_1$, is repeated s times ($s \leq n$) then

$$e^{r_1 x}, \ xe^{r_1 x}, \ x^2 e^{r_1 x}, \ \ldots, \ x^{s-1} e^{r_1 x} \tag{8}$$

are solutions of Eq. (1). To prove this, we observe that if r_1 is an s-fold zero of $Z(r)$, then Eq. (2) can be written as

$$L[e^{rx}] = e^{rx} a_0 (r - r_1)^s (r - r_{s+1}) \cdots (r - r_n)$$
$$= e^{rx}(r - r_1)^s H(r) \tag{9}$$

for all values of r, where $H(r_1) \neq 0$. Noting that $\partial e^{rx}/\partial r = xe^{rx}$, and observing that we can interchange differentiation with respect to x and r, we find on differentiating Eq. (9) with respect to r that

$$L[xe^{rx}] = e^{rx}[x(r - r_1)^s H(r) + s(r - r_1)^{s-1} H(r) + (r - r_1)^s H'(r)]. \tag{10}$$

Since $s \geq 2$ the right-hand side of Eq. (10) vanishes for $r = r_1$ and hence $xe^{r_1 x}$ is also a solution of Eq. (1). If $s \geq 3$, differentiating Eq. (10) again with respect to r and setting r equal to r_1 shows that $x^2 e^{r_1 x}$ is also a solution of Eq. (1). This process can be continued through $s - 1$ differentiations, which gives the desired result. Notice that the sth derivative of the right-hand side of Eq. (9) will not vanish for $r = r_1$ since the sth derivative of $(r - r_1)^s$ is a constant and $H(r_1) \neq 0$. It is reasonable to expect that $e^{r_1 x}$, $xe^{r_1 x}$, $\ldots$, $x^{s-1} e^{r_1 x}$ are linearly independent, and we will accept this fact without proof.

Finally, if a complex root $\lambda + i\mu$ is repeated s times the complex conjugate $\lambda - i\mu$ is also repeated s times. Corresponding to these $2s$ complex-valued solutions we can find $2s$ real-valued solutions by noting that the real and imaginary parts of $e^{(\lambda+i\mu)x}$, $xe^{(\lambda+i\mu)x}$, $\ldots$, $x^{s-1} e^{(\lambda+i\mu)x}$ are also linearly independent solutions:

$$e^{\lambda x} \cos \mu x, \qquad e^{\lambda x} \sin \mu x, \qquad xe^{\lambda x} \cos \mu x, \qquad xe^{\lambda x} \sin \mu x,$$
$$\ldots, \ x^{s-1} e^{\lambda x} \cos \mu x, \qquad x^{s-1} e^{\lambda x} \sin \mu x.$$

Hence the general solution of Eq. (1) can always be expressed as a linear combination of n real-valued solutions. Consider the following example.

Example 2. Find the general solution of

$$y^{iv} + 2y'' + y = 0. \tag{11}$$

The auxiliary equation is

$$r^4 + 2r^2 + 1 = (r^2 + 1)(r^2 + 1) = 0.$$

The roots are $r = i, i, -i, -i$, and the general solution of Eq. (11) is

$$y = c_1 \cos x + c_2 \sin x + c_3 x \cos x + c_4 x \sin x.$$

In determining the roots of the auxiliary equation it is often necessary to compute the cube roots, or fourth roots, or even higher roots of a (possibly complex) number. This can usually be done most conveniently by using Euler's formula $e^{ix} = \cos x + i \sin x$, and the algebraic laws given in Section 3.5.1. This is illustrated in the following example, and is also discussed in Problems 1 and 2.

Example 3. Find the general solution of

$$y^{iv} + y = 0. \tag{12}$$

The auxiliary equation is

$$r^4 + 1 = 0.$$

In this case the polynomial is not readily factored. We must compute the fourth roots of -1. Now

$$-1 = \cos \pi + i \sin \pi = e^{i\pi}$$
$$= \cos(\pi + 2m\pi) + i \sin(\pi + 2m\pi) = e^{i(\pi + 2m\pi)},$$

where m is zero or any positive or negative integer. Thus

$$(-1)^{\frac{1}{4}} = e^{i(\pi/4 + m\pi/2)} = \cos\left(\frac{\pi}{4} + \frac{m\pi}{2}\right) + i \sin\left(\frac{\pi}{4} + \frac{m\pi}{2}\right).$$

The four fourth roots of -1 are obtained by setting $m = 0, 1, 2,$ and 3; they are

$$\frac{1+i}{\sqrt{2}}, \quad \frac{-1+i}{\sqrt{2}}, \quad \frac{-1-i}{\sqrt{2}}, \quad \frac{1-i}{\sqrt{2}}.$$

It is easy to verify that for any other value of m we obtain one of these four roots. For example, corresponding to $m = 4$ we obtain $(1 + i)/\sqrt{2}$. The general solution of Eq. (12) is

$$y = e^{x/\sqrt{2}}\left(c_1 \cos \frac{x}{\sqrt{2}} + c_2 \sin \frac{x}{\sqrt{2}}\right) + e^{-x/\sqrt{2}}\left(c_3 \cos \frac{x}{\sqrt{2}} + c_4 \sin \frac{x}{\sqrt{2}}\right).$$

In conclusion we mention that the problem of determining the roots of $Z(r) = 0$ for $n > 2$ may require the use of numerical methods if they cannot be found by inspection or by a simple process of trial and error. Although there are formulas similar to the quadratic formula for the roots of cubic and quartic polynomial equations, there is no formula* for $n > 4$; and even for third and fourth degree polynomial equations it is usually more efficient to use numerical methods rather than the exact formula for determining the roots.

If the constants $a_0, a_1, \ldots, a_n$ in Eq. (1) are complex numbers, the solution of Eq. (1) is still of the form (4). In this case, however, the roots of the auxiliary equation will, in general, be complex numbers; and it is no longer true that the complex conjugate of a root will also be a root. The corresponding solutions will be complex-valued.

PROBLEMS

1. Express each of the following complex numbers in the form

$$R(\cos \theta + i \sin \theta) = Re^{i\theta}.$$

Note that $e^{i(\theta + 2m\pi)} = e^{i\theta}$, $m = 0, \pm 1, \pm 2, \ldots$.

(a) $1 + i$ (b) $-1 + i\sqrt{3}$ (c) -1

(d) $-i$ (e) $\sqrt{3} - i$ (f) $-1 - i$

2. Observing that $e^{i(\theta + 2m\pi)} = e^{i\theta}$ for m an integer, and that (one form of DeMoivre's formula, Problem 12, Section 3.5.1)

$$[e^{i(\theta + 2m\pi)}]^{1/n} = e^{i[(\theta + 2m\pi)/n]} = \cos\left(\frac{\theta}{n} + \frac{2m\pi}{n}\right) + i\sin\left(\frac{\theta}{n} + \frac{2m\pi}{n}\right),$$

determine the indicated roots of each of the following complex numbers.

(a) $1^{1/3}$ (b) $(1 - i)^{1/2}$

(c) $1^{1/4}$ (d) $\left[2\left(\cos\dfrac{\pi}{3} + i\sin\dfrac{\pi}{3}\right)\right]^{1/2}$

In each of Problems 3 through 13 determine the general solution of the given differential equation.

3. $y''' - y'' - y' + y = 0$ 4. $y''' - 3y'' + 3y' - y = 0$
5. $2y''' - 4y'' - 2y' + 4y = 0$ 6. $y^{iv} - 4y''' + 4y'' = 0$
7. $y^{vi} + y = 0$ 8. $y^{iv} - 5y'' + 4y = 0$

* The formula for solving the cubic equation is usually attributed to Cardano (1501–1576), and that for the quartic equation to his pupil Ferrari (1522–1565). That it is impossible to express the roots of a general algebraic equation of degree higher than four by a formula involving only rational operations (addition, multiplication, etc.) and root extractions was established by Abel and Galois (1811–1832). A discussion of methods of solving algebraic equations can be found in Uspensky.

9. $y^{vi} - 3y^{iv} + 3y'' - y = 0$ 10. $y^{vi} - y'' = 0$

11. $y^{v} - 3y^{iv} + 3y''' - 3y'' + 2y' = 0$

12. $y^{iv} - 8y' = 0$ 13. $y^{viii} + 8y^{iv} + 16y = 0$

14. Solve the initial value problem

$$y''' + y' = 0; \qquad y(0) = 0, \qquad y'(0) = 1, \qquad y''(0) = 2.$$

15. Show that the general solution of the differential equation

$$y^{iv} - y = 0$$

can be written as

$$y = c_1 \cos x + c_2 \sin x + c_3 \cosh x + c_4 \sinh x.$$

Determine the solution satisfying the initial conditions $y(0) = y'(0) = 0$, $y''(0) = y'''(0) = 1$. Why is it convenient to use $\cosh x$ and $\sinh x$ rather than e^x and e^{-x}?

Problems 16 through 19 deal with the nth order Euler equation.

*16. The nth order Euler or equidimensional equation is

$$L[y] = x^n y^{(n)} + a_1 x^{n-1} y^{(n-1)} + \cdots + a_{n-1} xy' + a_n y = 0 \qquad (i)$$

where $a_1, a_2, \ldots, a_n$ are real constants. Consider only the interval $x > 0$.
   (a) Show that

$$L[x^r] = x^r F(r)$$

where

$$F(r) = r(r - 1) \cdots (r - n + 1) + a_1[r(r - 1) \cdots (r - n + 2)]$$
$$+ \cdots + a_{n-1}r + a_n$$

is a polynomial of degree n in r. The functions $x^{r_1}, x^{r_2}, \ldots, x^{r_n}$ corresponding to the roots $r_1, r_2, \ldots, r_n$ of $F(r) = 0$ are solutions of Eq. (i).
   (b) Show that if r_1 is an s-fold root of $F(r) = 0$ then $x^{r_1}, x^{r_1} \ln x, x^{r_1}(\ln x)^2, \ldots, x^{r_1}(\ln x)^{s-1}$ are solutions of Eq. (i).
   When the roots of $F(r) = 0$ are complex, real-valued solutions can be obtained in the manner described for the second order Euler equation. See Section 4.4.

*17. Using the results of Problem 16 determine the general solution of each of the following differential equations. Consider only the interval $x > 0$.

   (a) $x^3 y''' + x^2 y'' - 2xy' + 2y = 0$
   (b) $x^3 y''' + xy' - y = 0$
   (c) $x^3 y''' + 2x^2 y'' + xy' - y = 0$

*18. In determining the drag on a very small sphere of radius a placed in a uniform viscous flow it is necessary to solve the following differential equation

$$\rho^3 f''''(\rho) + 8\rho^2 f'''(\rho) + 8\rho f''(\rho) - 8f'(\rho) = 0, \qquad \rho > a,$$

where ρ is the distance from the center of the sphere. Note this is an Euler equation for f' and show, using the results of Problem 16, that the general solution is

$$f(\rho) = \frac{A}{\rho^3} + \frac{B}{\rho} + C + D\rho^2$$

where A, B, C, and D are constants. Show that the solution satisfying the boundary conditions $f(a) = 0$, $f'(a) = 0$ and $f(\rho) \to U$ (the velocity at ∞) as $\rho \to \infty$ is $f(\rho) = Ua^3/2\rho^3 - 3Ua/2\rho + U$. The formula for the drag (Stokes' formula) on the sphere turns out to be $6\pi\mu aU$ where μ is the viscosity of the fluid. This result was used by R. A. Millikan (1868–1953) in his famous experiment to measure the charge on an electron.

*19. Show, for $x > 0$, that the change of variable $x = e^z$ reduces the third order Euler equation $x^3y''' + a_1x^2y'' + a_2xy' + a_3y = 0$ to a third order linear equation with constant coefficients. This transformation also reduces the nth order Euler equation to an nth order linear equation with constant coefficients. Solve Problem 17b by this method.

*20. It is often of importance in engineering applications to know whether all possible solutions of a linear homogeneous equation approach zero as x approaches infinity. If so, the equation is said to be *asymptotically stable*. If x represents time and y the response of a physical system, the condition that the differential equation is stable (asymptotically stable) means that regardless of the initial conditions the response of the system to the initial conditions will eventually decay to zero as x becomes large. For the second order equation $ay'' + by' + cy = 0$, it was shown in Section 3.7.1 (also see Section 3.5.1, Problem 10) that a sufficient condition for stability is that a, b, and c be positive. More generally the equation

$$a_0y^{(n)} + a_1y^{(n-1)} + \cdots + a_ny = 0, \qquad \text{(i)}$$

where $a_0, a_1, \ldots, a_n$ are real, will be stable if all the roots of the corresponding auxiliary equation have negative real parts. A necessary and sufficient condition for determining whether Eq. (i) is stable, without solving the equation, has been given by Hurwitz (1859–1919). For $n = 4$ the Hurwitz stability criterion can be stated as follows: Eq. (i) is stable if and only if for $a_0 > 0$,

$$a_1, \quad \begin{vmatrix} a_1 & a_0 \\ a_3 & a_2 \end{vmatrix}, \quad \begin{vmatrix} a_1 & a_0 & 0 \\ a_3 & a_2 & a_1 \\ 0 & a_4 & a_3 \end{vmatrix}, \quad \begin{vmatrix} a_1 & a_0 & 0 & 0 \\ a_3 & a_2 & a_1 & a_0 \\ 0 & a_4 & a_3 & a_2 \\ 0 & 0 & 0 & a_4 \end{vmatrix}$$

are all positive. For $n = 3$ the condition just applies to the first three expressions with $a_4 = 0$, and for $n = 2$ to the first two expressions with $a_3 = 0$. A complete discussion of the stability criterion of Hurwitz can be found in Guillemin [Chapter 6, Article 26].

Determine whether each of the following equations is stable, and verify your result if possible by actually computing the general solution.

(a) $y''' + 3y'' + 3y' + y = 0$ (b) $y''' - y = 0$

(c) $y''' + y'' - y' + y = 0$ (d) $y^{iv} + 2y'' + y = 0$

(e) $y''' + 0.1y'' + 1.2y' - 0.4y = 0$ (f) $y''' + 3.2y'' + 2.41y' + 0.21y = 0$

5.4 THE METHOD OF UNDETERMINED COEFFICIENTS

A particular solution of the nonhomogeneous nth order linear equation with constant coefficients

$$L[y] = a_0 y^{(n)} + a_1 y^{(n-1)} + \cdots + a_{n-1} y' + a_n y = g(x) \tag{1}$$

can be obtained by the method of undetermined coefficients provided that $g(x)$ is of an appropriate form. While the method of undetermined coefficients is not as general as the method of variation of parameters that is described in the next section, it is usually much easier to use when applicable.

Just as for the second order linear equation, it is clear that when the constant coefficient linear differential operator L is applied to a polynomial $A_0 x^m + A_1 x^{m-1} + \cdots + A_m$, an exponential function $e^{\alpha x}$, or a sine function $\sin \beta x$, or a cosine function $\cos \beta x$, the result is a polynomial, an exponential function, or a linear combination of sine and cosine functions respectively. Hence if $g(x)$ is the sum of polynomials, exponentials, sines and cosines, or even products of such functions, we can expect that it is possible to find $y_p(x)$ by choosing a suitable combination of polynomials, exponentials, etc., with a number of undetermined constants. The constants are then determined so that Eq. (1) is satisfied.

First consider the case that $g(x)$ is a polynomial of degree m

$$g(x) = b_0 x^m + b_1 x^{m-1} + \cdots + b_m, \tag{2}$$

where $b_0, b_1, \ldots, b_m$ are given constants. It is natural to look for a particular solution of the form

$$y_p(x) = A_0 x^m + A_1 x^{m-1} + \cdots + A_m. \tag{3}$$

Substituting for y in Eq. (1), and equating the coefficients of like powers of x, we find from the terms in x^m that $a_n A_0 = b_0$. Provided that $a_n \neq 0$ we have $A_0 = b_0/a_n$. The constants $A_1, \ldots, A_m$ are determined from the coefficients of the terms $x^{m-1}, x^{m-2}, \ldots, x^0$.

If $a_n = 0$, that is, if a constant is a solution of the homogeneous equation, we cannot solve for A_0; in this case it is necessary to assume for $y_p(x)$ a polynomial of degree $m + 1$ in order to obtain a term in $L[y_p](x)$ to balance against $b_0 x^m$. However, it is not necessary to carry the constant in the assumed form for $y_p(x)$. More generally it is easy to verify that if zero is an s-fold root of the auxiliary polynomial, in which case $1, x, x^2, \ldots, x^{s-1}$ are solutions of the homogeneous equation, then a suitable form for $y_p(x)$ is

$$y_p(x) = x^s(A_0 x^m + A_1 x^{m-1} + \cdots + A_m). \tag{4}$$

As a second problem suppose that $g(x)$ is of the form

$$g(x) = e^{\alpha x}(b_0 x^m + b_1 x^{m-1} + \cdots + b_m). \tag{5}$$

Then we would expect $y_p(x)$ to be of the form

$$y_p(x) = e^{\alpha x}(A_0 x^m + A_1 x^{m-1} + \cdots + A_m), \tag{6}$$

provided that $e^{\alpha x}$ is not a solution of the homogeneous equation. If α is an s-fold root of the auxiliary equation, a suitable form for $y_p(x)$ is

$$y_p(x) = x^s e^{\alpha x}(A_0 x^m + A_1 x^{m-1} + \cdots + A_m). \tag{7}$$

These results can be proved, as for the second order linear nonhomogeneous equation, by reducing this problem to the previous one by the substitution $y = e^{\alpha x}u(x)$. The function u will satisfy an nth order linear nonhomogeneous equation with constant coefficients—the nonhomogeneous term being precisely the polynomial (2). See Problem 18.

Similarly, if $g(x)$ is of the form

$$g(x) = e^{\alpha x}(b_0 x^m + b_1 x^{m-1} + \cdots + b_m)\begin{cases}\sin \beta x, \\ \cos \beta x,\end{cases} \tag{8}$$

then a suitable form for $y_p(x)$, provided that $\alpha + i\beta$ is not a root of the auxiliary equation, is

$$y_p(x) = e^{\alpha x}(A_0 x^m + A_1 x^{m-1} + \cdots + A_m) \cos \beta x$$
$$+ e^{\alpha x}(B_0 x^m + B_1 x^{m-1} + \cdots + B_m) \sin \beta x. \tag{9}$$

If $\alpha + i\beta$ is an s-fold root of the auxiliary equation, it is necessary to multiply the right-hand side of Eq. (9) by x^s.

These results are summarized in Table 5.1.

TABLE 5.1

$g(x)$	$y_p(x)$
$P_m(x) = b_0 x^m + b_1 x^{m-1} + \cdots + b_m$	$x^s(A_0 x^m + \cdots + A_m)$
$P_m(x)e^{\alpha x}$	$x^s(A_0 x^m + \cdots + A_m)e^{\alpha x}$
$P_m(x)e^{\alpha x}\begin{cases}\sin \beta x \\ \cos \beta x\end{cases}$	$x^s[(A_0 x^m + \cdots + A_m)e^{\alpha x} \cos \beta x$ $+ (B_0 x^m + \cdots + B_m)e^{\alpha x} \sin \beta x]$

Here s is the smallest nonnegative integer for which every term in $y_p(x)$ differs from every term in the complementary function $y_c(x)$.

If $g(x)$ is a sum of terms of the form (2), (5), and (8), it is usually easier in practice to compute separately the particular solution corresponding to each term in $g(x)$. Then using the principle of superposition (since the differential equation is linear), the particular solution of the complete problem is the sum of the particular solutions of the individual problems. This is illustrated in the following example.

Example. Find a particular solution of

$$y''' - 4y' = x + 3\cos x + e^{-2x}. \tag{10}$$

First we solve the homogeneous equation. The auxiliary equation is $r^3 - 4r = 0$, and the roots are $0, \pm 2$; hence

$$y_c(x) = c_1 + c_2 e^{2x} + c_3 e^{-2x}.$$

Using the superposition principle, a particular solution will be the sum of particular solutions corresponding to the differential equations

$$y''' - 4y' = x, \qquad y''' - 4y' = 3\cos x, \qquad y''' - 4y' = e^{-2x}.$$

Our initial guess for a particular solution, y_{p_1}, of the first equation is $A_0 x + A_1$; but since a constant is a solution of the homogeneous equation we multiply by x. Thus

$$y_{p_1}(x) = x(A_0 x + A_1).$$

For the second equation we guess

$$y_{p_2}(x) = B\cos x + C\sin x,$$

and there is no need to modify this initial guess since $\cos x$ and $\sin x$ are not solutions of the homogeneous equation. Finally for the third equation, since e^{-2x} is a solution of the homogeneous equation, we assume that

$$y_{p_3}(x) = Exe^{-2x}.$$

The constants are determined by substituting into the individual differential equations; they are $A_0 = -\frac{1}{8}$, $A_1 = 0$, $B = 0$, $C = -\frac{3}{5}$, and $E = \frac{1}{8}$. Hence a particular solution of Eq. (10) is

$$y_p(x) = -\tfrac{1}{8}x^2 - \tfrac{3}{5}\sin x + \tfrac{1}{8}xe^{-2x}.$$

The method of undetermined coefficients can be used whenever it is possible to guess the correct form for $y_p(x)$. However, this is usually impossible for other than constant coefficient differential equations, and for other than nonhomogeneous terms of the type described above. For more complicated problems we can use the method of variation of parameters, which is discussed in the next section.

PROBLEMS

In each of Problems 1 through 11 determine the general solution of the given differential equation. Where specified find the solution satisfying the given initial conditions.

1. $y''' + 4y' = x$, $y(0) = y'(0) = 0$, $y''(0) = 1$
2. $y''' - y'' - y' + y = 2e^{-x} + 3$

3. $y''' + y'' + y' + y = e^{-x} + 4x$

4. $y''' - y' = 2 \sin x$

5. $y^{iv} + 2y'' + y = 3x + 4,$ $y(0) = y'(0) = 0,$ $y''(0) = y'''(0) = 1$

6. $y^{iv} - 4y'' = x^2 + e^x$

7. $y^{iv} + 2y'' + y = 3 + \cos 2x$

8. $y''' - 3y'' + 2y' = x + e^x$

9. $y^{vi} + y''' = x$

10. $y^{iv} + y''' = \sin 2x$

11. $y^{iv} - y = 3x + \cos x$

In each of Problems 12 through 17 determine a suitable form for $y_p(x)$ if the method of undetermined coefficients is to be used. Do not evaluate the constants.

12. $y''' - 2y'' + y' = x^3 + 2e^x$

13. $y''' - y' = xe^{-x} + 2\cos x$

14. $y^{iv} - 2y'' + y = e^x + \sin x$

15. $y^{iv} - y''' - y'' + y' = x^2 + 4 + x\sin x$

16. $y^{iv} + 4y'' = \sin 2x + xe^x + 4$

17. $y^{iv} + 2y''' + 2y'' = 3e^x + 2xe^{-x} + e^{-x}\sin x$

18. Consider the nonhomogeneous nth order linear differential equation

$$a_0 y^{(n)} + a_1 y^{(n-1)} + \cdots + a_n y = g(x)$$

where $a_0, \ldots, a_n$ are constants. Verify that if $g(x)$ is of the form

$$e^{\alpha x}(b_0 x^m + \cdots + b_m),$$

then the substitution $y = e^{\alpha x} u(x)$ reduces the above equation to the form

$$t_0 u^{(n)} + t_1 u^{(n-1)} + \cdots + t_n u = b_0 x^m + \cdots + b_m,$$

where $t_0, \ldots, t_n$ are constants. Determine t_0 and t_n in terms of the a's and α. Thus the problem of determining a particular solution of the original equation is reduced to the simpler problem of determining a particular solution of an equation with constant coefficients and a polynomial for the nonhomogeneous term.

5.5 THE METHOD OF VARIATION OF PARAMETERS

The method of variation of parameters for determining a particular solution of the nonhomogeneous nth order linear differential equation

$$L[y] = y^{(n)} + p_1(x)y^{(n-1)} + \cdots + p_{n-1}(x)y' + p_n(x)y = g(x) \qquad (1)$$

is a direct extension of the theory for the second order differential equation (see Section 3.6.2). As before, in order to use the method of variation of parameters, it is first necessary to solve the corresponding homogeneous differential equation. In general this may be difficult unless the coefficients are constants. However, the method of variation of parameters is still more general than the method of undetermined coefficients in the following sense. The method of undetermined coefficients is usually applicable only for constant coefficient equations, and a limited class of functions g; for constant coefficient equations the homogeneous equation can be solved and hence a particular solution for *any* continuous function g can be determined by the method of variation of parameters. Suppose then that we know a fundamental set of solutions $y_1, y_2, \ldots, y_n$ of the homogeneous equation. Then

$$y_c(x) = c_1 y_1(x) + c_2 y_2(x) + \cdots + c_n y_n(x). \tag{2}$$

The method of variation of parameters for determining a particular solution of Eq. (1) rests on the possibility of determining n functions $u_1, u_2, \ldots, u_n$ such that $y_p(x)$ is of the form

$$y_p(x) = u_1(x) y_1(x) + u_2(x) y_2(x) + \cdots + u_n(x) y_n(x). \tag{3}$$

Since we have n functions to determine, we will have to specify n conditions. One of these is clearly that y_p satisfy Eq. (1). The other $n - 1$ conditions are chosen so as to facilitate the calculations. Since we can hardly expect a simplification in determining y_p if we must solve high order differential equations for the u_i, $i = 1, 2, \ldots, n$, it is natural to impose conditions that will suppress the terms which would lead to higher derivatives of the u_i. From Eq. (3) we obtain

$$y_p' = (u_1 y_1' + u_2 y_2' + \cdots + u_n y_n') + (u_1' y_1 + u_2' y_2 + \cdots + u_n' y_n). \tag{4}$$

Thus the first condition that we impose on the u_i is that

$$u_1' y_1 + u_2' y_2 + \cdots + u_n' y_n = 0. \tag{5}$$

Continuing this process in a similar manner through $n - 1$ derivatives of y_p gives

$$y_p^{(m)} = u_1 y_1^{(m)} + u_2 y_2^{(m)} + \cdots + u_n y_n^{(m)}, \qquad m = 0, 1, 2, \ldots, n - 1; \tag{6}$$

and the following $n - 1$ conditions on the functions $u_1, \ldots, u_n$:

$$u_1' y_1^{(m-1)} + u_2' y_2^{(m-1)} + \cdots + u_n' y_n^{(m-1)} = 0, \qquad m = 1, 2, \ldots, n - 1. \tag{7}$$

The nth derivative of y_p is

$$y_p^{(n)} = (u_1 y_1^{(n)} + \cdots + u_n y_n^{(n)}) + (u_1' y_1^{(n-1)} + \cdots + u_n' y_n^{(n-1)}). \tag{8}$$

The condition that y_p be a solution of Eq. (1) gives, on substituting for the derivatives of y_p from Eqs. (6) and (8), collecting terms, and noting that $L[y_i] = 0$, $i = 1, 2, \ldots, n$,

$$u_1' y_1^{(n-1)} + u_2' y_2^{(n-1)} + \cdots + u_n' y_n^{(n-1)} = g. \tag{9}$$

Equation (9), coupled with the $n - 1$ equations (7), represent n simultaneous linear nonhomogeneous equations for $u_1', u_2', \ldots, u_n'$:

$$y_1 u_1' + y_2 u_2' + \cdots + y_n u_n' = 0,$$
$$y_1' u_1' + y_2' u_2' + \cdots + y_n' u_n' = 0,$$
$$y_1'' u_1' + y_2'' u_2' + \cdots + y_n'' u_n' = 0,$$
$$\vdots$$
$$y_1^{(n-1)} u_1' + \cdots + y_n^{(n-1)} u_n' = g. \tag{10}$$

A sufficient condition for the existence of a solution of the system of equations (10) is that the determinant of the coefficients does not vanish. However, the determinant of the coefficients is precisely $W(y_1, y_2, \ldots, y_n)$, and it cannot vanish since $y_1, \ldots, y_n$ are linearly independent solutions of the homogeneous equation. Hence it is possible to determine $u_1', \ldots, u_n'$. Using Cramer's rule, the solution of the system of equations (10) is

$$u_m'(x) = \frac{g(x) W_m(x)}{W(x)}, \qquad m = 1, 2, \ldots, n \tag{11}$$

where $W(x) = W(y_1, y_2, \ldots, y_n)(x)$ and W_m is the determinant, obtained from $W(y_1, y_2, \ldots, y_n)$ by replacing the mth column by the column $(0, 0, \ldots, 0, \ldots, 0, 1)$:

$$W_m = \begin{vmatrix} y_1 & \cdots & y_{m-1} & 0 & y_{m+1} & \cdots & y_n \\ \cdot & & \cdot & \cdot & \cdot & & \cdot \\ \cdot & & \cdot & \cdot & \cdot & & \cdot \\ y_1^{(n-1)} & \cdots & y_{m-1}^{(n-1)} & 1 & y_{m+1}^{(n-1)} & \cdots & y_n^{(n-1)} \end{vmatrix}. \tag{12}$$

With this notation a particular solution of Eq. (1) is given by

$$y_p(x) = \sum_{m=1}^{n} y_m(x) \int^x \frac{g(t) W_m(t)}{W(t)} \, dt. \tag{13}$$

While the procedure is straightforward, the computational problem of evaluating $y_p(x)$ from Eq. (13) for n greater than 2 is not a trivial one. The calculation may be simplified to some extent by using Abel's identity:

$$W(x) = W(y_1, y_2, \ldots, y_n)(x) = c \exp\left[-\int^x p_1(t) \, dt \right].$$

(See Problem 2 of Section 5.2.) The constant c can be determined by evaluating $W(y_1, y_2, \ldots, y_n)$ at a conveniently chosen point.

PROBLEMS

In each of Problems 1 through 3 use the method of variation of parameters to determine a particular solution of the given differential equation.

1. $y''' + y' = \tan x$, $0 < x < \pi/2$
2. $y''' - y' = x$
3. $y''' - 2y'' - y' + 2y = e^{4x}$

4. Given that x, x^2, and $1/x$ are solutions of the homogeneous equation corresponding to

$$x^3 y''' + x^2 y'' - 2xy' + 2y = 2x^4, \qquad x > 0,$$

determine a particular solution.

5. Find a formula involving integrals for a particular solution of the differential equation

$$y''' - y'' + y' - y = g(x).$$

6. Find a formula involving integrals for a particular solution of the differential equation

$$y^{\text{iv}} - y = g(x).$$

Hint: The functions $\sin x$, $\cos x$, $\sinh x$, $\cosh x$ form a fundamental set of solutions of the homogeneous equation.

7. Find a formula involving integrals for a particular solution of the differential equation

$$x^3 y''' - 3x^2 y'' + 6xy' - 6y = g(x), \qquad x > 0.$$

Hint: Verify that x, x^2, and x^3 are solutions of the homogeneous equation.

REFERENCES

Coddington, E. A., *An Introduction to Ordinary Differential Equations*, Prentice-Hall, Englewood Cliffs, N.J., 1961.

Coddington, E. A. and Levinson, N., *Theory of Ordinary Differential Equations*, McGraw-Hill, New York, 1955.

Guillemin, E. A., *The Mathematics of Circuit Analysis*, Wiley, New York, 1949.

Ince, E. L., *Ordinary Differential Equations*, Longmans, Green, London, 1927.

Uspensky, J. V., *Theory of Equations*, McGraw-Hill, New York, 1948.

The Laplace Transform

6.1 INTRODUCTION. DEFINITION OF THE LAPLACE TRANSFORM

In this chapter we will introduce the Laplace* transform, a very useful tool in the study of linear differential equations. Although by no means limited to this class of problems, Laplace transforms are particularly effective in solving initial value problems for linear differential equations with constant coefficients having nonhomogeneous terms of a discontinuous or impulsive nature. Such problems occur frequently in the analysis of electric circuits, and are also of importance in other applications. They are relatively awkward to handle by the methods previously discussed.

Since the Laplace transform is defined by a certain integral over the range from zero to infinity, it is useful to mention first some basic facts about such integrals. In the first place, an integral over an unbounded interval is called an improper integral, and is defined as a limit of integrals over finite intervals; thus

$$\int_a^\infty f(t)\, dt = \lim_{A \to \infty} \int_a^A f(t)\, dt, \tag{1}$$

where A is a positive real number. If the integral from a to A exists for each $A > a$, and if the limit as $A \to \infty$ exists, then the improper integral is said to *converge* to that limiting value. Otherwise the integral is said to *diverge*, or to fail to exist. The following example illustrates both possibilities.

Example 1. Let $f(t) = e^{ct}$, $t \geq 0$, where c is a real nonzero constant. Then

$$\int_0^\infty e^{ct}\, dt = \lim_{A \to \infty} \int_0^A e^{ct}\, dt = \lim_{A \to \infty} \frac{e^{ct}}{c}\bigg|_0^A$$

$$= \lim_{A \to \infty} \frac{1}{c}(e^{cA} - 1).$$

---

* P. S. Laplace (1749–1827), one of the greatest of all French mathematicians, is especially famous for his work in astronomy and probability.

It follows that the improper integral converges if $c < 0$, and diverges if $c > 0$. If $c = 0$ the integrand is unity, and the integral again diverges.

Before discussing the possible existence of $\int_a^\infty f(t)\, dt$, it is helpful to define certain properties of a function f. A function f is said to have a *jump discontinuity* at the point $t = t_0$ if f has finite, but unequal, right- and left-hand limits as t approaches t_0. Note that $f(t_0)$ need not be equal to either of these limits. If f is continuous on an interval $\alpha \le t \le \beta$, or $t \ge \alpha$, except for a

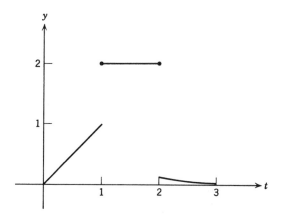

FIGURE 6.1   A piecewise continuous function.

finite number of points where it has jump discontinuities, then f is said to be *piecewise continuous* on the given interval. For example, the function f defined by

$$f(t) = \begin{cases} t, & 0 \le t < 1, \\ 2, & 1 \le t \le 2, \\ e^{-t}, & 2 < t \le 3, \end{cases}$$

is piecewise continuous on $0 \le t \le 3$. The graph of $y = f(t)$ is shown in Figure 6.1.

If f is piecewise continuous on the interval $a \le t \le A$, then it can be shown that $\int_a^A f(t)\, dt$ exists. Hence, if f is piecewise continuous for $t \ge a$, then $\int_a^A f(t)\, dt$ exists for each $A > a$. However, piecewise continuity is not enough to insure convergence of the improper integral $\int_a^\infty f(t)\, dt$, as Example 1 shows for $c > 0$. To illustrate further what may happen consider the following examples.

Example 2.   Let $f(t) = 1/t$, $t \geq 1$. Then

$$\int_1^\infty \frac{dt}{t} = \lim_{A \to \infty} \int_1^A \frac{dt}{t} = \lim_{A \to \infty} \ln A.$$

Since $\lim_{A \to \infty} \ln A$ does not exist, the improper integral diverges.

Example 3.   Let $f(t) = t^{-p}$, $t \geq 1$, where p is a real constant and $p \neq 1$; the case $p = 1$ was considered in Example 2.   Then

$$\int_1^\infty t^{-p} \, dt = \lim_{A \to \infty} \int_1^A t^{-p} \, dt = \lim_{A \to \infty} \frac{1}{1-p}(A^{1-p} - 1).$$

As $A \to \infty$, $A^{1-p} \to 0$ if $p > 1$, but $A^{1-p} \to \infty$ if $p < 1$. Hence $\int_1^\infty t^{-p} \, dt$ converges for $p > 1$, but (incorporating the result of Example 2) diverges for $p \leq 1$. These results are analogous to those for the infinite series $\sum_{n=1}^\infty n^{-p}$.

If f cannot be easily integrated in terms of elementary functions, the definition of convergence of $\int_a^\infty f(t) \, dt$ may be difficult to apply. Frequently, the most convenient way to test the convergence or divergence of an improper integral is by the following comparison theorem, which is analogous to a similar theorem for infinite series.

Theorem 6.1.   *If f is piecewise continuous for $t \geq a$; if $|f(t)| \leq g(t)$ when $t \geq M$, for some positive constant M; and if $\int_M^\infty g(t) \, dt$ converges; then $\int_a^\infty f(t) \, dt$ also converges. On the other hand, if $f(t) \geq g(t) \geq 0$ for $t \geq M$, and if $\int_M^\infty g(t) \, dt$ diverges, then $\int_a^\infty f(t) \, dt$ also diverges.*

The proof of this result from the calculus will not be given here. It is made plausible, however, by comparing the areas represented by $\int_M^\infty g(t) \, dt$ and $\int_M^\infty |f(t)| \, dt$. The functions most useful for comparison purposes are e^{ct} and t^{-p}, which were considered in Examples 1, 2, and 3.

Now suppose that $f(t)$ is defined for all $t \geq 0$. The Laplace transform of f, which we will denote by $\mathscr{L}\{f(t)\}$ or by $F(s)$, is defined by the equation

$$\mathscr{L}\{f(t)\} = F(s) = \int_0^\infty e^{-st} f(t) \, dt, \tag{2}$$

whenever this improper integral converges. In general the parameter s may be complex, but for our discussion we need consider only real values of s.

According to the foregoing discussion of integrals the function f must satisfy certain conditions in order for its Laplace transform F to exist. The simplest and most useful of these conditions are stated in the following theorem.

Theorem 6.2.   *Suppose that*
   (i) *f is piecewise continuous on the interval $0 \leq t \leq A$ for any positive A;*
   (ii) *$|f(t)| \leq Ke^{at}$ when $t \geq M$. In this inequality K, a, and M are real constants, K and M necessarily positive.*
   Then the Laplace transform $\mathscr{L}\{f(t)\} = F(s)$, defined by Eq. (2), exists for $s > a$.

To establish this theorem it is necessary to show only that the integral in Eq. (2) converges for $s > a$. Splitting the improper integral into two parts, we have

$$\int_0^\infty e^{-st}f(t)\,dt = \int_0^M e^{-st}f(t)\,dt + \int_M^\infty e^{-st}f(t)\,dt. \tag{3}$$

The first integral on the right side of Eq. (3) exists by hypothesis (i) of the theorem; hence the existence of $F(s)$ depends on the convergence of the second integral. By hypothesis (ii) we have, for $t \geq M$,

$$|e^{-st}f(t)| \leq Ke^{-st}e^{at} = Ke^{(a-s)t},$$

and thus, by Theorem 6.1, $F(s)$ exists provided $\displaystyle\int_M^\infty e^{(a-s)t}\,dt$ converges. Referring to Example 1 with c replaced by $a - s$, we see that this latter integral converges when $a - s < 0$, which establishes Theorem 6.2.

Unless the contrary is specifically stated, we will, in this chapter, deal only with functions satisfying the conditions of Theorem 6.2. Such functions will be described as piecewise continuous, and of *exponential order* as $t \to \infty$. The Laplace transforms of some important elementary functions are given in the examples below.

Example 4.   Let $f(t) = 1, t \geq 0$. Then

$$\mathscr{L}\{1\} = \int_0^\infty e^{-st}\,dt = \frac{1}{s}, \qquad s > 0.$$

Example 5.   Let $f(t) = e^{at}, t \geq 0$. Then

$$\mathscr{L}\{e^{at}\} = \int_0^\infty e^{-st}e^{at}\,dt = \int_0^\infty e^{-(s-a)t}\,dt$$

$$= \frac{1}{s - a}, \qquad s > a.$$

Example 6. Let $f(t) = \sin at, t \geq 0$. Then

$$\mathscr{L}\{\sin at\} = F(s) = \int_0^\infty e^{-st} \sin at \, dt, \qquad s > 0.$$

Since

$$F(s) = \lim_{A \to \infty} \int_0^A e^{-st} \sin at \, dt,$$

upon integrating by parts we obtain

$$F(s) = \lim_{A \to \infty} \left[-\frac{e^{-st} \cos at}{a} \Big|_0^A - \frac{s}{a} \int_0^A e^{-st} \cos at \, dt \right]$$

$$= \frac{1}{a} - \frac{s}{a} \int_0^\infty e^{-st} \cos at \, dt.$$

A second integration by parts then yields

$$F(s) = \frac{1}{a} - \frac{s^2}{a^2} \int_0^\infty e^{-st} \sin at \, dt$$

$$= \frac{1}{a} - \frac{s^2}{a^2} F(s).$$

Hence, solving for $F(s)$,

$$F(s) = \frac{a}{s^2 + a^2}, \qquad s > 0.$$

Now let us suppose that f_1 and f_2 are two functions whose Laplace transforms exist for $s > a_1$ and $s > a_2$, respectively. Then, for s greater than the maximum of a_1 and a_2,

$$\mathscr{L}\{c_1 f_1(t) + c_2 f_2(t)\} = \int_0^\infty e^{-st}[c_1 f_1(t) + c_2 f_2(t)] \, dt$$

$$= c_1 \int_0^\infty e^{-st} f_1(t) \, dt + c_2 \int_0^\infty e^{-st} f_2(t) \, dt,$$

and hence

$$\mathscr{L}\{c_1 f_1(t) + c_2 f_2(t)\} = c_1 \mathscr{L}\{f_1(t)\} + c_2 \mathscr{L}\{f_2(t)\}. \tag{4}$$

Equation (4) is a statement of the fact that the Laplace transform is a *linear operator*. This property is of paramount importance, and we will make frequent use of it later.

PROBLEMS

1. Sketch the graph of each of the following functions. In each case determine whether f is continuous, piecewise continuous, or neither on the interval $0 \leq t \leq 3$.

(a) $f(t) = \begin{cases} t^2, & 0 \leq t \leq 1 \\ 2 + t, & 1 < t \leq 2 \\ 6 - t, & 2 < t \leq 3 \end{cases}$

(b) $f(t) = \begin{cases} t^2, & 0 \leq t \leq 1 \\ (t - 1)^{-1}, & 1 < t \leq 2 \\ 1, & 2 < t \leq 3 \end{cases}$

(c) $f(t) = \begin{cases} t^2, & 0 \leq t \leq 1 \\ 1, & 1 < t \leq 2 \\ 3 - t, & 2 < t \leq 3 \end{cases}$

2. Find the Laplace transform of each of the following functions.

(a) t (b) t^2 (c) t^n, where n is a positive integer

3. Find the Laplace transform of $f(t) = \cos at$, where a is a real constant.

4. Recalling that $2 \cosh bt = e^{bt} + e^{-bt}$ and $2 \sinh bt = e^{bt} - e^{-bt}$, find the Laplace transform of each of the following functions; a and b are real constants.

(a) $\cosh bt$ (b) $\sinh bt$
(c) $e^{at} \cosh bt$ (d) $e^{at} \sinh bt$

5. Recall that $2 \cos bt = e^{ibt} + e^{-ibt}$ and $2i \sin bt = e^{ibt} - e^{-ibt}$. Assuming that the necessary elementary integration formulas extend to this case, find the Laplace transform of each of the following functions; a and b are real constants.

(a) $\sin bt$ (b) $\cos bt$
(c) $e^{at} \sin bt$ (d) $e^{at} \cos bt$

6. Using integration by parts, find the Laplace transform of each of the following functions; n is a positive integer and a is a real constant.

(a) te^{at} (b) $t \sin at$
(c) $t \cosh at$ (d) $t^n e^{at}$
(e) $t^n \sin at$ (f) $t^n \sinh at$

7. Determine whether each of the following integrals converges or diverges.

(a) $\displaystyle\int_0^\infty (t^2 + 1)^{-1} \, dt$ (b) $\displaystyle\int_0^\infty te^{-t} \, dt$ (c) $\displaystyle\int_1^\infty t^{-2}e^t \, dt$

8. Suppose that f and f' are continuous for $t \geq 0$, and of exponential order as $t \to \infty$. Show by integration by parts that if $F(s) = \mathcal{L}\{f(t)\}$, then $\lim\limits_{s \to \infty} F(s) = 0$. The result is actually true under less restrictive conditions, such as those of Theorem 6.2.

9. Consider the Laplace transform of $f(t) = t^p$, where we first assume that p is a positive real constant.

(a) Show that

$$\mathcal{L}\{t^p\} = \int_0^\infty e^{-st}t^p \, dt = \frac{1}{s^{p+1}} \int_0^\infty e^{-u}u^p \, du, \qquad s > 0.$$

(b) Show by integrating by parts that if $p = n$, then

$$\int_0^\infty e^{-u}u^n \, du = n!,$$

and hence

$$\mathcal{L}\{t^n\} = \frac{n!}{s^{n+1}}, \qquad s > 0.$$

For $p < 0$ the integral $\int_0^\infty e^{-u}u^p \, du$ is also improper at $u = 0$ since the integrand becomes unbounded as $u \to 0$. However, this integral can be shown to converge for $p > -1$; therefore, on this interval it defines a function of p, which is known as the Gamma function. It is conventional to write

$$\Gamma(p + 1) = \int_0^\infty e^{-u}u^p \, du.$$

From parts (a) and (b) it follows that

$$\mathcal{L}\{t^p\} = \frac{\Gamma(p + 1)}{s^{p+1}}, \qquad s > 0,$$

whether or not p is an integer, provided that $p > -1$.

6.2 SOLUTION OF INITIAL VALUE PROBLEMS

In this section we will show how the Laplace transform can be used to solve initial value problems for differential equations with constant coefficients. The usefulness of the Laplace transform in this connection rests primarily on the fact that the transform of f' is related in a simple way to the transform of f. The relationship is made clear in the following theorem.

Theorem 6.3.   *Suppose that f is continuous and that f' is piecewise continuous on any interval $0 \leq t \leq A$. Suppose further that there exist constants K, a, and M such that $|f(t)| \leq Ke^{at}$ for $t \geq M$. Then $\mathcal{L}\{f'(t)\}$ exists for $s > a$, and moreover*

$$\mathcal{L}\{f'(t)\} = s\mathcal{L}\{f(t)\} - f(0). \tag{1}$$

In order to prove this theorem we consider the integral

$$\int_0^A e^{-st} f'(t)\, dt.$$

Letting $t_1, t_2, \ldots, t_n$ be the points in the interval $0 \le t \le A$ where f' is discontinuous, we obtain

$$\int_0^A e^{-st} f'(t)\, dt = \int_0^{t_1} e^{-st} f'(t)\, dt + \int_{t_1}^{t_2} e^{-st} f'(t)\, dt + \cdots + \int_{t_n}^A e^{-st} f'(t)\, dt.$$

Integrating each term on the right by parts yields

$$\int_0^A e^{-st} f'(t)\, dt = e^{-st} f(t)\Big|_0^{t_1} + e^{-st} f(t)\Big|_{t_1}^{t_2} + \cdots + e^{-st} f(t)\Big|_{t_n}^A$$

$$+ s\left[\int_0^{t_1} e^{-st} f(t)\, dt + \int_{t_1}^{t_2} e^{-st} f(t)\, dt + \cdots + \int_{t_n}^A e^{-st} f(t)\, dt\right].$$

Since f is continuous, the contributions of the integrated terms at $t_1, t_2, \ldots, t_n$ cancel. Combining the integrals gives

$$\int_0^A e^{-st} f'(t)\, dt = e^{-sA} f(A) - f(0) + s\int_0^A e^{-st} f(t)\, dt.$$

As $A \to \infty$, $e^{-sA} f(A) \to 0$ whenever $s > a$. Hence, for $s > a$,

$$\mathscr{L}\{f'(t)\} = s\mathscr{L}\{f(t)\} - f(0), \tag{1}$$

which establishes the theorem.

If f' and f'' satisfy the same conditions that are imposed on f and f' respectively in Theorem 6.3, then it follows that the Laplace transform of f'' also exists for $s > a$ and is given by

$$\mathscr{L}\{f''(t)\} = s^2\mathscr{L}\{f(t)\} - sf(0) - f'(0). \tag{2}$$

Indeed, provided the function f and its derivatives satisfy suitable conditions, an expression for the transform of the nth derivative $f^{(n)}$ can be derived by successive applications of this theorem. The result is given in the following corollary.

Corollary. *Suppose that the functions $f, f', \ldots, f^{(n-1)}$ are continuous, and that $f^{(n)}$ is piecewise continuous on any interval $0 \le t \le A$. Suppose further that there exist constants K, a, and M such that $|f(t)| \le Ke^{at}$, $|f'(t)| \le Ke^{at}, \ldots, |f^{(n-1)}(t)| \le Ke^{at}$ for $t \ge M$. Then $\mathscr{L}\{f^{(n)}(t)\}$ exists for $s > a$ and is given by*

$$\mathscr{L}\{f^{(n)}(t)\} = s^n\mathscr{L}\{f(t)\} - s^{n-1}f(0) - \cdots - sf^{(n-2)}(0) - f^{(n-1)}(0). \tag{3}$$

Now let us consider the initial value problem consisting of the differential equation

$$y'' - y' - 2y = 0 \tag{4}$$

and the initial conditions

$$y(0) = 1, \qquad y'(0) = 0. \tag{5}$$

This simple problem is easily solved by the methods of Section 3.5. The auxiliary equation is

$$r^2 - r - 2 = (r - 2)(r + 1) = 0, \tag{6}$$

and consequently the general solution of Eq. (4) is

$$y = c_1 e^{-t} + c_2 e^{2t}. \tag{7}$$

The initial conditions (5) require that $c_1 + c_2 = 1$, $-c_1 + 2c_2 = 0$; hence $c_1 = \frac{2}{3}$ and $c_2 = \frac{1}{3}$, so that the solution of the initial value problem (4) and (5) is

$$y = \phi(t) = \tfrac{2}{3} e^{-t} + \tfrac{1}{3} e^{2t}. \tag{8}$$

Now let us solve the given problem by means of the Laplace transform. To do this we must assume that the problem has a solution $y = \phi(t)$, which with its first two derivatives satisfies the conditions of the Corollary. Then, taking the Laplace transform of the differential equation (4), we obtain

$$\mathscr{L}\{y''\} - \mathscr{L}\{y'\} - 2\mathscr{L}\{y\} = 0, \tag{9}$$

where we have used the linear character of the transform to write the transform of a sum as the sum of the separate transforms. Upon using the Corollary to express $\mathscr{L}\{y''\}$ and $\mathscr{L}\{y'\}$ in terms of $\mathscr{L}\{y\}$, we find that Eq. (9) then takes the form

$$s^2 \mathscr{L}\{y\} - sy(0) - y'(0) - [s\mathscr{L}\{y\} - y(0)] - 2\mathscr{L}\{y\} = 0,$$

or

$$(s^2 - s - 2)Y(s) + (1 - s)y(0) - y'(0) = 0, \tag{10}$$

where $Y(s) = \mathscr{L}\{y\}$. Substituting for $y(0)$ and $y'(0)$ in Eq. (10) from the initial conditions (5), and then solving for $Y(s)$, we obtain

$$Y(s) = \frac{s - 1}{s^2 - s - 2} = \frac{s - 1}{(s - 2)(s + 1)}. \tag{11}$$

We have thus obtained an expression for the Laplace transform $Y(s)$ of the solution $y = \phi(t)$ of the given initial value problem. To determine the function ϕ we must find the function whose Laplace transform is $Y(s)$, as given by Eq. (11).

In the present case this can be done most easily by expanding the right side of Eq. (11) in partial fractions. Thus we find that

$$Y(s) = \frac{\frac{1}{3}}{s-2} + \frac{\frac{2}{3}}{s+1}. \tag{12}$$

Finally, using the result of Example 5 of Section 6.1, it follows that $\frac{1}{3}e^{2t}$ has the transform $\frac{1}{3}(s-2)^{-1}$; similarly $\frac{2}{3}e^{-t}$ has the transform $\frac{2}{3}(s+1)^{-1}$. Hence, by the linearity of the Laplace transform,

$$y = \phi(t) = \tfrac{1}{3}e^{2t} + \tfrac{2}{3}e^{-t}$$

has the transform (12). This is the same solution, of course, as that obtained earlier in a different way.

While in this simple problem the use of the Laplace transform offers no particular advantages, we can nevertheless point out some of the essential features of the transform method. In the first place, the transform $Y(s)$ of the unknown function $y = \phi(t)$ is found by solving an *algebraic equation*, Eq. (10), rather than a *differential equation*. Next, the solution satisfying the initial conditions (5) as well as the differential equation (4) is automatically found. Thus the task of determining appropriate values for the arbitrary constants appearing in the general solution does not arise. The reader should also note that the coefficient of $Y(s)$ in Eq. (10) is precisely the polynomial that also appears in the auxiliary equation (6); in fact, this is always the case. Since the use of the partial fraction expansion of $Y(s)$ in order to determine $\phi(t)$ requires that this polynomial be factored, the use of Laplace transforms does not avoid the necessity of finding the roots of the auxiliary equation. For equations of higher than second order this may be a difficult algebraic problem, particularly if the roots are irrational or complex.

The main difficulty that occurs in solving initial value problems by the transform technique lies in the problem of determining the function $y = \phi(t)$ corresponding to the transform $Y(s)$. This problem is known as the inversion problem for the Laplace transform; $\phi(t)$ is called the inverse transform corresponding to $Y(s)$, and the process of finding $\phi(t)$ from $Y(s)$ is known as "inverting the transform." We will also use the notation $\mathscr{L}^{-1}\{Y(s)\}$ to denote the inverse transform of $Y(s)$. There is a general formula for the inverse Laplace transform, but its use requires a knowledge of the theory of functions of a complex variable, and we will not consider it in this book. However, it is still possible to develop many important properties of the Laplace transform, and to solve many interesting problems, without the use of complex variables.

In solving the initial value problem (4), (5) we did not consider the question of whether there may be functions other than that given by Eq. (8) which also have the transform (12). In fact, it can be shown that if f is a continuous function with the Laplace transform F, then there is no other

TABLE 6.1 Elementary Laplace Transforms

$f(t) = \mathcal{L}^{-1}\{F(s)\}$	$F(s) = \mathcal{L}\{f(t)\}$	Notes
1	$\dfrac{1}{s}, \quad s > 0$	
e^{at}	$\dfrac{1}{s - a}, \quad s > a$	
$\sin at$	$\dfrac{a}{s^2 + a^2}, \quad s > 0$	
t^n, n = positive integer	$\dfrac{n!}{s^{n+1}}, \quad s > 0$	
$t^p, p > -1$	$\dfrac{\Gamma(p + 1)}{s^{p+1}}, \quad s > 0$	Sec. 6.1; Prob. 9
$\cos at$	$\dfrac{s}{s^2 + a^2}, \quad s > 0$	
$\sinh at$	$\dfrac{a}{s^2 - a^2}, \quad s > |a|$	
$\cosh at$	$\dfrac{s}{s^2 - a^2}, \quad s > |a|$	
$e^{at} \sin bt$	$\dfrac{b}{(s - a)^2 + b^2}, \quad s > a$	
$e^{at} \cos bt$	$\dfrac{s - a}{(s - a)^2 + b^2}, \quad s > a$	
$t^n e^{at}$, n = positive integer	$\dfrac{n!}{(s - a)^{n+1}}, \quad s > a$	
$u_c(t)$	$\dfrac{e^{-cs}}{s}, \quad s > 0$	Sec. 6.3
$u_c(t)f(t - c)$	$e^{-cs}F(s)$	Sec. 6.3
$e^{ct}f(t)$	$F(s - c)$	Sec. 6.3
$f(ct)$	$\dfrac{1}{c} F\left(\dfrac{s}{c}\right), \quad c > 0$	Sec. 6.3; Prob. 4
$\displaystyle\int_0^t f(t - u)g(u)\,du$	$F(s)G(s)$	Sec. 6.5
$\delta(t - c)$	e^{-cs}	Sec. 6.4
$f^{(n)}(t)$	$s^n F(s) - s^{n-1}f(0) - \cdots - f^{(n-1)}(0)$	Sec. 6.2
$(-t)^n f(t)$	$F^{(n)}(s)$	Sec. 6.2; Prob. 14

continuous function having the same transform. In other words, there is essentially a one-to-one correspondence between functions and their Laplace transforms. This fact suggests the compilation of a table (somewhat analogous to a table of integrals) giving the transforms of functions which are frequently encountered, and vice versa; see Table 6.1.* The entries in the second column are the transforms of those in the first column. Perhaps more important, the functions in the first column are the inverse transforms of those in the second column. Thus, for example, if the transform of the solution of a differential equation is known, the solution itself can often be found merely by looking it up in the table. Some of the entries in Table 6.1 have been used as examples, or appear as problems in Section 6.1, while others will be developed later in the chapter. The third column of the table indicates where the derivation of some of the given transforms may be found.

Frequently, a Laplace transform $F(s)$ will be expressible as a sum of several terms,

$$F(s) = F_1(s) + F_2(s) + \cdots + F_n(s). \tag{13}$$

Suppose that $f_1(t) = \mathcal{L}^{-1}\{F_1(s)\}, \ldots, f_n(t) = \mathcal{L}^{-1}\{F_n(s)\}$. Then the function

$$f(t) = f_1(t) + \cdots + f_n(t)$$

has the Laplace transform $F(s)$. By the uniqueness property stated above there is no other continuous function f having the same transform. Thus

$$\mathcal{L}^{-1}\{F(s)\} = \mathcal{L}^{-1}\{F_1(s)\} + \cdots + \mathcal{L}^{-1}\{F_n(s)\}; \tag{14}$$

that is, the inverse Laplace transform is also a linear operator. In many problems it is convenient to make use of this property by decomposing a given transform into a sum of functions whose inverse transforms are already known or can be found in the table.

As a further illustration of the technique of solving initial value problems by means of the Laplace transform, consider the following example.

Example.   Find the solution of the differential equation

$$y'' + y = \sin 2t, \tag{15}$$

which satisfies the initial conditions

$$y(0) = 0, \qquad y'(0) = 1. \tag{16}$$

We will assume that this initial value problem has a solution $y = \phi(t)$, which with its first two derivatives satisfies the conditions of the Corollary to Theorem 6.3. Then, taking the Laplace transform of the differential equation gives

$$s^2 Y(s) - sy(0) - y'(0) + Y(s) = \frac{2}{s^2 + 4},$$

* Larger tables are also available. See the references at the end of the chapter.

where the transform of sin $2t$ has been obtained from Table 6.1. Substituting for $y(0)$ and $y'(0)$ from the initial conditions and solving for $Y(s)$ yields

$$Y(s) = \frac{s^2 + 6}{(s^2 + 1)(s^2 + 4)}.$$

Using partial fractions we can write $Y(s)$ in the form

$$Y(s) = \frac{as + b}{s^2 + 1} + \frac{cs + d}{s^2 + 4}.$$

Upon determining the constants a, b, c, and d, we find that

$$Y(s) = \frac{\frac{5}{3}}{s^2 + 1} - \frac{\frac{2}{3}}{s^2 + 4}.$$

Referring to Example 6 of Section 6.1, or to Table 6.1, it follows that

$$y = \phi(t) = \tfrac{5}{3}\sin t - \tfrac{1}{3}\sin 2t. \tag{17}$$

The reader should note that in solving a differential equation, such as Eq. (15), by means of the Laplace transform, we *assume* at the beginning that the solution $y = \phi(t)$ *has* a transform $Y(s)$. Once the solution has been found, this assumption should be justified. For example, the expression on the right side of Eq. (17) clearly satisfies the conditions of the Corollary to Theorem 6.3 for $n = 2$. This example also illustrates that nonhomogeneous equations are solved in the same manner as homogeneous ones. Again the solution satisfying the initial conditions is found directly, without first finding the general solution of the differential equation.

PROBLEMS

In each of Problems 1 through 10 use the Laplace transform to solve the given initial value problem.

1. $y'' - y' - 6y = 0$; $y(0) = 1$, $y'(0) = -1$
2. $y'' + 3y' + 2y = 0$; $y(0) = 1$, $y'(0) = 0$
3. $y'' - 2y' + 2y = 0$; $y(0) = 0$, $y'(0) = 1$
4. $y'' - 4y' + 4y = 0$; $y(0) = 1$, $y'(0) = 1$
5. $y^{\mathrm{iv}} - 4y''' + 6y'' - 4y' + y = 0$;

   $y(0) = 0$, $y'(0) = 1$, $y''(0) = 0$, $y'''(0) = 1$
6. $y^{\mathrm{iv}} - y = 0$; $y(0) = 1$, $y'(0) = 0$, $y''(0) = 1$, $y'''(0) = 0$
7. $y'' - 2y' - 2y = 0$; $y(0) = 2$, $y'(0) = 0$
8. $y'' + \omega^2 y = \cos 2t$, $\omega^2 \neq 4$; $y(0) = 1$, $y'(0) = 0$
9. $y'' - 2y' + 2y = \cos t$; $y(0) = 1$, $y'(0) = 0$
10. $y'' - 2y' + 2y = e^{-t}$; $y(0) = 0$, $y'(0) = 1$

In each of Problems 11 and 12 find the Laplace transform $Y(s) = \mathcal{L}\{y\}$ of the solution of the given initial value problem. A method for determining the inverse transforms will be developed in Section 6.3.

11. $y'' + 4y = \begin{cases} 1, & 0 \leq t < \pi, \\ 0, & \pi \leq t < \infty; \end{cases}$ $y(0) = 1, \quad y'(0) = 0$

12. $y'' + y = \begin{cases} t, & 0 \leq t < 1, \\ 0, & 1 \leq t < \infty; \end{cases}$ $y(0) = 0, \quad y'(0) = 0$

*13. The Laplace transform of certain functions can be conveniently found from their Taylor series expansions.

(a) Using the Taylor series for $\sin t$,

$$\sin t = \sum_{n=0}^{\infty} \frac{(-1)^n t^{2n+1}}{(2n+1)!},$$

and assuming that the Laplace transform of this series can be computed term by term, verify that

$$\mathcal{L}\{\sin t\} = \frac{1}{s^2 + 1}, \quad s > 1.$$

(b) Let

$$f(t) = \begin{cases} (\sin t)/t, & t \neq 0, \\ 1, & t = 0. \end{cases}$$

Find the Taylor series for f about $t = 0$. Assuming that the Laplace transform of this function can be computed term by term, verify that

$$\mathcal{L}\{f(t)\} = \arctan \frac{1}{s}, \quad s > 1.$$

(c) The Bessel function of the first kind of order zero J_0 has the Taylor series (see Section 4.7)

$$J_0(t) = \sum_{n=0}^{\infty} \frac{(-1)^n t^{2n}}{2^{2n}(n!)^2}.$$

Assuming that the following Laplace transforms can be computed term by term, verify that

$$\mathcal{L}\{J_0(t)\} = (s^2 + 1)^{-1/2}, \quad s > 1,$$

and that

$$\mathcal{L}\{J_0(\sqrt{t})\} = \frac{1}{s} e^{-1/4s}, \quad s > 0.$$

Problems 14 through 17 are concerned with differentiation of the Laplace transform.

14. Let

$$F(s) = \int_0^\infty e^{-st} f(t) \, dt.$$

represent the Laplace transform of f. It is possible to show that as long as f satisfies the conditions of Theorem 6.2, it is legitimate to differentiate under the integral sign with respect to the parameter s when $s > a$.

(a) Show that

$$F'(s) = \mathcal{L}\{-tf(t)\}.$$

(b) Show that

$$F^{(n)}(s) = \mathcal{L}\{(-t)^n f(t)\};$$

hence differentiating the Laplace transform corresponds to multiplying the original function by $-t$.

15. Use the result of Problem 14 to find the Laplace transform of each of the following functions.

(a) $f(t) = t^n e^{at}$, where a is a real constant and n is a positive integer

(b) $f(t) = t^2 \sin t$

(c) $f(t) = t^n$, where n is a positive integer

*16. Consider Bessel's equation of order zero

$$ty'' + y' + ty = 0.$$

Recall from Section 4.3 that $t = 0$ is a regular singular point for this equation, and therefore solutions may become unbounded as $t \to 0$. However, let us try to determine whether there are any solutions which remain finite at $t = 0$, and have finite derivatives there. Assuming that there is such a solution $y = \phi(t)$, let $Y(s) = \mathcal{L}\{\phi(t)\}$.

(a) Show that $Y(s)$ satisfies

$$(1 + s^2) Y'(s) + s Y(s) = 0.$$

(b) Show that $Y(s) = c(1 + s^2)^{-1/2}$, where c is an arbitrary constant.

(c) Expanding $(1 + s^2)^{-1/2}$ in a binomial series valid for $s > 1$, and assuming that it is permissible to take the inverse transform term by term, show that

$$y = c \sum_{n=0}^{\infty} \frac{(-1)^n t^{2n}}{2^{2n}(n!)^2} = c J_0(t),$$

where J_0 is the Bessel function of the first kind of order zero. Note that $J_0(0) = 1$, and that J_0 has finite derivatives of all orders at $t = 0$. It was shown in Section 4.7 that the second solution of this equation becomes unbounded as $t \to 0$.

17. For each of the following initial value problems use the results of Problem 14 to find the differential equation satisfied by $Y(s) = \mathcal{L}\{\phi(t)\}$, where $y = \phi(t)$ is the solution of the given initial value problem.

(a) $y'' + ty = 0;$ $y(0) = 1,$ $y'(0) = 0$ (Airy's equation)

(b) $(1 - t^2)y'' - 2ty' + \alpha(\alpha + 1)y = 0;$ $y(0) = 0,$ $y'(0) = 1$
(Legendre's equation)

Note that the differential equation for $Y(s)$ is of first order in part (a), but of second order in part (b). This is due to the fact that t appears at most to the first power in the equation of part (a), whereas it appears to the second power in that of part (b). This illustrates that the Laplace transform is not often useful in solving differential equations with variable coefficients, unless all of the coefficients are at most linear functions of the independent variable.

*18. The functions

$$erf(t) = \frac{2}{\sqrt{\pi}} \int_0^t e^{-u^2} \, du, \qquad erfc(t) = \frac{2}{\sqrt{\pi}} \int_t^\infty e^{-u^2} \, du,$$

known as the error function and complementary error function respectively, occur frequently in heat conduction and probability problems, for example. These functions are well-tabulated and may be considered as known. Since it can be shown that

$$\int_0^\infty e^{-u^2} \, du = \frac{\sqrt{\pi}}{2},$$

it follows that $erf(t) + erfc(t) = 1$. Assuming that it is permissible to interchange the order of integration, show that

$$\mathcal{L}\{erf(t)\} = \frac{1}{s} e^{s^2/4} erfc(s/2), \qquad s > 0.$$

Also find $\mathcal{L}\{erfc(t)\}$.

6.3 STEP FUNCTIONS

In Section 6.2 the general procedure involved in solving initial value problems by means of the Laplace transform was outlined. Some of the most interesting elementary applications of the transform method occur in the solution of linear differential equations with discontinuous or impulsive forcing functions. Equations of this type frequently arise in the analysis of the flow of current in electric circuits or the vibrations of mechanical systems. In this section and the following ones we will develop some additional properties of the Laplace transform which are useful in the solution of such problems. Unless a specific statement is made to the contrary, all functions appearing below will be assumed to be piecewise continuous and of exponential order, so that their Laplace transforms exist, at least for s sufficiently large.

In order to deal effectively with functions having jump discontinuities, it is very helpful to introduce a function known as the *unit step function*. This function will be denoted by u_c, and is defined by

$$u_c(t) = \begin{cases} 0, & t < c, \\ 1, & t \geq c, \end{cases} \qquad c \geq 0. \tag{1}$$

The graph of $y = u_c(t)$ is shown in Figure 6.2.

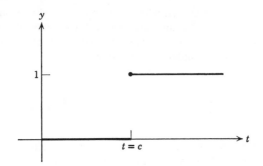

FIGURE 6.2 $y = u_c(t)$.

Example 1.   Sketch the graph of $y = h(t)$, where
$$h(t) = u_\pi(t) - u_{2\pi}(t), \qquad t \geq 0.$$
From the definition of $u_c(t)$ in Eq. (1) we have
$$h(t) = \begin{cases} 0 - 0 = 0, & 0 \leq t < \pi, \\ 1 - 0 = 1, & \pi \leq t < 2\pi, \\ 1 - 1 = 0, & 2\pi \leq t < \infty. \end{cases}$$
Thus the equation $y = h(t)$ has the graph shown in Figure 6.3.

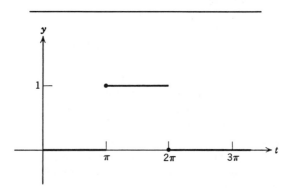

FIGURE 6.3 $y = u_\pi(t) - u_{2\pi}(t)$.

The unit step function u_c can also be used to translate a given function f, with domain $t \geq 0$, a distance c to the right. For example, the function defined by
$$y = u_c(t)f(t - c) = \begin{cases} 0, & 0 \leq t < c, \\ f(t - c), & t \geq c, \end{cases}$$
represents a translation of the function f a distance c in the positive t direction; see Figure 6.4.

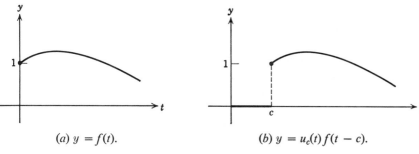

(a) $y = f(t)$.

(b) $y = u_c(t) f(t - c)$.

FIGURE 6.4

The Laplace transform of u_c is easily determined:

$$\mathcal{L}\{u_c(t)\} = \int_0^\infty e^{-st} u_c(t) \, dt$$

$$= \int_c^\infty e^{-st} \, dt$$

$$= \frac{e^{-cs}}{s}, \qquad s > 0. \tag{2}$$

The unit step function is particularly important in transform theory because of the following relation between the transform of $f(t)$ and that of its translation $u_c(t)f(t - c)$.

Theorem 6.4. *If $F(s) = \mathcal{L}\{f(t)\}$ exists for $s > a \geq 0$, and if c is a positive constant, then*

$$\mathcal{L}\{u_c(t)f(t - c)\} = e^{-cs}\mathcal{L}\{f(t)\} = e^{-cs}F(s), \qquad s > a. \tag{3}$$

Conversely, if $f(t) = \mathcal{L}^{-1}\{F(s)\}$, then

$$u_c(t)f(t - c) = \mathcal{L}^{-1}\{e^{-cs}F(s)\}. \tag{4}$$

To prove Theorem 6.4 it is sufficient to compute the transform of $u_c(t)f(t - c)$. Clearly

$$\mathcal{L}\{u_c(t)f(t - c)\} = \int_0^\infty e^{-st} u_c(t)f(t - c) \, dt$$

$$= \int_c^\infty e^{-st} f(t - c) \, dt.$$

Introducing a new integration variable $\xi = t - c$, we have

$$\mathcal{L}\{u_c(t)f(t - c)\} = \int_0^\infty e^{-(\xi+c)s} f(\xi) \, d\xi$$

$$= e^{-cs} \int_0^\infty e^{-s\xi} f(\xi) \, d\xi$$

$$= e^{-cs} F(s).$$

Thus Eq. (3) is established; Eq. (4) follows by taking the inverse transform of both sides of Eq. (3).

A simple example of this theorem occurs if we take $f(t) = 1$. Recalling that $\mathcal{L}\{1\} = 1/s$, we immediately have from Eq. (3) that $\mathcal{L}\{u_c(t)\} = e^{-cs}/s$. This result agrees with that of Eq. (2). Examples 2 and 3 illustrate further how Theorem 6.4 can be used in the calculation of transforms and inverse transforms.

Example 2.   If the function f is defined by

$$f(t) = \begin{cases} \sin t, & 0 \le t < 2\pi, \\ \sin t + \cos t, & t \ge 2\pi, \end{cases}$$

find $\mathcal{L}\{f(t)\}$.

Note that $f(t) = \sin t + g(t)$, where

$$g(t) = \begin{cases} 0, & t < 2\pi, \\ \cos t, & t \ge 2\pi. \end{cases}$$

Thus

$$g(t) = u_{2\pi}(t) \cos (t - 2\pi)$$

and

$$\mathcal{L}\{f(t)\} = \mathcal{L}\{\sin t\} + \mathcal{L}\{u_{2\pi}(t) \cos (t - 2\pi)\}$$
$$= \mathcal{L}\{\sin t\} + e^{-2\pi s}\mathcal{L}\{\cos t\}.$$

Introducing the transforms of $\sin t$ and $\cos t$, we obtain

$$\mathcal{L}\{f(t)\} = \frac{1}{s^2 + 1} + e^{-2\pi s}\frac{s}{s^2 + 1}$$
$$= \frac{1 + e^{-2\pi s}s}{s^2 + 1}.$$

The reader should compare this method with the calculation of $\mathcal{L}\{f(t)\}$ directly from the definition.

Example 3.   Find the inverse transform of

$$F(s) = \frac{1 - e^{-2s}}{s^2}.$$

From the linearity of the inverse transform we have

$$f(t) = \mathcal{L}^{-1}\{F(s)\} = \mathcal{L}^{-1}\left\{\frac{1}{s^2}\right\} - \mathcal{L}^{-1}\left\{\frac{e^{-2s}}{s^2}\right\}$$
$$= t - u_2(t)(t - 2).$$

The function f may also be written as

$$f(t) = \begin{cases} t, & 0 \le t < 2, \\ 2, & t \ge 2. \end{cases}$$

The following theorem contains another very useful property of Laplace transforms which is somewhat analogous to that given in Theorem 6.4.

Theorem 6.5.   *If* $F(s) = \mathcal{L}\{f(t)\}$ *exists for* $s > a \ge 0,$ *and if* c *is a* constant, then

$$\mathcal{L}\{e^{ct}f(t)\} = F(s - c), \qquad s > a + c. \tag{5}$$

Conversely, if $f(t) = \mathcal{L}^{-1}\{F(s)\},$ *then*

$$e^{ct}f(t) = \mathcal{L}^{-1}\{F(s - c)\}. \tag{6}$$

According to Theorem 6.5, multiplication of $f(t)$ by e^{ct} results in a translation of the transform $F(s)$ a distance c in the positive s-direction, and conversely. The proof of this theorem requires merely the evaluation of $\mathcal{L}\{e^{ct}f(t)\}$. Thus

$$\mathcal{L}\{e^{ct}f(t)\} = \int_0^\infty e^{-st}e^{ct}f(t)\,dt$$
$$= \int_0^\infty e^{-(s-c)t}f(t)\,dt$$
$$= F(s - c).$$

which is Eq. (5). The restriction $s > a + c$ follows from the observation that, according to hypothesis (ii) of Theorem 6.2, $|f(t)| \le Ke^{at}$; hence $|e^{ct}f(t)| \le Ke^{(a+c)t}$. Equation (6) follows by taking the inverse transform of Eq. (5), and the proof is complete.

The principal application of Theorem 6.5 is in the evaluation of certain inverse transforms, as illustrated by Example 4.

Example 4.   Find the inverse transform of

$$G(s) = \frac{1}{s^2 - 4s + 5}.$$

By completing the square in the denominator we can write

$$G(s) = \frac{1}{(s - 2)^2 + 1} = F(s - 2),$$

where $F(s) = (s^2 + 1)^{-1}$. Since $\mathcal{L}^{-1}\{F(s)\} = \sin t$, it follows from Theorem 6.5 that

$$g(t) = \mathcal{L}^{-1}\{G(s)\} = e^{2t}\sin t.$$

The results of this section are often useful in solving differential equations, particularly those having discontinuous forcing functions. The next section is devoted to an example illustrating this fact.

PROBLEMS

1. Sketch the graph of each of the following functions on the interval $t \geq 0$.

(a) $u_1(t) + 2u_3(t) - 6u_4(t)$

(b) $(t - 3)u_2(t) - (t - 2)u_3(t)$

(c) $f(t - \pi)u_\pi(t)$,   where $f(t) = t^2$

(d) $f(t - 3)u_3(t)$,   where $f(t) = \sin t$

(e) $f(t - 1)u_2(t)$,   where $f(t) = 2t$

2. Find the Laplace transform of each of the following functions.

(a) $f(t) = \begin{cases} 0, & t < 2 \\ (t - 2)^2, & t \geq 2 \end{cases}$ (b) $f(t) = \begin{cases} 0, & t < 1 \\ t^2 - 2t + 2, & t \geq 1 \end{cases}$

(c) $f(t) = \begin{cases} 0, & t < \pi \\ t - \pi, & \pi \leq t < 2\pi \\ 0, & t \geq 2\pi \end{cases}$ (d) $f(t) = u_1(t) + 2u_3(t) - 6u_4(t)$

(e) $f(t) = (t - 3)u_2(t) - (t - 2)u_3(t)$

3. Find the inverse Laplace transform of each of the following functions.

(a) $F(s) = \dfrac{3!}{(s - 2)^4}$ (b) $F(s) = \dfrac{e^{-2s}}{s^2 + s - 2}$

(c) $F(s) = \dfrac{2(s - 1)e^{-2s}}{s^2 - 2s + 2}$ (d) $F(s) = \dfrac{2e^{-2s}}{s^2 - 4}$

(e) $F(s) = \dfrac{(s - 2)e^{-s}}{s^2 - 4s + 3}$

4. Suppose that $F(s) = \mathcal{L}\{f(t)\}$ exists for $s > a \geq 0$.

(a) Show that if c is a positive constant, then

$$\mathcal{L}\{f(ct)\} = \frac{1}{c} F\left(\frac{s}{c}\right), \qquad s > ca.$$

(b) Show that if k is a positive constant, then

$$\mathcal{L}^{-1}\{F(ks)\} = \frac{1}{k} f\left(\frac{t}{k}\right).$$

(c) Show that if a and b are constants with $a > 0$, then

$$\mathcal{L}^{-1}\{F(as + b)\} = \frac{1}{a} e^{-bt/a} f\left(\frac{t}{a}\right).$$

5. Using the results of Problem 4, find the inverse Laplace transform of each of the following functions.

(a) $F(s) = \dfrac{2^{n+1}n!}{s^{n+1}}$

(b) $F(s) = \dfrac{2s + 1}{4s^2 + 4s + 5}$

(c) $F(s) = \dfrac{1}{9s^2 - 12s + 3}$

(d) $F(s) = \dfrac{e^2 e^{-4s}}{2s - 1}$

6. Find the Laplace transform of each of the following functions. In part (d) assume that term by term integration of the infinite series is permissible.

(a) $f(t) = \begin{cases} 1, & 0 \le t < 1 \\ 0, & t \ge 1 \end{cases}$

(b) $f(t) = \begin{cases} 1, & 0 \le t < 1 \\ 0, & 1 \le t < 2 \\ 1, & 2 \le t < 3 \\ 0, & t \ge 3 \end{cases}$

(c) $f(t) = 1 - u_1(t) + \cdots + u_{2n}(t) - u_{2n+1}(t)$

$\qquad = 1 + \displaystyle\sum_{k=1}^{2n+1} (-1)^k u_k(t)$

(d) $f(t) = 1 + \displaystyle\sum_{k=1}^{\infty} (-1)^k u_k(t).$ See Figure 6.5.

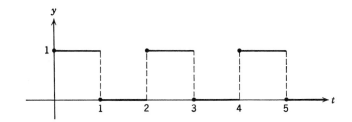

FIGURE 6.5   Square wave.

*7. Let f satisfy $f(t + T) = f(t)$ for all $t \ge 0$ and for some fixed positive number T; f is said to be periodic with period T on $0 \le t < \infty$.

$$\mathcal{L}\{f(t)\} = \frac{\displaystyle\int_0^T e^{-st} f(t)\, dt}{1 - e^{-sT}}$$

*8. Use the result of Problem 7 to find the Laplace transform of each of the following functions.

(a) $f(t) = \begin{cases} 1, & 0 \le t < 1, \\ 0, & 1 \le t < 2; \end{cases}$ $f(t + 2) = f(t).$ Compare with Problem 6(d).

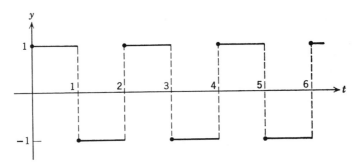

FIGURE 6.6   Square wave.

(b) $f(t) = \begin{cases} 1, & 0 \le t < 1, \\ -1, & 1 \le t < 2; \end{cases}$ $f(t + 2) = f(t)$.   See Figure 6.6.

(c) $f(t) = t$ for $0 \le t < 1$; $f(t + 1) = f(t)$.   See Figure 6.7.

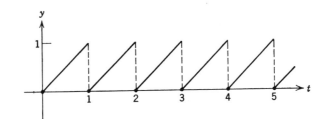

FIGURE 6.7   Sawtooth wave.

(d) $f(t) = \sin t$ for $0 \le t < \pi$; $f(t + \pi) = f(t)$.   See Figure 6.8.

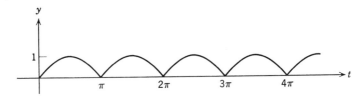

FIGURE 6.8   Rectified sine wave.

*9. (a) If $f(t) = 1 - u_1(t)$, find $\mathscr{L}\{f(t)\}$; compare with Problem 6(a). Sketch the graph of $y = f(t)$.

(b) Let $g(t) = \int_0^t f(\xi) \, d\xi$, where the function f is defined in part (a). Sketch the graph of $y = g(t)$, and find $\mathscr{L}\{g(t)\}$.

(c) Let $h(t) = g(t) - u_1(t)g(t - 1)$, where g is defined in part (b). Sketch the graph of $y = h(t)$, and find $\mathscr{L}\{h(t)\}$.

*10. Consider the function p defined by

$$p(t) = \begin{cases} t, & 0 \le t < 1 \\ 2 - t, & 1 \le t < 2; \end{cases} \qquad p(t + 2) = p(t).$$

(a) Sketch the graph of $y = p(t)$.

(b) Find $\mathcal{L}\{p(t)\}$ by noting that p is the periodic extension of the function h in Problem 9(c) and using the result of Problem 7.

(c) Find $\mathcal{L}\{p(t)\}$ by noting that

$$p(t) = \int_0^t f(t)\, dt,$$

where f is the function in Problem 8(b), and using Theorem 6.3.

6.3.1 A DIFFERENTIAL EQUATION WITH A DISCONTINUOUS FORCING FUNCTION

Let us now turn our attention to a typical problem involving a discontinuous forcing function. Consider the differential equation

$$y'' + 4y = h(t), \tag{1}$$

where (see Figure 6.3)

$$h(t) = \begin{cases} 1, & \pi \le t < 2\pi, \\ 0, & 0 \le t < \pi \text{ and } t \ge 2\pi. \end{cases} \tag{2}$$

Assume that the initial conditions are

$$y(0) = 1, \qquad y'(0) = 0. \tag{3}$$

This problem governs, for example, the charge on the condenser in a simple electric circuit containing no resistor and with an impressed voltage of the form (2). Alternatively, y may represent the response of an undamped harmonic oscillator subject to the applied force $h(t)$.

Before taking the transform of Eq. (1) it is convenient to write $h(t)$ in the form (see Example 1 of Section 6.3)

$$h(t) = u_\pi(t) - u_{2\pi}(t). \tag{4}$$

Then the Laplace transform of Eq. (1) is

$$(s^2 + 4)Y(s) - sy(0) - y'(0) = \mathcal{L}\{u_\pi(t)\} - \mathcal{L}\{u_{2\pi}(t)\}$$

$$= \frac{e^{-\pi s}}{s} - \frac{e^{-2\pi s}}{s}.$$

Introducing the initial values (3) and solving for $Y(s)$, we obtain

$$Y(s) = \frac{s}{s^2 + 4} + \frac{e^{-\pi s}}{s(s^2 + 4)} - \frac{e^{-2\pi s}}{s(s^2 + 4)}. \tag{5}$$

To compute $y = \phi(t)$ we must obtain the inverse transform of each term on the right side of Eq. (5). From Table 6.1 the inverse transform of the first term is given by

$$\mathscr{L}^{-1}\left\{\frac{s}{s^2 + 4}\right\} = \cos 2t. \tag{6}$$

To compute the inverse transform of the second term we note that, according to Theorem 6.4,

$$\mathscr{L}^{-1}\left\{\frac{e^{-\pi s}}{s(s^2 + 4)}\right\} = u_\pi(t)g(t - \pi),$$

where

$$g(t) = \mathscr{L}^{-1}\left\{\frac{1}{s(s^2 + 4)}\right\}.$$

Using partial fractions, we obtain

$$\frac{1}{s(s^2 + 4)} = \frac{1}{4}\left(\frac{1}{s} - \frac{s}{s^2 + 4}\right),$$

and it follows from Table 6.1 that

$$g(t) = \tfrac{1}{4}(1 - \cos 2t).$$

Hence

$$\mathscr{L}^{-1}\left\{\frac{e^{-\pi s}}{s(s^2 + 4)}\right\} = \tfrac{1}{4}u_\pi(t)[1 - \cos 2(t - \pi)]. \tag{7}$$

Similarly

$$\mathscr{L}^{-1}\left\{\frac{e^{-2\pi s}}{s(s^2 + 4)}\right\} = \tfrac{1}{4}u_{2\pi}(t)[1 - \cos 2(t - 2\pi)]. \tag{8}$$

Combining Eqs. (6), (7), and (8) we obtain finally

$$\phi(t) = \mathscr{L}^{-1}\{Y(s)\}$$
$$= \cos 2t + \tfrac{1}{4}u_\pi(t)[1 - \cos 2(t - \pi)] - \tfrac{1}{4}u_{2\pi}(t)[1 - \cos 2(t - 2\pi)]. \tag{9}$$

The graph of $y = \phi(t)$ is sketched in Figure 6.9.

Note that the second and third terms on the right side of Eq. (9) are zero for $t < \pi$ and $t < 2\pi$ respectively. If $\phi(t)$ is written without use of the unit step functions u_π and $u_{2\pi}$, then

$$\phi(t) = \begin{cases} \cos 2t, & 0 \le t < \pi, \\ \tfrac{3}{4}\cos 2t + \tfrac{1}{4}, & \pi \le t < 2\pi, \\ \cos 2t, & 2\pi \le t < \infty. \end{cases} \tag{10}$$

The initial value problem we have just solved involves a differential equation with a forcing function having jump discontinuities. It therefore does not quite fall within the scope of the fundamental existence and uniqueness theorem (Theorem 3.2). In particular, although the solution $y = \phi(t)$

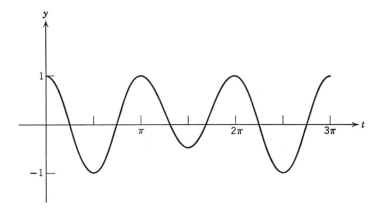

FIGURE 6.9 Solution of initial value problem (1), (2), (3).

given by Eq. (10) is continuous and has a continuous first derivative for all $t > 0$, it does not have a second derivative at the points $t = \pi$ and $t = 2\pi$ where the forcing function h has jump discontinuities. From Eq. (10) we have

$$\phi''(t) = \begin{cases} -4\cos 2t, & 0 < t < \pi, \\ -3\cos 2t, & \pi < t < 2\pi, \\ -4\cos 2t, & 2\pi < t < \infty. \end{cases}$$

In the neighborhood of $t = \pi$, for example, $\phi''(t) \to -4$ as $t \to \pi$ from the left, but $\phi''(t) \to -3$ as $t \to \pi$ from the right. Thus ϕ'' has a jump discontinuity at $t = \pi$, and the situation is the same at $t = 2\pi$.

Consider now the general second order linear equation,

$$y'' + p(t)y' + q(t)y = g(t), \tag{11}$$

where p and q are continuous on some interval $\alpha < t < \beta$, but g is only piecewise continuous there. If $y = \psi(t)$ is a solution of Eq. (11) then ψ and ψ' will be continuous on $\alpha < t < \beta$, but ψ'' will have jump discontinuities at the same points as g. Similar remarks apply to higher order equations; the highest derivative of the solution appearing in the differential equation will have jump discontinuities at the same points as the forcing function, but the solution itself and its lower derivatives will be continuous even at those points.

An alternate way to solve the initial value problem (1), (2), and (3) is to solve the differential equation in the three separate intervals $0 < t < \pi$, $\pi < t < 2\pi$, and $t > 2\pi$. In the first of these intervals the arbitrary constants in the general solution are chosen so as to satisfy the given initial conditions. In the second interval the constants are chosen so as to make the solution ϕ and its derivative ϕ' continuous at $t = \pi$. Similarly, in the third interval the constants are chosen so that ϕ and ϕ' will be continuous at $t = 2\pi$. The same general procedure can be used in other problems having piecewise continuous forcing functions. However, once the necessary theory is developed, it is often easier to use the Laplace transform to solve such problems all at once.

PROBLEMS

In each of Problems 1 through 7 find the solution of the given initial value problem.

1. $y'' + y = f(t)$; $y(0) = 0$, $y'(0) = 1$

$$f(t) = \begin{cases} 1, & 0 \le t < \pi/2 \\ 0, & \pi/2 \le t < \infty \end{cases}$$

2. $y'' + 2y' + 2y = h(t)$; $y(0) = 0$, $y'(0) = 1$

$$h(t) = \begin{cases} 1, & \pi \le t < 2\pi \\ 0, & 0 \le t < \pi \text{ and } t \ge 2\pi \end{cases}$$

3. $y'' + 4y = \sin t - u_{2\pi}(t) \sin (t - 2\pi)$; $y(0) = 0$, $y'(0) = 0$

4. $y'' + 4y = \sin t + u_\pi(t) \sin (t - \pi)$; $y(0) = 0$, $y'(0) = 0$

5. $y'' + 2y' + y = f(t)$; $y(0) = 1$, $y'(0) = 0$

$$f(t) = \begin{cases} 1, & 0 \le t < 1 \\ 0, & t \ge 1 \end{cases}$$

6. $y'' + 3y' + 2y = u_2(t)$; $y(0) = 0$, $y'(0) = 1$

7. $y'' + y = u_\pi(t)$; $y(0) = 1$, $y'(0) = 0$

*8. Let the function f be defined by

$$f(t) = \begin{cases} 1, & 0 \le t < \pi, \\ 0, & \pi \le t < 2\pi, \end{cases}$$

and for all other positive values of t so that $f(t + 2\pi) = f(t)$. That is, f is periodic with period 2π; see Problem 7 in Section 6.3. Find the solution of the initial value problem

$$y'' + y = f(t); \qquad y(0) = 1, y'(0) = 0.$$

*9. Suppose that the function f is given by

$$f(t) = \begin{cases} t, & 0 \le t < 1, \\ 1, & t \ge 1. \end{cases}$$

(a) Find $\mathcal{L}\{f(t)\}$.

(b) Solve the initial value problem

$$y'' + 4y = f(t); \qquad y(0) = 0, y'(0) = 1.$$

6.4 IMPULSE FUNCTIONS

In some applications it is necessary to deal with phenomena of an impulsive nature, for example, voltages or forces of large magnitude which act over very short time intervals. Such problems often lead to differential equations of the form

$$ay'' + by' + cy = g(t), \tag{1}$$

where $g(t)$ is large during the short interval $t_0 - \tau < t < t_0 + \tau$, and is otherwise zero.

The integral $I(\tau)$, defined by

$$I(\tau) = \int_{t_0-\tau}^{t_0+\tau} g(t)\, dt, \tag{2}$$

or, since $g(t) = 0$ outside of the interval $(t_0 - \tau, t_0 + \tau)$,

$$I(\tau) = \int_{-\infty}^{\infty} g(t)\, dt \tag{3}$$

is a measure of the strength of the forcing function. In a mechanical system, where $g(t)$ is a force, then $I(\tau)$ is the total *impulse* of the force $g(t)$ over the time interval $(t_0 - \tau, t_0 + \tau)$. Similarly, if y is the current in an electric circuit and $g(t)$ is the time derivative of the voltage, then $I(\tau)$ represents the total voltage impressed on the circuit during the interval $(t_0 - \tau, t_0 + \tau)$.

In particular, let us suppose that t_0 is zero, and that $g(t)$ is given by

$$g(t) = d_\tau(t) = \begin{cases} 1/2\tau, & -\tau < t < \tau, \\ 0, & t \leq -\tau \text{ or } t \geq \tau, \end{cases} \tag{4}$$

where τ is a small positive constant. See Figure 6.10. According to Eq. (2) or Eq. (3) it follows immediately that in this case $I(\tau) = 1$ independent of the value of τ, as long as $\tau \neq 0$. Now let us idealize the forcing function d_τ by prescribing it to act over shorter and shorter time intervals; that is, we will require that $\tau \to 0$. As a result of this limiting operation we obtain

$$\lim_{\tau \to 0} d_\tau(t) = 0, \qquad t \neq 0. \tag{5}$$

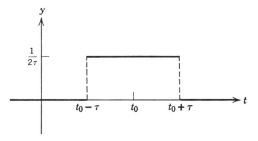

FIGURE 6.10 $y = d_\tau(t)$.

Further, since $I(\tau) = 1$ for each $\tau \neq 0$, it follows that

$$\lim_{\tau \to 0} I(\tau) = 1. \tag{6}$$

Equations (5) and (6) can be used to define an idealized "unit impulse function" δ, which imparts an impulse of magnitude one at $t = 0$, but is zero for all values of t other than zero. That is, the "function" δ is defined to have the properties

$$\delta(t) = 0, \qquad t \neq 0; \tag{7}$$

$$\int_{-\infty}^{\infty} \delta(t) \, dt = 1. \tag{8}$$

Clearly, there is no ordinary function of the kind studied in elementary calculus that satisfies both of Eqs. (7) and (8). The "function" δ, defined by those equations, is an example of what are known as *generalized functions* and is usually called the Dirac* "delta function." It is frequently convenient to represent impulsive forcing functions by means of the delta function. Since $\delta(t)$ corresponds to a unit impulse at $t = 0$, a unit impulse at an arbitrary point $t = t_0$ is given by $\delta(t - t_0)$. From Eqs. (7) and (8) it follows that

$$\delta(t - t_0) = 0, \qquad t \neq t_0; \tag{9}$$

$$\int_{-\infty}^{\infty} \delta(t - t_0) \, dt = 1. \tag{10}$$

The delta function does not satisfy the conditions of Theorem 6.2, but its Laplace transform can nevertheless be formally defined. Since $\delta(t)$ is defined as the limit of $d_\tau(t)$ as $\tau \to 0$, it is natural to define the Laplace transform of δ as a similar limit of the transform of d_τ. In particular, we will assume that $t_0 > 0$, and define $\mathscr{L}\{\delta(t - t_0)\}$ by the equation

$$\mathscr{L}\{\delta(t - t_0)\} = \lim_{\tau \to 0} \mathscr{L}\{d_\tau(t - t_0)\}. \tag{11}$$

If $\tau < t_0$, which must eventually be the case as $\tau \to 0$, then

$$\mathscr{L}\{d_\tau(t - t_0)\} = \int_0^{\infty} e^{-st} d_\tau(t - t_0) \, dt$$

$$= \int_{t_0-\tau}^{t_0+\tau} e^{-st} d_\tau(t - t_0) \, dt,$$

since $d_\tau(t - t_0) = 0$ if $t < t_0 - \tau$ or $t > t_0 + \tau$. Substituting for $d_\tau(t - t_0)$

---

* Paul A. M. Dirac (1902–   ) was awarded the Nobel Prize (with Erwin Schrödinger) in 1933 for his work in quantum mechanics.

from Eq. (4), we obtain

$$\mathcal{L}\{d_r(t - t_0)\} = \frac{1}{2\tau} \int_{t_0-\tau}^{t_0+\tau} e^{-st} \, dt$$

$$= -\frac{1}{2\tau s} e^{-st} \Big|_{t=t_0-\tau}^{t=t_0+\tau}$$

$$= \frac{1}{2\tau s} e^{-st_0}(e^{s\tau} - e^{-s\tau})$$

or

$$\mathcal{L}\{d_r(t - t_0)\} = \frac{\sinh s\tau}{s\tau} e^{-st_0}. \tag{12}$$

The quotient $(\sinh s\tau)/s\tau$ is indeterminate as $\tau \to 0$, but its limit can be evaluated by L'Hospital's rule. We obtain

$$\lim_{\tau \to 0} \frac{\sinh s\tau}{s\tau} = \lim_{\tau \to 0} \frac{s \cosh s\tau}{s} = 1.$$

Then from Eq. (11) it follows that

$$\mathcal{L}\{\delta(t - t_0)\} = e^{-st_0}. \tag{13}$$

Since Eq. (13) holds for all $t_0 > 0$, we can define $\mathcal{L}\{\delta(t)\}$ by letting $t_0 \to 0$ in Eq. (13); thus

$$\mathcal{L}\{\delta(t)\} = \lim_{t_0 \to 0} e^{-st_0} = 1. \tag{14}$$

In a similar way it is possible to define the integral of the product of the delta function and any continuous function f. We have

$$\int_{-\infty}^{\infty} \delta(t - t_0)f(t) \, dt = \lim_{\tau \to 0} \int_{-\infty}^{\infty} d_r(t - t_0)f(t) \, dt. \tag{15}$$

Using the definition (4) of $d_r(t)$ and the mean value theorem for integrals gives

$$\int_{-\infty}^{\infty} d_r(t - t_0)f(t) \, dt = \frac{1}{2\tau} \int_{t_0-\tau}^{t_0+\tau} f(t) \, dt$$

$$= \frac{1}{2\tau} \cdot 2\tau \cdot f(t^*) = f(t^*),$$

where $t_0 - \tau < t^* < t_0 + \tau$. Hence, as $\tau \to 0$, $t^* \to t_0$, and from Eq. (15)

$$\int_{-\infty}^{\infty} \delta(t - t_0)f(t) \, dt = f(t_0). \tag{16}$$

It is often convenient to introduce the delta function when working with impulse problems, and to operate formally on it as though it were a function of the ordinary kind. This is illustrated in the example below. It is important to realize, however, that the ultimate justification of such procedures must rest on a careful analysis of the limiting operations involved. Such a rigorous mathematical theory has been developed, but it is much too difficult to discuss here.

As an example, let us consider the differential equation

$$y'' + 2y' + 2y = \delta(t - \pi) \tag{17}$$

with the initial conditions

$$y(0) = 0, \qquad y'(0) = 0. \tag{18}$$

This initial value problem might arise from the study of the flow of current in a certain electric circuit on which a unit impulsive voltage is impressed at $t = \pi$.

To solve the given problem we take the Laplace transform of the differential equation, obtaining

$$(s^2 + 2s + 2)Y(s) = e^{-\pi s},$$

where the initial conditions (18) have been used. Thus

$$Y(s) = \frac{e^{-\pi s}}{s^2 + 2s + 2} = e^{-\pi s} \frac{1}{(s + 1)^2 + 1}. \tag{19}$$

By Theorem 6.5 or from Table 6.1

$$\mathscr{L}^{-1}\left\{\frac{1}{(s + 1)^2 + 1}\right\} = e^{-t} \sin t. \tag{20}$$

Hence, by Theorem 6.4 we have

$$y = \mathscr{L}^{-1}\{Y(s)\} = u_\pi(t)e^{-(t-\pi)} \sin (t - \pi), \tag{21}$$

which is the formal solution of the given problem. It is also possible to write y in the form

$$y = \begin{cases} 0, & t < \pi, \\ e^{-(t-\pi)} \sin (t - \pi), & t \geq \pi. \end{cases} \tag{22}$$

The graph of Eq. (22) is shown in Figure 6.11.

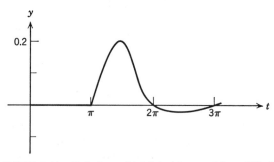

FIGURE 6.11 Solution of initial value problem (17), (18).

As the initial conditions at $t = 0$ are homogeneous, and there is no external excitation until $t = \pi$, there is no response in the interval $0 < t < \pi$. The impulse at $t = \pi$ produces a response which persists indefinitely, although it decays exponentially in the absence of any further external excitation. It is also interesting to note that the response is continuous at $t = \pi$ in spite of the singular nature of the forcing function at that point; however, the slope of the solution has a jump discontinuity at this point, and its second derivative is not defined there. This is required by the differential equation (17) since a singularity on one side of the equation must be balanced by one on the other.

PROBLEMS

In each of Problems 1 through 7 find the solution of the given initial value problem by means of the Laplace transform.

1. $y'' + 2y' + 2y = \delta(t - \pi);$ $y(0) = 1,$ $y'(0) = 0$
2. $y'' + 4y = \delta(t - \pi) - \delta(t - 2\pi);$ $y(0) = 0,$ $y'(0) = 0$
3. $y'' + 2y' + y = \delta(t) + u_{2\pi}(t);$ $y(0) = 0,$ $y'(0) = 1$
4. $y'' - y = 2\delta(t - 1);$ $y(0) = 1,$ $y'(0) = 0$
5. $y'' + 2y' + 3y = \sin t + \delta(t - \pi);$ $y(0) = 0,$ $y'(0) = 1$
6. $y'' + \omega^2 y = \delta(t - \pi/\omega);$ $y(0) = 1,$ $y'(0) = 0$
7. $y'' + y = \delta(t - \pi) \cos t;$ $y(0) = 0,$ $y'(0) = 1$

*8. (a) Show by the method of variation of parameters that the solution of the initial value problem

$$y'' + 2y' + 2y = f(t);   y(0) = 0,   y'(0) = 0$$

is

$$y = \int_0^t e^{-(t-\tau)}f(\tau) \sin (t - \tau) \, d\tau.$$

(b) Show that if $f(t) = \delta(t - \pi)$, then the solution of part (a) reduces to

$$y = u_\pi(t)e^{-(t-\pi)} \sin (t - \pi),$$

which agrees with Eq. (21) of the text.

6.5 THE CONVOLUTION INTEGRAL

Sometimes it is possible to identify a Laplace transform $H(s)$ as the product of two other transforms $F(s)$ and $G(s)$, the latter transforms corresponding to known functions f and g, respectively. In this event, we might anticipate that $H(s)$ would be the transform of the product of f and g. However, this is not the case; in other words, the Laplace transform cannot be commuted with ordinary multiplication. On the other hand, if an appropriately defined "generalized product" is introduced, then the situation changes, as stated in the following theorem.

Theorem 6.6. *If $F(s) = \mathscr{L}\{f(t)\}$ and $G(s) = \mathscr{L}\{g(t)\}$ both exist for $s > a \geq 0$, then*

$$H(s) = F(s)G(s) = \mathscr{L}\{h(t)\}, \qquad s > a, \tag{1}$$

where

$$h(t) = \int_0^t f(t - u)g(u)\, du = \int_0^t f(u)g(t - u)\, du. \tag{2}$$

The function h is known as the convolution of f and g; the integrals in Eq. (2) are known as convolution integrals.

The equality of the two integrals in Eq. (2) follows by making the change of variable $t - u = \xi$ in the first integral. Before giving the proof of this theorem let us make some observations about the convolution integral. According to this theorem, the transform of the convolution of two functions, rather than the transform of their ordinary product, is given by the product of the separate transforms. It is conventional to emphasize that the convolution integral can be thought of as a "generalized product" by writing

$$h(t) = (f * g)(t). \tag{3}$$

In particular, the notation $(f * g)(t)$ serves to indicate the first integral appearing in Eq. (2).

The convolution $f * g$ has many of the properties of ordinary multiplication. For example, it is relatively simple to show that

$$f * g = g * f \qquad \text{(commutative law)} \tag{4}$$
$$f * (g_1 + g_2) = f * g_1 + f * g_2 \qquad \text{(distributive law)} \tag{5}$$
$$(f * g) * h = f * (g * h) \qquad \text{(associative law)} \tag{6}$$
$$f * 0 = 0 * f = 0. \tag{7}$$

The proofs of these properties are left to the reader. However, there are other properties of ordinary multiplication which the convolution integral does not have. For example, it is not true in general that $f * 1$ is equal to f. To see this, note that

$$(f * 1)(t) = \int_0^t f(t - u) \cdot 1 \, du$$
$$= \int_0^t f(t - u) \, du.$$

If, for example, $f(t) = \cos t$, then

$$(f * 1)(t) = \int_0^t \cos(t - u)\, du = \sin(t - u)\Big|_{u=0}^{u=t}$$
$$= \sin 0 - \sin t$$
$$= -\sin t.$$

Clearly, $(f * 1)(t) \neq f(t)$. Similarly, it may not be true that $f * f$ is non-negative. See Problem 3 for an example.

Convolution integrals arise in various applications in which the behavior of the system at time t depends not only on its state at time t, but on its past history as well. Systems of this kind are sometimes called hereditary systems, and occur in such diverse fields as neutron transport, viscoelasticity, and population growth.

Turning now to the proof of Theorem 6.6, we note first that if

$$F(s) = \int_0^\infty e^{-s\xi} f(\xi) \, d\xi$$

and

$$G(s) = \int_0^\infty e^{-s\eta} g(\eta) \, d\eta,$$

then

$$F(s)G(s) = \int_0^\infty e^{-s\xi} f(\xi) \, d\xi \int_0^\infty e^{-s\eta} g(\eta) \, d\eta. \tag{8}$$

Since the integrand of the first integral does not depend on the integration variable of the second, we can write $F(s)G(s)$ as an iterated integral,

$$F(s)G(s) = \int_0^\infty g(\eta) \, d\eta \int_0^\infty e^{-s(\xi+\eta)} f(\xi) \, d\xi. \tag{9}$$

This expression can be put into a more convenient form by introducing new variables of integration. First let $\xi = t - \eta$, for fixed η. Then the integral with respect to ξ in Eq. (9) is transformed into one with respect to t; hence

$$F(s)G(s) = \int_0^\infty g(\eta) \, d\eta \int_\eta^\infty e^{-st} f(t - \eta) \, dt. \tag{10}$$

Next let $\eta = u$; then Eq. (10) becomes

$$F(s)G(s) = \int_0^\infty g(u) \, du \int_u^\infty e^{-st} f(t - u) \, dt. \tag{11}$$

The integral on the right side of Eq. (11) is carried out over the shaded wedge-shaped region in the tu plane shown in Figure 6.12. Assuming that

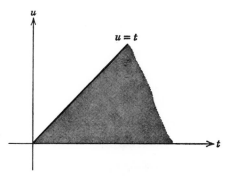

FIGURE 6.12

the order of integration can be reversed, we finally obtain

$$F(s)G(s) = \int_0^\infty e^{-st} \, dt \int_0^t f(t-u)g(u) \, du, \qquad (12)$$

or

$$F(s)G(s) = \int_0^\infty e^{-st} h(t) \, dt$$

$$= \mathscr{L}\{h(t)\}, \qquad (13)$$

where $h(t)$ is defined by Eq. (2). This completes the proof of Theorem 6.6.

Example. Find the inverse transform of

$$H(s) = \frac{a}{s^2(s^2 + a^2)}.$$

It is convenient to think of $H(s)$ as the product of s^{-2} and $a/(s^2 + a^2)$, which, according to Table 6.1, are the transforms of t and $\sin at$ respectively. Hence, by Theorem 6.6, the inverse transform of $H(s)$ is

$$h(t) = \int_0^t (t-u)\sin au \, du$$

$$= \frac{at - \sin at}{a^2}.$$

The reader may show that the same result is obtained if $h(t)$ is written in the alternate form

$$h(t) = \int_0^t u \sin a(t-u) \, du,$$

which verifies Eq. (2) in this case.

PROBLEMS

1. Establish the commutative, distributive, and associative properties of the convolution integral.

(a) $f * g = g * f$

(b) $f * (g_1 + g_2) = f * g_1 + f * g_2$

(c) $f * (g * h) = (f * g) * h$

2. Find an example different from the one in the text which shows that $(f * 1)(t)$ need not be equal to $f(t)$.

3. Show, by means of the example $f(t) = \sin t$, that $f * f$ is not necessarily nonnegative.

4. Find the Laplace transform of each of the following functions.

(a) $f(t) = \displaystyle\int_0^t (t - u)^2 \cos 2u \, du$

(b) $f(t) = \displaystyle\int_0^t e^{-(t-u)} \sin u \, du$

(c) $f(t) = \displaystyle\int_0^t (t - u)e^u \, du$

5. Find the inverse Laplace transform of each of the following functions by using the convolution theorem.

(a) $F(s) = \dfrac{1}{s^4(s^2 + 1)}$

(b) $F(s) = \dfrac{s}{(s + 1)(s^2 + 4)}$

(c) $F(s) = \dfrac{1}{(s + 1)^2(s^2 + 4)}$

(d) $F(s) = \dfrac{G(s)}{s^2 + 1}$

6. Find the solution of the initial value problem

$$y'' + 2y' + 2y = f(t); \qquad y(0) = 0, \, y'(0) = 0,$$

where $f(t) = 1 - u_{2\pi}(t)$.

7. Find the solution of the initial value problem

$$y'' + 2y' + 2y = \sin \alpha t; \qquad y(0) = 0, \, y'(0) = 0,$$

where α is a constant.

8. Consider the equation

$$\phi(t) + \int_0^t k(t - \xi)\phi(\xi) \, d\xi = f(t),$$

in which f and k are known functions, and ϕ is to be determined. Since the unknown function ϕ appears under an integral sign, the given equation is called an *integral equation*; in particular, it belongs to a class of integral equations known as Volterra (1860–1940) integral equations. Take the Laplace transform of the given integral equation, and obtain an expression for $\mathscr{L}\{\phi(t)\}$ in terms of the transforms $\mathscr{L}\{f(t)\}$ and $\mathscr{L}\{k(t)\}$ of the given functions f and k. The inverse transform of $\mathscr{L}\{\phi(t)\}$ is the solution of the original integral equation.

9. Consider the Volterra integral equation

$$\phi(t) + \int_0^t (t - \xi)\phi(\xi) \, d\xi = \sin 2t.$$

(a) Show that if u is a function such that $u''(t) = \phi(t)$, then

$$u''(t) + u(t) - tu'(0) - u(0) = \sin 2t.$$

(b) Show that the given integral equation is equivalent to the initial value problem

$$u''(t) + u(t) = \sin 2t; \qquad u(0) = 0, \qquad u'(0) = 0.$$

(c) Solve the given integral equation by using the Laplace transform.

(d) Solve the initial value problem of part (b) and verify that the solution is the same as that obtained in (c).

10. Obtain the Laplace transform of the solution of each of the following integral equations.

(a) $\phi(t) + \int_0^t (t - \xi)^2 \phi(\xi)\, d\xi = 2t$

(b) $\phi(t) + \int_0^t \sin(t - \xi)\phi(\xi)\, d\xi = 1 - u_{2\pi}(t)$

(c) $\phi(t) + \int_0^t e^{-(t-\xi)} \cos(t - \xi)\phi(\xi)\, d\xi = \sin 2t$

(d) $\phi(t) + 2\int_0^t (1 + t - \xi)\phi(\xi)\, d\xi = \sin t - 2$

6.6 GENERAL DISCUSSION AND SUMMARY

In concluding this chapter, we will briefly discuss some more general aspects of the transform method. Consider the initial value problem consisting of the differential equation

$$ay'' + by' + cy = f(t), \tag{1}$$

where a, b, and c are real constants and f is a given function, together with the initial conditions

$$y(0) = y_0, \qquad y'(0) = y_0'. \tag{2}$$

As indicated in Sections 3.7 and 3.8, initial value problems of this kind are of frequent importance in various applications. For example, for a vibrating spring-mass system, a represents the mass, b the damping coefficient, c the spring constant, y the displacement, and $f(t)$ the external force. Alternatively, a could denote the inductance, b the resistance, c the reciprocal of the capacitance, and y the charge on the condenser in an electric circuit subject to the impressed voltage $f(t)$.

The Laplace transform of Eq. (1) is

$$(as^2 + bs + c)Y(s) - (as + b)y(0) - ay'(0) = F(s), \tag{3}$$

where $Y(s)$ and $F(s)$ are the transforms of y and $f(t)$ respectively. Using the initial conditions (2) and solving for $Y(s)$, we obtain

$$Y(s) = \frac{F(s) + (as + b)y_0 + ay_0'}{as^2 + bs + c}. \tag{4}$$

Thus $Y(s)$ can be thought of as the product of the functions

$$H(s) = (as^2 + bs + c)^{-1} \tag{5}$$

and

$$G(s) = F(s) + (as + b)y_0 + ay_0'. \tag{6}$$

The first function H is characterized entirely by the properties of the system under consideration, and may be called the *system function*. The second, G, is dependent on the forcing function and initial conditions, and may be called the *excitation function*. Further, the excitation function also consists of two parts: the function F which is the transform of the forcing function f, and the function $(as + b)y_0 + ay_0'$, which depends on the initial conditions.

At this point it is tempting to write

$$Y(s) = H(s)G(s) \tag{7}$$

and, by invoking the convolution theorem, to obtain

$$y = \int_0^t h(t - u)g(u)\, du \tag{8}$$

as the solution of Eqs. (1) and (2). However, the function $(as + b)y_0 + ay_0'$ cannot be a Laplace transform, at least not of an ordinary function.* Consequently, it is necessary to write $Y(s)$ as

$$Y(s) = H(s)F(s) + \frac{(as + b)y_0 + ay_0'}{as^2 + bs + c}. \tag{9}$$

It then follows that

$$y = \int_0^t h(t - u)f(u)\, du + \mathcal{L}^{-1}\left\{\frac{(as + b)y_0 + ay_0'}{as^2 + bs + c}\right\}. \tag{10}$$

Once specific values of a, b, and c are given, the inverse transform indicated in Eq. (10) can be found from Table 6.1 or by the method of partial fractions. Using the linearity of the inverse transform we can write Eq. (10) as

$$y = \int_0^t h(t - u)f(u)\, du + y_0\mathcal{L}^{-1}\left\{\frac{as + b}{as^2 + bs + c}\right\}$$

$$+ y_0'\mathcal{L}^{-1}\left\{\frac{a}{as^2 + bs + c}\right\}. \tag{11}$$

Then, if we let

$$y_1(t) = \mathcal{L}^{-1}\left\{\frac{as + b}{as^2 + bs + c}\right\}, \qquad y_2(t) = \mathcal{L}^{-1}\left\{\frac{a}{as^2 + bs + c}\right\}, \tag{12}$$

we have

$$y = \int_0^t h(t - u)f(u)\, du + y_0 y_1(t) + y_0' y_2(t). \tag{13}$$

The first term on the right side of Eq. (13) is the response of the system to the forcing function f. In the terminology of Chapter 3 it is a particular solution of the nonhomogeneous equation (1). The remaining terms on

---

* If it were it would approach zero as $s \to \infty$; see Problem 4 of Section 6.1. It is possible, however, to interpret this function as the transform of a certain combination of the delta function and its "derivative."

the right side of Eq. (13) represent the response of the system to the initial conditions. If we think of y_0 and y_0' as arbitrary constants, these terms comprise the complementary function, or the general solution of the homogeneous equation corresponding to Eq. (1).

REFERENCES

The books listed below contain additional information on the Laplace transform and its applications.

Churchill, R. V., *Operational Mathematics*, second edition, McGraw-Hill, New York, 1958.

Doetsch, Gustave, *Guide to the Applications of Laplace Transforms*, Van Nostrand, London, 1967.

Kaplan, W., *Operational Methods for Linear Systems*, Addison-Wesley, Reading, Mass., 1962.

McLachlan, N. W., *Modern Operational Calculus*, Dover, New York, 1962.

Each of the books mentioned above contains a table of transforms. Very extensive tables are also available; see, for example, the following books.

Erdelyi, A. (editor), *Tables of Integral Transforms, Vol. 1*, McGraw-Hill, New York, 1954.

Roberts, G. E. and Kaufman, H., *Table of Laplace Transforms*, Saunders, Philadelphia, 1966.

Systems of First Order Equations

7.1 INTRODUCTION

This chapter is devoted to a discussion of systems of simultaneous ordinary differential equations. Such systems arise naturally in problems involving several dependent variables, each of which is a function of a single independent variable. We will denote the independent variable by t, and let $x_1, x_2, x_3, \ldots$ represent dependent variables which are functions of t. Differentiation with respect to t will be denoted by a prime.

For example, the motion of a particle in space is governed by Newton's law in three dimensions,

$$m \frac{d^2 x_1}{dt^2} = F_1\left(t, x_1, x_2, x_3, \frac{dx_1}{dt}, \frac{dx_2}{dt}, \frac{dx_3}{dt}\right),$$

$$m \frac{d^2 x_2}{dt^2} = F_2\left(t, x_1, x_2, x_3, \frac{dx_1}{dt}, \frac{dx_2}{dt}, \frac{dx_3}{dt}\right), \qquad (1)$$

$$m \frac{d^2 x_3}{dt^2} = F_3\left(t, x_1, x_2, x_3, \frac{dx_1}{dt}, \frac{dx_2}{dt}, \frac{dx_3}{dt}\right),$$

where m is the mass of the particle; x_1, x_2, and x_3 are its spatial coordinates; and F_1, F_2, and F_3 are the forces acting on the particle in the x_1, x_2, and x_3 directions, respectively. If the particle is an idealization of a space vehicle, for instance, then F_1, F_2, and F_3 include the gravitational forces exerted upon the vehicle by neighboring celestial bodies, any forces produced by the vehicle's own propulsive system, and also drag forces if the vehicle is within the earth's atmosphere.

As another example, consider the spring-mass system shown in Figure 7.1. The two masses move on a frictionless surface under the influence of external forces $F_1(t)$ and $F_2(t)$, and they are also constrained by the three springs whose constants are k_1, k_2, and k_3, respectively. Using arguments similar to those in Section 3.7, we find the following equations for the

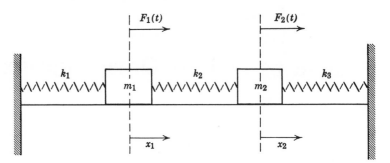

FIGURE 7.1   A two degree of freedom spring mass system.

coordinates x_1 and x_2 of the two masses:

$$m_1 \frac{d^2x_1}{dt^2} = k_2(x_2 - x_1) - k_1x_1 + F_1(t)$$

$$= -(k_1 + k_2)x_1 + k_2x_2 + F_1(t),$$

$$m_2 \frac{d^2x_2}{dt^2} = -k_3x_2 - k_2(x_2 - x_1) + F_2(t)$$

$$= k_2x_1 - (k_2 + k_3)x_2 + F_2(t). \tag{2}$$

Systems of differential equations also occur frequently in the study of electric circuits. A transformer, for example, involves two circuits, each of which affects the current in the other by magnetic induction; see Figure .7.2. The corresponding system of differential equations for the currents I_1 and I_2 is

$$L_1 \frac{dI_1}{dt} + M \frac{dI_2}{dt} + R_1I_1 = E_1(t),$$

$$L_2 \frac{dI_2}{dt} + M \frac{dI_1}{dt} + R_2I_2 = E_2(t), \tag{3}$$

where M is the coefficient of mutual inductance. Systems of equations also occur in many other applications, such as the chemical mixing of several

FIGURE 7.2   A transformer circuit.

ingredients and the growth of two or more populations which interact or prey upon one another.

From a theoretical point of view there is an important connection between systems of equations and single equations of arbitrary order. In fact, an nth order equation

$$y^{(n)} = F(t, y, y', \ldots, y^{(n-1)}) \tag{4}$$

can always be reduced to a system of n first order equations having a rather special form. To show this we introduce the variables $x_1, x_2, \ldots, x_n$ defined by

$$x_1 = y, \; x_2 = y', \; x_3 = y'', \ldots, x_n = y^{(n-1)}. \tag{5}$$

It then follows immediately that

$$x_1' = x_2,$$
$$x_2' = x_3,$$
$$\cdot$$
$$\cdot \tag{6}$$
$$\cdot$$
$$x_{n-1}' = x_n,$$

and from Eq. (4)

$$x_n' = F(t, x_1, x_2, \ldots, x_n). \tag{7}$$

In a similar way the systems (1) and (2) can also be reduced to systems of first order equations containing, respectively, six and four equations. By solving algebraically for dI_1/dt and dI_2/dt, the system (3) can also be written as a system of two equations each of which contains only one of the derivatives, dI_1/dt or dI_2/dt.

Thus it is sufficient to consider systems of first order equations of the form

$$x_1' = F_1(t, x_1, \ldots, x_n),$$
$$x_2' = F_2(t, x_1, \ldots, x_n),$$
$$\cdot$$
$$\cdot \tag{8}$$
$$\cdot$$
$$x_n' = F_n(t, x_1, \ldots, x_n).$$

Because systems of the form (8) include all cases of interest, it is customary in an advanced study of the theory of differential equations to deal mainly with such systems.

The system of equations (8) is said to have a *solution* on the interval $\alpha < t < \beta$ if there exists a set of n functions $x_1 = \phi_1(t), \ldots, x_n = \phi_n(t)$ which are differentiable at all points in $\alpha < t < \beta$, and which satisfy the system (8) at all points in this interval. In addition to the given system of differential equations there may also be given initial conditions of the form

$$x_1(t_0) = x_1^0, \ x_2(t_0) = x_2^0, \ \ldots, \ x_n(t_0) = x_n^0, \tag{9}$$

where t_0 is a specified value of t in $\alpha < t < \beta$, and $x_1^0, \ldots, x_n^0$ are prescribed numbers. The differential equations (8) and initial conditions (9) together form an initial value problem.

In order to guarantee that the initial value problem (8) and (9) has a solution and that the solution is unique, it is necessary to impose certain conditions upon the functions $F_1, F_2, \ldots, F_n$. The following theorem is analogous to the existence and uniqueness theorems for single equations of first and second order, Theorems 2.2 and 3.1, respectively.

Theorem 7.1. *Let each of the functions $F_1, \ldots, F_n$ and the partial derivatives $\partial F_1/\partial x_1, \ldots, \partial F_1/\partial x_n, \ldots, \partial F_n/\partial x_1, \ldots, \partial F_n/\partial x_n$ be continuous in a region R of $tx_1 x_2 \cdots x_n$-space containing the point $(t_0, x_1^0, x_2^0, \ldots, x_n^0)$. Then there is an interval $|t - t_0| < h$ in which there exists a unique solution $x_1 = \phi_1(t), \ldots, x_n = \phi_n(t)$ of the system of differential equations (8), which also satisfies the initial conditions (9).*

The proof of this theorem can be constructed by generalizing the argument in Section 2.11, but we will not give it here. Note, however, that in the hypotheses of the theorem nothing is said about the partial derivatives of the functions $F_1, F_2, \ldots, F_n$ with respect to t. Also, in the conclusion, the length $2h$ of the interval in which the solution exists is not specified exactly, and in some cases may be very short. Finally, the theorem is not the most general one known, and the given conditions are sufficient, but not necessary, to ensure the conclusion.

If each of the functions $F_1, \ldots, F_n$ in Eqs. (8) is a linear function of the dependent variables $x_1, \ldots, x_n$, then the system of equations is said to be *linear*. Thus the most general system of n linear first order equations has the form

$$x_1' = p_{11}(t)x_1 + \cdots + p_{1n}(t)x_n + g_1(t),$$

$$\cdot$$
$$\cdot \tag{10}$$
$$\cdot$$

$$x_n' = p_{n1}(t)x_1 + \cdots + p_{nn}(t)x_n + g_n(t).$$

If each of the functions $g_1, \ldots, g_n$ is identically zero, then the system (10) is said to be homogeneous; otherwise it is nonhomogeneous. For the linear system (10) the existence and uniqueness theorem is somewhat simpler and also has a stronger conclusion. It is analogous to Theorems 2.1 and 3.2.

Theorem 7.2. *If the functions $p_{11}, \ldots, p_{nn}, g_1, \ldots, g_n$ are continuous on an open interval $\alpha < t < \beta$, containing the point $t = t_0$, then there exists* *a unique solution* $x_1 = \phi_1(t), \ldots, x_n = \phi_n(t)$ *of the system of differential equations* (10), *which also satisfies the initial conditions* (9). *This solution is valid throughout the interval* $\alpha < t < \beta$.

Note that in contrast to the situation for a nonlinear system the existence and uniqueness of the solution of a linear system is guaranteed throughout the interval in which the hypotheses are satisfied. Furthermore, for a linear system the initial values $x_1^0, \ldots, x_n^0$ at $t = t_0$ are completely arbitrary, whereas in the nonlinear case the initial point must lie in the region R defined in Theorem 7.1.

The rest of this chapter is devoted to systems of linear first order equations. The exposition is most effectively phrased in terms of certain results from matrix theory and, beginning in Section 7.3, the rest of the chapter is based on the use of matrices. The necessary facts about matrices are summarized in Sections 7.3 and 7.6. For readers completely unfamiliar with matrix theory, Section 7.2 contains a discussion of elementary elimination techniques by which systems of equations can be replaced by a single equation of higher order. This procedure does not provide an adequate foundation for a general discussion of linear systems, but is sometimes quite efficient as a means of solving systems of only a few equations.

PROBLEMS

1. Reduce each of the systems (1), (2), and (3) to a system of first order equations of the form (8).

2. Consider the initial value problem $u'' + p(t)u' + q(t)u = g(t)$, $u(0) = u_0$, $u'(0) = u_0'$. Transform this problem into an initial value problem for two first order linear equations.

3. Show that if a_{11}, a_{12}, a_{21}, and a_{22} are constants with a_{12} and a_{21} not both zero, and if the functions g_1 and g_2 are differentiable, then the initial value problem

$$x_1' = a_{11}x_1 + a_{12}x_2 + g_1(t), \qquad x_1(0) = x_1^0$$

$$x_2' = a_{21}x_1 + a_{22}x_2 + g_2(t), \qquad x_2(0) = x_2^0$$

can be transformed into an initial value problem for a single second order equation. Can the same procedure be carried out if $a_{11}, \ldots, a_{22}$ are functions of t?

4. Consider the linear homogeneous system

$$x' = p_{11}(t)x + p_{12}(t)y,$$

$$y' = p_{21}(t)x + p_{22}(t)y.$$

Show that if $x = x_1(t)$, $y = y_1(t)$ and $x = x_2(t)$, $y = y_2(t)$ are two solutions of the given system, then $x = c_1x_1(t) + c_2x_2(t)$, $y = c_1y_1(t) + c_2y_2(t)$ is also a solution for any constants c_1 and c_2. This is the principle of superposition.

5. Let $x = x_1(t)$, $y = y_1(t)$ and $x = x_2(t)$, $y = y_2(t)$ be any two solutions of the linear nonhomogeneous system

$$x' = p_{11}(t)x + p_{12}(t)y + g_1(t),$$
$$y' = p_{21}(t)x + p_{22}(t)y + g_2(t).$$

Show that $x = x_1(t) - x_2(t)$, $y = y_1(t) - y_2(t)$ is a solution of the corresponding homogeneous system

$$x' = p_{11}(t)x + p_{12}(t)y,$$
$$y' = p_{21}(t)x + p_{22}(t)y.$$

7.2 SOLUTION OF LINEAR SYSTEMS BY ELIMINATION

The most elementary way of solving a system of linear differential equations with constant coefficients is by the direct process of elimination. That is, dependent variables are successively eliminated with the object of eventually obtaining a single higher order equation containing only one dependent variable. After solving this equation, the other dependent variables can be found in turn.

For systems of only two or three first order equations such methods are quite efficient. They can be applied to nonhomogeneous systems as well as to homogeneous ones, and can also be used to advantage in some problems involving systems of higher order differential equations. Elimination methods do not, however, lend themselves readily to theoretical discussions; nor are they a convenient way to solve large systems of equations.

To illustrate the method of elimination let us consider the system of differential equations

$$\begin{align} x_1' &= x_1 + x_2, \\ x_2' &= 4x_1 + x_2. \end{align} \tag{1}$$

Solving the first of Eqs. (1) for x_2 gives

$$x_2 = x_1' - x_1. \tag{2}$$

Hence $x_2' = x_1'' - x_1'$, and from the second of Eqs. (1) we obtain, after some minor algebraic simplification,

$$x_1'' - 2x_1' - 3x_1 = 0. \tag{3}$$

The general solution of Eq. (3) is

$$x_1 = \phi_1(t) = c_1 e^{3t} + c_2 e^{-t}, \tag{4}$$

where c_1 and c_2 are arbitrary constants. From Eq. (2) it follows at once that

$$x_2 = \phi_2(t) = 2c_1 e^{3t} - 2c_2 e^{-t}. \tag{5}$$

The solution of the system (1) given by Eqs. (4) and (5) contains two arbitrary constants. It is easy to show that these constants can be chosen so as to satisfy any prescribed initial conditions at any given point. Therefore any solution of the system (1) can be written in the form (4), (5) for suitable choices of c_1 and c_2. Equations (4) and (5) are thus said to form the general solution of the system (1). The reader may verify that the same solution is obtained if x_1 is eliminated from Eqs. (1) instead of x_2.

The same procedure can be applied to the nonhomogeneous system

$$
\begin{aligned}
x_1' &= x_1 + x_2 + g_1(t), \\
x_2' &= 4x_1 + x_2 + g_2(t).
\end{aligned}
\tag{6}
$$

The only differences are that now $x_2 = x_1' - x_1 - g_1(t)$, and that the second order equation (3) for x_1 is replaced by a nonhomogeneous equation.

As mentioned earlier, the method of elimination can also be used to solve systems of higher order equations. Such systems may occur naturally in various applications; they also arise when the method of elimination just described is applied to a system of more than two first-order equations.

Thus let us consider the system

$$
\begin{aligned}
L_1[x_1] + L_2[x_2] &= g_1(t), \\
L_3[x_1] + L_4[x_2] &= g_2(t),
\end{aligned}
\tag{7}
$$

where L_1, L_2, L_3, and L_4 are linear differential operators, not necessarily of first order, with constant coefficients, and g_1 and g_2 are given functions. For example, suppose that L_1 is the second order differential operator

$$
L_1[x] = ax'' + bx' + cx.
\tag{8}
$$

It is convenient to let $D = d/dt$, and to write Eq. (8) in the form

$$
L_1[x] = (aD^2 + bD + c)x.
\tag{9}
$$

Before proceeding further it is necessary to discuss the meaning of an expression such as $L_2L_1[x]$, which indicates the successive applications of the operators L_1 and L_2 to the function x. Suppose for the moment that

$$
L_1[x] = (aD + b)x,
\tag{10}
$$

and

$$
L_2[x] = (cD + d)x,
\tag{11}
$$

where a, b, c, and d are constants. Then $L_2L_1[x]$ is defined by

$$
\begin{aligned}
L_2L_1[x] &= cD[(aD + b)x] + d[(aD + b)x] \\
&= caD^2x + cbDx + daDx + dbx \\
&= [caD^2 + (cb + da)D + db]x.
\end{aligned}
\tag{12}
$$

Note that Eq. (12) can be written as

$$L_2L_1[x] = [(cD + d)(aD + b)]x, \tag{13}$$

where D is treated as an algebraic quantity in expanding the right-hand side. Similarly

$$L_1L_2[x] = aD[(cD + d)x] + b[(cD + d)x]$$

$$= [acD^2 + (ad + bc)D + bd]x. \tag{14}$$

It is clear from Eqs. (12) and (14) that

$$L_2L_1[x] = L_1L_2[x], \tag{15}$$

that is, L_1 and L_2 are commutative. It is possible to show that the property of commutativity is possessed not only by the operators L_1 and L_2 defined by Eqs. (10) and (11), but by any two linear differential operators L_1 and L_2 having constant coefficients, regardless of their order. On the other hand, operators with variable coefficients do not in general possess the property of commutativity; see Problem 22.

Returning to the system (7) it is now a simple matter to eliminate either of the dependent variables x_1 or x_2. To eliminate x_1 we need only apply L_3 to the first equation, L_1 to the second equation, and then subtract the first from the second. Thus

$$L_3L_1[x_1] + L_3L_2[x_2] = L_3[g_1], \tag{16}$$

$$L_1L_3[x_1] + L_1L_4[x_2] = L_1[g_2], \tag{17}$$

and subtraction of Eq. (16) from Eq. (17) gives

$$L_1L_4[x_2] - L_3L_2[x_2] = L_1[g_2] - L_3[g_1]. \tag{18}$$

Equation (18) does not involve x_1 and can be solved by standard methods. Once x_2 is determined from Eq. (18), x_1 can be found by solving either of Eqs. (7). Alternatively, x_2 can be eliminated from the system in a similar way. Note that in using this method the functions g_1 and g_2 must possess sufficiently many derivatives so that it is possible to compute such quantities as $L_1[g_2]$ and $L_3[g_1]$ in Eq. (18).

In general, a number of extraneous constants will be introduced during this procedure. In solving Eq. (18) for x_2 the number of arbitrary constants will be equal to the order* of the operator $L_1L_4 - L_3L_2$. Additional constants are introduced when x_1 is determined by solving either of Eqs. (7). The relations among the constants can be found, and the extraneous ones

---

* By the order of $L_1L_4 - L_3L_2$ we mean the order of the highest derivative appearing in it. If $L_1L_4 - L_3L_2$ is zero the system (7) is said to be *degenerate*. In this case there may be either infinitely many solutions or else none, depending on whether the right side of Eq. (18) does, or does not, vanish. See Problems 18 through 21. The situation here is similar to that for a system of linear algebraic equations whose determinant of coefficients vanishes.

eliminated, by substituting for x_1 and x_2 in whichever of Eqs. (7) was not used in solving for x_1. This is illustrated in the example below.

The question of the number of arbitrary constants which should appear in the general solution of the system (7) can be answered in the following way. If the system (7) were reduced to a system of first order equations, then the number of independent constants in the general solution would be equal to the number of equations in the system. This will be established in Section 7.4. By eliminating x_1 we obtain a single equation whose order is that of the operator $L_1 L_4 - L_3 L_2$. This latter equation could in turn be transformed into a system of first order equations equal in number to the order of $L_1 L_4 - L_3 L_2$. Thus it is reasonable to expect, and it can be proved to be true, that the number of independent arbitrary constants in the general solution of the system (7) is equal to the order of $L_1 L_4 - L_3 L_2$, provided that $L_1 L_4 - L_3 L_2$ is not zero. This fact can be used to check that the correct number of arbitrary constants appears in the final solution. The result can also be extended to larger systems of equations; see Problem 23.

Example. Find the general solution of

$$(x_1'' + x_1' - x_1) + (x_2'' - 3x_2' + 2x_2) = 0, \tag{19}$$

$$(x_1' + 2x_1) + \qquad (2x_2' - 4x_2) = 0. \tag{20}$$

In this case $L_1[x_1] = (D^2 + D - 1)x_1$, $L_2[x_2] = (D^2 - 3D + 2)x_2$, $L_3[x_1] = (D + 2)x_1$, and $L_4[x_2] = (2D - 4)x_2$. Applying L_3 and L_1 to Eqs. (19) and (20) respectively, and subtracting the results, yields

$$(L_1 L_4 - L_3 L_2)[x_2]$$
$$= [(D^2 + D - 1)(2D - 4) - (D + 2)(D^2 - 3D + 2)]x_2 = 0$$

or

$$(D^3 - D^2 - 2D)x_2 = 0. \tag{21}$$

Thus the general solution of the system (19), (20) should contain three arbitrary constants. The general solution of Eq. (21) is

$$x_2 = \phi_2(t) = c_1 + c_2 e^{2t} + c_3 e^{-t}. \tag{22}$$

Substituting this expression for x_2 in Eq. (20) gives

$$x_1' + 2x_1 = 4c_1 + 6c_3 e^{-t} \tag{23}$$

whose general solution is

$$x_1 = \phi_1(t) = 2c_1 + 6c_3 e^{-t} + c_4 e^{-2t}. \tag{24}$$

To eliminate the extraneous constant we substitute for x_1 and x_2 in Eq. (19), and find that $c_4 = 0$. Note that if we had substituted for x_2 in Eq. (19) and then solved this second order equation for x_1 we would have introduced two extraneous constants instead of one. These would have been eliminated by substituting for x_1 and x_2 in Eq. (20).

PROBLEMS

In each of Problems 1 through 11 solve the given system of equations.

1. $x_1' = x_1 + x_2$
   $x_2' = 4x_1 - 2x_2$

2. $x_1' = x_1 + x_2 + 2e^t$
   $x_2' = 4x_1 + x_2 - e^t$

3. $x_1' = 2x_1 - 5x_2 - \sin 2t,$ $x_1(0) = 0$
   $x_2' = x_1 - 2x_2 + t,$ $x_2(0) = 1$

4. $x_1' = x_1 - x_2 - t^2$
   $x_2' = x_1 + 3x_2 + 2t$

5. $x_1' = 3x_1 - 4x_2 + e^t,$ $x_1(0) = 1$
   $x_2' = x_1 - x_2 - e^t,$ $x_2(0) = -1$

6. $x_1' = 4x_1 - 2x_2 + 2t$
   $x_2' = 8x_1 - 4x_2 + 1$

7. $x_1' = 3x_1 - 2x_2 - e^{-t} \sin t$
   $x_2' = 4x_1 - x_2 + 2e^{-t} \cos t$

8. $x_1' = x_1 - 5x_2,$ $x_1(0) = 1$
   $x_2' = 2x_1 - 5x_2,$ $x_2(0) = 0$

9. $x_1' = x_1$
   $x_2' = -x_2 + \sqrt{2}x_3$
   $x_3' = \sqrt{2}x_2$

10. $x_1' = x_1 - x_2 + 4x_3$
    $x_2' = 3x_1 + 2x_2 - x_3$
    $x_3' = 2x_1 + x_2 - x_3$

11. $x_1' = x_1 + x_2 + x_3$
    $x_2' = 2x_1 + x_2 - x_3$
    $x_3' = -8x_1 - 5x_2 - 3x_3$

12. Solve the example problem, Eqs. (19) and (20), by substituting for x_2 from Eq. (22) in Eq. (19).

In each of Problems 13 through 17 solve the given system of equations. Make sure that the proper number of arbitrary constants appears in the general solution.

13. $(D^2 - 3D + 2)x_1 + (D - 1)x_2 = 0$
    $(D - 2)x_1 + (D + 1)x_2 = 0$

14. $(2D + 1)x_1 + Dx_2 = t$
    $(D - 1)x_1 + Dx_2 = 2$

15. $(D^2 - 4D + 4)x_1 + \qquad 3Dx_2 = 1$
    $(D - 2)x_1 + (D + 2)x_2 = 0$

16. $\qquad D^2x_1 + (D + 1)x_2 = 0$
    $(D - 1)x_1 + \qquad x_2 = \sin t$

17. $(D^2 - 4D + 4)x_1 + \qquad (D^2 + 2D)x_2 = 0$
    $(D^2 - 2D)x_1 + (D^2 + 4D + 4)x_2 = 0$

In each of Problems 18 through 21 show that the given system of equations is degenerate. Determine by attempting to solve the system whether there are no solutions or infinitely many.

18. $Dx_1 + (D + 1)x_2 = t$
    $Dx_1 + (D + 1)x_2 = t + 2$

19. $(D + 2)x_1 + (D + 2)x_2 = e^{2t}$
    $(D - 2)x_1 + (D - 2)x_2 = e^{-2t}$ Hint: Let $u = x_1 + x_2$

20. $(D^2 - 1)x_1 + (D - 1)x_2 = \sin t$
    $(D + 1)x_1 + \qquad x_2 = 2e^t$

21. $(D^2 + 3D + 2)x_1 + (D^2 + 2D)x_2 = 0$
    $(D + 1)x_1 + \qquad Dx_2 = 0$

22. Linear differential operators with variable coefficients may not be commutative. Consider the operators

$$L_1[x] = x' + tx, \qquad L_2[x] = x' + t^2x.$$

Show that

$$L_1L_2[x] = L_1\{L_2[x]\} = x'' + (t^2 + t)x' + (2t + t^3)x,$$

and that

$$L_2L_1[x] = L_2\{L_1[x]\} = x'' + (t + t^2)x' + (1 + t^3)x.$$

Hence

$$L_1L_2[x] \neq L_2L_1[x].$$

23. Consider the system of equations

$$L_{11}[x_1] + L_{12}[x_2] + L_{13}[x_3] = g_1(t),$$
$$L_{21}[x_1] + L_{22}[x_2] + L_{23}[x_3] = g_2(t),$$
$$L_{31}[x_1] + L_{32}[x_2] + L_{33}[x_3] = g_3(t),$$

where $L_{11}, \ldots, L_{33}$ are linear differential operators with constant coefficients, but are not necessarily of first order. It can be shown that the order of this system, that is, the number of arbitrary constants appearing in its general solution, is equal to the order of the operator L defined by

$$L = \begin{vmatrix} L_{11} & L_{12} & L_{13} \\ L_{21} & L_{22} & L_{23} \\ L_{31} & L_{32} & L_{33} \end{vmatrix}.$$

This determinant is evaluated by treating $L_{11}, \ldots, L_{33}$ as polynomials in the operator D, and formally using the customary methods of expanding determinants. Determine the order of each of the following systems.

(a) $(D^2 + 1)x_1 + (D^2 + 2)x_2 \qquad\qquad\qquad = 0$
    $\qquad\qquad (D - 1)x_2 + (D^2 - 2)x_3 = 0$
    $\quad D^2x_1 \qquad\qquad\qquad - (D^3 + 1)x_3 = 0$

(b) $\qquad (D + 1)x_1 + \qquad Dx_2 + (D^2 + 1)x_3 = 0$
    $(D^2 + 2D + 2)x_1 + (D - 1)x_2 + \quad (D + 2)x_3 = 2te^t$
    $\quad (D - 2)x_1 + (D + 3)x_2 + (D^2 + 3D)x_3 = te^{2t}$

7.3 REVIEW OF MATRICES

Whereas the process of elimination discussed in the last section is often a satisfactory way of solving systems of linear differential equations when the number of equations is small, it rapidly becomes unwieldy when larger systems are to be considered. More important, it does not provide an adequate basis for a systematic development of the theory associated with such equations. For both of these reasons it is advisable to bring to bear some of the results of matrix theory upon the initial value problem for a system of linear differential equations. For reference purposes this section is devoted to a brief summary* of some of the facts which will be needed later. We will assume, however, that the reader is familiar with determinants and how to evaluate them.

We will designate matrices by bold-faced capitals $\mathbf{A}$, $\mathbf{B}$, $\mathbf{C}$, $\ldots$, occasionally using bold-faced Greek capitals $\mathbf{\Phi}$, $\mathbf{\Psi}$, $\ldots$. A matrix $\mathbf{A}$ consists of a rectangular array of numbers, or elements, arranged in m rows and n columns, that is,

$$\mathbf{A} = \begin{pmatrix} a_{11} & a_{12} & \cdots & a_{1n} \\ a_{21} & a_{22} & \cdots & a_{2n} \\ \cdot & \cdot & & \cdot \\ \cdot & \cdot & & \cdot \\ \cdot & \cdot & & \cdot \\ a_{m1} & a_{m2} & \cdots & a_{mn} \end{pmatrix}. \tag{1}$$

We speak of $\mathbf{A}$ as an $m \times n$ matrix. Although later in the chapter we will often assume that the elements of certain matrices are real numbers, we will assume that the elements of the matrices in this section may be complex numbers. The element lying in the ith row and jth column is designated by a_{ij}, the first subscript identifying its row and the second its column. Sometimes the notation (a_{ij}) is used to denote the matrix whose generic element is a_{ij}.

Associated with each matrix $\mathbf{A}$ is the matrix $\mathbf{A}^T$, known as the *transpose* of $\mathbf{A}$, and obtained from $\mathbf{A}$ by interchanging the rows and columns of $\mathbf{A}$. Thus, if $\mathbf{A} = (a_{ij})$, then $\mathbf{A}^T = (a_{ji})$. Also, we will denote by $\bar{a}_{ij}$ the complex conjugate of a_{ij}, and by $\bar{\mathbf{A}}$ the matrix obtained from $\mathbf{A}$ by replacing each element a_{ij} by its conjugate $\bar{a}_{ij}$. The matrix $\bar{\mathbf{A}}$ is called the *conjugate* of $\mathbf{A}$. It will also be necessary to consider the transpose of the conjugate matrix $\bar{\mathbf{A}}^T$. This matrix is called the *adjoint* of $\mathbf{A}$ and will be denoted by $\mathbf{A}^*$.

We will be particularly interested in two somewhat special kinds of matrices: square matrices, which have the same number of rows and columns,

---

* There are many books dealing with the elements of matrix algebra. A representative list appears at the end of the chapter.

that is, $m = n$; and vectors (or column vectors), which can be thought of as $n \times 1$ matrices, or matrices having only one column. Square matrices having n rows and n columns are said to be of order n. We will denote (column) vectors by bold-faced lowercase letters $\mathbf{x}$, $\mathbf{y}$, $\boldsymbol{\xi}$, $\boldsymbol{\eta}$, ... The transpose $\mathbf{x}^T$ of an $n \times 1$ column vector is a $1 \times n$ row vector, that is, the matrix consisting of one row whose elements are the same as the elements in the corresponding position of $\mathbf{x}$.

Algebraic Operations

(1) *Equality.* Two $m \times n$ matrices $\mathbf{A}$ and $\mathbf{B}$ are said to be equal if corresponding elements are equal, that is, if $a_{ij} = b_{ij}$ for each i and j.

(2) *Addition.* The sum of two $m \times n$ matrices is defined as the matrix obtained by adding corresponding elements:

$$\mathbf{A} + \mathbf{B} = (a_{ij}) + (b_{ij}) = (a_{ij} + b_{ij}). \tag{2}$$

Matrix addition is commutative and associative, so that

$$\mathbf{A} + \mathbf{B} = \mathbf{B} + \mathbf{A}, \qquad \mathbf{A} + (\mathbf{B} + \mathbf{C}) = (\mathbf{A} + \mathbf{B}) + \mathbf{C}. \tag{3}$$

(3) *Multiplication by a Number.* The product of a matrix $\mathbf{A}$ by a complex number α is defined as follows:

$$\alpha \mathbf{A} = \alpha(a_{ij}) = (\alpha a_{ij}). \tag{4}$$

The distributive laws

$$\alpha(\mathbf{A} + \mathbf{B}) = \alpha \mathbf{A} + \alpha \mathbf{B}, \qquad (\alpha + \beta)\mathbf{A} = \alpha \mathbf{A} + \beta \mathbf{A} \tag{5}$$

are satisfied for this type of multiplication.

(4) *Multiplication.* The product $\mathbf{AB}$ of two matrices is defined whenever the number of columns of the first factor is the same as the number of rows in the second. If $\mathbf{A}$ and $\mathbf{B}$ are $m \times n$ and $n \times r$ matrices, respectively, then the product $\mathbf{C} = \mathbf{AB}$ is an $m \times r$ matrix. The element in the ith row and jth column of $\mathbf{C}$ is found by multiplying each element of the ith row of $\mathbf{A}$ by the corresponding element of the jth column of $\mathbf{B}$ and then adding the resulting products. Symbolically,

$$c_{ij} = \sum_{k=1}^{n} a_{ik} b_{kj}. \tag{6}$$

Matrix multiplication satisfies the associative law

$$(\mathbf{AB})\mathbf{C} = \mathbf{A}(\mathbf{BC}), \tag{7}$$

and the distributive law

$$\mathbf{A}(\mathbf{B} + \mathbf{C}) = \mathbf{AB} + \mathbf{AC}. \tag{8}$$

However, in general, matrix multiplication is not commutative. In order for both products AB and BA to exist it is necessary that A and B be square matrices of the same order. Even in that case the two products need not be equal, so that, in general

$$AB \neq BA. \tag{9}$$

Example 1.   To illustrate the multiplication of matrices, and also the fact that matrix multiplication is not necessarily commutative, consider the matrices

$$A = \begin{pmatrix} 1 & -2 & 1 \\ 0 & 2 & -1 \\ 2 & 1 & 1 \end{pmatrix}, \qquad B = \begin{pmatrix} 2 & 1 & -1 \\ 1 & -1 & 0 \\ 2 & -1 & 1 \end{pmatrix}.$$

From the definition of multiplication given in Eq. (6) we have

$$AB = \begin{pmatrix} 2-2+2 & 1+2-1 & -1+0+1 \\ 0+2-2 & 0-2+1 & 0+0-1 \\ 4+1+2 & 2-1-1 & -2+0+1 \end{pmatrix}$$

$$= \begin{pmatrix} 2 & 2 & 0 \\ 0 & -1 & -1 \\ 7 & 0 & -1 \end{pmatrix}.$$

Similarly, we find that

$$BA = \begin{pmatrix} 0 & -3 & 0 \\ 1 & -4 & 2 \\ 4 & -5 & 4 \end{pmatrix}.$$

Clearly, $AB \neq BA$.

(5) *Multiplication of Vectors.*   Matrix multiplication as described above also applies as a special case if the matrices A and B are $1 \times n$ and $n \times 1$ row and column vectors, respectively. Denoting these vectors by $\mathbf{x}^T$ and $\mathbf{y}$ we have

$$\mathbf{x}^T \mathbf{y} = \sum_{i=1}^{n} x_i y_i. \tag{10}$$

The result of such an operation is a (complex) number, and it is clear from Eq. (10) that

$$\mathbf{x}^T \mathbf{y} = \mathbf{y}^T \mathbf{x}, \qquad \mathbf{x}^T(\mathbf{y} + \mathbf{z}) = \mathbf{x}^T \mathbf{y} + \mathbf{x}^T \mathbf{z}, \qquad (\alpha \mathbf{x})^T \mathbf{y} = \alpha(\mathbf{x}^T \mathbf{y}) = \mathbf{x}^T(\alpha \mathbf{y}).$$

$$\tag{11}$$

There is another very useful type of vector multiplication, which is also defined for any two vectors having the same number of components. This product, denoted by $(\mathbf{x}, \mathbf{y})$, is called the scalar or inner product, and is defined by

$$(\mathbf{x}, \mathbf{y}) = \sum_{i=1}^{n} x_i \bar{y}_i. \tag{12}$$

The scalar product is also a (complex) number, and by comparing Eqs. (10) and (12) we see that

$$(\mathbf{x}, \mathbf{y}) = \mathbf{x}^T \bar{\mathbf{y}}. \tag{13}$$

From Eq. (12) it follows that

$$(\mathbf{x}, \mathbf{y}) = \overline{(\mathbf{y}, \mathbf{x})}, \qquad (\mathbf{x}, \mathbf{y} + \mathbf{z}) = (\mathbf{x}, \mathbf{y}) + (\mathbf{x}, \mathbf{z})$$
$$(\alpha\mathbf{x}, \mathbf{y}) = \alpha(\mathbf{x}, \mathbf{y}), \qquad (\mathbf{x}, \alpha\mathbf{y}) = \bar{\alpha}(\mathbf{x}, \mathbf{y}). \tag{14}$$

Even if the vector $\mathbf{x}$ has elements with nonzero imaginary parts, the inner product of $\mathbf{x}$ with itself yields a nonnegative real number,

$$(\mathbf{x}, \mathbf{x}) = \sum_{i=1}^{n} x_i \bar{x}_i = \sum_{i=1}^{n} |x_i|^2; \tag{15}$$

however, the matrix product

$$\mathbf{x}^T \mathbf{x} = \sum_{i=1}^{n} x_i^2 \tag{16}$$

may not be a real number. If all of the components of the second factor $\mathbf{y}$ are real, then the two products are identical, and both reduce to the dot product usually encountered in physical and geometrical contexts with $n = 3$.

(6) *Identity.*   The multiplicative identity, or simply the identity matrix $\mathbf{I}$, is given by

$$\mathbf{I} = \begin{pmatrix} 1 & 0 & \cdots & 0 \\ 0 & 1 & \cdots & 0 \\ \cdot & \cdot & & \cdot \\ \cdot & \cdot & & \cdot \\ \cdot & \cdot & & \cdot \\ 0 & 0 & \cdots & 1 \end{pmatrix}. \tag{17}$$

From the definition of matrix multiplication we have

$$\mathbf{AI} = \mathbf{IA} = \mathbf{A} \tag{18}$$

for any (square) matrix $\mathbf{A}$. Hence, the commutative law does hold for square matrices if one of the matrices is the identity.

(7) *Zero.*   The symbol $\mathbf{0}$ will be used to denote the matrix (or vector) each of whose elements is zero.

Solution of Algebraic Equations.   A set of n simultaneous linear algebraic equations in n variables

$$a_{11}x_1 + a_{12}x_2 + \cdots + a_{1n}x_n = b_1,$$

$$\vdots \tag{19}$$

$$a_{n1}x_1 + a_{n2}x_2 + \cdots + a_{nn}x_n = b_n,$$

can be written as

$$\mathbf{Ax} = \mathbf{b}, \tag{20}$$

where the $n \times n$ matrix $\mathbf{A}$ and the vector $\mathbf{b}$ are given, and the components of $\mathbf{x}$ are to be determined. If $\mathbf{b} = \mathbf{0}$, the system is said to be homogeneous; otherwise, it is nonhomogeneous. If the determinant of coefficients det $\mathbf{A}$ is not zero, then there is a unique solution of the system (20). In particular, if $\mathbf{b} = \mathbf{0}$, then the trivial solution $\mathbf{x} = \mathbf{0}$ is the only solution. However, if det $\mathbf{A}$ is zero, then the situation is more complicated. In this case the homogeneous system

$$\mathbf{Ax} = \mathbf{0} \tag{21}$$

has (infinitely many) nonzero solutions. On the other hand, the nonhomogeneous system (20) has no solution unless the vector $\mathbf{b}$ satisfies a certain further condition, namely

$$(\mathbf{b}, \mathbf{y}) = 0, \tag{22}$$

for all vectors $\mathbf{y}$ satisfying $\mathbf{A^*y} = \mathbf{0}$. If condition (22) is met, then the system (20) has (infinitely many) solutions. Each of these solutions has the form

$$\mathbf{x} = \mathbf{x}^{(0)} + \boldsymbol{\xi}, \tag{23}$$

where $\mathbf{x}^{(0)}$ is a particular solution of Eq. (20), and $\boldsymbol{\xi}$ is some solution of the homogeneous system (21). Note the resemblance between Eq. (23) and the solution of a nonhomogeneous linear differential equation (Eq. (4) of Section 3.6); $\mathbf{x}^{(0)}$ and $\boldsymbol{\xi}$ correspond, respectively, to the particular solution y_p and the complementary solution y_c. The proofs of some of the above statements are outlined in Problems 21 through 25.

Linear Independence.   A set of k vectors $\mathbf{x}^{(1)}, \ldots, \mathbf{x}^{(k)}$ is said to be *linearly dependent* if there exists a set of (complex) numbers $c_1, \ldots, c_k$, at least one of which is nonzero, such that

$$c_1\mathbf{x}^{(1)} + \cdots + c_k\mathbf{x}^{(k)} = \mathbf{0}. \tag{24}$$

In other words, $\mathbf{x}^{(1)}, \ldots, \mathbf{x}^{(k)}$ are linearly dependent if there is a linear relation among them. On the other hand, if the only set $c_1, \ldots, c_k$ for which Eq. (24) is satisfied is $c_1 = c_2 = \cdots = c_k = 0$, then $\mathbf{x}^{(1)}, \ldots, \mathbf{x}^{(k)}$ are said to be *linearly independent*.

Consider now a set of n vectors, each of which has n components. Let $x_{ij} = x_i^{(j)}$ be the ith component of the vector $\mathbf{x}^{(j)}$, and let $\mathbf{X} = (x_{ij})$.

Then Eq. (24) can be written as

$$\begin{pmatrix} x_1^{(1)}c_1 + \cdots + x_1^{(n)}c_n \\ \cdot \\ \cdot \\ \cdot \\ x_n^{(1)}c_1 + \cdots + x_n^{(n)}c_n \end{pmatrix} = \begin{pmatrix} x_{11}c_1 + \cdots + x_{1n}c_n \\ \cdot \\ \cdot \\ \cdot \\ x_{n1}c_1 + \cdots + x_{nn}c_n \end{pmatrix} = \mathbf{Xc} = \mathbf{0}.$$

(25)

If $\det \mathbf{X} \neq 0$, then the only solution of Eq. (25) is $\mathbf{c} = \mathbf{0}$, but if $\det \mathbf{X} = 0$, there are nonzero solutions. Thus the set of vectors $\mathbf{x}^{(1)}, \ldots, \mathbf{x}^{(n)}$ is linearly independent if and only if $\det \mathbf{X} \neq 0$.

Example 2.   Consider the vectors

$$\mathbf{x}^{(1)} = \begin{pmatrix} 1 \\ 2 \\ -1 \end{pmatrix}, \qquad \mathbf{x}^{(2)} = \begin{pmatrix} 2 \\ 1 \\ 3 \end{pmatrix}, \qquad \mathbf{x}^{(3)} = \begin{pmatrix} -4 \\ 1 \\ -11 \end{pmatrix}.$$

To determine whether $\mathbf{x}^{(1)}$, $\mathbf{x}^{(2)}$, and $\mathbf{x}^{(3)}$ are linearly dependent we compute $\det (x_{ij})$ whose columns are the components of $\mathbf{x}^{(1)}$, $\mathbf{x}^{(2)}$, and $\mathbf{x}^{(3)}$, respectively. Thus

$$\det (x_{ij}) = \begin{vmatrix} 1 & 2 & -4 \\ 2 & 1 & 1 \\ -1 & 3 & -11 \end{vmatrix},$$

and an elementary calculation shows that it is zero. Thus $\mathbf{x}^{(1)}$, $\mathbf{x}^{(2)}$, and $\mathbf{x}^{(3)}$ are linearly dependent, and there are constants c_1, c_2, and c_3 such that

$$c_1\mathbf{x}^{(1)} + c_2\mathbf{x}^{(2)} + c_3\mathbf{x}^{(3)} = \mathbf{0}.$$

(26)

Since the determinant of coefficients is zero, the homogeneous system (26) has nontrivial solutions, and two of the constants c_1, c_2, and c_3 can be determined in terms of the third. Equation (26) is equivalent to the system

$$c_1 + 2c_2 = 4c_3,$$

$$2c_1 + c_2 = -c_3,$$

$$-c_1 + 3c_2 = 11c_3.$$

For convenience we take $c_3 = -1$. Then solving the first two of these equations gives $c_1 = 2$, $c_2 = -3$, and these values also satisfy the third equation. Thus the relation among $\mathbf{x}^{(1)}$, $\mathbf{x}^{(2)}$, and $\mathbf{x}^{(3)}$ is $2\mathbf{x}^{(1)} - 3\mathbf{x}^{(2)} - \mathbf{x}^{(3)} = \mathbf{0}$.

Frequently it is useful to think of the columns (or rows) or a matrix $\mathbf{A}$ as vectors. These column (or row) vectors are linearly independent if and only if $\det \mathbf{A} \neq 0$. Further, if $\mathbf{C} = \mathbf{AB}$, then it can be shown that $\det \mathbf{C} = (\det \mathbf{A})(\det \mathbf{B})$. Therefore, if the columns (or rows) of both $\mathbf{A}$ and $\mathbf{B}$ are linearly independent, then the columns (or rows) of $\mathbf{C}$ will also be linearly independent.

Matrix Functions. We will sometimes need to consider vectors or matrices whose elements are functions of a real variable t. We write

$$
\mathbf{x}(t) = \begin{pmatrix} x_1(t) \\ \cdot \\ \cdot \\ \cdot \\ x_n(t) \end{pmatrix}, \qquad \mathbf{A}(t) = \begin{pmatrix} a_{11}(t) \cdots a_{1n}(t) \\ \cdot \qquad \cdot \\ \cdot \qquad \cdot \\ \cdot \qquad \cdot \\ a_{n1}(t) \cdots a_{nn}(t) \end{pmatrix}, \tag{27}
$$

respectively. The vectors $\mathbf{x}^{(1)}(t), \ldots, \mathbf{x}^{(k)}(t)$ are said to be linearly dependent on an interval $\alpha < t < \beta$ if there exists a set of constants $c_1, \ldots, c_k$, not all of which are zero, such that $c_1\mathbf{x}^{(1)}(t) + \cdots + c_k\mathbf{x}^{(k)}(t) = \mathbf{0}$ for all t in the interval. Otherwise, $\mathbf{x}^{(1)}(t), \ldots, \mathbf{x}^{(k)}(t)$ are said to be linearly independent. Note that if $\mathbf{x}^{(1)}(t), \ldots, \mathbf{x}^{(k)}(t)$ are linearly dependent on an interval, they are linearly dependent at each point in the interval. However, if $\mathbf{x}^{(1)}(t), \ldots, \mathbf{x}^{(k)}(t)$ are linearly independent on an interval, they may or may not be linearly independent at each point; they may, in fact, be linearly dependent at each point, but with different sets of constants at different points. See Problem 15 for an example.

The matrix $\mathbf{A}(t)$ is said to be continuous at $t = t_0$ or on an interval $\alpha < t < \beta$ if each element of $\mathbf{A}$ is a continuous function at the given point or on the given interval. Similarly $\mathbf{A}(t)$ is said to be differentiable if each of its elements is differentiable, and its derivative $d\mathbf{A}/dt$ is defined by

$$
\frac{d\mathbf{A}}{dt} = \left(\frac{da_{ij}}{dt}\right); \tag{28}
$$

that is, each element of $d\mathbf{A}/dt$ is the derivative of the corresponding element of $\mathbf{A}$. In the same way the integral of a matrix function is defined as

$$
\int_a^b \mathbf{A}(t)\, dt = \left(\int_a^b a_{ij}(t)\, dt\right). \tag{29}
$$

Many of the rules of elementary calculus can be easily extended to matrix functions; in particular,

$$
\frac{d}{dt}(\mathbf{CA}) = \mathbf{C}\frac{d\mathbf{A}}{dt}, \text{ where } \mathbf{C} \text{ is a constant matrix;} \tag{30}
$$

$$
\frac{d}{dt}(\mathbf{A} + \mathbf{B}) = \frac{d\mathbf{A}}{dt} + \frac{d\mathbf{B}}{dt}; \tag{31}
$$

$$
\frac{d}{dt}(\mathbf{AB}) = \mathbf{A}\frac{d\mathbf{B}}{dt} + \frac{d\mathbf{A}}{dt}\mathbf{B}. \tag{32}
$$

In Eqs. (30) and (32) care must be taken in each term to avoid carelessly interchanging the order of multiplication. The definitions expressed by Eqs. (28) and (29) also apply as special cases to vectors.

PROBLEMS

1.   If $A = \begin{pmatrix} 1 & -2 & 0 \\ 3 & 2 & -1 \\ -2 & 1 & 3 \end{pmatrix}$ and $B = \begin{pmatrix} 4 & -2 & 3 \\ -1 & 5 & 0 \\ 6 & 1 & 2 \end{pmatrix}$,

find

(a) $2A + B$ (b) $A - 4B$ (c) AB (d) BA

2.   If $A = \begin{pmatrix} -2 & 1 & 2 \\ 1 & 0 & -3 \\ 2 & -1 & 1 \end{pmatrix}$ and $B = \begin{pmatrix} 1 & 2 & 3 \\ 3 & -1 & -1 \\ -2 & 1 & 0 \end{pmatrix}$,

find

(a) A^T (b) B^T (c) $A^T + B^T$ (d) $(A + B)^T$

3.   If $A = \begin{pmatrix} 3 & 2 & -1 \\ 2 & -1 & 2 \\ 1 & 2 & 1 \end{pmatrix}$ and $B = \begin{pmatrix} 2 & 1 & -1 \\ -2 & 3 & 3 \\ 1 & 0 & 2 \end{pmatrix}$,

verify that $2(A + B) = 2A + 2B$.

4.   If $A = \begin{pmatrix} 1 & -2 & 0 \\ 3 & 2 & -1 \\ -2 & 0 & 3 \end{pmatrix}$, $B = \begin{pmatrix} 2 & 1 & -1 \\ -2 & 3 & 3 \\ 1 & 0 & 2 \end{pmatrix}$,

and $C = \begin{pmatrix} 2 & 1 & 0 \\ 1 & 2 & 2 \\ 0 & 1 & -1 \end{pmatrix}$,

verify that

(a) $(AB)C = A(BC)$ (b) $(A + B) + C = A + (B + C)$

(c) $A(B + C) = AB + AC$

5. Prove each of the following laws of matrix algebra.

(a) $A + B = B + A$ (b) $A + (B + C) = (A + B) + C$

(c) $\alpha(A + B) = \alpha A + \alpha B$ (d) $(\alpha + \beta)A = \alpha A + \beta A$

(e) $A(BC) = (AB)C$ (f) $A(B + C) = AB + AC$

In each of Problems 6 through 10 either solve the given set of equations, or else show that there is no solution.

6. $\quad x_1 \quad - \quad x_3 = 0$

$\quad 3x_1 + x_2 + \quad x_3 = 1$

$\quad -x_1 + x_2 + 2x_3 = 2$

7. $\quad x_1 + 2x_2 - \quad x_3 = 1$

$\quad 2x_1 + \quad x_2 + \quad x_3 = 1$

$\quad x_1 - \quad x_2 + 2x_3 = 1$

8. $\quad x_1 + 2x_2 - \quad x_3 = 2$

$\quad 2x_1 + \quad x_2 + \quad x_3 = 1$

$\quad x_1 - \quad x_2 + 2x_3 = -1$

9. $\quad x_1 + 2x_2 - \quad x_3 = 0$

$\quad 2x_1 + \quad x_2 + \quad x_3 = 0$

$\quad x_1 - \quad x_2 + 2x_3 = 0$

10. $\quad x_1 \quad - \quad x_3 = 0$

$\quad 3x_1 + x_2 + \quad x_3 = 0$

$\quad -x_1 + x_2 + 2x_3 = 0$

11. Determine whether each of the following sets of vectors is linearly independent. If linearly dependent, find the linear relation among them. The vectors are written as row vectors to save space, but may be considered as column vectors if you wish; that is, the transposes of the given vectors may be used instead of the vectors themselves.

(a) $\mathbf{x}^{(1)} = (1, 1, 0), \qquad \mathbf{x}^{(2)} = (0, 1, 1), \qquad \mathbf{x}^{(3)} = (1, 0, 1)$

(b) $\mathbf{x}^{(1)} = (2, 1, 0), \qquad \mathbf{x}^{(2)} = (0, 1, 0), \qquad \mathbf{x}^{(3)} = (-1, 2, 0)$

(c) $\mathbf{x}^{(1)} = (1, 2, 2, 3), \qquad \mathbf{x}^{(2)} = (-1, 0, 3, 1), \qquad \mathbf{x}^{(3)} = (-2, -1, 1, 0)$
$\mathbf{x}^{(4)} = (-3, 0, -1, 3)$

(d) $\mathbf{x}^{(1)} = (1, 2, -1, 0), \qquad \mathbf{x}^{(2)} = (2, 3, 1, -1), \qquad \mathbf{x}^{(3)} = (-1, 0, 2, 2)$
$\mathbf{x}^{(4)} = (3, -1, 1, 3)$

(e) $\mathbf{x}^{(1)} = (1, 2, -2), \qquad \mathbf{x}^{(2)} = (3, 1, 0), \qquad \mathbf{x}^{(3)} = (2, -1, 1),$
$\mathbf{x}^{(4)} = (4, 3, -2)$

12. Suppose that the vectors $\mathbf{x}^{(1)}, \ldots, \mathbf{x}^{(m)}$ each have n components where $n < m$. Show that $\mathbf{x}^{(1)}, \ldots, \mathbf{x}^{(m)}$ are linearly dependent.

13. If $A(t) = \begin{pmatrix} e^t & 2e^{-t} & e^{2t} \\ 2e^t & e^{-t} & -e^{2t} \\ -e^t & 3e^{-t} & 2e^{2t} \end{pmatrix}$ and $B(t) = \begin{pmatrix} 2e^t & e^{-t} & 3e^{2t} \\ -e^t & 2e^{-t} & e^{2t} \\ 3e^t & -e^{-t} & -e^{2t} \end{pmatrix},$

find

(a) $A + 3B$

(b) AB

(c) dA/dt

(d) $\int_0^1 A(t)\, dt$

14. Determine whether each of the following sets of vectors is linearly independent for $-\infty < t < \infty$. If linearly dependent, find the linear relation among them. As in Problem 11 the vectors are written as row vectors to save space.

(a) $\mathbf{x}^{(1)}(t) = (e^{-t}, 2e^{-t})$, $\mathbf{x}^{(2)}(t) = (e^{-t}, e^{-t})$, $\mathbf{x}^{(3)}(t) = (3e^{-t}, 0)$

(b) $\mathbf{x}^{(1)}(t) = (2 \sin t, \sin t)$, $\mathbf{x}^{(2)}(t) = (\sin t, 2 \sin t)$

15. Let

$$\mathbf{x}^{(1)}(t) = \begin{pmatrix} e^t \\ te^t \end{pmatrix}, \qquad \mathbf{x}^{(2)}(t) = \begin{pmatrix} 1 \\ t \end{pmatrix}.$$

Show that $\mathbf{x}^{(1)}(t)$ and $\mathbf{x}^{(2)}(t)$ are linearly dependent at each point in the interval $0 \le t \le 1$. Nevertheless, show that $\mathbf{x}^{(1)}(t)$ and $\mathbf{x}^{(2)}(t)$ are linearly independent on the interval $0 \le t \le 1$.

In each of Problems 16 through 18 verify that the given vector satisfies the given differential equation.

16. $\mathbf{x}' = \begin{pmatrix} 3 & -2 \\ 2 & -2 \end{pmatrix} \mathbf{x}$, $\mathbf{x} = \begin{pmatrix} 4 \\ 2 \end{pmatrix} e^{2t}$

17. $\mathbf{x}' = \begin{pmatrix} 2 & -1 \\ 3 & -2 \end{pmatrix} \mathbf{x} + \begin{pmatrix} 1 \\ -1 \end{pmatrix} e^t$, $\mathbf{x} = \begin{pmatrix} 1 \\ 0 \end{pmatrix} e^t + 2 \begin{pmatrix} 1 \\ 1 \end{pmatrix} te^t$

18. $\mathbf{x}' = \begin{pmatrix} 1 & 1 & 1 \\ 2 & 1 & -1 \\ 0 & -1 & 1 \end{pmatrix} \mathbf{x}$, $\mathbf{x} = \begin{pmatrix} 6 \\ -8 \\ -4 \end{pmatrix} e^{-t} + 2 \begin{pmatrix} 0 \\ 1 \\ -1 \end{pmatrix} e^{2t}$

In each of Problems 19 and 20 verify that the given matrix satisfies the given differential equation.

19. $\mathbf{\Psi}' = \begin{pmatrix} 1 & 1 \\ 4 & -2 \end{pmatrix} \mathbf{\Psi}$, $\mathbf{\Psi}(t) = \begin{pmatrix} e^{-3t} & e^{2t} \\ -4e^{-3t} & e^{2t} \end{pmatrix}$

20. $\mathbf{\Psi}' = \begin{pmatrix} 1 & -1 & 4 \\ 3 & 2 & -1 \\ 2 & 1 & -1 \end{pmatrix} \mathbf{\Psi}$, $\mathbf{\Psi}(t) = \begin{pmatrix} e^t & e^{-2t} & e^{3t} \\ -4e^t & -e^{-2t} & 2e^{3t} \\ -e^t & -e^{-2t} & e^{3t} \end{pmatrix}$

Problems 21 through 25 deal with the problem of solving $\mathbf{Ax} = \mathbf{b}$ when $\det \mathbf{A} = 0$.

21. Suppose that, for a given matrix $\mathbf{A}$, there is a nonzero vector $\mathbf{x}$ such that $\mathbf{Ax} = \mathbf{0}$. Show that there is also a nonzero vector $\mathbf{y}$ such that $\mathbf{A}^*\mathbf{y} = \mathbf{0}$.

22. Show that $(\mathbf{Ax}, \mathbf{y}) = (\mathbf{x}, \mathbf{A}^*\mathbf{y})$ for any vectors $\mathbf{x}$ and $\mathbf{y}$.

23. Suppose that det $\mathbf{A} = 0$ but that $\mathbf{Ax} = \mathbf{b}$ has solutions. Show that $(\mathbf{b}, \mathbf{y}) = 0$, where $\mathbf{y}$ is any solution of $\mathbf{A}^*\mathbf{y} = \mathbf{0}$. Verify that this statement is true for the set of equations in Problem 8. *Hint:* Use the result of Problem 22.

24. Suppose that det $\mathbf{A} = 0$ but that $\mathbf{x} = \mathbf{x}^{(0)}$ is a solution of $\mathbf{Ax} = \mathbf{b}$. Show that if $\boldsymbol{\xi}$ is a solution of $\mathbf{A}\boldsymbol{\xi} = \mathbf{0}$ and α is any constant, then $\mathbf{x} = \mathbf{x}^{(0)} + \alpha\boldsymbol{\xi}$ is also a solution of $\mathbf{Ax} = \mathbf{b}$.

*25. Suppose that det $\mathbf{A} = 0$, and that $\mathbf{y}$ is a solution of $\mathbf{A}^*\mathbf{y} = \mathbf{0}$. Show that if $(\mathbf{b}, \mathbf{y}) = 0$ then $\mathbf{Ax} = \mathbf{b}$ has solutions. Note that this is the converse of Problem 23; the form of the solution is given by Problem 24.

7.4 BASIC THEORY OF SYSTEMS OF FIRST ORDER LINEAR EQUATIONS

The general theory of a system of n first order linear equations

$$x_1' = p_{11}(t)x_1 + \cdots + p_{1n}(t)x_n + g_1(t),$$

$$\vdots \tag{1}$$

$$x_n' = p_{n1}(t)x_1 + \cdots + p_{nn}(t)x_n + g_n(t),$$

closely parallels that of a single linear equation of nth order. The discussion in this section therefore follows the same general lines as that in Sections 3.2, 3.3, and 5.2. In order to discuss the system (1) most effectively, we will write it in matrix notation. That is, we will consider $x_1 = \phi_1(t), \ldots, x_n = \phi_n(t)$ to be components of a vector $\mathbf{x} = \boldsymbol{\phi}(t)$; similarly $g_1(t), \ldots, g_n(t)$ are components of a vector $\mathbf{g}(t)$, and $p_{11}(t), \ldots, p_{nn}(t)$ are elements of an $n \times n$ matrix $\mathbf{P}(t)$. Equation (1) then takes the form

$$\mathbf{x}' = \mathbf{P}(t)\mathbf{x} + \mathbf{g}(t). \tag{2}$$

The use of vectors and matrices not only saves a great deal of space and facilitates calculations but also emphasizes the similarity between systems of equations and single (scalar) equations.

A vector $\mathbf{x} = \boldsymbol{\phi}(t)$ is said to be a solution of Eq. (2) if its components satisfy the system of equations (1). Throughout this section we will assume that $\mathbf{P}$ and $\mathbf{g}$ are continuous on some interval $\alpha < t < \beta$; that is, each of the scalar functions $p_{11}, \ldots, p_{nn}, g_1, \ldots, g_n$ is continuous there. According to Theorem 7.2, this is sufficient to guarantee the existence of solutions of Eq. (2) on the interval $\alpha < t < \beta$.

It is convenient to consider first the homogeneous equation,

$$\mathbf{x}' = \mathbf{P}(t)\mathbf{x}, \tag{3}$$

obtained from Eq. (2) by setting $\mathbf{g}(t) = \mathbf{0}$. Once the homogeneous equation has been solved, the method of variation of parameters can be used to solve the nonhomogeneous equation (2); this is taken up in Section 7.10. We will use the notation

$$
\mathbf{x}^{(1)}(t) = \begin{pmatrix} x_{11}(t) \\ x_{21}(t) \\ \cdot \\ \cdot \\ \cdot \\ x_{n1}(t) \end{pmatrix}, \dots, \mathbf{x}^{(k)}(t) = \begin{pmatrix} x_{1k}(t) \\ x_{2k}(t) \\ \cdot \\ \cdot \\ \cdot \\ x_{nk}(t) \end{pmatrix}, \dots \quad (4)
$$

to designate specific solutions of the system (3). Note that $x_{ij}(t) = x_i^{(j)}(t)$ refers to the ith component of the jth solution $\mathbf{x}^{(j)}(t)$. The main facts about the structure of solutions of the system (3) are stated in Theorems 7.3 to 7.6. They closely resemble the corresponding theorems in Sections 3.2, 3.3, and 5.2; some of the proofs are left to the reader as exercises.

Theorem 7.3. *If the vector functions* $\mathbf{x}^{(1)}$ *and* $\mathbf{x}^{(2)}$ *are solutions of the system (3), then the linear combination* $c_1\mathbf{x}^{(1)} + c_2\mathbf{x}^{(2)}$ *is also a solution for any constants* c_1 *and* c_2.

This is the principle of superposition; it is proved simply by differentiating $c_1\mathbf{x}^{(1)} + c_2\mathbf{x}^{(2)}$ and using the fact that $\mathbf{x}^{(1)}$ and $\mathbf{x}^{(2)}$ satisfy Eq. (3). By repeated application of Theorem 7.3 we reach the conclusion that if $\mathbf{x}^{(1)}, \dots, \mathbf{x}^{(k)}$ are solutions of Eq. (3) then

$$
\mathbf{x} = c_1\mathbf{x}^{(1)}(t) + \cdots + c_k\mathbf{x}^{(k)}(t) \quad (5)
$$

is also a solution for any constants $c_1, \dots, c_k$. As an example, it can be verified that

$$
\mathbf{x}^{(1)}(t) = \begin{pmatrix} e^{3t} \\ 2e^{3t} \end{pmatrix} = \begin{pmatrix} 1 \\ 2 \end{pmatrix}e^{3t}, \quad \mathbf{x}^{(2)}(t) = \begin{pmatrix} e^{-t} \\ -2e^{-t} \end{pmatrix} = \begin{pmatrix} 1 \\ -2 \end{pmatrix}e^{-t} \quad (6)
$$

satisfy the equation

$$
\mathbf{x}' = \begin{pmatrix} 1 & 1 \\ 4 & 1 \end{pmatrix}\mathbf{x}. \quad (7)
$$

According to Theorem 7.3

$$
\mathbf{x} = c_1\begin{pmatrix} 1 \\ 2 \end{pmatrix}e^{3t} + c_2\begin{pmatrix} 1 \\ -2 \end{pmatrix}e^{-t}
$$
$$
= c_1\mathbf{x}^{(1)}(t) + c_2\mathbf{x}^{(2)}(t) \quad (8)
$$

also satisfies Eq. (7). This solution of the system (7) was found in Section 7.2 by the method of elimination.

As we indicated above, by repeatedy applying Theorem 7.3, it follows that every finite linear combination of solutions of Eq. (3) is again a solution. The question now arises as to whether all solutions of Eq. (3) can be found in this way. By analogy with previous cases it is reasonable to expect that for a system of the form (3) of nth order it is sufficient to form linear combinations of n properly chosen solutions. Therefore let $x^{(1)}, \ldots, x^{(n)}$ be n solutions of the nth order system (3), and consider the matrix $X(t)$ whose columns are the vectors $x^{(1)}(t), \ldots, x^{(n)}(t)$;

$$
X(t) = \begin{pmatrix} x_{11}(t) & \cdots & x_{1n}(t) \\ & & \\ \cdot & & \cdot \\ \cdot & & \cdot \\ \cdot & & \cdot \\ x_{n1}(t) & \cdots & x_{nn}(t) \end{pmatrix}. \tag{9}
$$

Recall from Section 7.3 that the columns of $X(t)$ are linearly independent for a given value of t if and only if $\det X \neq 0$ for that value of t. This determinant is called the Wronskian of the n solutions $x^{(1)}, \ldots, x^{(n)}$ and is also denoted by $W[x^{(1)}, \ldots, x^{(n)}]$; that is

$$
W[x^{(1)}, \ldots, x^{(n)}] = \det X. \tag{10}
$$

The solutions $x^{(1)}, \ldots, x^{(n)}$ are then linearly independent at a point if and only if $W[x^{(1)}, \ldots, x^{(n)}]$ is not zero there.

Theorem 7.4. *If the vector functions* $x^{(1)}, \ldots, x^{(n)}$ *are linearly independent solutions of the system* (3) *for each point in the interval* $\alpha < t < \beta$, *then each solution* $x = \phi(t)$ *of the system* (3) *can be expressed as a linear combination of* $x^{(1)}, \ldots, x^{(n)}$,

$$
x = c_1 x^{(1)}(t) + \cdots + c_n x^{(n)}(t), \tag{11}
$$

in exactly one way.

Before proving Theorem 7.4, note that according to Theorem 7.3 all expressions of the form (11) are solutions of the system (3), while by Theorem 7.4 all solutions of Eq. (3) can be written in the form (11). If the constants $c_1, \ldots, c_n$ are thought of as arbitrary, then Eq. (11) includes all solutions of the system (3), and it is customary to call it the *general solution*. Any set of solutions $x^{(1)}, \ldots, x^{(n)}$ of Eq. (3), which is linearly independent at each point in the interval $\alpha < t < \beta$, is said to be a *fundamental set of solutions* for that interval.

To prove Theorem 7.4 we will show, given any solution ϕ of Eq. (3), that $\phi(t) = c_1 x^{(1)}(t) + \cdots + c_n x^{(n)}(t)$ for suitable values of $c_1, \ldots, c_n$. Let $t = t_0$ be some point in the interval $\alpha < t < \beta$, and let $\xi = \phi(t_0)$. We now wish to determine whether there is any solution of the form $x = c_1 x^{(1)}(t) + \cdots + c_n x^{(n)}(t)$ which also satisfies the same initial condition, $x(t_0) = \xi$. That is, we wish to know whether there are values of $c_1, \ldots, c_n$

such that

$$c_1 \mathbf{x}^{(1)}(t_0) + \cdots + c_n \mathbf{x}^{(n)}(t_0) = \boldsymbol{\xi}, \tag{12}$$

or in scalar form

$$c_1 x_{11}(t_0) + \cdots + c_n x_{1n}(t_0) = \xi_1,$$

$$\cdot$$
$$\cdot \tag{13}$$
$$\cdot$$

$$c_1 x_{n1}(t_0) + \cdots + c_n x_{nn}(t_0) = \xi_n.$$

The necessary and sufficient condition that Eqs. (13) possess a unique solution $c_1, \ldots, c_n$ is precisely the nonvanishing of the determinant of coefficients, which is the Wronskian $W[\mathbf{x}^{(1)}, \ldots, \mathbf{x}^{(n)}]$ evaluated at $t = t_0$. The hypothesis that $\mathbf{x}^{(1)}, \ldots, \mathbf{x}^{(n)}$ are linearly independent throughout $\alpha < t < \beta$ guarantees that $W[\mathbf{x}^{(1)}, \ldots, \mathbf{x}^{(n)}]$ is not zero at $t = t_0$, and therefore there is a (unique) solution of Eq. (3) of the form $\mathbf{x} = c_1 \mathbf{x}^{(1)}(t) + \cdots + c_n \mathbf{x}^{(n)}(t)$ which also satisfies the initial condition (12). By the uniqueness part of Theorem 7.2 this solution is identical to $\boldsymbol{\phi}(t)$, and hence $\boldsymbol{\phi}(t) = c_1 \mathbf{x}^{(1)}(t) + \cdots + c_n \mathbf{x}^{(n)}(t)$, as was to be proved.

Theorem 7.5. *If $\mathbf{x}^{(1)}, \ldots, \mathbf{x}^{(n)}$ are solutions of Eq. (3) on the interval $\alpha < t < \beta$, then in this interval $W[\mathbf{x}^{(1)}, \ldots, \mathbf{x}^{(n)}]$ either is identically zero or else never vanishes.*

The significance of Theorem 7.5 lies in the fact that it relieves us of the necessity of examining $W[\mathbf{x}^{(1)}, \ldots, \mathbf{x}^{(n)}]$ at all points in the interval of interest, and enables us to determine whether $\mathbf{x}^{(1)}, \ldots, \mathbf{x}^{(n)}$ form a fundamental set of solutions merely by evaluating their Wronskian at any convenient point in the interval.

Theorem 7.5 is proved by first establishing that the Wronskian of $\mathbf{x}^{(1)}, \ldots, \mathbf{x}^{(n)}$ satisfies the differential equation (see Problem 2)

$$\frac{dW}{dt} = (p_{11} + p_{22} + \cdots + p_{nn})W. \tag{14}$$

Hence W is an exponential function, and the conclusion of the theorem follows immediately. The expression for W obtained by solving Eq. (14) is known as Abel's formula; note the analogy with Eq. (13) of Section 3.2.

Alternatively, Theorem 7.5 can be established by showing that if n solutions $\mathbf{x}^{(1)}, \ldots, \mathbf{x}^{(n)}$ of Eq. (3) are linearly dependent at one point $t = t_0$, then they must be linearly dependent at each point in $\alpha < t < \beta$; see Problem 8. Consequently, if $\mathbf{x}^{(1)}, \ldots, \mathbf{x}^{(n)}$ are linearly independent at one point, they must be linearly independent at each point in the interval.

The next theorem states that the system (3) always has at least one fundamental set of solutions.

Theorem 7.6. *Let*

$$\mathbf{e}^{(1)} = \begin{pmatrix} 1 \\ 0 \\ 0 \\ \cdot \\ \cdot \\ \cdot \\ 0 \end{pmatrix}, \quad \mathbf{e}^{(2)} = \begin{pmatrix} 0 \\ 1 \\ 0 \\ \cdot \\ \cdot \\ \cdot \\ 0 \end{pmatrix}, \quad \dots, \quad \mathbf{e}^{(n)} = \begin{pmatrix} 0 \\ \cdot \\ \cdot \\ \cdot \\ 0 \\ 1 \end{pmatrix};$$

further let $\mathbf{x}^{(1)}, \dots, \mathbf{x}^{(n)}$ *be the solutions of the system* (3) *which satisfy the initial conditions*

$$\mathbf{x}^{(1)}(t_0) = \mathbf{e}^{(1)}, \dots, \mathbf{x}^{(n)}(t_0) = \mathbf{e}^{(n)}, \tag{15}$$

respectively, where t_0 *is any point in* $\alpha < t < \beta$. *Then* $\mathbf{x}^{(1)}, \dots, \mathbf{x}^{(n)}$ *form a fundamental set of solutions of the system* (3).

To prove this theorem, note that the existence and uniqueness of the solutions $\mathbf{x}^{(1)}, \dots, \mathbf{x}^{(n)}$ mentioned in Theorem 7.6 is assured by Theorem 7.2. It is not hard to see that the Wronskian of these solutions is equal to one when $t = t_0$; therefore $\mathbf{x}^{(1)}, \dots, \mathbf{x}^{(n)}$ are a fundamental set of solutions.

Once one fundamental set of solutions has been found, other sets can be generated by forming (independent) linear combinations of the first set. For theoretical purposes the set given by Theorem 7.6 is usually the simplest.

To summarize, any set of n linearly independent solutions of the system (3) constitutes a fundamental set of solutions. Under the conditions given in this section, such fundamental sets always exist, and every solution of the system (3) can be represented as a linear combination of any fundamental set of solutions.

PROBLEMS

1. Using matrix algebra, prove the statement following Theorem 7.3 for an arbitrary value of the integer k.

2. In this problem we outline a proof of Theorem 7.5 in the case $n = 2$. Let $\mathbf{x}^{(1)}$ and $\mathbf{x}^{(2)}$ be solutions of Eq. (3) for $\alpha < t < \beta$, and let W be the Wronskian of $\mathbf{x}^{(1)}$ and $\mathbf{x}^{(2)}$.

(a) Show that

$$\frac{dW}{dt} = \begin{vmatrix} \dfrac{dx_1^{(1)}}{dt} & \dfrac{dx_1^{(2)}}{dt} \\ x_2^{(1)} & x_2^{(2)} \end{vmatrix} + \begin{vmatrix} x_1^{(1)} & x_1^{(2)} \\ \dfrac{dx_2^{(1)}}{dt} & \dfrac{dx_2^{(2)}}{dt} \end{vmatrix}.$$

(b) Using Eq. (3), show that

$$\frac{dW}{dt} = (p_{11} + p_{22})W.$$

(c) Find $W(t)$ by solving the differential equation obtained in part (b). Use **this expression** to obtain the conclusion stated in Theorem 7.5.

*(d) Generalize this procedure so as to prove Theorem 7.5 for an arbitrary value of n.

3. Show that the Wronskians of two fundamental sets of solutions of the system (3) can differ at most by a multiplicative constant.
Hint: Use Eq. (14).

4. If $x_1 = y$ and $x_2 = y'$, then the second order equation

$$y'' + p(t)y' + q(t)y = 0 \tag{i}$$

corresponds to the system

$$\begin{aligned} x_1' &= x_2, \\ x_2' &= -q(t)x_1 - p(t)x_2. \end{aligned} \tag{ii}$$

Show that if $x^{(1)}$ and $x^{(2)}$ are a fundamental set of solutions of Eqs. (ii), and if $y^{(1)}$ and $y^{(2)}$ are a fundamental set of solutions of Eq. (i), then $W[y^{(1)}, y^{(2)}] = cW[x^{(1)}, x^{(2)}]$, where c is a nonzero constant.
Hint: $y^{(1)}(t)$ and $y^{(2)}(t)$ must be linear combinations of $x_{11}(t)$ and $x_{12}(t)$.

5. Show that the general solution of $x' = P(t)x + g(t)$ is the sum of any particular solution $x^{(p)}$ of this equation and the general solution $x^{(c)}$ of the corresponding homogeneous equation.

6. Consider the vectors $x^{(1)}(t) = \begin{pmatrix} t \\ 1 \end{pmatrix}$ and $x^{(2)}(t) = \begin{pmatrix} t^2 \\ 2t \end{pmatrix}$.
   (a) Compute the Wronskian of $x^{(1)}$ and $x^{(2)}$.
   (b) In what intervals are $x^{(1)}$ and $x^{(2)}$ linearly independent?
   (c) What conclusion can you draw about the coefficients in the system of homogeneous differential equations satisfied by $x^{(1)}$ and $x^{(2)}$?
   (d) Find this system of equations and verify your conclusions of part (b).

7. Consider the vectors $x^{(1)}(t) = \begin{pmatrix} t^2 \\ 2t \end{pmatrix}$ and $x^{(2)}(t) = \begin{pmatrix} e^t \\ e^t \end{pmatrix}$, and answer the same questions as in Problem 6.

The following two problems indicate an alternative derivation of Theorem 7.4.

8. Let $x^{(1)}, \ldots, x^{(m)}$ be solutions of $x' = P(t)x$ on the interval $\alpha < t < \beta$. Assume that P is continuous and let t_0 be an arbitrary point in the given interval. Show that $x^{(1)}, \ldots, x^{(m)}$ are linearly dependent for $\alpha < t < \beta$ if (and only if) $x^{(1)}(t_0), \ldots, x^{(m)}(t_0)$ are linearly dependent. In other words, $x^{(1)}, \ldots, x^{(m)}$ are linearly dependent on the interval (α, β) if they are linearly dependent at any point in it.
Hint: There are constants $c_1, \ldots, c_m$ such that $c_1 x^{(1)}(t_0) + \cdots + c_m x^{(m)}(t_0) = 0$. Let $z(t) = c_1 x^{(1)}(t) + \cdots + c_m x^{(m)}(t)$, and use the uniqueness theorem to show that $z(t) = 0$ for each t in $\alpha < t < \beta$.

9. Let $x^{(1)}, \ldots, x^{(n)}$ be linearly independent solutions of $x' = P(t)x$, where P is continuous on $\alpha < t < \beta$.
   (a) Show that any solution $x = z(t)$ can be written in the form

$$z(t) = c_1 x^{(1)}(t) + \cdots + c_n x^{(n)}(t)$$

for suitable constants $c_1, \ldots, c_n$.
Hint: Use the result of Problem 12 of Section 7.3, and also Problem 8 above.

(b) Show that the expression for the solution $z(t)$ in part (a) is unique; that is, if $z(t) = k_1 x^{(1)}(t) + \cdots + k_n x^{(n)}(t)$, then $k_1 = c_1, \ldots, k_n = c_n$.
Hint: Show that $(k_1 - c_1)x^{(1)}(t) + \cdots + (k_n - c_n)x^{(n)}(t) = 0$ for each t in $\alpha < t < \beta$ and use the linear independence of $x^{(1)}, \ldots, x^{(n)}$.

7.5 LINEAR HOMOGENEOUS SYSTEMS WITH CONSTANT COEFFICIENTS

In this section we will begin to show how to construct the general solution of a system of linear homogeneous equations with constant coefficients, that is, a system of the form

$$x' = Ax, \tag{1}$$

where A is a constant* $n \times n$ matrix. Before dealing with the problem in this generality we will exhibit some of the ideas as they occur in the simple example:

$$\begin{aligned} x_1' &= x_1 + x_2, \\ x_2' &= 4x_1 + x_2, \end{aligned} \tag{2}$$

or

$$x' = \begin{pmatrix} 1 & 1 \\ 4 & 1 \end{pmatrix} x. \tag{3}$$

This system was solved in Section 7.2 by the method of elimination, but we will now consider an alternative process.

By analogy with the treatment of linear second order equations in Section 3.5, we will seek solutions of Eq. (3) of the form

$$x = \xi e^{rt}, \tag{4}$$

where r and the constant vector ξ are to be determined. Substituting from Eq. (4) for x in the system (3) leads immediately to

$$r\xi = \begin{pmatrix} 1 & 1 \\ 4 & 1 \end{pmatrix} \xi,$$

or in scalar form,

$$\begin{aligned} (1 - r)\xi_1 + \quad \xi_2 &= 0, \\ 4\xi_1 + (1 - r)\xi_2 &= 0. \end{aligned} \tag{5}$$

Equations (5) have a nontrivial solution if and only if the determinant of coefficients vanishes. Thus

$$\begin{vmatrix} 1 - r & 1 \\ 4 & 1 - r \end{vmatrix} = r^2 - 2r - 3 = 0 \tag{6}$$

---

* The procedure described here applies whether A is real or complex valued. However, we will consider only systems with real coefficients in examples and problems, and the reader may wish to think of A as real throughout.

is the condition which determines allowable values of r. Equation (6) is called the auxiliary equation for the system (3), and its roots are $r_1 = 3$, $r_2 = -1$. For $r_1 = 3$ Eqs. (5) have the solution ξ defined by $\xi^T = (c_1, 2c_1) = c_1(1, 2)$, where c_1 is an arbitrary constant; a corresponding solution $x^{(1)}$ of the differential equation (3) is given by

$$x^{(1)}(t) = \begin{pmatrix} 1 \\ 2 \end{pmatrix} e^{3t}. \tag{7}$$

Similarly, for $r_2 = -1$, $\xi^T = (c_2, -2c_2) = c_2(1, -2)$, where c_2 is also arbitrary; hence a second solution of the system (3) is

$$x^{(2)}(t) = \begin{pmatrix} 1 \\ -2 \end{pmatrix} e^{-t}. \tag{8}$$

By superposition we obtain the general solution

$$x = c_1 \begin{pmatrix} 1 \\ 2 \end{pmatrix} e^{3t} + c_2 \begin{pmatrix} 1 \\ -2 \end{pmatrix} e^{-t}, \tag{9}$$

which is the same as that found in Section 7.2.

The same procedure can also be applied to the general system

$$x' = Ax, \tag{10}$$

where A is any constant $n \times n$ matrix. Assuming that

$$x = \xi e^{rt} \tag{11}$$

and substituting for x in Eq. (10), we obtain the system of algebraic equations

$$(A - rI)\xi = 0, \tag{12}$$

where I is the identity matrix. Once again nontrivial solutions of the algebraic equations (12) exist if and only if r is chosen so as to make the determinant of coefficients zero, that is, if r is a root of the *auxiliary equation**

$$\det(A - rI) = 0. \tag{13}$$

Equation (13) is a polynomial equation in r of degree n, and hence has n roots $r_1, \ldots, r_n$, some of which, however, may be repeated.

If all of the roots $r_1, \ldots, r_n$ are different, then corresponding to each r_k Eq. (12) determines (up to an arbitrary multiplicative constant) the corresponding vector $\xi^{(k)}$. Hence the corresponding solutions of the differential system (10) are

$$x^{(1)}(t) = \xi^{(1)} e^{r_1 t}, \ldots, x^{(n)}(t) = \xi^{(n)} e^{r_n t}. \tag{14}$$

---

* The values of r which satisfy Eq. (13) are called *eigenvalues* of the matrix A. A fuller discussion of eigenvalues and their importance in solving systems of differential equations appears in Sections 7.6 and 7.7.

The Wronskian of these solutions is

$$W[\mathbf{x}^{(1)}, \ldots, \mathbf{x}^{(n)}](t) = \begin{vmatrix} \xi_1^{(1)}e^{r_1 t} \cdots \xi_1^{(n)}e^{r_n t} \\ \cdot \qquad\qquad \cdot \\ \cdot \qquad\qquad \cdot \\ \cdot \qquad\qquad \cdot \\ \xi_n^{(1)}e^{r_1 t} \cdots \xi_n^{(n)}e^{r_n t} \end{vmatrix} = e^{(r_1 + \cdots + r_n)t} \begin{vmatrix} \xi_1^{(1)} \cdots \xi_1^{(n)} \\ \cdot \qquad \cdot \\ \cdot \qquad \cdot \\ \cdot \qquad \cdot \\ \xi_n^{(1)} \cdots \xi_n^{(n)} \end{vmatrix}.$$

$$(15)$$

It is possible to show that the vectors $\boldsymbol{\xi}^{(1)}, \ldots, \boldsymbol{\xi}^{(n)}$ are linearly independent, and hence the determinant in Eq. (15) is not zero.* Since the exponential function is never zero, it follows from Eq. (15) that $W[\mathbf{x}^{(1)}, \ldots, \mathbf{x}^{(n)}]$ is nonvanishing, and hence $\mathbf{x}^{(1)}, \ldots, \mathbf{x}^{(n)}$ form a fundamental set of solutions. In other words, when the roots of Eq. (13) are all different the general solution of the system (10) is

$$\mathbf{x} = c_1 \boldsymbol{\xi}^{(1)}e^{r_1 t} + \cdots + c_n \boldsymbol{\xi}^{(n)}e^{r_n t}. \tag{16}$$

If the coefficient matrix $\mathbf{A}$ is real, then the vector $\boldsymbol{\xi}^{(k)}$ corresponding to a real root r_k of Eq. (13) is also real. Hence, if $\mathbf{A}$ is real and if all of the roots $r_1, \ldots, r_n$ are real and no two are equal, then the general solution (16) is real-valued. If some of the roots are complex, then the solution (16) is complex-valued. However, if $\mathbf{A}$ is real, then any complex roots of Eq. (13) must occur in conjugate pairs. In this case it is always possible to construct a new fundamental set of solutions, all of which are real-valued. This is done in a manner similar to that for scalar equations, and is discussed further in Section 7.8. If $\mathbf{A}$ is complex, then it is usually not possible to construct a fundamental set of real-valued solutions, regardless of whether the roots of Eq. (13) are real.

A more serious problem may occur if some of the roots of Eq. (13) are repeated. Even in this case it may be possible to find n independent solutions of the system (10) having the form (11). For example, even if $r = r_1$ is a double root of Eq. (13), it may still be possible to find two linearly independent solutions $\boldsymbol{\xi}^{(1)}$ and $\boldsymbol{\xi}^{(2)}$ of Eq. (12). If so, then $\boldsymbol{\xi}^{(1)}e^{r_1 t}$ and $\boldsymbol{\xi}^{(2)}e^{r_2 t}$ are two linearly independent solutions of Eq. (10) corresponding to the double root $r = r_1$. An important class of problems is that for which $\mathbf{A} = \mathbf{A}^*$; in this event not only are all of the roots real, but also it is always possible to find n solutions of the form $\boldsymbol{\xi}e^{rt}$. However, when $\mathbf{A} \neq \mathbf{A}^*$, and when Eq. (13) has repeated roots, it is not generally possible to find n linearly independent solutions of the form $\boldsymbol{\xi}e^{rt}$. It is then necessary to seek other solutions, not of this form, in order to completely determine a fundamental set of solutions. These other solutions can be found in several ways, and one method is

* We will omit the proof of this fact; see, however, Problem 16 where the proof is outlined for the case $n = 2$.

discussed in Section 7.9. The method of reduction of order can sometimes be used to advantage also; see Problems 17 through 19.

Example. Find the general solution of the system

$$\mathbf{x}' = \begin{pmatrix} 1 & -1 & 0 \\ 1 & 2 & 1 \\ -2 & 1 & -1 \end{pmatrix} \mathbf{x}, \tag{17}$$

or, in scalar form,

$$\begin{aligned} x_1' &= x_1 - x_2 \\ x_2' &= x_1 + 2x_2 + x_3 \\ x_3' &= -2x_1 + x_2 - x_3. \end{aligned}$$

Assuming that $\mathbf{x} = \boldsymbol{\xi} e^{rt}$, we obtain the system of algebraic equations

$$\begin{aligned} (1-r)\xi_1 &- \xi_2 = 0 \\ \xi_1 + (2-r)\xi_2 + & \xi_3 = 0 \\ -2\xi_1 + &\xi_2 + (-1-r)\xi_3 = 0, \end{aligned} \tag{18}$$

whose determinant of coefficients is

$$\Delta(r) = \begin{vmatrix} 1-r & -1 & 0 \\ 1 & 2-r & 1 \\ -2 & 1 & -1-r \end{vmatrix} = -(1-r)(2-r)(1+r). \tag{19}$$

Hence the allowable values of r are $r_1 = 1$, $r_2 = 2$, and $r_3 = -1$. Corresponding to each of these values of r, Eqs. (18) have a solution which is determined only up to an arbitrary multiplicative constant. Choosing this constant in each case so that the first component is one, we obtain

$$\boldsymbol{\xi}^{(1)} = \begin{pmatrix} 1 \\ 0 \\ -1 \end{pmatrix}, \quad \boldsymbol{\xi}^{(2)} = \begin{pmatrix} 1 \\ -1 \\ -1 \end{pmatrix}, \quad \boldsymbol{\xi}^{(3)} = \begin{pmatrix} 1 \\ 2 \\ -7 \end{pmatrix}. \tag{20}$$

The general solution of the system (17) is then

$$\mathbf{x} = c_1 \boldsymbol{\xi}^{(1)} e^{r_1 t} + c_2 \boldsymbol{\xi}^{(2)} e^{r_2 t} + c_3 \boldsymbol{\xi}^{(3)} e^{r_3 t} \tag{21}$$

or

$$\mathbf{x} = c_1 \begin{pmatrix} 1 \\ 0 \\ -1 \end{pmatrix} e^t + c_2 \begin{pmatrix} 1 \\ -1 \\ -1 \end{pmatrix} e^{2t} + c_3 \begin{pmatrix} 1 \\ 2 \\ -7 \end{pmatrix} e^{-t}. \tag{22}$$

Note that even for a system of three equations the algebraic calculations required may be complicated, particularly those involved in factoring the determinantal polynomial $\Delta(r)$. This example was selected so as to make these calculations simple, and therefore it is not altogether typical in this respect.

PROBLEMS

In each of Problems 1 through 6 find the general solution of the given system of equations.

1. $\mathbf{x}' = \begin{pmatrix} 3 & -2 \\ 2 & -2 \end{pmatrix} \mathbf{x}$

2. $\mathbf{x}' = \begin{pmatrix} 4 & -3 \\ 8 & -6 \end{pmatrix} \mathbf{x}$

3. $\mathbf{x}' = \begin{pmatrix} 2 & -1 \\ 3 & -2 \end{pmatrix} \mathbf{x}$

4. $\mathbf{x}' = \begin{pmatrix} 1 & 1 \\ 4 & -2 \end{pmatrix} \mathbf{x}$

5. $\mathbf{x}' = \begin{pmatrix} 1 & 1 & 1 \\ 2 & 1 & -1 \\ -8 & -5 & -3 \end{pmatrix} \mathbf{x}$

6. $\mathbf{x}' = \begin{pmatrix} 1 & -1 & 4 \\ 3 & 2 & -1 \\ 2 & 1 & -1 \end{pmatrix} \mathbf{x}$

In each of Problems 7 through 10 solve the given initial value problem.

7. $\mathbf{x}' = \begin{pmatrix} 5 & -1 \\ 3 & 1 \end{pmatrix} \mathbf{x}, \qquad \mathbf{x}(0) = \begin{pmatrix} 2 \\ -1 \end{pmatrix}$

8. $\mathbf{x}' = \begin{pmatrix} -2 & 1 \\ -5 & 4 \end{pmatrix} \mathbf{x}, \qquad \mathbf{x}(0) = \begin{pmatrix} 1 \\ 3 \end{pmatrix}$

9. $\mathbf{x}' = \begin{pmatrix} 1 & 1 & 2 \\ 0 & 2 & 2 \\ -1 & 1 & 3 \end{pmatrix} \mathbf{x}, \qquad \mathbf{x}(0) = \begin{pmatrix} 2 \\ 0 \\ 1 \end{pmatrix}$

10. $\mathbf{x}' = \begin{pmatrix} 0 & 0 & -1 \\ 2 & 0 & 0 \\ -1 & 2 & 4 \end{pmatrix} \mathbf{x}, \qquad \mathbf{x}(0) = \begin{pmatrix} 7 \\ 5 \\ 5 \end{pmatrix}$

11. The system $t\mathbf{x}' = A\mathbf{x}$ is analogous to the second order Euler equation (Section 4.4). Assuming that $\mathbf{x} = \xi t^r$, where ξ is a constant vector, show that ξ and r must satisfy $(A - rI)\xi = 0$; also show that to obtain nontrivial solutions of the given differential equation, r must be a root of the auxiliary equation det $(A - rI) = 0$.

Referring to Problem 11, solve the given system of equations in each of Problems 12 through 15. Assume that $t > 0$.

12. $t\mathbf{x}' = \begin{pmatrix} 2 & -1 \\ 3 & -2 \end{pmatrix} \mathbf{x}$

13. $t\mathbf{x}' = \begin{pmatrix} 5 & -1 \\ 3 & 1 \end{pmatrix} \mathbf{x}$

14. $t\mathbf{x}' = \begin{pmatrix} 4 & -3 \\ 8 & -6 \end{pmatrix} \mathbf{x}$

15. $t\mathbf{x}' = \begin{pmatrix} 3 & -2 \\ 2 & -2 \end{pmatrix} \mathbf{x}$

16. Consider a second order system $\mathbf{x}' = \mathbf{A}\mathbf{x}$. Assuming that $r_1 \neq r_2$, the general solution is $\mathbf{x} = c_1 \boldsymbol{\xi}^{(1)} e^{r_1 t} + c_2 \boldsymbol{\xi}^{(2)} e^{r_2 t}$, provided $\boldsymbol{\xi}^{(1)}$ and $\boldsymbol{\xi}^{(2)}$ are linearly independent. In this problem we will establish the linear independence of $\boldsymbol{\xi}^{(1)}$ and $\boldsymbol{\xi}^{(2)}$ by assuming that they are linearly dependent, and then showing that this leads to a contradiction.

(a) Note that $\boldsymbol{\xi}^{(1)}$ satisfies the matrix equation $(\mathbf{A} - r_1 \mathbf{I})\boldsymbol{\xi}^{(1)} = \mathbf{0}$; similarly, note that $(\mathbf{A} - r_2 \mathbf{I})\boldsymbol{\xi}^{(2)} = \mathbf{0}$.

(b) Show that $(\mathbf{A} - r_2 \mathbf{I})\boldsymbol{\xi}^{(1)} = (r_1 - r_2)\boldsymbol{\xi}^{(1)}$.

(c) Suppose that $\boldsymbol{\xi}^{(1)}$ and $\boldsymbol{\xi}^{(2)}$ are linearly dependent. Then $c_1 \boldsymbol{\xi}^{(1)} + c_2 \boldsymbol{\xi}^{(2)} = \mathbf{0}$ and at least one of c_1 and c_2 is not zero; suppose $c_1 \neq 0$. Show that $(\mathbf{A} - r_2 \mathbf{I})(c_1 \boldsymbol{\xi}^{(1)} + c_2 \boldsymbol{\xi}^{(2)}) = \mathbf{0}$, and also show that $(\mathbf{A} - r_2 \mathbf{I})(c_1 \boldsymbol{\xi}^{(1)} + c_2 \boldsymbol{\xi}^{(2)}) = c_1(r_1 - r_2)\boldsymbol{\xi}^{(1)}$. Hence $c_1 = 0$ which is a contradiction. Therefore $\boldsymbol{\xi}^{(1)}$ and $\boldsymbol{\xi}^{(2)}$ are linearly independent.

(d) Modify the argument of part (c) in case c_1 is zero but c_2 is not.

(e) Carry out a similar argument for the case in which $n = 3$; note that the procedure can be extended to cover an arbitrary value of n.

17. In this problem we show how the method of reduction of order can be used for systems of equations. It provides a method for dealing with systems which do not have a complete set of solutions of the form $\boldsymbol{\xi} e^{rt}$. Consider the system

$$\mathbf{x}' = \begin{pmatrix} 3 & -2 \\ 2 & -2 \end{pmatrix} \mathbf{x}. \tag{i}$$

(a) Verify that $\mathbf{x} = \begin{pmatrix} 2 \\ 1 \end{pmatrix} e^{2t}$ satisfies the given differential equation.

(b) Introduce a new dependent variable by the transformation

$$\mathbf{x} = \begin{pmatrix} 1 & 2e^{2t} \\ 0 & e^{2t} \end{pmatrix} \mathbf{y}. \tag{ii}$$

Observe that this transformation is obtained by replacing the second column of the identity matrix by the known solution. By substituting for $\mathbf{x}$ in Eq. (i), show that $\mathbf{y}$ satisfies the system of equations

$$\begin{pmatrix} 1 & 2e^{2t} \\ 0 & e^{2t} \end{pmatrix} \mathbf{y}' = \begin{pmatrix} 3 & 0 \\ 2 & 0 \end{pmatrix} \mathbf{y}. \tag{iii}$$

(c) Solve Eq. (iii) and show that

$$\mathbf{y} = c_1 \begin{pmatrix} \frac{1}{2} e^{-t} \\ -\frac{1}{3} e^{-3t} \end{pmatrix} + c_2 \begin{pmatrix} 0 \\ 1 \end{pmatrix} \tag{iv}$$

where c_1 and c_2 are arbitrary constants.

(d) Using Eq. (ii), show that

$$\mathbf{x} = -\frac{c_1}{6}\binom{1}{2}e^{-t} + c_2\binom{2}{1}e^{2t}; \tag{v}$$

thus a second solution of Eq. (i) has been found. This is the method of reduction of order as it applies to a system of equations.

In Problems 18 and 19 use the method of reduction of order (Problem 17) to solve the given system of equations.

18. $\mathbf{x}' = \begin{pmatrix} 1 & -4 \\ 4 & -7 \end{pmatrix}\mathbf{x}$ 19. $\mathbf{x}' = \begin{pmatrix} 3 & -4 \\ 1 & -1 \end{pmatrix}\mathbf{x}$

7.6 INVERSES, EIGENVALUES, AND EIGENVECTORS

To continue our study of systems of linear differential equations, some further results about matrices are required. This section contains a summary of the additional properties of matrices which will be needed in the rest of this chapter.

In order to define an operation for square matrices analogous to division for numbers, we need to know whether, given a square matrix $\mathbf{A}$, there is another matrix $\mathbf{B}$ such that $\mathbf{AB} = \mathbf{I}$, where $\mathbf{I}$ is the identity. If so, $\mathbf{B}$ is called the multiplicative inverse, or simply the inverse, of $\mathbf{A}$, and we write $\mathbf{B} = \mathbf{A}^{-1}$. It is possible to show that if $\mathbf{A}^{-1}$ exists, then

$$\mathbf{A}^{-1}\mathbf{A} = \mathbf{A}\mathbf{A}^{-1} = \mathbf{I}. \tag{1}$$

In other words, multiplication is commutative between any matrix and its inverse. If $\mathbf{A}$ has a multiplicative inverse $\mathbf{A}^{-1}$, then $\mathbf{A}$ is said to be *nonsingular*; otherwise $\mathbf{A}$ is called *singular*.

There are various ways to compute $\mathbf{A}^{-1}$ from $\mathbf{A}$, assuming that it exists. One way involves the use of determinants. Associated with each element a_{ij} of a given matrix is the minor M_{ij}, which is the determinant of the matrix obtained by deleting the ith row and jth column of the original matrix, that is, the row and column containing a_{ij}. Also associated with each element a_{ij} is the cofactor C_{ij} defined by the equation

$$C_{ij} = (-1)^{i+j}M_{ij}. \tag{2}$$

If $\mathbf{B} = \mathbf{A}^{-1}$, then it can be shown that the general element b_{ij} is given by

$$b_{ij} = \frac{C_{ji}}{\det \mathbf{A}}. \tag{3}$$

While Eq. (3) is not an efficient way* to calculate A^{-1}, it does suggest a condition which A must satisfy in order that it have an inverse. In fact, the condition is both necessary and sufficient: A is nonsingular if and only if det $A \neq 0$. If det $A = 0$, then A is singular.

Another and usually better way to compute A^{-1} is by means of elementary row operations. There are three such operations:

(i) Interchange of two rows.

(ii) Multiplication of a row by a nonzero scalar.

(iii) Addition of any multiple of one row to another row.

Any nonsingular matrix A can be transformed into the identity I by a systematic sequence of these operations. It is possible to show that if the same sequence of operations is then performed upon I, it is transformed into A^{-1}. The following example illustrates the process.

Example.   Find the inverse of $A = \begin{pmatrix} 1 & -1 & -1 \\ 3 & -1 & 2 \\ 2 & 2 & 3 \end{pmatrix}$.

The matrix A can be transformed into I by the following sequence of operations. The result of each step appears in the right hand column.

(a) Obtain zeros in the off-diagonal positions in the first column by adding (-3) times the first row to the second row and adding (-2) times the first row to the third row.
$\begin{pmatrix} 1 & -1 & -1 \\ 0 & 2 & 5 \\ 0 & 4 & 5 \end{pmatrix}$

(b) Obtain a one in the diagonal position in the second column by multiplying the second row by $\frac{1}{2}$.
$\begin{pmatrix} 1 & -1 & -1 \\ 0 & 1 & \frac{5}{2} \\ 0 & 4 & 5 \end{pmatrix}$

(c) Obtain zeros in the off-diagonal positions in the second column by adding the second row to the first row and adding (-4) times the second row to the third row.
$\begin{pmatrix} 1 & 0 & \frac{3}{2} \\ 0 & 1 & \frac{5}{2} \\ 0 & 0 & -5 \end{pmatrix}$

---

* For large n the number of multiplications required to evaluate A^{-1} by Eq. (3) is proportional to $n!$. If one uses more efficient methods, such as the elimination procedure described below, the number of multiplications is proportional only to n^3. Even for small values of n (such as $n = 4$), determinants are not an economical tool in calculating inverses, and elimination methods are to be preferred.

(d) Obtain a one in the diagonal position in the third column by multiplying the third row by $(-\frac{1}{5})$.

$$\begin{pmatrix} 1 & 0 & \frac{3}{2} \\ 0 & 1 & \frac{5}{2} \\ 0 & 0 & 1 \end{pmatrix}$$

(e) Obtain zeros in the off-diagonal positions in the third column by adding $(-\frac{3}{2})$ times the third row to the first row and adding $(-\frac{5}{2})$ times the third row to the first row.

$$\begin{pmatrix} 1 & 0 & 0 \\ 0 & 1 & 0 \\ 0 & 0 & 1 \end{pmatrix}$$

If we perform the same sequence of operations in the same order upon **I**, we obtain the following sequence of matrices:

$$\begin{pmatrix} 1 & 0 & 0 \\ 0 & 1 & 0 \\ 0 & 0 & 1 \end{pmatrix}, \quad \begin{pmatrix} 1 & 0 & 0 \\ -3 & 1 & 0 \\ -2 & 0 & 1 \end{pmatrix}, \quad \begin{pmatrix} 1 & 0 & 0 \\ -\frac{3}{2} & \frac{1}{2} & 0 \\ -2 & 0 & 1 \end{pmatrix}, \quad \begin{pmatrix} -\frac{1}{2} & \frac{1}{2} & 0 \\ -\frac{3}{2} & \frac{1}{2} & 0 \\ 4 & -2 & 1 \end{pmatrix},$$

$$\begin{pmatrix} -\frac{1}{2} & \frac{1}{2} & 0 \\ -\frac{3}{2} & \frac{1}{2} & 0 \\ -\frac{4}{5} & \frac{2}{5} & -\frac{1}{5} \end{pmatrix}, \quad \begin{pmatrix} \frac{7}{10} & -\frac{1}{10} & \frac{3}{10} \\ \frac{1}{2} & -\frac{1}{2} & \frac{1}{2} \\ -\frac{4}{5} & \frac{2}{5} & -\frac{1}{5} \end{pmatrix}.$$

The last of these matrices is $\mathbf{A}^{-1}$, a result that can be verified by direct multiplication.

This example is made slightly simpler by the fact that the original matrix **A** had a one in the upper left corner ($a_{11} = 1$). If this is not the case, then the first step is to produce a one there by multiplying the first row by $1/a_{11}$, so long as $a_{11} \neq 0$. If $a_{11} = 0$, then the first row must be interchanged with some other row in order to bring a nonzero element into the upper left position before proceeding as above.

Eigenvalues and Eigenvectors.   The equation

$$\mathbf{A}\mathbf{x} = \mathbf{y} \tag{4}$$

can be viewed as a linear transformation that maps (or transforms) a given vector **x** into a new vector **y**. Vectors that are transformed into multiples of themselves play an important role in many applications. To find such vectors we set $\mathbf{y} = \lambda\mathbf{x}$, where λ is a scalar proportionality factor, and seek solutions of the equations

$$\mathbf{A}\mathbf{x} = \lambda\mathbf{x}, \tag{5}$$

or

$$(\mathbf{A} - \lambda\mathbf{I})\mathbf{x} = 0. \tag{6}$$

The latter equation will have nonzero solutions if and only if λ is chosen so that

$$\Delta(\lambda) = \det(\mathbf{A} - \lambda\mathbf{I}) = 0. \tag{7}$$

Values of λ which satisfy Eq. (7) are called *eigenvalues* of the matrix $\mathbf{A}$, and the solutions of Eq. (5) or (6) which are obtained by using such a value of λ are called the *eigenvectors* corresponding to that eigenvalue. Eigenvectors are determined only up to an arbitrary multiplicative constant, which is usually chosen for some reason of convenience, such as to make one of the components of the eigenvector equal to one.

Since Eq. (7) is a polynomial equation of degree n in λ, there are n eigenvalues $\lambda_1, \ldots, \lambda_n$, some of which may be repeated. If a given eigenvalue appears m times as a root of Eq. (7), then that eigenvalue is said to have *multiplicity m*. Each eigenvalue has at least one associated eigenvector, and an eigenvalue of multiplicity m may have q linearly independent eigenvectors, where

$$1 \leq q \leq m. \tag{8}$$

We will not try to give a proof of Eq. (8), but the result is illustrated by several of the problems at the end of the section. If all of the eigenvalues of a matrix $\mathbf{A}$ are *simple* (have multiplicity one), then it is possible to show that the n eigenvectors of $\mathbf{A}$, one for each eigenvalue, are linearly independent.* On the other hand, if $\mathbf{A}$ has one or more repeated eigenvalues, then there may be fewer than n linearly independent eigenvectors associated with $\mathbf{A}$, since the right side of Eq. (8) may be a strict inequality for one or more of the repeated eigenvalues. This fact leads to complications later on.

Now suppose that $\mathbf{A}$ has a full set of n linearly independent eigenvectors (whether the eigenvalues of $\mathbf{A}$ are all simple or not). Letting $\mathbf{x}^{(1)}, \ldots, \mathbf{x}^{(n)}$ denote these eigenvectors and $\lambda_1, \ldots, \lambda_n$ the corresponding eigenvalues, form the matrix $\mathbf{T}$ whose columns are the eigenvectors $\mathbf{x}^{(1)}, \ldots, \mathbf{x}^{(n)}$. Since the columns of $\mathbf{T}$ are linearly independent vectors, $\det \mathbf{T} \neq 0$; hence $\mathbf{T}$ is nonsingular and $\mathbf{T}^{-1}$ exists. A straightforward calculation shows that the columns of the matrix $\mathbf{AT}$ are just the vectors $\mathbf{A}\mathbf{x}^{(1)}, \ldots, \mathbf{A}\mathbf{x}^{(n)}$. Since $\mathbf{A}\mathbf{x}^{(k)} = \lambda_k \mathbf{x}^{(k)}$, it follows that

$$\mathbf{AT} = \begin{pmatrix} \lambda_1 x_1^{(1)} & \cdots & \lambda_n x_1^{(n)} \\ \cdot & & \cdot \\ \cdot & & \cdot \\ \cdot & & \cdot \\ \lambda_1 x_n^{(1)} & \cdots & \lambda_n x_n^{(n)} \end{pmatrix}$$

$$= \mathbf{TD}, \tag{9}$$

* For the proof of a special case of this result see Problem 16 in Section 7.5.

where

$$D = \begin{pmatrix} \lambda_1 & 0 & \cdots & 0 \\ 0 & \lambda_2 & \cdots & 0 \\ \cdot & \cdot & & \cdot \\ \cdot & \cdot & & \cdot \\ \cdot & \cdot & & \cdot \\ 0 & 0 & \cdots & \lambda_n \end{pmatrix} \tag{10}$$

is a diagonal matrix whose diagonal elements are the eigenvalues of A. From Eq. (9) it follows that

$$T^{-1}AT = D. \tag{11}$$

Thus, if the eigenvalues and eigenvectors of A are known, A can be transformed into a diagonal matrix by the process shown in Eq. (11). This process is known as a *similarity transformation*, and Eq. (11) is summed up in words by saying that A is *similar* to the diagonal matrix D. The possibility of carrying out such a diagonalization will be of vital importance later in the chapter.

If, on the other hand, A has fewer than n linearly independent eigenvectors, then there is no matrix T such that $T^{-1}AT = D$. In other words, A is not similar to a diagonal matrix.

An important special class of matrices, called *self-adjoint* or *Hermitian* matrices, are those for which $A^* = A$, that is $\bar{a}_{ji} = a_{ij}$. Hermitian matrices include as a subclass real symmetric matrices, that is, matrices which have real elements and for which $A^T = A$. The eigenvalues and eigenvectors of Hermitian matrices always have the following properties.

(i) All eigenvalues of a Hermitian matrix are real.

(ii) If $x^{(1)}$ and $x^{(2)}$ are eigenvectors which correspond to different eigenvalues, then $(x^{(1)}, x^{(2)}) = 0$.

(iii) There always exists a full set of n eigenvectors, regardless of the multiplicities of the eigenvalues.

The proofs of the first two of these statements are outlined in Problems 23 through 25.

PROBLEMS

In each of Problems 1 through 10 either compute the inverse of the given matrix, or else show that it is singular.

1. $\begin{pmatrix} 1 & 4 \\ -2 & 3 \end{pmatrix}$

2. $\begin{pmatrix} 3 & -1 \\ 6 & 2 \end{pmatrix}$

3. $\begin{pmatrix} 1 & 2 & 3 \\ 2 & 4 & 5 \\ 3 & 5 & 6 \end{pmatrix}$

4. $\begin{pmatrix} 1 & 1 & -1 \\ 2 & -1 & 1 \\ 1 & 1 & 2 \end{pmatrix}$

5. $\begin{pmatrix} 1 & 2 & 1 \\ -2 & 1 & 8 \\ 1 & -2 & -7 \end{pmatrix}$

6. $\begin{pmatrix} 2 & 1 & 0 \\ 0 & 2 & 1 \\ 0 & 0 & 2 \end{pmatrix}$

7. $\begin{pmatrix} 1 & -1 & -1 \\ 2 & 1 & 0 \\ 3 & -2 & 1 \end{pmatrix}$

8. $\begin{pmatrix} 2 & 3 & 1 \\ -1 & 2 & 1 \\ 4 & -1 & -1 \end{pmatrix}$

9. $\begin{pmatrix} 1 & 0 & 0 & -1 \\ 0 & -1 & 1 & 0 \\ -1 & 0 & 1 & 0 \\ 0 & 1 & -1 & 1 \end{pmatrix}$

10. $\begin{pmatrix} 1 & -1 & 2 & 0 \\ -1 & 2 & -4 & 2 \\ 1 & 0 & 1 & 3 \\ -2 & 2 & 0 & -1 \end{pmatrix}$

11. Prove that if **A** is nonsingular, then $\mathbf{A}^{-1}$ is uniquely determined; that is, show that there cannot be two different matrices **B** and **C** such that $\mathbf{AB} = \mathbf{I}$ and $\mathbf{AC} = \mathbf{I}$.

12. Prove that if **A** is nonsingular, then $\mathbf{AA}^{-1} = \mathbf{A}^{-1}\mathbf{A}$; that is, multiplication is commutative between any nonsingular matrix and its inverse.

In each of Problems 13 through 21 find all eigenvalues and eigenvectors of the given matrix.

13. $\begin{pmatrix} 5 & -1 \\ 3 & 1 \end{pmatrix}$

14. $\begin{pmatrix} 3 & -2 \\ 4 & -1 \end{pmatrix}$

15. $\begin{pmatrix} 1 & -4 \\ 4 & -7 \end{pmatrix}$

16. $\begin{pmatrix} 1 & -1 & 4 \\ 3 & 2 & -1 \\ 2 & 1 & -1 \end{pmatrix}$

17. $\begin{pmatrix} 1 & 0 & 0 \\ 2 & 1 & -2 \\ 3 & 2 & 1 \end{pmatrix}$

18. $\begin{pmatrix} 1 & 0 & 0 \\ -4 & 1 & 0 \\ 3 & 6 & 2 \end{pmatrix}$

19. $\begin{pmatrix} 3 & 2 & 2 \\ 1 & 4 & 1 \\ -2 & -4 & -1 \end{pmatrix}$

20. $\begin{pmatrix} 1 & 1 & 1 \\ 2 & 1 & -1 \\ -3 & 2 & 4 \end{pmatrix}$

21. $\begin{pmatrix} 3 & 2 & 4 \\ 2 & 0 & 2 \\ 4 & 2 & 3 \end{pmatrix}$

22. Prove that $\lambda = 0$ is an eigenvalue of $\mathbf{A}$ if and only if $\mathbf{A}$ is singular.

23. Prove that if $\mathbf{A}$ is Hermitian, then $(\mathbf{A}\mathbf{x}, \mathbf{y}) = (\mathbf{x}, \mathbf{A}\mathbf{y})$, where $\mathbf{x}$ and $\mathbf{y}$ are any vectors.
Hint: Use the definition of the scalar product.

24. In this problem we show that the eigenvalues of a Hermitian matrix $\mathbf{A}$ are real. Let $\mathbf{x}$ be an eigenvector corresponding to the eigenvalue λ.
   (a) Show that $(\mathbf{A}\mathbf{x}, \mathbf{x}) = (\mathbf{x}, \mathbf{A}\mathbf{x})$. *Hint:* See Problem 23.
   (b) Show that $\lambda(\mathbf{x}, \mathbf{x}) = \bar{\lambda}(\mathbf{x}, \mathbf{x})$. *Hint:* Recall that $\mathbf{A}\mathbf{x} = \lambda\mathbf{x}$.
   (c) Show that $\lambda = \bar{\lambda}$, that is, the eigenvalue λ is real.

25. Show that if λ_1 and λ_2 are eigenvalues of a Hermitian matrix $\mathbf{A}$, and if $\lambda_1 \neq \lambda_2$, then the corresponding eigenvectors $\mathbf{x}^{(1)}$ and $\mathbf{x}^{(2)}$ are orthogonal.
Hint: Use the results of Problems 23 and 24 to show that $(\lambda_1 - \lambda_2)(\mathbf{x}^{(1)}, \mathbf{x}^{(2)}) = 0$.

7.7 FUNDAMENTAL MATRICES

The theory of systems of linear differential equations can be further illuminated by introducing the idea of a *fundamental matrix*. Suppose that $\mathbf{x}^{(1)}, \ldots, \mathbf{x}^{(n)}$ form a fundamental set of solutions for the equation

$$\mathbf{x}' = \mathbf{P}(t)\mathbf{x} \tag{1}$$

on some interval $\alpha < t < \beta$. Then the matrix

$$\Psi(t) = \begin{pmatrix} x_1^{(1)}(t) \cdots x_1^{(n)}(t) \\ \cdot \quad\quad \cdot \\ \cdot \quad\quad \cdot \\ \cdot \quad\quad \cdot \\ x_n^{(1)}(t) \cdots x_n^{(n)}(t) \end{pmatrix}, \tag{2}$$

whose columns are the vectors $\mathbf{x}^{(1)}, \ldots, \mathbf{x}^{(n)}$, is said to be a fundamental matrix for the system (1). Note that any fundamental matrix is nonsingular since its columns are linearly independent vectors.

Example 1. Find a fundamental matrix for the system

$$\mathbf{x}' = \begin{pmatrix} 1 & 1 \\ 4 & 1 \end{pmatrix}\mathbf{x}. \tag{3}$$

In Section 7.5 we found that

$$\mathbf{x}^{(1)}(t) = \begin{pmatrix} e^{3t} \\ 2e^{3t} \end{pmatrix}, \qquad \mathbf{x}^{(2)}(t) = \begin{pmatrix} e^{-t} \\ -2e^{-t} \end{pmatrix} \tag{4}$$

are linearly independent solutions of Eq. (3). Thus a fundamental matrix for the system (3) is

$$\Psi(t) = \begin{pmatrix} e^{3t} & e^{-t} \\ 2e^{3t} & -2e^{-t} \end{pmatrix}. \tag{5}$$

The solution of an initial value problem can be written very compactly in terms of a fundamental matrix. The general solution of Eq. (1) is

$$x = c_1 x^{(1)}(t) + \cdots + c_n x^{(n)}(t) \tag{6}$$

or, in terms of $\Psi(t)$,

$$x = \Psi(t)c, \tag{7}$$

where c is a constant vector with arbitrary components $c_1, \ldots, c_n$. For an initial value problem consisting of the differential equation (1) and the initial condition

$$x(t_0) = x^0, \tag{8}$$

where t_0 is a given point in $\alpha < t < \beta$, and x^0 is a given initial vector, it is only necessary to choose the vector c in Eq. (7) so as to satisfy the initial condition (8). Hence c must satisfy

$$\Psi(t_0)c = x^0. \tag{9}$$

Therefore, since $\Psi(t)$ is nonsingular,

$$c = \Psi^{-1}(t_0)x^0, \tag{10}$$

and

$$x = \Psi(t)\Psi^{-1}(t_0)x^0 \tag{11}$$

is the solution of the given initial value problem.

Sometimes it is convenient to make use of the special fundamental matrix, denoted by $\Phi(t)$, whose columns are the vectors $x^{(1)}, \ldots, x^{(n)}$ designated in Theorem 7.6 of Section 7.4. Besides the differential equation (1) these vectors satisfy the initial conditions

$$x^{(1)}(t_0) = \begin{pmatrix} 1 \\ 0 \\ 0 \\ \cdot \\ \cdot \\ \cdot \\ 0 \end{pmatrix}, \quad x^{(2)}(t_0) = \begin{pmatrix} 0 \\ 1 \\ 0 \\ \cdot \\ \cdot \\ 0 \end{pmatrix}, \ldots, x^{(n)}(t_0) = \begin{pmatrix} 0 \\ \cdot \\ \cdot \\ \cdot \\ 0 \\ 0 \\ 1 \end{pmatrix}. \tag{12}$$

Thus $\boldsymbol{\Phi}(t)$ has the property that

$$\boldsymbol{\Phi}(t_0) = \begin{pmatrix} 1 & 0 & \cdots & 0 \\ 0 & 1 & \cdots & 0 \\ \cdot & \cdot & & \cdot \\ \cdot & \cdot & & \cdot \\ \cdot & \cdot & & \cdot \\ 0 & 0 & \cdots & 1 \end{pmatrix} = \mathbf{I}. \tag{13}$$

We will always reserve the symbol $\boldsymbol{\Phi}$ to denote the fundamental matrix satisfying the initial condition (13), and use $\boldsymbol{\Psi}$ when an arbitrary fundamental matrix is intended. In terms of $\boldsymbol{\Phi}(t)$ the solution of the initial value problem (1) and (8) is even simpler in appearance; since $\boldsymbol{\Phi}^{-1}(t_0) = \mathbf{I}$, it follows from Eq. (11) that

$$\mathbf{x} = \boldsymbol{\Phi}(t)\mathbf{x}^0. \tag{14}$$

Example 2. For the system (3)

$$\mathbf{x}' = \begin{pmatrix} 1 & 1 \\ 4 & 1 \end{pmatrix}\mathbf{x},$$

just discussed in Example 1, find the fundamental matrix $\boldsymbol{\Phi}$ such that $\boldsymbol{\Phi}(0) = \mathbf{I}$.

The columns of $\boldsymbol{\Phi}$ are solutions of Eq. (3) which satisfy the initial conditions

$$\mathbf{x}^{(1)}(0) = \begin{pmatrix} 1 \\ 0 \end{pmatrix}, \qquad \mathbf{x}^{(2)}(0) = \begin{pmatrix} 0 \\ 1 \end{pmatrix}. \tag{15}$$

Since the general solution of Eq. (3) is

$$\mathbf{x} = c_1 \begin{pmatrix} 1 \\ 2 \end{pmatrix} e^{3t} + c_2 \begin{pmatrix} 1 \\ -2 \end{pmatrix} e^{-t},$$

we can find the solution satisfying the first set of these initial conditions by choosing $c_1 = c_2 = \frac{1}{2}$; similarly we obtain the solution satisfying the second set of initial conditions by choosing $c_1 = \frac{1}{4}$ and $c_2 = -\frac{1}{4}$. Hence

$$\boldsymbol{\Phi}(t) = \begin{pmatrix} \frac{1}{2}e^{3t} + \frac{1}{2}e^{-t} & \frac{1}{4}e^{3t} - \frac{1}{4}e^{-t} \\ e^{3t} - e^{-t} & \frac{1}{2}e^{3t} + \frac{1}{2}e^{-t} \end{pmatrix}. \tag{16}$$

Note that the elements of $\boldsymbol{\Phi}(t)$ are more complicated than those of the fundamental matrix $\boldsymbol{\Psi}(t)$ given by Eq. (5).

Now let us turn again to the system

$$\mathbf{x}' = \mathbf{A}\mathbf{x} \tag{17}$$

where $\mathbf{A}$ is a given constant matrix. We have already described two methods of solving such systems: in Section 7.2 by the method of elimination, and in Section 7.5 by assuming that $x = \xi e^{rt}$, although for the latter we have not yet discussed the procedure when roots of the auxiliary equation are repeated. Here we wish to provide still another viewpoint. The basic reason why a system of equations presents some difficulty is that the equations are usually coupled; in other words, some or all of the equations involve more than one, perhaps all, of the dependent variables. This occurs whenever the coefficient matrix A is not a diagonal matrix. Hence the equations in the system must be solved *simultaneously*, rather than *consecutively*. This observation suggests that one way to solve a system of equations might be by transforming it into an equivalent *uncoupled* system in which each equation contains only one dependent variable. This corresponds to transforming the coefficient matrix A into a *diagonal* matrix.

According to the results quoted in Section 7.6, in certain circumstances A can be transformed into a diagonal matrix by introducing the transformation matrix T whose columns are the eigenvectors of A. We assume that A has a full set of n linearly independent eigenvectors $\xi^{(1)}, \ldots, \xi^{(n)}$ corresponding to the eigenvalues $r_1, \ldots, r_n$. Then

$$T = \begin{pmatrix} \xi_1^{(1)} & \cdots & \xi_1^{(n)} \\ \vdots & & \vdots \\ \xi_n^{(1)} & \cdots & \xi_n^{(n)} \end{pmatrix}. \tag{18}$$

Defining a new dependent variable y by the relation

$$x = Ty, \tag{19}$$

we have from Eq. (17) that

$$Ty' = ATy, \tag{20}$$

or

$$y' = (T^{-1}AT)y. \tag{21}$$

From Eq. (11) of Section 7.6,

$$T^{-1}AT = D = \begin{pmatrix} r_1 & 0 & \cdots & 0 \\ 0 & r_2 & \cdots & 0 \\ \vdots & \vdots & & \vdots \\ 0 & 0 & \cdots & r_n \end{pmatrix} \tag{22}$$

is the diagonal matrix whose diagonal elements are the eigenvalues of A. Thus y satisfies the uncoupled system of equations

$$y' = Dy, \tag{23}$$

for which a fundamental matrix is the diagonal matrix

$$Q(t) = \begin{pmatrix} e^{r_1 t} & 0 & \cdots & 0 \\ 0 & e^{r_2 t} & \cdots & 0 \\ \cdot & \cdot & & \cdot \\ \cdot & \cdot & & \cdot \\ \cdot & \cdot & & \cdot \\ 0 & 0 & \cdots & e^{r_n t} \end{pmatrix}. \tag{24}$$

A fundamental matrix Ψ for the system (17) is then found from Q by the transformation (19),

$$\Psi = TQ; \tag{25}$$

that is,

$$\Psi(t) = \begin{pmatrix} \xi_1^{(1)} e^{r_1 t} & \cdots & \xi_1^{(n)} e^{r_n t} \\ \cdot & & \cdot \\ \cdot & & \cdot \\ \cdot & & \cdot \\ \xi_n^{(1)} e^{r_1 t} & \cdots & \xi_n^{(n)} e^{r_n t} \end{pmatrix}. \tag{26}$$

Equation (26) is the same result that was obtained in Section 7.5. The procedure of this section does not offer any computational advantages over that of Section 7.5, since in any event the main obstacle is the calculation of the eigenvalues and eigenvectors of A, which may be difficult if $n \geq 3$. The viewpoint described here, however, does provide additional insight into the structure of the underlying theory.

Example 3. Consider again the system (3)

$$x' = \begin{pmatrix} 1 & 1 \\ 4 & 1 \end{pmatrix} x.$$

The eigenvalues and eigenvectors of the coefficient matrix are determined from the algebraic system

$$\begin{pmatrix} 1 - r & 1 \\ 4 & 1 - r \end{pmatrix} \begin{pmatrix} \xi_1 \\ \xi_2 \end{pmatrix} = \begin{pmatrix} 0 \\ 0 \end{pmatrix}.$$

We find that

$$\xi^{(1)} = \begin{pmatrix} 1 \\ 2 \end{pmatrix}, \qquad \xi^{(2)} = \begin{pmatrix} 1 \\ -2 \end{pmatrix},$$

corresponding to the eigenvalues $r_1 = 3$ and $r_2 = -1$, respectively. Thus

$$T = \begin{pmatrix} 1 & 1 \\ 2 & -2 \end{pmatrix};$$

straightforward calculation shows that

$$\mathbf{T}^{-1} = \begin{pmatrix} \frac{1}{2} & \frac{1}{4} \\ \frac{1}{2} & -\frac{1}{4} \end{pmatrix},$$

and

$$\mathbf{T}^{-1}\mathbf{A}\mathbf{T} = \begin{pmatrix} 3 & 0 \\ 0 & -1 \end{pmatrix}.$$

Hence the transformation $\mathbf{x} = \mathbf{T}\mathbf{y}$ reduces the system (3) to the form

$$\mathbf{y}' = \begin{pmatrix} 3 & 0 \\ 0 & -1 \end{pmatrix}\mathbf{y}. \tag{27}$$

A fundamental matrix for the uncoupled system (27) is

$$\mathbf{Q}(t) = \begin{pmatrix} e^{3t} & 0 \\ 0 & e^{-t} \end{pmatrix};$$

corresponding to it a fundamental matrix for the original system is

$$\mathbf{\Psi}(t) = \mathbf{T}\mathbf{Q}(t) = \begin{pmatrix} e^{3t} & e^{-t} \\ 2e^{3t} & -2e^{-t} \end{pmatrix}.$$

This is the same result that has been obtained previously by other methods.

PROBLEMS

In each of Problems 1 through 6 find a fundamental matrix for the given system of equations. In each case also find the fundamental matrix $\mathbf{\Phi}(t)$ satisfying $\mathbf{\Phi}(0) = \mathbf{I}$.

1. $\mathbf{x}' = \begin{pmatrix} 3 & -2 \\ 2 & -2 \end{pmatrix}\mathbf{x}$

2. $\mathbf{x}' = \begin{pmatrix} 4 & -3 \\ 8 & -6 \end{pmatrix}\mathbf{x}$

3. $\mathbf{x}' = \begin{pmatrix} 2 & -1 \\ 3 & -2 \end{pmatrix}\mathbf{x}$

4. $\mathbf{x}' = \begin{pmatrix} 1 & 1 \\ 4 & -2 \end{pmatrix}\mathbf{x}$

5. $\mathbf{x}' = \begin{pmatrix} 1 & 1 & 1 \\ 2 & 1 & -1 \\ -8 & -5 & -3 \end{pmatrix}\mathbf{x}$

6. $\mathbf{x}' = \begin{pmatrix} 1 & -1 & 4 \\ 3 & 2 & -1 \\ 2 & 1 & -1 \end{pmatrix}\mathbf{x}$

7. Show that $\Phi(t) = \Psi(t)\Psi^{-1}(t_0)$, where $\Phi(t)$ and $\Psi(t)$ are as defined in this section.

*8. The method of successive approximations (see Section 2.11) can also be applied to systems of equations. In this problem we indicate formally how it works for linear systems with constant coefficients. Consider the initial value problem

$$x' = Ax, \qquad x(0) = \eta \tag{i}$$

where A is a constant matrix, and η a prescribed initial vector.

(a) Assuming that a solution $x = \Phi(t)$ of Eq. (i) exists, show that it must satisfy the integral equation

$$\Phi(t) = \eta + \int_0^t A\Phi(s)\, ds. \tag{ii}$$

(b) Start with the initial approximation $\Phi^{(0)}(t) = \eta$. Substitute this expression for $\Phi(s)$ in the right side of Eq. (ii), and obtain a new approximation $\Phi^{(1)}(t)$. Show that

$$\Phi^{(1)}(t) = (I + At)\eta. \tag{iii}$$

(c) Repeat this process by substituting the expression in Eq. (iii) for $\Phi(s)$ in the right side of Eq. (ii) to obtain a new approximation $\Phi^{(2)}(t)$. Show that

$$\Phi^{(2)}(t) = \left(I + At + A^2 \frac{t^2}{2}\right)\eta. \tag{iv}$$

(d) By continuing this process obtain a sequence of approximations $\Phi^{(0)}$, $\Phi^{(1)}, \Phi^{(2)}, \ldots, \Phi^{(n)}, \ldots$. Show by induction that

$$\Phi^{(n)}(t) = \left(I + At + A^2 \frac{t^2}{2!} + \cdots + A^n \frac{t^n}{n!}\right)\eta. \tag{v}$$

(e) The sum appearing in Eq. (v) is a sum of matrices. It is possible to show that each component of this sum converges as $n \to \infty$, and therefore a new matrix $M(t)$ can be defined as

$$M(t) = \lim_{n \to \infty} \left(I + At + A^2 \frac{t^2}{2!} + \cdots + A^n \frac{t^n}{n!}\right) = I + \sum_{k=1}^{\infty} A^k \frac{t^k}{k!}. \tag{vi}$$

Assuming that term-by-term differentiation is permissible, show that $M(t)$ satisfies $M'(t) = AM(t)$, $M(0) = I$. Hence show that $M(t) = \Phi(t)$.

(f) The series in Eq. (vi) resembles the exponential series. Thus it is natural to adopt the notation e^{At} for this sum:

$$e^{At} = I + \sum_{k=1}^{\infty} A^k \frac{t^k}{k!}. \tag{vii}$$

Show that the solution of the initial value problem (i) can then be written as $x = e^{At}\eta$.

9. Let $\Phi(t)$ denote the fundamental matrix which satisfies $\Phi' = A\Phi$, $\Phi(0) = I$. In Problem 8 we indicated that it was also reasonable to denote this matrix by e^{At}. In this problem we show that Φ does indeed have the principal algebraic properties associated with the exponential function.

(a) Show that $\Phi(t)\Phi(s) = \Phi(t + s)$; that is, $e^{At}e^{As} = e^{A(t+s)}$. *Hint:* Show that if s is fixed and t is variable, then both $\Phi(t)\Phi(s)$ and $\Phi(t + s)$ satisfy the initial value problem $Z' = AZ$, $Z(0) = \Phi(s)$.

(b) Show that $\Phi(t)\Phi(-t) = I$, or $e^{At}e^{A(-t)} = I$, and hence that $\Phi(-t) = \Phi^{-1}(t)$.

(c) Show that $\Phi(t - s) = \Phi(t)\Phi^{-1}(s)$.

7.8 COMPLEX ROOTS

In Sections 7.5 and 7.7 we showed that the general solution of

$$x' = Ax, \tag{1}$$

where A is a real constant $n \times n$ matrix with distinct eigenvalues, can be expressed in terms of the fundamental matrix

$$\Psi(t) = \begin{pmatrix} \xi_1^{(1)}e^{r_1 t} & \cdots & \xi_1^{(n)}e^{r_n t} \\ & \cdot & \\ & \cdot & \\ & \cdot & \\ \xi_n^{(1)}e^{r_1 t} & \cdots & \xi_n^{(n)}e^{r_n t} \end{pmatrix}. \tag{2}$$

Here $\xi^{(1)}, \ldots, \xi^{(n)}$ are the eigenvectors of A corresponding to the eigenvalues $r_1, \ldots, r_n$. If some of the r_i are complex, then $\Psi(t)$ will be complex-valued, and it may be desirable to construct another fundamental matrix all of whose elements are real. We will show how this can be done in this section. We emphasize that A must be real, since a real fundamental matrix may not exist otherwise.

As an example, let us first consider the system

$$x' = \begin{pmatrix} 1 & -1 \\ 5 & -3 \end{pmatrix} x. \tag{3}$$

Assuming that

$$x = \xi e^{rt} \tag{4}$$

leads to the set of linear algebraic equations

$$(1 - r)\xi_1 - \xi_2 = 0,$$
$$5\xi_1 - (3 + r)\xi_2 = 0, \tag{5}$$

which determine the eigenvalues and eigenvectors of **A**. The auxiliary equation is

$$\begin{vmatrix} 1 - r & -1 \\ 5 & -(3 + r) \end{vmatrix} = r^2 + 2r + 2 = 0; \tag{6}$$

therefore the eigenvalues are $r_1 = -1 + i$ and $r_2 = -1 - i$, and from Eq. (5) the corresponding eigenvectors are

$$\xi^{(1)} = \begin{pmatrix} 1 \\ 2 - i \end{pmatrix}, \qquad \xi^{(2)} = \begin{pmatrix} 1 \\ 2 + i \end{pmatrix}. \tag{7}$$

Hence a fundamental matrix for the system (3) is

$$\Psi(t) = \begin{pmatrix} e^{(-1+i)t} & e^{(-1-i)t} \\ (2 - i)e^{(-1+i)t} & (2 + i)e^{(-1-i)t} \end{pmatrix}, \tag{8}$$

and the general solution of Eq. (3) is

$$\mathbf{x} = k_1 \begin{pmatrix} 1 \\ 2 - i \end{pmatrix} e^{(-1+i)t} + k_2 \begin{pmatrix} 1 \\ 2 + i \end{pmatrix} e^{(-1-i)t}, \tag{9}$$

where k_1 and k_2 are arbitrary constants.

To obtain the solution in terms of real-valued functions we make use of Euler's formula

$$e^{i\mu t} = \cos \mu t + i \sin \mu t, \tag{10}$$

thus obtaining

$$x_1 = (k_1 + k_2)e^{-t} \cos t + i(k_1 - k_2)e^{-t} \sin t,$$
$$x_2 = (k_1 + k_2)e^{-t}(2 \cos t + \sin t) + i(k_1 - k_2)e^{-t}(2 \sin t - \cos t). \tag{11}$$

Setting $c_1 = k_1 + k_2$ and $c_2 = i(k_1 - k_2)$ gives

$$\mathbf{x} = c_1 e^{-t} \begin{pmatrix} \cos t \\ 2 \cos t + \sin t \end{pmatrix} + c_2 e^{-t} \begin{pmatrix} \sin t \\ -\cos t + 2 \sin t \end{pmatrix}, \tag{12}$$

which satisfies Eq. (3) for all values of c_1 and c_2. Consequently

$$\mathbf{x}^{(1)}(t) = e^{-t} \begin{pmatrix} \cos t \\ 2 \cos t + \sin t \end{pmatrix}, \qquad \mathbf{x}^{(2)}(t) = e^{-t} \begin{pmatrix} \sin t \\ -\cos t + 2 \sin t \end{pmatrix} \tag{13}$$

are solutions. That $\mathbf{x}^{(1)}$ and $\mathbf{x}^{(2)}$ form a fundamental set of solutions follows from the fact that $W[\mathbf{x}^{(1)}, \mathbf{x}^{(2)}](t) = -e^{-2t}$, which is never zero. Thus the matrix

$$\hat{\Psi}(t) = \begin{pmatrix} e^{-t} \cos t & e^{-t} \sin t \\ e^{-t}(2 \cos t + \sin t) & e^{-t}(-\cos t + 2 \sin t) \end{pmatrix}, \tag{14}$$

whose columns are $\mathbf{x}^{(1)}(t)$ and $\mathbf{x}^{(2)}(t)$, is a real-valued fundamental matrix for the system (3). Alternatively, the solutions (13) can be obtained by computing the real and imaginary parts, respectively, of either of the original solutions given by Eqs. (8) or (9).

The matrix $\hat{\mathbf{\Psi}}$ can also be obtained by operating directly upon the original matrix $\mathbf{\Psi}$ given by Eq. (8). By essentially the calculations just described, it is straightforward to show that the first column of $\hat{\mathbf{\Psi}}$ is simply one half the sum of the columns of $\mathbf{\Psi}$. Similarly, the second column of $\hat{\mathbf{\Psi}}$ is the difference of the columns of $\mathbf{\Psi}$ divided by $2i$. These elementary column operations can be expressed by means of a matrix product

$$\hat{\mathbf{\Psi}} = \mathbf{\Psi}\mathbf{\Gamma}, \tag{15}$$

where

$$\mathbf{\Gamma} = \begin{pmatrix} \dfrac{1}{2} & \dfrac{1}{2i} \\[2mm] \dfrac{1}{2} & -\dfrac{1}{2i} \end{pmatrix}, \tag{16}$$

Since $\mathbf{\Gamma}$ and $\mathbf{\Psi}$ are both nonsingular, it follows that $\hat{\mathbf{\Psi}}$ is also nonsingular and is, therefore, also a fundamental matrix for the system (3).

The same procedure can be followed in the general case. In order to be definite we assume that in the fundamental matrix $\mathbf{\Psi}$ given by Eq. (2) the first two columns arise from a pair of complex conjugate roots $r_1, r_2 = \lambda \pm i\mu$. Then define $\mathbf{\Gamma}$ by

$$\mathbf{\Gamma} = \begin{pmatrix} \dfrac{1}{2} & \dfrac{1}{2i} & 0 & \cdots & 0 \\[2mm] \dfrac{1}{2} & -\dfrac{1}{2i} & 0 & \cdots & 0 \\[2mm] 0 & 0 & 1 & \cdots & 0 \\ \cdot & \cdot & \cdot & & \cdot \\ \cdot & \cdot & \cdot & & \cdot \\ \cdot & \cdot & \cdot & & \cdot \\ 0 & 0 & 0 & \cdots & 1 \end{pmatrix}; \tag{17}$$

and observe that $\mathbf{\Gamma}$ is nonsingular. It follows that

$$\hat{\mathbf{\Psi}} = \mathbf{\Psi}\mathbf{\Gamma} \tag{18}$$

is also a fundamental matrix for the system (1). Furthermore, the first two columns of $\hat{\mathbf{\Psi}}$ are real-valued, whereas the first two columns of $\mathbf{\Psi}$ were not. If $\mathbf{A}$ has other complex eigenvalues so that other columns of $\mathbf{\Psi}$ are also complex, then the corresponding block of elements in $\mathbf{\Gamma}$ should be defined as indicated in Eq. (17). While the multiplication shown in Eq. (18) can be carried out and a general formula for $\hat{\mathbf{\Psi}}$ exhibited, it is usually simpler in practice to apply the given procedure in each specific problem as it arises.

Example. Find a real-valued fundamental matrix for the system

$$\mathbf{x}' = \begin{pmatrix} 2 & -5 & 0 \\ 1 & -2 & -3 \\ 0 & 1 & 2 \end{pmatrix} \mathbf{x}. \tag{19}$$

Assuming that $\mathbf{x} = \boldsymbol{\xi} e^{rt}$, we find that

$$
\begin{aligned}
(2 - r)\xi_1 - \quad\quad 5\xi_2 \quad\quad\quad\quad &= 0, \\
\xi_1 + (-2 - r)\xi_2 - \quad 3\xi_3 &= 0, \\
\xi_2 + (2 - r)\xi_3 &= 0.
\end{aligned} \tag{20}
$$

Hence the auxiliary polynomial is

$$
\Delta(r) = \begin{vmatrix} 2 - r & -5 & 0 \\ 1 & -2 - r & -3 \\ 0 & 1 & 2 - r \end{vmatrix}
$$

$$= (4 + r^2)(2 - r), \tag{21}$$

so that the eigenvalues are $r_1 = 2i$, $r_2 = -2i$, and $r_3 = 2$. The corresponding eigenvectors are found from Eq. (20) to be

$$
\boldsymbol{\xi}^{(1)} = \begin{pmatrix} -5 \\ -2 + 2i \\ 1 \end{pmatrix}, \quad
\boldsymbol{\xi}^{(2)} = \begin{pmatrix} -5 \\ -2 - 2i \\ 1 \end{pmatrix}, \quad
\boldsymbol{\xi}^{(3)} = \begin{pmatrix} 3 \\ 0 \\ 1 \end{pmatrix}. \tag{22}
$$

Hence a fundamental matrix is

$$
\mathbf{\Psi}(t) = \begin{pmatrix} -5e^{2it} & -5e^{-2it} & 3e^{2t} \\ (-2 + 2i)e^{2it} & (-2 - 2i)e^{-2it} & 0 \\ e^{2it} & e^{-2it} & e^{2t} \end{pmatrix}. \tag{23}
$$

To find a real-valued fundamental matrix we can either use Euler's formula as in the earlier transition from Eq. (8) to Eq. (14), or else accomplish the same result by post-multiplying Ψ by the matrix

$$\Gamma = \begin{pmatrix} \dfrac{1}{2} & \dfrac{1}{2i} & 0 \\[2mm] \dfrac{1}{2} & -\dfrac{1}{2i} & 0 \\[2mm] 0 & 0 & 1 \end{pmatrix}. \tag{24}$$

The result is

$$\hat{\Psi}(t) = \Psi(t)\Gamma = \begin{pmatrix} -5\cos 2t & -5\sin 2t & 3e^{2t} \\ -2(\cos 2t + \sin 2t) & 2(\cos 2t - \sin 2t) & 0 \\ \cos 2t & \sin 2t & e^{2t} \end{pmatrix}.$$

PROBLEMS

In each of Problems 1 through 6, express the general solution of the given system of equations in terms of real-valued functions only.

1. $\mathbf{x}' = \begin{pmatrix} 3 & -2 \\ 4 & -1 \end{pmatrix}\mathbf{x}$

2. $\mathbf{x}' = \begin{pmatrix} -1 & -1 \\ 2 & -1 \end{pmatrix}\mathbf{x}$

3. $\mathbf{x}' = \begin{pmatrix} 2 & -5 \\ 1 & -2 \end{pmatrix}\mathbf{x}$

4. $\mathbf{x}' = \begin{pmatrix} 2 & -\frac{5}{2} \\ \frac{9}{5} & -1 \end{pmatrix}\mathbf{x}$

5. $\mathbf{x}' = \begin{pmatrix} 1 & 0 & 0 \\ 2 & 1 & -2 \\ 3 & 2 & 1 \end{pmatrix}\mathbf{x}$

6. $\mathbf{x}' = \begin{pmatrix} -3 & 0 & 2 \\ 1 & -1 & 0 \\ -2 & -1 & 0 \end{pmatrix}\mathbf{x}$

In each of Problems 7 and 8 find the solution of the given initial value problem.

7. $\mathbf{x}' = \begin{pmatrix} 1 & -5 \\ 1 & -3 \end{pmatrix}\mathbf{x}, \qquad \mathbf{x}(0) = \begin{pmatrix} 1 \\ 1 \end{pmatrix}$

8. $\mathbf{x}' = \begin{pmatrix} -3 & 2 \\ -1 & -1 \end{pmatrix}\mathbf{x}, \qquad \mathbf{x}(0) = \begin{pmatrix} 1 \\ -2 \end{pmatrix}$

In each of Problems 9 and 10 solve the given system of equations by the method of Problem 11 of Section 7.5. Assume that $t > 0$.

9. $t\mathbf{x}' = \begin{pmatrix} -1 & -1 \\ 2 & -1 \end{pmatrix}\mathbf{x}$

10. $t\mathbf{x}' = \begin{pmatrix} 2 & -5 \\ 1 & -2 \end{pmatrix}\mathbf{x}$

7.9 REPEATED ROOTS

We conclude our consideration of the linear homogeneous system with constant coefficients,

$$\mathbf{x}' = \mathbf{Ax}, \tag{1}$$

with a discussion of the case in which the matrix $\mathbf{A}$ has a repeated eigenvalue.* If $r = \rho$ is a k-fold root of the determinantal equation

$$\det(\mathbf{A} - r\mathbf{I}) = 0, \tag{2}$$

then ρ is said to be an eigenvalue of multiplicity k of the matrix $\mathbf{A}$. In this event, there are two possibilities: either there are k linearly independent eigenvectors corresponding to the eigenvalue ρ, or else there are fewer than k such eigenvectors. In the first case, let $\boldsymbol{\xi}^{(1)}, \ldots, \boldsymbol{\xi}^{(k)}$ be the eigenvectors associated with the eigenvalue ρ. Then $\mathbf{x}^{(1)}(t) = \boldsymbol{\xi}^{(1)}e^{\rho t}, \ldots, \mathbf{x}^{(k)}(t) = \boldsymbol{\xi}^{(k)}e^{\rho t}$ are k linearly independent solutions of Eq. (1). Thus in this case it really makes no difference that the eigenvalue $r = \rho$ is repeated; there is still a full complement of solutions of Eq. (1) of the form $\boldsymbol{\xi}e^{rt}$.

A great many problems arising in applications lead to coefficient matrices which are Hermitian, or self-adjoint; see Section 7.6. In this case the situation is as described in the preceding paragraph whenever repeated eigenvalues occur, and no further analysis is required. However, if the coefficient matrix is not Hermitian, then there may be fewer than k independent eigenvectors corresponding to an eigenvalue ρ of multiplicity k, and if so, there will be fewer than k solutions of Eq. (1) of the form $\boldsymbol{\xi}e^{rt}$ associated with this eigenvalue. Therefore, in order to construct a fundamental matrix of Eq. (1) it is necessary to find other solutions of a different form. By analogy with previous results for linear equations of order n, it is natural to seek additional solutions involving products of polynomials and exponential functions. We will first consider a simple example.

Let

$$\mathbf{x}' = \begin{pmatrix} 1 & -1 \\ 1 & 3 \end{pmatrix} \mathbf{x} = \mathbf{Ax}. \tag{3}$$

Assuming that $\mathbf{x} = \boldsymbol{\xi}e^{rt}$ and substituting for $\mathbf{x}$ in Eq. (3) gives

$$\begin{aligned}(1 - r)\xi_1 - \quad \xi_2 &= 0, \\ \xi_1 + (3 - r)\xi_2 &= 0,\end{aligned} \tag{4}$$

from which it follows that the eigenvalues of $\mathbf{A}$ are $r_1 = r_2 = 2$. For this value of r, Eqs. (4) imply that $\xi_1 + \xi_2 = 0$. Hence there is only the one eigenvector $\boldsymbol{\xi}$ given by $\boldsymbol{\xi}^T = (1, -1)$ corresponding to the double eigenvalue.

---

* Once again, the discussion in this section is valid whether $\mathbf{A}$ is real or complex.

Thus one solution of the system (3) is

$$\mathbf{x}^{(1)}(t) = \begin{pmatrix} 1 \\ -1 \end{pmatrix} e^{2t}, \tag{5}$$

but there is no second solution of the form $\mathbf{x} = \boldsymbol{\xi} e^{rt}$. It is natural to attempt to find a second solution of the system (3) of the form

$$\mathbf{x} = \boldsymbol{\eta} t e^{2t}, \tag{6}$$

where $\boldsymbol{\eta}$ is a constant vector. Substituting for $\mathbf{x}$ in Eq. (3) gives

$$2\boldsymbol{\eta} t e^{2t} + \boldsymbol{\eta} e^{2t} - \mathbf{A}\boldsymbol{\eta} t e^{2t} = \mathbf{0}. \tag{7}$$

In order for Eq. (7) to be satisfied for all t it is necessary for the coefficients of te^{2t} and e^{2t} each to be zero. From the term in e^{2t} we find that

$$\boldsymbol{\eta} = \mathbf{0}. \tag{8}$$

Hence there is no nonzero solution of the system (3) of the form (6).

Since Eq. (7) contains terms in both te^{2t} and e^{2t}, it appears that in addition to $\boldsymbol{\eta} t e^{2t}$ the second solution must contain a term of the form $\boldsymbol{\zeta} e^{2t}$; in other words, we need to assume that

$$\mathbf{x} = \boldsymbol{\eta} t e^{2t} + \boldsymbol{\zeta} e^{2t}, \tag{9}$$

where $\boldsymbol{\eta}$ and $\boldsymbol{\zeta}$ are constant vectors. Upon substituting this expression for $\mathbf{x}$ in Eq. (3) we obtain

$$2\boldsymbol{\eta} t e^{2t} + (\boldsymbol{\eta} + 2\boldsymbol{\zeta}) e^{2t} = \mathbf{A}(\boldsymbol{\eta} t e^{2t} + \boldsymbol{\zeta} e^{2t}). \tag{10}$$

Equating coefficients of te^{2t} and e^{2t} on each side of Eq. (10) gives the conditions

$$(\mathbf{A} - 2\mathbf{I})\boldsymbol{\eta} = \mathbf{0}, \tag{11}$$

and

$$(\mathbf{A} - 2\mathbf{I})\boldsymbol{\zeta} = \boldsymbol{\eta}. \tag{12}$$

for the determination of $\boldsymbol{\eta}$ and $\boldsymbol{\zeta}$. Equation (11) is satisfied if $\boldsymbol{\eta}$ is the eigenvector of $\mathbf{A}$ corresponding to the eigenvalue $r = 2$, that is, $\boldsymbol{\eta}^T = (1, -1)$. Since det $(\mathbf{A} - 2\mathbf{I})$ is zero, we might expect that Eq. (12) cannot be solved. However, by direct calculation we can show that the eigenvector $\boldsymbol{\eta}$ satisfies the condition $(\boldsymbol{\eta}, \mathbf{y}) = 0$, where $\mathbf{y}$ is any solution of $(\mathbf{A}^* - 2\mathbf{I})\mathbf{y} = \mathbf{0}$. This is precisely the condition under which Eq. (12) does have solutions; see Section 7.3 and Problem 10 below. The solution of Eq. (12) is not unique since an arbitrary multiple of $\boldsymbol{\eta}$ can be included. Upon solving Eq. (12) we find that

$$\boldsymbol{\zeta} = \begin{pmatrix} 0 \\ 1 \end{pmatrix} + k \begin{pmatrix} 1 \\ -1 \end{pmatrix}, \tag{13}$$

where k is an arbitrary constant. Substituting for $\boldsymbol{\eta}$ and $\boldsymbol{\zeta}$ in Eq. (9) gives

$$\mathbf{x} = \begin{pmatrix} 1 \\ -1 \end{pmatrix} te^{2t} + \begin{pmatrix} 0 \\ 1 \end{pmatrix} e^{2t} + k \begin{pmatrix} 1 \\ -1 \end{pmatrix} e^{2t}. \tag{14}$$

The last term in Eq. (14) is merely a multiple of the first solution $\mathbf{x}^{(1)}(t)$, and may be ignored, but the first two terms constitute a new solution $\mathbf{x}^{(2)}(t)$,

$$\mathbf{x}^{(2)}(t) = \begin{pmatrix} 1 \\ -1 \end{pmatrix} te^{2t} + \begin{pmatrix} 0 \\ 1 \end{pmatrix} e^{2t}. \tag{15}$$

An elementary calculation shows that $W[\mathbf{x}^{(1)}, \mathbf{x}^{(2)}](t) = e^{-4t}$, and therefore $\mathbf{x}^{(1)}$ and $\mathbf{x}^{(2)}$ form a fundamental set of solutions of the system (3). The general solution is

$$\mathbf{x} = c_1 \mathbf{x}^{(1)}(t) + c_2 \mathbf{x}^{(2)}(t)$$

$$= c_1 \begin{pmatrix} 1 \\ -1 \end{pmatrix} e^{2t} + c_2 \left[\begin{pmatrix} 1 \\ -1 \end{pmatrix} te^{2t} + \begin{pmatrix} 0 \\ 1 \end{pmatrix} e^{2t} \right], \tag{16}$$

and the corresponding fundamental matrix is

$$\mathbf{\Psi}(t) = \begin{pmatrix} e^{2t} & te^{2t} \\ -e^{2t} & -te^{2t} + e^{2t} \end{pmatrix} \tag{17}$$

or

$$\mathbf{\Psi}(t) = e^{2t} \begin{pmatrix} 1 & t \\ -1 & -t+1 \end{pmatrix}. \tag{18}$$

One difference between a system of two first order equations and a single second order equation is evident at this point. Recall that for a second order linear equation with a repeated root r_1 of the auxiliary equation a term $ce^{r_1 t}$ in the second solution is not required, since it is a multiple of the first solution. On the other hand, for a system of two first order equations the term $\boldsymbol{\zeta} e^{r_1 t}$ is not a multiple of the first solution unless $\boldsymbol{\zeta}$ is proportional to the eigenvector associated with the eigenvalue r_1. Since this is not generally the case, the term $\boldsymbol{\zeta} e^{r_1 t}$ must be retained.

Now let us consider the same problem in more generality. Consider again the system (1), and suppose that $r = \rho$ is a double eigenvalue of $\mathbf{A}$, but that there is only one corresponding eigenvector $\boldsymbol{\xi}$. Then one solution (similar to Eq. (5)) is

$$\mathbf{x}^{(1)}(t) = \boldsymbol{\xi} e^{\rho t}. \tag{19}$$

The second solution is of the form given by Eq. (9),

$$\mathbf{x} = \boldsymbol{\eta} te^{\rho t} + \boldsymbol{\zeta} e^{\rho t}, \tag{20}$$

where $\boldsymbol{\eta}$ and $\boldsymbol{\zeta}$ must satisfy the equations (similar to Eqs. (11) and (12))

$$(\mathbf{A} - \rho\mathbf{I})\boldsymbol{\eta} = \mathbf{0}, \tag{21}$$

$$(\mathbf{A} - \rho\mathbf{I})\boldsymbol{\zeta} = \boldsymbol{\eta}. \tag{22}$$

From Eq. (21) we have that $\boldsymbol{\eta}$ is equal to the eigenvector $\boldsymbol{\xi}$. Since det $(\mathbf{A} - \rho\mathbf{I}) = 0$, Eq. (22) will have solutions only if $\boldsymbol{\eta}$ satisfies the necessary consistency condition $(\boldsymbol{\eta}, \mathbf{y}) = 0$, for each solution $\mathbf{y}$ of $(\mathbf{A}^* - \rho\mathbf{I})\mathbf{y} = \mathbf{0}$. The fact that the eigenvector $\boldsymbol{\eta} = \boldsymbol{\xi}$ always satisfies this condition can be established, but it is beyond the scope of this book to do so. The solution of Eq (22) is determined only up to an arbitrary multiple of $\boldsymbol{\xi}$, and can be written as

$$\boldsymbol{\zeta} = \boldsymbol{\zeta}^{(1)} + \alpha_1\boldsymbol{\xi}. \tag{23}$$

Hence

$$\mathbf{x} = \boldsymbol{\xi}te^{\rho t} + \boldsymbol{\zeta}^{(1)}e^{\rho t} + \alpha_1\boldsymbol{\xi}e^{\rho t}. \tag{24}$$

The last term is a multiple of the first solution $\mathbf{x}^{(1)}(t)$, and can be discarded here, but the first two terms constitute a new solution

$$\mathbf{x}^{(2)}(t) = \boldsymbol{\xi}te^{\rho t} + \boldsymbol{\zeta}^{(1)}e^{\rho t}. \tag{25}$$

The same procedure can also be applied if the eigenvalue has multiplicity greater than two. Suppose, for example, that the matrix $\mathbf{A}$ in Eq. (1) has an eigenvalue ρ of multiplicity three, but with only one corresponding eigenvector. Then one solution is given by Eq. (19) and a second by Eq. (25). A third independent solution must be sought in the form

$$\mathbf{x} = \boldsymbol{\eta}^{(1)}\frac{t^2}{2}e^{\rho t} + \boldsymbol{\eta}^{(2)}te^{\rho t} + \boldsymbol{\eta}^{(3)}e^{\rho t}. \tag{26}$$

Upon substituting Eq. (26) for $\mathbf{x}$ in Eq. (1) it follows that $\boldsymbol{\eta}^{(1)}$, $\boldsymbol{\eta}^{(2)}$, and $\boldsymbol{\eta}^{(3)}$ must satisfy the equations

$$(\mathbf{A} - \rho\mathbf{I})\boldsymbol{\eta}^{(1)} = \mathbf{0}, \tag{27}$$

$$(\mathbf{A} - \rho\mathbf{I})\boldsymbol{\eta}^{(2)} = \boldsymbol{\eta}^{(1)}, \tag{28}$$

and

$$(\mathbf{A} - \rho\mathbf{I})\boldsymbol{\eta}^{(3)} = \boldsymbol{\eta}^{(2)}. \tag{29}$$

We have already stated that $\boldsymbol{\eta}^{(1)}$ will always be such that Eq. (28) can be solved for $\boldsymbol{\eta}^{(2)}$. It is also true that $\boldsymbol{\eta}^{(2)}$ will satisfy the necessary condition so that Eq. (29) can be solved for $\boldsymbol{\eta}^{(3)}$.

In conclusion we note that the above discussion can be extended so as to deal with an eigenvalue of arbitrary multiplicity, or with the case in which several different eigenvalues each have multiplicities greater than one. By making use of more advanced concepts from matrix theory, a very elegant theory can be developed.

PROBLEMS

In each of Problems 1 through 4 find the general solution of the given system of equations.

1. $\mathbf{x}' = \begin{pmatrix} 3 & -4 \\ 1 & -1 \end{pmatrix} \mathbf{x}$

2. $\mathbf{x}' = \begin{pmatrix} 4 & -2 \\ 8 & -4 \end{pmatrix} \mathbf{x}$

3. $\mathbf{x}' = \begin{pmatrix} 1 & 1 & 1 \\ 2 & 1 & -1 \\ 0 & -1 & 1 \end{pmatrix} \mathbf{x}$

4. $\mathbf{x}' = \begin{pmatrix} 0 & 1 & 1 \\ 1 & 0 & 1 \\ 1 & 1 & 0 \end{pmatrix} \mathbf{x}$

In each of Problems 5 and 6 find the solution of the given initial value problem.

5. $\mathbf{x}' = \begin{pmatrix} 1 & -4 \\ 4 & -7 \end{pmatrix} \mathbf{x}, \qquad \mathbf{x}(0) = \begin{pmatrix} 3 \\ 2 \end{pmatrix}$

6. $\mathbf{x}' = \begin{pmatrix} 1 & 0 & 0 \\ -4 & 1 & 0 \\ 3 & 6 & 2 \end{pmatrix} \mathbf{x}, \qquad \mathbf{x}(0) = \begin{pmatrix} -1 \\ 2 \\ -30 \end{pmatrix}$

7. Show that $r = 2$ is a triple root of the auxiliary equation for the system

$$\mathbf{x}' = \begin{pmatrix} 1 & 1 & 1 \\ 2 & 1 & -1 \\ -3 & 2 & 4 \end{pmatrix} \mathbf{x},$$

and find three linearly independent solutions of this system.

In each of Problems 8 and 9 solve the given system of equations by the method of Problem 11 of Section 7.5. Assume that $t > 0$.

8. $t\mathbf{x}' = \begin{pmatrix} 3 & -4 \\ 1 & -1 \end{pmatrix} \mathbf{x}$

9. $t\mathbf{x}' = \begin{pmatrix} 1 & -4 \\ 4 & -7 \end{pmatrix} \mathbf{x}$

10. Consider the example problem in the text,

$$\mathbf{x}' = \begin{pmatrix} 1 & -1 \\ 1 & 3 \end{pmatrix} \mathbf{x} = A\mathbf{x}$$

with the eigenvector ξ given by $\xi^T = (1, -1)$ corresponding to the eigenvalue $r = 2$. Find all solutions of $(A^* - 2I)\mathbf{y} = \mathbf{0}$, and show directly that ξ is orthogonal to each of them.

7.10 NONHOMOGENEOUS LINEAR SYSTEMS

In this section we will briefly discuss ways of solving nonhomogeneous linear systems, that is, systems of the form

$$\mathbf{x}' = \mathbf{P}(t)\mathbf{x} + \mathbf{g}(t). \tag{1}$$

We assume that the elements of $\mathbf{P}$ and $\mathbf{g}$ are continuous functions on $\alpha < t < \beta$, and that a fundamental matrix $\mathbf{\Psi}(t)$ for the corresponding homogeneous system

$$\mathbf{x}' = \mathbf{P}(t)\mathbf{x} \tag{2}$$

has been found. Then the method of variation of parameters can be used to construct a particular solution, and hence the general solution, of the nonhomogeneous system (1).

Since the general solution of the homogeneous system (2) is $\mathbf{\Psi}(t)\mathbf{c}$, it is natural to seek a solution of the nonhomogeneous system (1) of the form

$$\mathbf{x} = \mathbf{\Psi}(t)\mathbf{u}(t), \tag{3}$$

where $\mathbf{u}(t)$ is a vector to be found below. Upon differentiating $\mathbf{x}$ as given by Eq. (3) and requiring that Eq. (1) be satisfied, we obtain

$$\mathbf{\Psi}'(t)\mathbf{u}(t) + \mathbf{\Psi}(t)\mathbf{u}'(t) = \mathbf{P}(t)\mathbf{\Psi}(t)\mathbf{u}(t) + \mathbf{g}(t). \tag{4}$$

Since $\mathbf{\Psi}(t)$ is a fundamental matrix, $\mathbf{\Psi}'(t) = \mathbf{P}(t)\mathbf{\Psi}(t)$, and hence Eq. (4) reduces to

$$\mathbf{\Psi}(t)\mathbf{u}'(t) = \mathbf{g}(t). \tag{5}$$

Recall that $\mathbf{\Psi}(t)$ is nonsingular on any interval where $\mathbf{P}$ is continuous. Hence $\mathbf{\Psi}^{-1}(t)$ exists, and therefore

$$\mathbf{u}'(t) = \mathbf{\Psi}^{-1}(t)\mathbf{g}(t). \tag{6}$$

Thus for $\mathbf{u}(t)$ we can select any vector from the class of vectors that satisfy Eq. (6); these vectors are determined only up to an arbitrary additive constant (vector); therefore we denote $\mathbf{u}(t)$ by

$$\mathbf{u}(t) = \int^t \mathbf{\Psi}^{-1}(s)\mathbf{g}(s)\, ds + \mathbf{c}, \tag{7}$$

where the constant vector $\mathbf{c}$ is arbitrary. Finally, substituting for $\mathbf{u}(t)$ in Eq. (3) gives the solution $\mathbf{x}$ of the system (1):

$$\mathbf{x} = \mathbf{\Psi}(t)\mathbf{c} + \mathbf{\Psi}(t)\int^t \mathbf{\Psi}^{-1}(s)\mathbf{g}(s)\, ds. \tag{8}$$

Since $\mathbf{c}$ is arbitrary, any initial condition at a point $t = t_0$ can be satisfied by an appropriate choice of $\mathbf{c}$. Thus every solution of the system (1) is contained in the expression given by Eq. (8); it is therefore the general solution of Eq. (1). Note that the first term on the right side of Eq. (8) is the general solution of the homogeneous system (2), whereas the second term is a particular solution of the nonhomogeneous system (1). Hence the solution obtained here has the same basic structure as that obtained for linear scalar equations in Chapters 3 and 5.

Further, just as for linear scalar equations, once the general solution of the homogeneous system is known, the method of variation of parameters can be used to solve the nonhomogeneous system regardless of the nature of the nonhomogeneous term **g**, so long as it is continuous. Note also that for a system of equations $\mathbf{u}(t)$ is completely determined by the differential equations, whereas for a scalar equation of second or higher order it was necessary to introduce additional requirements in order to solve for the unknown functions.

Now let us consider the initial value problem consisting of the differential equation (1) and the initial condition

$$\mathbf{x}(t_0) = \mathbf{x}^0. \tag{9}$$

We can write the solution of this problem most conveniently if we choose for the particular solution in Eq. (8) the specific one which is zero when $t = t_0$. This can be done by using $t = t_0$ as the lower limit of integration in Eq. (8), so that the general solution of the differential equation takes the form

$$\mathbf{x} = \mathbf{\Psi}(t)\mathbf{c} + \mathbf{\Psi}(t)\int_{t_0}^{t} \mathbf{\Psi}^{-1}(s)\mathbf{g}(s)\, ds. \tag{10}$$

The initial condition (9) can also be satisfied provided

$$\mathbf{c} = \mathbf{\Psi}^{-1}(t_0)\mathbf{x}^0. \tag{11}$$

Therefore

$$\mathbf{x} = \mathbf{\Psi}(t)\mathbf{\Psi}^{-1}(t_0)\mathbf{x}^0 + \mathbf{\Psi}(t)\int_{t_0}^{t} \mathbf{\Psi}^{-1}(s)\mathbf{g}(s)\, ds \tag{12}$$

is the solution of the given initial value problem.

Example.   Find the general solution of the system

$$\mathbf{x}' = \begin{pmatrix} 2 & -5 \\ 1 & -2 \end{pmatrix}\mathbf{x} + \begin{pmatrix} \csc t \\ \sec t \end{pmatrix} \tag{13}$$

on any interval not containing zero or any multiple of $\pi/2$.

Using the methods of Section 7.8 we find that

$$\mathbf{x}^{(1)}(t) = \begin{pmatrix} 5\cos t \\ 2\cos t + \sin t \end{pmatrix} \tag{14}$$

and

$$\mathbf{x}^{(2)}(t) = \begin{pmatrix} 5\sin t \\ -\cos t + 2\sin t \end{pmatrix} \tag{15}$$

form a fundamental set of solutions of the corresponding homogeneous system; therefore a fundamental matrix $\boldsymbol{\Psi}$ is given by

$$\boldsymbol{\Psi}(t) = \begin{pmatrix} 5\cos t & 5\sin t \\ 2\cos t + \sin t & -\cos t + 2\sin t \end{pmatrix}. \tag{16}$$

A straightforward calculation (see Section 7.6) shows that

$$\boldsymbol{\Psi}^{-1}(t) = \begin{pmatrix} \frac{1}{5}\cos t - \frac{2}{5}\sin t & \sin t \\ \frac{1}{5}\sin t + \frac{2}{5}\cos t & -\cos t \end{pmatrix}. \tag{17}$$

In this particular problem

$$\mathbf{g}(t) = \begin{pmatrix} \csc t \\ \sec t \end{pmatrix} \tag{18}$$

and therefore

$$\mathbf{u}'(t) = \boldsymbol{\Psi}^{-1}(t)\mathbf{g}(t) = \begin{pmatrix} \frac{1}{5}\cot t + \tan t - \frac{2}{5} \\ \frac{2}{5}\cot t - \frac{4}{5} \end{pmatrix}. \tag{19}$$

Thus, omitting the constants of integration,

$$\mathbf{u}(t) = \begin{pmatrix} \frac{1}{5}\ln|\sin t| - \ln|\cos t| - \frac{2}{5}t \\ \frac{2}{5}\ln|\sin t| - \frac{4}{5}t \end{pmatrix} \tag{20}$$

and the general solution of Eq. (13) can be written as

$$\mathbf{x} = c_1\mathbf{x}^{(1)}(t) + c_2\mathbf{x}^{(2)}(t) + \tfrac{1}{5}(\ln|\sin t| - 5\ln|\cos t| - 2t)\mathbf{x}^{(1)}(t)$$
$$+ \tfrac{1}{5}(2\ln|\sin t| - 4t)\mathbf{x}^{(2)}(t), \tag{21}$$

or, more compactly, as

$$\mathbf{x} = \boldsymbol{\Psi}(t)\mathbf{c} + \boldsymbol{\Psi}(t)\mathbf{u}(t). \tag{22}$$

In some cases a more convenient way to find a particular solution of the nonhomogeneous system (1) is the method of undetermined coefficients. To make use of this method one assumes the form of the solution with some or all of the coefficients unspecified, and then seeks to determine these coefficients so as to satisfy the differential equation. As a practical matter this method is applicable only if $\mathbf{P}$ is a constant matrix, and if the components of $\mathbf{g}$ are polynomial, exponential, or sinusoidal functions, or sums of products of these. Only in these cases can the correct form of the solution be predicted in a simple and systematic manner. The procedure for choosing the form of the solution is substantially the same as that given in Section 3.6.1 for linear second order equations. Several cases are illustrated in Problems 9 through 16.

PROBLEMS

In each of Problems 1 through 5 use the method of variation of parameters to solve the given system of equations.

1. $\mathbf{x}' = \begin{pmatrix} 2 & -1 \\ 3 & -2 \end{pmatrix} \mathbf{x} + \begin{pmatrix} e^t \\ t \end{pmatrix}$

2. $\mathbf{x}' = \begin{pmatrix} 2 & -5 \\ 1 & -2 \end{pmatrix} \mathbf{x} + \begin{pmatrix} -\cos t \\ \sin t \end{pmatrix}$

3. $\mathbf{x}' = \begin{pmatrix} 1 & 1 \\ 4 & -2 \end{pmatrix} \mathbf{x} + \begin{pmatrix} e^{-2t} \\ -2e^t \end{pmatrix}$

4. $\mathbf{x}' = \begin{pmatrix} 4 & -2 \\ 8 & -4 \end{pmatrix} \mathbf{x} + \begin{pmatrix} t^{-3} \\ -t^{-2} \end{pmatrix}, \qquad t > 0$

5. $\mathbf{x}' = \begin{pmatrix} 2 & -5 \\ 1 & -2 \end{pmatrix} \mathbf{x} + \begin{pmatrix} 0 \\ \cot t \end{pmatrix}, \qquad 0 < t < \pi$

In each of Problems 6 and 7 verify that the given vector is the general solution of the corresponding homogeneous system, and use the method of variation of parameters to solve the nonhomogeneous system. Assume that $t > 0$.

6. $t\mathbf{x}' = \begin{pmatrix} 2 & -1 \\ 3 & -2 \end{pmatrix} \mathbf{x} + \begin{pmatrix} 1 - t^2 \\ 2t \end{pmatrix}, \qquad \mathbf{x}^{(c)} = c_1 \begin{pmatrix} 1 \\ 1 \end{pmatrix} t + c_2 \begin{pmatrix} 1 \\ 3 \end{pmatrix} t^{-1}$

7. $t\mathbf{x}' = \begin{pmatrix} 3 & -2 \\ 2 & -2 \end{pmatrix} \mathbf{x} + \begin{pmatrix} -2t \\ t^4 - 1 \end{pmatrix}, \qquad \mathbf{x}^{(c)} = c_1 \begin{pmatrix} 1 \\ 2 \end{pmatrix} t^{-1} + c_2 \begin{pmatrix} 2 \\ 1 \end{pmatrix} t^2$

8. Show that the general solution of the system $\mathbf{x}' = \mathbf{P}(t)\mathbf{x} + \mathbf{g}(t)$ may be expressed as $\mathbf{x} = \mathbf{x}^{(c)}(t) + \mathbf{x}^{(p)}(t)$, where $\mathbf{x}^{(c)}$ is the general solution of the corresponding homogeneous system, and $\mathbf{x}^{(p)}$ is any solution of the given nonhomogeneous system.

Problems 9 through 16 illustrate how the method of undetermined coefficients may be extended to systems of equations.

9. Consider the system

$$\mathbf{x}' = \begin{pmatrix} 3 & -2 \\ 2 & -2 \end{pmatrix} \mathbf{x} + \begin{pmatrix} t \\ 3e^t \end{pmatrix}. \tag{i}$$

(a) Show that the general solution of the corresponding homogeneous system is

$$\mathbf{x}^{(c)}(t) = c_1 \begin{pmatrix} 1 \\ 2 \end{pmatrix} e^{-t} + c_2 \begin{pmatrix} 2 \\ 1 \end{pmatrix} e^{2t}. \tag{ii}$$

(b) The nonhomogeneous terms may be written as

$$\begin{pmatrix} 1 \\ 0 \end{pmatrix} t + \begin{pmatrix} 0 \\ 3 \end{pmatrix} e^t.$$

Corresponding to these terms it is natural to look for solutions of the form $\mathbf{a} + \mathbf{b}t + \mathbf{c}e^t$, where $\mathbf{a}$, $\mathbf{b}$, and $\mathbf{c}$ are undetermined vectors. Show by direct computation that

$$\mathbf{x}^{(p)}(t) = \frac{1}{2} \begin{pmatrix} 0 \\ 1 \end{pmatrix} - \begin{pmatrix} 1 \\ 1 \end{pmatrix} t + 3 \begin{pmatrix} 1 \\ 1 \end{pmatrix} e^t. \tag{iii}$$

By the result of Problem 8 the general solution of Eq. (i) is $\mathbf{x}^{(c)}(t) + \mathbf{x}^{(p)}(t)$.

10. Consider the system

$$\mathbf{x}' = \begin{pmatrix} 3 & -2 \\ 2 & -2 \end{pmatrix} \mathbf{x} - \begin{pmatrix} 0 \\ 1 \end{pmatrix} e^{2t}. \tag{i}$$

(a) Show that the general solution of the corresponding homogeneous system is

$$\mathbf{x}^{(c)}(t) = c_1 \begin{pmatrix} 1 \\ 2 \end{pmatrix} e^{-t} + c_2 \begin{pmatrix} 2 \\ 1 \end{pmatrix} e^{2t}. \tag{ii}$$

(b) Because of the form of the nonhomogeneous term in Eq. (i), it is natural to assume that $\mathbf{x}^{(p)}(t)$ is of the form $\mathbf{x}^{(p)}(t) = \mathbf{a}e^{2t}$. Show, however, that it is impossible to satisfy Eq. (i) with this expression regardless of the choice of $\mathbf{a}$. Explain.

(c) Assume that $\mathbf{x}^{(p)}(t) = \mathbf{a}te^{2t}$. Show that it is impossible to satisfy Eq. (i) with an expression of this form.

(d) Assume that $\mathbf{x}^{(p)}(t) = \mathbf{a}e^{2t} + \mathbf{b}te^{2t}$. Show that

$$\mathbf{x}^{(p)}(t) = \frac{2}{3} \begin{pmatrix} 1 \\ 0 \end{pmatrix} e^{2t} + \frac{1}{3} \begin{pmatrix} 2 \\ 1 \end{pmatrix} te^{2t}. \tag{iii}$$

Note that the term $\mathbf{a}e^{2t}$ must be retained in $\mathbf{x}^{(p)}(t)$, since it cannot in general be absorbed in the second term of the homogeneous solution $\mathbf{x}^{(c)}(t)$.

In each of Problems 11 through 16 find the general solution of the given equation by the method of undetermined coefficients.

11. $\mathbf{x}' = \begin{pmatrix} 1 & 1 \\ 4 & 1 \end{pmatrix} \mathbf{x} + \begin{pmatrix} 2 \\ -1 \end{pmatrix} e^t$

12. $\mathbf{x}' = \begin{pmatrix} 2 & -5 \\ 1 & -2 \end{pmatrix} \mathbf{x} + \begin{pmatrix} -\sin 2t \\ t \end{pmatrix}$

13. $\mathbf{x}' = \begin{pmatrix} 3 & -2 \\ 4 & -1 \end{pmatrix} \mathbf{x} + \begin{pmatrix} -e^{-t} \sin t \\ 2e^{-t} \cos t \end{pmatrix}$

14. $\mathbf{x}' = \begin{pmatrix} 2 & -1 \\ 3 & -2 \end{pmatrix} \mathbf{x} + \begin{pmatrix} 1 \\ -1 \end{pmatrix} e^t$

15. $\mathbf{x}' = \begin{pmatrix} 4 & -2 \\ 8 & -4 \end{pmatrix} \mathbf{x} + \begin{pmatrix} 2t \\ 1 \end{pmatrix}$

16. $\mathbf{x}' = \begin{pmatrix} 3 & -4 \\ 1 & -1 \end{pmatrix} \mathbf{x} + \begin{pmatrix} 1 \\ -1 \end{pmatrix} e^t$

7.11   THE LAPLACE TRANSFORM FOR SYSTEMS OF EQUATIONS

The Laplace transform, described in Chapter 6, is just as useful for solving systems of linear equations as for solving a single equation. It is particularly well adapted to solving initial value problems for linear systems with constant coefficients and nonhomogeneous terms corresponding to discontinuous or impulsive forcing functions.

First it is necessary to extend the definition of the Laplace transform to vector and matrix functions. Let $\mathbf{x}$ be a vector each of whose components is piecewise continuous and of exponential order (see Section 6.1) as $t \to \infty$. Then the Laplace transform of $\mathbf{x}$, denoted by $\mathscr{L}\{\mathbf{x}(t)\}$ or $\mathbf{X}(s)$, is defined to be the vector whose components are the transforms of the corresponding components of $\mathbf{x}$. In other words,

$$X_i(s) = \mathscr{L}\{x_i(t)\} = \int_0^\infty e^{-st} x_i(t)\, dt; \qquad i = 1, \ldots, n \tag{1}$$

for s sufficiently large. Further, if each of the components of $\mathbf{x}$ and $\mathbf{x}'$ satisfy the conditions of Theorem 6.3 (x_i continuous, x_i' piecewise continuous, and x_i of exponential order), then the Laplace transform of $\mathbf{x}'$ also exists and is given by

$$\mathscr{L}\{\mathbf{x}'(t)\} = s\mathscr{L}\{\mathbf{x}(t)\} - \mathbf{x}(0). \tag{2}$$

Similarly, the Laplace transform of a matrix whose generic element is $a_{ij}(t)$ is a matrix whose corresponding element $A_{ij}(s)$ is the transform of $a_{ij}(t)$. An equation similar to Eq. (2) also gives the Laplace transform of the derivative of such a matrix.

Now let us find the Laplace transform of a fundamental matrix for the differential equation $\mathbf{x}' = \mathbf{Ax}$, where $\mathbf{A}$ is a constant matrix. In particular, consider the fundamental matrix $\mathbf{\Phi}$, which satisfies the initial condition

$$\mathbf{\Phi}(0) = \mathbf{I} \tag{3}$$

as well as the differential equation

$$\mathbf{\Phi}' = \mathbf{A\Phi}. \tag{4}$$

Taking the transform of Eq. (4) and using the initial condition (3) yields

$$s\mathscr{L}\{\mathbf{\Phi}(t)\} - \mathbf{I} = \mathbf{A}\mathscr{L}\{\mathbf{\Phi}(t)\},$$

or

$$(\mathbf{A} - s\mathbf{I})\mathscr{L}\{\mathbf{\Phi}(t)\} = -\mathbf{I}. \tag{5}$$

In order to solve Eq. (5) for $\mathscr{L}\{\mathbf{\Phi}(t)\}$ we must compute $(\mathbf{A} - s\mathbf{I})^{-1}$. The matrix $\mathbf{A} - s\mathbf{I}$ is nonsingular provided s is not equal to an eigenvalue of $\mathbf{A}$. Hence, by restricting s to be sufficiently large, we can be sure that $(\mathbf{A} - s\mathbf{I})^{-1}$ exists. Therefore

$$\mathscr{L}\{\boldsymbol{\Phi}(t)\} = -(\mathbf{A} - s\mathbf{I})^{-1} \tag{6}$$

or

$$\boldsymbol{\Phi}(t) = \mathscr{L}^{-1}\{-(\mathbf{A} - s\mathbf{I})^{-1}\}. \tag{7}$$

Next, consider the nonhomogeneous initial value problem

$$\mathbf{x}' = \mathbf{A}\mathbf{x} + \mathbf{g}(t), \qquad \mathbf{x}(0) = \mathbf{x}^0, \tag{8}$$

where $\mathbf{A}$ is a constant matrix, $\mathbf{x}^0$ is a constant vector, and $\mathbf{g}(t)$ is a given forcing vector. Transforming Eq. (8) yields

$$s\mathbf{X}(s) - \mathbf{x}^0 = \mathbf{A}\mathbf{X}(s) + \mathbf{G}(s), \tag{9}$$

where $\mathbf{G}(s)$ is the Laplace transform of $\mathbf{g}(t)$. Solving Eq. (9) for $\mathbf{X}(s)$, we obtain

$$\mathbf{X}(s) = -(\mathbf{A} - s\mathbf{I})^{-1}\mathbf{x}^0 - (\mathbf{A} - s\mathbf{I})^{-1}\mathbf{G}(s). \tag{10}$$

To determine $\mathbf{x}(t) = \mathscr{L}^{-1}\{\mathbf{X}(s)\}$ we must find the inverse transform of each term on the right side of Eq. (10). The inverse transform of the first term follows directly from Eq. (7); in fact, since $\mathbf{x}^0$ is a constant vector,

$$\mathscr{L}^{-1}\{-(\mathbf{A} - s\mathbf{I})^{-1}\mathbf{x}^0\} = \mathscr{L}^{-1}\{-(\mathbf{A} - s\mathbf{I})^{-1}\}\mathbf{x}^0$$
$$= \boldsymbol{\Phi}(t)\mathbf{x}^0. \tag{11}$$

The second term is the product of two factors, one of which is the transform of the fundamental matrix $\boldsymbol{\Phi}(t)$ while the other is the transform of $\mathbf{g}(t)$. Hence, the inverse transform of this term is the convolution (see Theorem 6.6) of $\boldsymbol{\Phi}(t)$ and $\mathbf{g}(t)$, that is,

$$\mathscr{L}^{-1}\{-(\mathbf{A} - s\mathbf{I})^{-1}\mathbf{G}(s)\} = \boldsymbol{\Phi}(t) * \mathbf{g}(t)$$
$$= \int_0^t \boldsymbol{\Phi}(t - u)\mathbf{g}(u)\,du. \tag{12}$$

Thus the inverse transform of $\mathbf{X}(s)$ is

$$\mathbf{x} = \boldsymbol{\Phi}(t)\mathbf{x}^0 + \int_0^t \boldsymbol{\Phi}(t - u)\mathbf{g}(u)\,du. \tag{13}$$

If $\mathbf{x}^0$ is thought of as an arbitrary initial vector, then the first term on the right side of Eq. (13) constitutes the general solution of the homogeneous system $\mathbf{x}' = \mathbf{A}\mathbf{x}$. This term represents the response of the nonhomogeneous system to the initial conditions. The last term in Eq. (13) represents the response to the forcing term $\mathbf{g}(t)$ in Eq. (8).

It is worthwhile to compare the result (13) with that obtained in Section 7.10 by the method of variation of parameters:

$$x = \Phi(t)x^0 + \Phi(t)\int_0^t \Phi^{-1}(u)g(u)\,du. \tag{14}$$

In comparing Eqs. (13) and (14) it is important to realize that Eq. (14) is valid for problems with variable coefficients whereas Eq. (13) was obtained only for systems with constant coefficients. For the case to which both apply (constant coefficients), they must yield the same result because of the uniqueness theorem, and hence it can be shown that

$$\Phi(t - u) = \Phi(t)\Phi^{-1}(u). \tag{15}$$

Equation (15) is interesting because it reflects the fact that Φ has some of the properties of the exponential function. For a fuller discussion see Problems 8 and 9 of Section 7.7.

The chief significance of the Laplace transform procedure, however, does not rest upon the derivation of Eq. (13), which is essentially a special case of the more general result obtained earlier. In practice, one often does not use Eq. (13) at all, but rather proceeds directly to transform the given initial value problem, solve algebraically for the transform vector $X(s)$, and then find the inverse transform $x(t)$ by using partial fraction expansions and a table of transforms. This procedure is illustrated in the following example.

Example.   Solve the initial value problem

$$x' = \begin{pmatrix} 3 & -2 \\ 2 & -2 \end{pmatrix}x + \begin{pmatrix} 1 - u_\pi(t) \\ 0 \end{pmatrix}, \tag{16}$$

$$x(0) = \begin{pmatrix} 1 \\ 0 \end{pmatrix}, \tag{17}$$

where $u_\pi(t)$ is the unit step function defined in Section 6.3:

$$u_\pi(t) = \begin{cases} 0, & t < \pi, \\ 1, & t \geq \pi. \end{cases} \tag{18}$$

Taking the transform of each component of Eq. (16), using the initial conditions (17), and collecting terms leads to the system of algebraic equations

$$(s - 3)X_1(s) \qquad + 2X_2(s) = 1 + \frac{1}{s} - \frac{e^{-\pi s}}{s} \tag{19}$$

$$-2X_1(s) + (s + 2)X_2(s) = 0$$

for $X_1(s)$ and $X_2(s)$. The solution of Eqs. (19) is

$$X_1(s) = \frac{(s+2)\left(1 + \dfrac{1}{s} - \dfrac{e^{-\pi s}}{s}\right)}{(s+1)(s-2)}, \qquad X_2(s) = \frac{2\left(1 + \dfrac{1}{s} - \dfrac{e^{-\pi s}}{s}\right)}{(s+1)(s-2)}. \quad (20)$$

In order to compute the inverse transforms $x_1(t)$ and $x_2(t)$, it is convenient to rewrite Eqs. (20) in the form

$$X_1(s) = \frac{s+2}{(s+1)(s-2)} + \frac{s+2}{(s+1)(s-2)} \frac{1 - e^{-\pi s}}{s},$$

$$X_2(s) = \frac{2}{(s+1)(s-2)} + \frac{2}{(s+1)(s-2)} \frac{1 - e^{-\pi s}}{s}, \quad (21)$$

or

$$X_1(s) = H_1(s) + H_1(s)G(s),$$
$$X_2(s) = H_2(s) + H_2(s)G(s), \quad (22)$$

where

$$H_1(s) = \frac{s+2}{(s+1)(s-2)}, \qquad H_2(s) = \frac{2}{(s+1)(s-2)}, \qquad G(s) = \frac{1 - e^{-\pi s}}{s}. \quad (23)$$

If $h_1(t)$, $h_2(t)$, and $g(t)$ are the inverse transforms of $H_1(s)$, $H_2(s)$, and $G(s)$, respectively, then it follows at once from the convolution theorem that

$$x_1(t) = \mathcal{L}^{-1}\{X_1(s)\} = h_1(t) + \int_0^t h_1(t-u)g(u)\,du,$$

$$x_2(t) = \mathcal{L}^{-1}\{X_2(s)\} = h_2(t) + \int_0^t h_2(t-u)g(u)\,du. \quad (24)$$

The functions h_1, h_2, and g can be determined by using partial fraction expansions and Table 6.1. The results are

$$h_1(t) = \tfrac{1}{3}(-e^{-t} + 4e^{2t}), \quad h_2(t) = \tfrac{2}{3}(-e^{-t} + e^{2t}), \quad g(t) = 1 - u_\pi(t). \quad (25)$$

PROBLEMS

In each of Problems 1 through 5 use the Laplace transform to find the solution of the given initial value problem.

1. $\mathbf{x}' = \begin{pmatrix} 1 & 1 \\ 4 & -2 \end{pmatrix}\mathbf{x}, \qquad \mathbf{x}(0) = \begin{pmatrix} 0 \\ 1 \end{pmatrix}$

2. $\mathbf{x}' = \begin{pmatrix} 2 & -2 \\ 4 & -2 \end{pmatrix}\mathbf{x}, \qquad \mathbf{x}(0) = \begin{pmatrix} 1 \\ 0 \end{pmatrix}$

3. $\mathbf{x}' = \begin{pmatrix} 2 & -1 \\ 3 & -2 \end{pmatrix} \mathbf{x} + \begin{pmatrix} 1 \\ -1 \end{pmatrix} e^t, \qquad \mathbf{x}(0) = \begin{pmatrix} 1 \\ 1 \end{pmatrix}$

4. $\mathbf{x}' = \begin{pmatrix} 3 & -2 \\ 2 & -2 \end{pmatrix} \mathbf{x} + \begin{pmatrix} 1 \\ 2t \end{pmatrix} e^t, \qquad \mathbf{x}(0) = \begin{pmatrix} 1 \\ 0 \end{pmatrix}$

5. $\mathbf{x}' = \begin{pmatrix} -1 & -1 \\ -2 & -1 \end{pmatrix} \mathbf{x}, \qquad \mathbf{x}(0) = \begin{pmatrix} 1 \\ 0 \end{pmatrix}$

6. Consider the initial value problem

$$\mathbf{x}' = \begin{pmatrix} 2 & -2 \\ 4 & -2 \end{pmatrix} \mathbf{x} + \mathbf{g}(t), \qquad \mathbf{x}(0) = \begin{pmatrix} 1 \\ 0 \end{pmatrix}.$$

Find the solution of this problem if $\mathbf{g}^T = (g_1, g_2)$ is given by each of the following:

(a) $\mathbf{g}^T(t) = (\sin t, \cos t)$

(b) $\mathbf{g}^T(t) = (e^{-t}, 0)$

(c) $\mathbf{g}^T(t) = (1 - u_\pi(t), 0)$; see Section 6.3

(d) $\mathbf{g}^T(t) = (0, \delta(t - \pi))$; see Section 6.4

7. Consider the initial value problem

$$\mathbf{x}' = \begin{pmatrix} 1 & -5 \\ 2 & -5 \end{pmatrix} \mathbf{x} + \mathbf{g}(t), \qquad \mathbf{x}(0) = \begin{pmatrix} 0 \\ 1 \end{pmatrix}.$$

Find the solution of this problem if $\mathbf{g}^T = (g_1, g_2)$ is given by each of the following. The answer may be left in the form of an integral.

(a) $\mathbf{g}^T(t) = (\cos 2t, \sin 2t)$

(b) $\mathbf{g}^T(t) = (1 - u_\pi(t), 0)$

(c) $\mathbf{g}^T(t) = (0, e^{-t})$

In Problems 8 and 9 use the Laplace transform to solve the given initial value problem. Compare the Laplace transform method with the method of elimination (Section 7.2, Problems 13 and 15).

8. $x_1'' - 3x_1' + 2x_1 + x_2' - x_2 = 0$; $x_1(0) = 0$, $x_1'(0) = 1$
   $x_1' - 2x_1 + x_2' + x_2 = 0$; $x_2(0) = 0$

9. $x_1'' - 4x_1' + 4x_1 + 3x_2' = 1$; $x_1(0) = 1$, $x_1'(0) = 1$
   $x_1' - 2x_1 + x_2' + 2x_2 = 0$; $x_2(0) = 0$

10. Solve the example problem of this section by computing $-(\mathbf{A} - s\mathbf{I})^{-1}$ and then finding its inverse transform in order to obtain the fundamental matrix $\mathbf{\Phi}$. Show that this procedure leads to the same solution as given in the text.

REFERENCES

The books listed below are representative of many recent introductory books on matrices and linear algebra.

Cullen, C. G., *Matrices and Linear Transformations*, Addison-Wesley, Reading, Mass., 1966.

Schneider, H. and Barker, G. P., *Matrices and Linear Algebra*, Holt, Rinehart, and Winston, New York, 1968.

Shields, P. C., *Elementary Linear Algebra*, Worth, New York, 1968.

Stewart, F. M., *Introduction to Linear Algebra*, van Nostrand, Princeton, N.J., 1963.

Zelinsky, D., *A First Course in Linear Algebra*, Academic Press, New York, 1968.

Numerical Methods

8.1 INTRODUCTION

In this chapter we shall consider numerical methods by which we can construct, in tabular form, the solution of a given differential equation and initial conditions. For example, a table of values of e^x, which is the solution of the initial value problem

$$y' - y = 0, \qquad y(0) = 1,$$

would represent a numerical solution of this problem. We will primarily consider the first order differential equation

$$y' = f(x, y) \tag{1}$$

with the initial condition

$$y(x_0) = y_0. \tag{2}$$

We will also assume that the functions f and f_y are continuous in some rectangle in the xy plane including the point (x_0, y_0) so that, according to Theorem 2.2, there exists a unique solution $y = \phi(x)$ of the given problem in some interval about x_0. As we emphasized in Section 2.3, if Eq. (1) is nonlinear the interval about x_0 in which the solution ϕ exists may be difficult to determine, and may have no simple relationship to the function f. In all of our discussion of Eq. (1) we will assume that a unique solution satisfying the initial condition (2) exists on the interval of interest.

In some cases $f(x, y)$ is so simple that Eq. (1) can be integrated directly. However, in many engineering and scientific problems this is not the case, and it is natural to consider numerical procedures for obtaining an approximate solution of the problem. Even if Eq. (1) can be integrated directly, it may be more difficult to evaluate the analytic solution than to solve the original initial value problem numerically. For example, the analytic solution may be in the form of a complicated implicit relation $F(x, y) = 0$. Nevertheless the importance of analytic methods should not be underestimated. They provide valuable information about the existence, uniqueness, and qualitative behavior of solutions.

By a numerical procedure for solving the initial value problem given by Eqs. (1) and (2) is meant a procedure for constructing approximate values $y_0, y_1, y_2, \ldots, y_n, \ldots$ of the solution ϕ at the points $x_0 < x_1 < x_2 < \cdots < x_n < \cdots$; see Figure 8.1. More precisely, such a numerical procedure is referred to as a *discrete variable method* since we are replacing a problem involving continuous variables by one involving discrete variables.

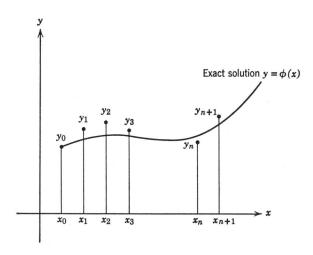

FIGURE 8.1

Our first concern is to determine y_1, knowing y_0 from the initial condition and $\phi'(x_0) = f(x_0, y_0)$ from the differential equation (1). Then knowing y_1 we determine y_2 and so on. In determining y_2 we can either use the same method as in going from x_0 to x_1, or we can use a different method which takes account of the fact that we know both y_0 at x_0 and y_1 at x_1.

In general, methods that require only a knowledge of y_n to determine y_{n+1} are known as *one-step*, or *stepwise*, or *starting methods*. Methods that make use of data at more than the previous point, say y_n, y_{n-1}, y_{n-2} to determine y_{n+1}, are known as *multistep* or *continuing methods*. Clearly, if a continuing method involving y_n and y_{n-1} is used, we must use a starting method (hence the name starting method) at the first step to determine y_1; the continuing method can then be used to determine y_2 and so on. On the other hand, a stepwise or starting method may be used for all of the computations. In Sections 8.2 through 8.7 we will discuss several stepwise methods, and in Section 8.8 we will discuss a typical multistep method. In Section 8.9 we will briefly consider systems of equations and higher order equations.

With the advent of high-speed electronic digital computers which can do tens or hundreds of thousands of computations per second, the use of numerical methods to solve initial value problems has become increasingly important. Many problems which are hopeless to solve analytically, and which would require years to solve by hand computation, can now be solved in a matter of minutes* using high-speed computers. On the other hand, not all questions about solving differential equations can be answered by using numerical methods. For example, it may be difficult to answer such questions as how a solution depends on y_0 (which is often of interest) or on other parameters in the problem. Such questions would be considerably simpler if the analytic solution were known.

Moreover, numerical methods raise serious questions of their own. In the first place, there is the question of convergence. That is, as the spacing between the points $x_0, x_1, x_2, \ldots, x_n, \ldots$ approaches zero, do the values of the numerical solution $y_1, y_2, \ldots, y_n, \ldots$ approach the values of the exact solution? There is also the question of estimating the error that is made in computing the values $y_1, y_2, \ldots, y_n$. This error arises from two sources: first, the formula used in the numerical method is only an approximate one, which causes a *formula error*, or *truncation error*, or *discretization error;* and second, it is possible to carry only a limited number of digits in any computation, which causes a *round-off error*. In Sections 8.3 and 8.7 we will discuss briefly the significance of formula and round-off errors.

The notation that will be used throughout this chapter is as follows. The exact solution of the initial value problem given by Eqs. (1) and (2) will be denoted by ϕ (or $y = \phi(x)$); then the value of the exact solution at x_n is $\phi(x_n)$. For a given numerical procedure the symbols y_n and $y'_n = f(x_n, y_n)$ will denote the approximate values of the exact solution and its derivative at the point x_n. Clearly $\phi(x_0) = y_0$, but in general $\phi(x_n) \neq y_n$ for $n \geq 1$. Similarly $\phi'(x_0) = y'_0$, but in general $\phi'(x_n) = f[x_n, \phi(x_n)]$ is not equal to $y'_n = f(x_n, y_n)$ for $n \geq 1$. Further, in all of the discussion we will use a uniform spacing or step size h on the x axis. Thus $x_1 = x_0 + h, x_2 = x_1 + h = x_0 + 2h$, and in general $x_n = x_0 + nh$.

Finally we would like to call the reader's attention to the following point. The first problem at the end of Sections 8.2 through 8.6 and 8.8 deals with the same initial value problem, and so do the second and third problems. By using one of these problems for practice work, it is possible to compare the accuracy and amount of labor required by the various numerical procedures.

8.2 THE EULER OR TANGENT LINE METHOD

One of the simplest stepwise methods of solving the initial value problem

$$y' = f(x, y), \qquad y(x_0) = y_0 \tag{1}$$

---

* That is, the actual computation may require only a few minutes, but much more time may be required to set up the problem for computation—perhaps weeks or even months. The preparation time depends strongly on whether this is the *first* such problem to be solved, or whether it falls into a class of problems for which a computational program is already available.

numerically is the tangent line method, which was first used by Euler. Since x_0 and y_0 are known, the slope of the tangent line to the solution at $x = x_0$, namely $\phi'(x_0) = f(x_0, y_0)$, is also known. Hence we can construct the tangent line to the solution at x_0, and then obtain an approximate value y_1 of $\phi(x_1)$ by moving along the tangent line to x_1; see Figure 8.2. Thus

$$y_1 = y_0 + \phi'(x_0)(x_1 - x_0)$$
$$= y_0 + f(x_0, y_0)(x_1 - x_0). \tag{2}$$

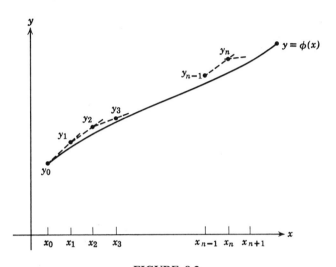

FIGURE 8.2

Once y_1 is determined we can compute $y_1' = f(x_1, y_1)$, which is an approximate value of $\phi'(x_1) = f[x_1, \phi(x_1)]$, the slope of the tangent line to the actual solution at x_1. Using this slope we obtain

$$y_2 = y_1 + y_1'(x_2 - x_1)$$
$$= y_1 + f(x_1, y_1)(x_2 - x_1),$$

and in general

$$y_{n+1} = y_n + f(x_n, y_n)(x_{n+1} - x_n).$$

If we assume that there is a uniform step size h between the points $x_0, x_1, x_2, \ldots$, then $x_{n+1} = x_n + h$ and we obtain the Euler formula

$$y_{n+1} = y_n + hf(x_n, y_n)$$
$$= y_n + hy_n', \qquad n = 0, 1, 2, \ldots. \tag{3}$$

The Euler formula is very simple to use, and in discussing the application of the formula it is possible to illustrate many of the important ideas in numerical methods for solving initial value problems. On the other hand it is not, in general, an accurate formula. Before discussing the Euler formula and methods of improving it, let us first illustrate how this result can be used to solve the initial value problem

$$y' = 1 - x + 4y, \tag{4}$$

$$y(0) = 1. \tag{5}$$

This example will be used throughout the rest of this chapter to illustrate and compare different numerical methods. While it is a very simple problem, it still illustrates the improvement that can be gained by using more accurate numerical procedures, and smaller step sizes h in the independent variable. Equation (4) is a linear first order equation, and it is easily verified that the solution satisfying the initial condition (5) is

$$y = \phi(x) = \tfrac{1}{4}x - \tfrac{3}{16} + \tfrac{19}{16}e^{4x}. \tag{6}$$

Example.   Using the Euler formula (3) and a step size $h = 0.1$, determine an approximate value of the solution $y = \phi(x)$ at $x = 0.2$ for the illustrative example $y' = 1 - x + 4y$, $y(0) = 1$.

First we compute $y'_0 = f(0, 1) = 5$; hence

$$y_1 = y_0 + hf(0, 1)$$
$$= 1 + (0.1)5 = 1.5.$$

Next

$$y_2 = y_1 + hf(x_1, y_1)$$
$$= 1.5 + (0.1)f(0.1, 1.5)$$
$$= 1.5 + (0.1)(1 - 0.1 + 6)$$
$$= 2.19.$$

This result should be compared with the exact value, which is $\phi(0.2) = 2.5053299$ correct through eight digits. The error is approximately $2.51 - 2.19 = 0.32$.

Normally, an error this large (a percentage error of 12%) is not acceptable.* A better result can be obtained by using a smaller step size. Thus using $h = 0.05$ and taking four steps to reach $x = 0.2$ gives the approximate value 2.3249 for $\phi(0.2)$ with a percentage error of 8%. A step size $h = 0.025$

---

* Lest the student be discouraged we emphasize again that we have purposely chosen an example which will illustrate the improvement to be gained by using more accurate procedures and/or a smaller step size h. On the other hand, the present example is extremely simple compared to what may be encountered in practice. It follows that in general more accurate procedures are used in constructing numerical solutions of initial value problems in engineering, physics, and other fields of applications.

leads to a value of 2.4080117 with a percentage error of 4%. Alternatively we can use more accurate procedures which will give satisfactory results without using a very small step size. For example, if the Runge-Kutta method, which is discussed in Section 8.6, is used with $h = 0.1$, the approximate value 2.5050062 for $\phi(0.2)$ is obtained. This result agrees with the exact solution through the first four figures. These points are discussed in more detail in the following sections. In this section we are primarily interested in developing a familiarity with the technique of using a numerical procedure to solve an initial value problem.

In carrying out the computations in any numerical procedure it is generally wise to construct a table in which to record, in a systematic way, the necessary results. Carrying out the computations in a systematic manner reduces the danger of making errors, and, if errors are made, makes it easier to locate and correct them. Further, if the table is set up correctly, the routine task of filling in the entries can be turned over to a person who knows nothing about differential equations. It is more likely that a high-speed electronic computer would be used. In this case we would draw a flow chart, and then write a program instructing the machine to carry out the calculations.

For the present problem we might set up Table 8.1, where we work from left to right along the rows. The student should check the table carefully so that he is satisfied he can compute $y_6, y_7, \ldots$ in a straightforward manner. In Table 8.1 the last two columns contain the values of the exact solution ϕ correct through eight digits and the differences $\phi(x_n) - y_n$. It should be evident from these results that for the present problem the Euler method with a step size of $h = 0.1$ is unsatisfactory.

A flow chart for the Euler method for solving the initial value problem (1) for $x_0 \leq x \leq x_0 + Nh$ is shown in Figure 8.3. Notice that in the flow chart the second box represents the calculation of $f(x_n, y_n)$ for given x_n and y_n. The first time this box is entered we have $x_n = x_0$ and $y_n = y_0$. In succeeding calculations the values of x_n and y_n are determined in the third box for entry into the second box until $x_n = x_0 + Nh$. When this happens the calculation stops.

In concluding this section we point out two alternate methods for deriving the Euler formula (3), which will suggest ways of obtaining better formulas and will also assist in our study of the error in using formula (3).

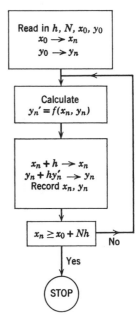

FIGURE 8.3 Flow chart for the Euler method.

TABLE 8.1 Numerical Solution of $y' = 1 - x + 4y$, $y(0) = 1$ Using the Euler Method with $h = 0.1$

n	x_n	y_n	$f(x_n, y_n) = 1 - x_n + 4y_n$	$hf(x_n, y_n)$	$y_{n+1} = y_n + hf(x_n, y_n)$	$\phi(x_{n+1})$	$\phi(x_{n+1}) - y_{n+1}$
0	0	1.0	5	0.5	1.5	1.6090418	0.1090418
1	0.1	1.5	6.9	0.69	2.19	2.5053299	0.3153299
2	0.2	2.19	9.56	0.956	3.146	3.8301388	0.6841388
3	0.3	3.146	13.284	1.3284	4.4744	5.7942260	1.3198260
4	0.4	4.4744	18.4976	1.84976	6.32416	8.7120041	2.3878441
5	0.5	6.32416				13.052522	
6	0.6					19.515518	
7	0.7						

First, since $y = \phi(x)$ is a solution of the initial value problem (1), on integrating from x_n to x_{n+1} we obtain

$$\int_{x_n}^{x_{n+1}} \phi'(x)\, dx = \int_{x_n}^{x_{n+1}} f[x, \phi(x)]\, dx$$

or

$$\phi(x_{n+1}) = \phi(x_n) + \int_{x_n}^{x_{n+1}} f[x, \phi(x)]\, dx. \tag{7}$$

If we approximate the integral in Eq. (7) by replacing $f[x, \phi(x)]$ by its value $f[x_n, \phi(x_n)]$ at $x = x_n$, as indicated in Figure 8.4, we obtain

$$\phi(x_{n+1}) \cong \phi(x_n) + f[x_n, \phi(x_n)](x_{n+1} - x_n)$$
$$= \phi(x_n) + hf[x_n, \phi(x_n)]. \tag{8}$$

Finally, to obtain an approximation y_{n+1} for $\phi(x_{n+1})$ we make a second approximation by replacing $\phi(x_n)$ by its approximate value y_n in Eq. (8).

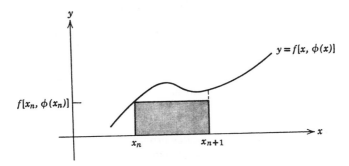

FIGURE 8.4

This gives the Euler formula $y_{n+1} = y_n + hf(x_n, y_n)$. A more accurate formula can be obtained by evaluating the integral more accurately. This is discussed in Section 8.4.

Second, suppose we assume that the solution $y = \phi(x)$ has a Taylor series about the point x_n. Then

$$\phi(x_n + h) = \phi(x_n) + \phi'(x_n)h + \phi''(x_n)\frac{h^2}{2!} + \cdots$$
$$= \phi(x_n) + f[x_n, \phi(x_n)]h + \phi''(x_n)\frac{h^2}{2!} + \cdots. \tag{9}$$

If the series is terminated after the first two terms, and $\phi(x_{n+1})$ and $\phi(x_n)$ are replaced by their approximate values y_{n+1} and y_n, we again obtain the Euler formula (3). If more terms in the series are retained, a more accurate formula is obtained. This is discussed in Section 8.5. Further, by using a Taylor series with a remainder it is possible to estimate the magnitude of the error in the formula. This is discussed in the next section.

PROBLEMS

In all computations, unless otherwise specified, retain four digits starting from the first nonzero digit. Thus, for example, the number 1.6846 *is to be rounded to* 1.685 *before further computation. If the fifth digit is* 5 *or more, round up.*

1. Consider the initial value problem

$$y' = 2y - 1, \qquad y(0) = 1.$$

(a) Determine the solution $y = \phi(x)$ and evaluate $\phi(x)$ at $x = 0.1, 0.2, 0.3$, and 0.4.

(b) Set up a table for determining y_n using the Euler formula (3). Take $h = 0.1$ and determine approximate values of $\phi(0.1)$, $\phi(0.2)$, $\phi(0.3)$, and $\phi(0.4)$. Compare your results with the exact values.

(c) Take $h = 0.05$ and determine approximate values of $\phi(0.05)$, $\phi(0.1)$, $\phi(0.15)$, and $\phi(0.2)$. Compare your results with the results of part (b) and the exact values. The differences in the results for $h = 0.1$ and $h = 0.05$ tend to indicate whether $h = 0.1$ is satisfactory, or whether a smaller step size must be used for this range of x.

2. Carry out parts (a), (b), and (c) of Problem 1 for the initial value problem

$$y' = \tfrac{1}{2} - x + 2y, \qquad y(0) = 1.$$

3. Consider the initial value problem

$$y' = x^2 + y^2, \qquad y(0) = 1.$$

The solution $y = \phi(x)$ of this initial value problem cannot be expressed in terms of elementary functions; hence the use of numerical procedures is more important in this case.

(a) Set up a table for determining y_n using the Euler formula (3). Take $h = 0.1$, and determine approximate values of $\phi(0.1)$, $\phi(0.2)$, $\phi(0.3)$, and $\phi(0.4)$.

(b) Take $h = 0.05$, and determine approximate values of $\phi(0.05)$, $\phi(0.1)$, $\phi(0.15)$, and $\phi(0.2)$. The differences in the results for $h = 0.1$ and $h = 0.05$ tend to indicate whether $h = 0.1$ is satisfactory, or whether a smaller step size should be used for this range of x.

4. Complete the rows corresponding to $n = 5$ and $n = 6$ in Table 8.1.

5. Using three terms in the Taylor series given in Eq. (9), and taking $h = 0.1$, determine approximate values of the solution of the illustrative example $y' = 1 - x + 4y$, $y(0) = 1$ at $x = 0.1$ and 0.2. Compare your results with those using the Euler method and the exact values.
Hint: If $y' = f(x, y)$, what is y''? See Section 8.5.

*6. It can be shown that under suitable conditions on f the numerical solution generated by the Euler method for the initial value problem $y' = f(x, y), y(x_0) = y_0$, converges to the exact solution as the step size h decreases. This is illustrated by the following example. Consider the initial value problem

$$y' = 1 - x + y, \qquad y(x_0) = y_0.$$

(a) Show that the exact solution is $y = \phi(x) = (y_0 - x_0)e^{(x-x_0)} + x$.

(b) Show, using the Euler formula, that

$$y_k = (1 + h)y_{k-1} + h - hx_{k-1}, \qquad k = 1, 2, \ldots.$$

(c) Noting that $y_1 = (1 + h)(y_0 - x_0) + x_1$ and using induction, show that

$$y_n = (1 + h)^n(y_0 - x_0) + x_n.$$

(d) Consider a fixed point $x > x_0$, and for a given n choose $h = (x - x_0)/n$. Then for any n, $x_n = x$. Substituting for h in the preceding formula and letting $n \to \infty$ gives the desired result. Note that $h \to 0$ as $n \to \infty$.
Hint: $\lim\limits_{n\to\infty} (1 + a/n)^n = e^a$.

*7. Using the technique discussed in Problem 6, show that the approximate solution obtained by the Euler method converges to the exact solution at any fixed point as $h \to 0$ for each of the following problems.

(a) $y' = y, \qquad y(0) = 1$

(b) $y' = 2y - 1, \qquad y(0) = 1$ *Hint:* $y_1 = (1 + 2h)/2 + 1/2$

(c) $y' = \frac{1}{2} - x + 2y, \qquad y(0) = 1$ *Hint:* $y_1 = (1 + 2h) + x_1/2$

8. An alternative procedure for constructing the solution $y = \phi(x)$ of the initial value problem $y' = f(x, y), y(x_0) = y_0$ is to use the method of *iteration*. Integrating the differential equation from x_0 to x gives

$$\phi(x) = y_0 + \int_{x_0}^{x} f[t, \phi(t)] \, dt. \tag{i}$$

If, on the right-hand side of Eq. (i), $\phi(t)$ is replaced by a particular function, the integral can be evaluated and a new function ϕ obtained. This suggests the iteration procedure

$$\phi_{n+1}(x) = y_0 + \int_{x_0}^{x} f[t, \phi_n(t)] \, dt.$$

It is this type of iteration procedure which is used to establish the existence of a solution for the given initial value problem under suitable conditions on $f(x, y)$. This was discussed in detail in Section 2.11. For actually computing $\phi(x)$ this procedure is generally unwieldy since it may be difficult, if not impossible, to evaluate the integral of $f[t, \phi_n(t)]$, $n = 0, 1, 2, \ldots$.

Taking $\phi_0(x) = 1$, determine $\phi_3(x)$ for each of the following initial value problems. Also compute $\phi_2(0.4)$ and $\phi_3(0.4)$ and compare with the result obtained using the Euler method.

(a) $y' = 2y - 1, \qquad y(0) = 1$

(b) $y' = \frac{1}{2} - x + 2y, \qquad y(0) = 1$

(c) $y' = x^2 + y^2, \qquad y(0) = 1;$ compute only $\phi_2(x)$

8.3 THE ERROR

As we mentioned in the introduction to this chapter there are two fundamental sources of error in solving the initial value problem

$$y' = f(x, y), \qquad y(x_0) = y_0 \tag{1}$$

by a numerical procedure such as the Euler method:

$$y_{n+1} = y_n + hf(x_n, y_n), \qquad x_n = x_0 + nh. \tag{2}$$

Let us first assume that our computing equipment is such that we can carry out all computations with complete accuracy, that is, we can retain an infinite number of decimal places. The difference between the exact solution $y = \phi(x)$ and the approximate solution of the initial value problem (1),

$$E_n = \phi(x_n) - y_n, \tag{3}$$

is known as the formula error, or the *accumulated formula error*. It arises from two causes: (i) at each step we use an approximate formula to determine y_{n+1}; (ii) the input data at each step do not agree with the exact solution, since in general $\phi(x_k)$ is not equal to y_k. If we assume that the input data are correct, the only error in going one step is that due to the use of an approximate formula, and is known as the *local formula error e_n*.

In practice, due to the limitations of all computing equipment, it is in general impossible to compute y_{n+1} exactly from the given formula. Thus we have a round-off error due to a lack of computational accuracy. For example, if a computing machine which can carry only eight digits is used, and y_0 is 1.017325842, the last two digits must be rounded off, which immediately introduces an error in the computation of y_1. Alternatively, if $f(x, y)$ should involve functions such as the logarithm or exponential we would have a round-off error in carrying out these operations. Just as for the formula error, it is possible to speak of the local round-off error and the accumulated round-off error. The *accumulated round-off error R_n* is defined as

$$R_n = y_n - Y_n, \tag{4}$$

where Y_n is the value *actually computed* by the given numerical procedure, for example the Euler formula (2)

The absolute value of the total error in computing $\phi(x_n)$ is given by

$$|\phi(x_n) - Y_n| = |\phi(x_n) - y_n + y_n - Y_n|. \tag{5}$$

Making use of the triangle inequality, $|a + b| \leq |a| + |b|$, we obtain from Eq. (5)

$$|\phi(x_n) - Y_n| \leq |\phi(x_n) - y_n| + |y_n - Y_n|$$
$$\leq |E_n| + |R_n|. \tag{6}$$

Thus the total error is bounded by the sum of the absolute values of the formula and round-off errors. For the numerical procedures discussed in this book it is possible to obtain useful estimates of the formula error. However, we shall limit our discussion primarily to the local formula error, which is somewhat simpler. The round-off error is clearly more random in nature. It depends on the type of computing machine used, the sequence in which the computations are carried out, the method of rounding off, etc. While an analysis of round-off error is beyond the scope of this introductory text, it is possible to say more about it than one would at first expect. See, for example, Henrici. Some of the dangers due to round-off error are discussed in Problems 10, 11, 12, and 13 and in Section 8.7.

Local Formula Error for the Euler Method. Let us assume that the solution $y = \phi(x)$ of the initial value problem (1) has a continuous second derivative in the interval of interest. This assumption is equivalent to assuming that f, f_x, and f_y are continuous in the region of interest. If f has these properties and if ϕ is a solution of the initial value problem (1), then

$$\phi'(x) = f[x, \phi(x)],$$

and by the chain rule

$$\phi''(x) = f_x[x, \phi(x)] + f_y[x, \phi(x)]\phi'(x)$$
$$= f_x[x, \phi(x)] + f_y[x, \phi(x)]f[x, \phi(x)]. \tag{7}$$

Since the right-hand side of this equation is continuous, ϕ'' is also continuous.

Then making use of a Taylor series with a remainder to expand ϕ about x_n, we obtain

$$\phi(x_n + h) = \phi(x_n) + \phi'(x_n)h + \tfrac{1}{2}\phi''(\bar{x}_n)h^2, \tag{8}$$

where $\bar{x}_n$ is some point in the interval $x_n < \bar{x}_n < x_n + h$. Subtracting Eq. (2) from Eq. (8), and noting that $\phi(x_n + h) = \phi(x_{n+1})$ and $\phi'(x_n) = f[x_n, \phi(x_n)]$, gives

$$\phi(x_{n+1}) - y_{n+1} = [\phi(x_n) - y_n] + h\{f[x_n, \phi(x_n)] - f(x_n, y_n)\}$$
$$+ \tfrac{1}{2}\phi''(\bar{x}_n)h^2. \tag{9}$$

To compute the local formula error we assume that the data at the nth step are correct, that is, $y_n = \phi(x_n)$. Then we immediately obtain from Eq. (9) that the local formula error e_{n+1} is

$$e_{n+1} = \phi(x_{n+1}) - y_{n+1} = \tfrac{1}{2}\phi''(\bar{x}_n)h^2. \tag{10}$$

Thus the local formula error for the Euler method is proportional to the square of the step size h and to the second derivative of ϕ. For the fixed interval $a = x_0 \leq x \leq b$, the absolute value of the local formula error for any step is bounded by $Mh^2/2$ where M is the maximum of $|\phi''(x)|$ on $a \leq x \leq b$. The primary difficulty in estimating the local formula error is that of obtaining an accurate estimate of M. However, notice that M is independent of h; hence, reducing h by a factor of $\frac{1}{2}$ reduces the error bound by a factor of $\frac{1}{4}$, and a reduction by a factor of $\frac{1}{10}$ in h reduces the error bound by a factor of $\frac{1}{100}$.

More meaningful than the local formula error is the accumulated formula error E_n. Nevertheless, an estimate of the local formula error does give a better understanding of the numerical procedure, and a means for comparing the accuracy of different numerical procedures. The analysis for estimating E_n is more difficult than that for e_n. However, knowing the local formula error we can make an *intuitive* estimate of the accumulated formula error at a fixed $\bar{x} > x_0$ as follows. Suppose we take n steps in going from x_0 to $\bar{x} = x_0 + nh$. In each step the error is at most $Mh^2/2$; thus the error in n steps is at most $nMh^2/2$. Noting that $n = (\bar{x} - x_0)/h$, we find that the accumulated formula error for the Euler method in going from x_0 to $\bar{x}$ is bounded by

$$n \frac{Mh^2}{2} = (\bar{x} - x_0) \frac{Mh}{2} . \tag{11}$$

While this argument is not correct, it is shown in Problem 5 that on any finite interval the accumulated formula error using the Euler method is no greater than a constant times h. Thus in going from x_0 to a fixed point $\bar{x}$, the accumulated formula error can be reduced by making the step size h smaller. Unfortunately, this is not the end of the story. If h is made too small, that is, too many steps are used in going from x_0 to $\bar{x}$, the accumulated round-off error may become more important than the accumulated formula error. In practice both sources of error must be considered and an "optimum" choice of h made so that neither is too large. This is discussed further in Section 8.7. A practical procedure for estimating the accumulated formula error, which requires computation with two different step sizes, is discussed in Problems 6 and 8.

As an example of how we can use the result (10) if we have a priori information about the solution of the given initial value problem consider the illustrative example

$$y' = 1 - x + 4y, \qquad y(0) = 1 \tag{12}$$

on the interval $0 \leq x \leq 1$. Let $y = \phi(x)$ be the solution of the initial value problem (12). Then $\phi'(x) = 1 - x + 4\phi(x)$, and

$$\phi''(x) = -1 + 4\phi'(x)$$
$$= -1 + 4[1 - x + 4\phi(x)]$$
$$= 3 - 4x + 16\phi(x).$$

From Eq. (10)

$$e_{n+1} = \frac{3 - 4\bar{x}_n + 16\phi(\bar{x}_n)}{2} h^2, \qquad x_n < \bar{x}_n < x_n + h. \tag{13}$$

Noting that $|3 - 4\bar{x}_n| \leq 3$ on $0 \leq x \leq 1$, a rough bound for e_{n+1} is given by

$$e_{n+1} \leq \left[\tfrac{3}{2} + 8 \max_{0 \leq x \leq 1} |\phi(x)| \right] h^2. \tag{14}$$

Since the right-hand side of Eq. (14) does not depend on n, this provides a uniform, although not necessarily an accurate, bound for the error at any step if a bound for $|\phi(x)|$ on $0 \leq x \leq 1$ is known. For the present problem, $\phi(x) = (4x - 3 + 19e^{4x})/16$. Substituting for $\phi(\bar{x}_n)$ in Eq. (13) gives

$$e_{n+1} = 19e^{4\bar{x}_n}h^2/2, \qquad x_n < \bar{x}_n < x_n + h. \tag{15}$$

The appearance of the factor 19 and the rapid growth of e^{4x} (at $x = 1$, $e^{4x} = 54.598$) explain why the results in the previous section with $h = 0.1$ were not very accurate. For example, the error in the first step is

$$e_1 = \phi(x_1) - y_1 = \frac{19e^{4\bar{x}_0}(0.01)}{2}, \qquad 0 < \bar{x}_0 < 0.1.$$

It is clear that e_1 is positive and, since $e^{4\bar{x}_0} < e^{0.4}$, we have

$$e_1 \leq \frac{19e^{0.4}(0.01)}{2} \simeq 0.142. \tag{16}$$

Note also that $e^{4\bar{x}_0} > 1$; hence $e_1 \geq 19(0.01)/2 = 0.095$. The actual error is 0.1090418. Notice also from Eq. (15) that the error becomes progressively worse with increasing x; this is clearly shown by the results in Table 8.1 of the last section. A similar computation for a bound for the local formula error in going from 0.4 to 0.5 gives

$$0.47 \simeq \frac{19e^{1.6}(0.01)}{2} \leq e_5 \leq \frac{19e^2(0.01)}{2} \simeq 0.7.$$

In practice, of course, we will not know the solution ϕ of the given initial value problem. However, if we have bounds on the functions f, f_x, and f_y we can obtain a bound on $|\phi''(x)|$, although not necessarily an accurate one, from Eq. (7). Then we can use Eq. (10) to estimate the local formula error. Even if we cannot find a useful bound for $|\phi''(x)|$, we still know that for the Euler method the local formula error and the accumulated formula error are bounded by a constant times h^2 and a constant times h, respectively.

We conclude this section with two practical comments which are based on experience.

1. One way of estimating whether the formula error is sufficiently small is, after completing the computations with a given h, to repeat the computations using a step size $h/2$. (See Problems 6 and 8.) If the changes are greater than we are willing to accept, then it is necessary to use a smaller step size or a more accurate numerical procedure or possibly both. More accurate

procedures are discussed in the following sections. The results* for the illustrative example using the Euler method with several different step sizes are given in Table 8.2. These results show that even with $h = 0.01$ it is not possible to obtain the first three digits correctly at $x = 0.10$. This could be expected without knowing the exact solution, since the results at $x = 0.1$ for $h = 0.025$ and $h = 0.01$ differ in the third digit.

2. It is possible to estimate the effect of the round-off error after completing the computations using a certain number of digits by repeating the computations carrying one or two more digits. Again, if the changes are more than we are willing to accept, it is necessary to retain more digits in the computations. Some examples of the difficulties that arise due to round-off errors are discussed in Problems 10 through 13.

TABLE 8.2 A Comparison of Results for the Numerical Solution of $y' = 1 - x + 4y, y(0) = 1$ Using the Euler Method for Different Step Sizes h

x	$h = 0.1$	$h = 0.05$	$h = 0.025$	$h = 0.01$	Exact
0	1.0000000	1.0000000	1.0000000	1.0000000	1.0000000
0.1	1.5000000	1.5475000	1.5761188	1.5952901	1.6090418
0.2	2.1900000	2.3249000	2.4080117	2.4644587	2.5053299
0.3	3.1460000	3.4333560	3.6143837	3.7390345	3.8301388
0.4	4.4744000	5.0185326	5.3690304	5.6137120	5.7942260
0.5	6.3241600	7.2901870	7.9264062	8.3766865	8.7120041
0.6	8.9038240	10.550369	11.659058	12.454558	13.052522
0.7	12.505354	15.234032	17.112430	18.478797	19.515518
0.8	17.537495	21.967506	25.085110	27.384136	29.144880
0.9	24.572493	31.652708	36.746308	40.554208	43.497903
1	34.411490	45.588400	53.807866	60.037126	64.897803

PROBLEMS

In Problems 1 and 2 estimate the local formula error in terms of the exact solution $y = \phi(x)$ if the Euler method is used. Obtain a bound for e_{n+1} in terms of x and $\phi(x)$ which is valid on the interval $0 \leq x \leq 1$. By using the exact solution obtain a more accurate error bound for e_{n+1}. For $h = 0.1$ compute a bound for e_1 and compare with the actual error at $x = 0.1$. Also compute a bound for the error e_4 in the fourth step.

1. $y' = 2y - 1$, $y(0) = 1$

2. $y' = \frac{1}{2} - x + 2y$, $y(0) = 1$

---

* In Table 8.2 as well as all others in this chapter except those in Section 8.7, all computations were carried out on an I.B.M. 1410 computer using twelve digits and the answers were rounded to eight digits.

3. Obtain a formula for the local formula error in terms of x and the exact solution ϕ if the Euler method is used for the initial value problem

$$y' = x^2 + y^2, \qquad y(0) = 1.$$

4. Consider the initial value problem

$$y' = \cos 5\pi x, \qquad y(0) = 1.$$

(a) Determine the exact solution $y = \phi(x)$, and draw a graph of $y = \phi(x) - 1$ for $0 \le x \le 1$. Use a scale for the ordinate so that $1/5\pi$ is about an inch.

(b) Determine approximate values of $\phi(x)$ at $x = 0.2$, 0.4, and 0.6 using the Euler method with $h = 0.2$. Draw a broken line graph for the approximate solution, and compare with the graph of the exact solution.

(c) Repeat the computations of part (b) for $0 \le x \le 0.4$, but take $h = 0.1$.

(d) Show by computing the local formula error that neither of these step sizes is sufficiently small. Determine a value of h which will insure that the local formula error is less than 0.05 throughout the interval $0 \le x \le 1$. That such a small value of h is required results from the fact that max $|\phi''(x)|$ is large; or, put in rough terms, that the solution is highly oscillatory.

*5. In this problem we will discuss the accumulated formula error associated with the Euler method for the initial value problem $y' = f(x, y)$, $y(x_0) = y_0$. Assuming that the functions f and f_y are continuous in a region R of the xy plane which includes the point (x_0, y_0) it can be shown that there exists a constant L such that $|f(x, y) - f(x, \tilde{y})| < L\,|y - \tilde{y}|$ where (x, y) and $(x, \tilde{y})$ are any two points in R with the same x coordinate. (See Problem 3 of Section 2.11.) Further we assume that f_x is continuous so that the solution ϕ has a continuous second derivative.

(a) Using Eq. (9) show that

$$|E_{n+1}| \le |E_n| + h\,|f[x_n, \phi(x_n)] - f(x_n, y_n)| + \tfrac{1}{2}h^2\,|\phi''(\bar{x}_n)| \le \alpha\,|E_n| + \beta h^2, \quad \text{(i)}$$

where $\alpha = 1 + hL$ and $\beta = \max |\phi''(x)|/2$ on $x_0 \le x \le x_n$.

(b) Accepting without proof that if $E_0 = 0$, and if $|E_n|$ satisfies Eq. (i), then $|E_n| \le \beta h^2(\alpha^n - 1)/(\alpha - 1)$ for $\alpha \ne 1$, show that

$$|E_n| \le \frac{(1 + hL)^n - 1}{L}\,\beta h. \qquad \text{(ii)}$$

Equation (ii) gives a bound for $|E_n|$ in terms of h, L, n, and β. Notice that for a fixed h, this error bound increases with increasing n; that is, the error bound increases with distance from the starting point x_0.

(c) Show that $(1 + hL)^n \le e^{nhL}$, and hence that

$$|E_n| \le \frac{e^{nhL} - 1}{L}\,\beta h$$

$$\le \frac{e^{(x_n - x_0)L} - 1}{L}\,\beta h.$$

For a fixed point $\bar{x} = x_0 + nh$ (that is, nh is constant and $h = (\bar{x} - x_0)/n$) this error bound is of the form constant times h and approaches zero as $h \to 0$. Also note that for $nhL = (\bar{x} - x_0)L$ small the right side of the above equation is approximately $nh^2\beta = (\bar{x} - x_0)\beta h$ which was obtained in Eq. (11) by an intuitive argument.

6. Let $y = \phi(x)$ be the solution of the initial value problem $y' = f(x, y)$, $y(x_0) = y_0$. As was discussed in the text (also see part (c) of Problem 5), the accumulated formula error using the Euler method to go from x_0 to a fixed point $\bar{x} = x_0 + nh$ is proportional to nh^2. Then $\phi(\bar{x}) = y_n(h) + C_1 nh^2$, where C_1 is an unknown constant. The dependence of y_n on h is indicated by writing $y_n(h)$. Next suppose that the computation is repeated using a step size $h/2$. Since $2n$ steps are now required to reach $\bar{x}$, we have $\phi(\bar{x}) = y_{2n}(h/2) + C_2(2n)(h/2)^2$. In general C_1 and C_2 will be different, but for small h this difference is small; and we will assume that it is permissible to set $C_2 = C_1$. By solving for nC_1 in terms of $y_n(h)$, $y_{2n}(h/2)$, and h, and then substituting for nC_2 in the second equation show that

$$\phi(\bar{x}) \cong y_{2n}(h/2) + [y_{2n}(h/2) - y_n(h)].$$

The quantity in brackets is a correction to the result using a step size $h/2$, and hence gives an *estimate of the error*.

By substituting for nC_1 in the first equation obtain an estimate of the error using a step size h. This procedure for computing a new approximation to $\phi(\bar{x})$ in terms of $y_n(h)$ and $y_{2n}(h/2)$ is often called Richardson's deferred approach to the limit.

7. Using the technique discussed in Problem 6 determine new estimates for the value of the exact solution $y = \phi(x)$ at $x = 0.2$, by making use of the results for $h = 0.2$ and $h = 0.1$ with the Euler method, for each of the following initial value problems. When possible compare your results with the values of the exact solution a $x = 0.2$.

(a) $y' = 2y$, $y(0) = 1$ (b) $y' = 2y - 1$, $y(0) = 1$

(c) $y' = \frac{1}{2} - x + 2y$, $y(0) = 1$ (d) $y' = x^2 + y^2$, $y(0) = 1$

8. A numerical method is said to have rth order accuracy if the error at $x_n = x_0 + nh$ is proportional to nh^{r+1}. Thus the Euler method has first order accuracy, since $r = 1$. Following the procedure of Problem 6, show that for a method with rth order accuracy an estimate of the error in $y_{2n}(h/2)$ is given by $[y_{2n}(h/2) - y_n(h)]/(2^r - 1)$. If the first digit affected by this quantity is the kth, it is reasonable to hope that the result is correct through $k - 1$ digits.

9. Consider the example problem $y' = 1 - x + 4y$, $y(0) = 1$. Following the method of Richardson's deferred approach to the limit (Problems 6 and 8), and using the approximate values of $\phi(1)$ for $h = 0.1, 0.05$, and 0.025 which are given in Table 8.2, obtain new estimates for $\phi(1)$ for

(a) $h = 0.1$ and $h = 0.05$ (b) $h = 0.05$ and $h = 0.025$

Compare your results with the value of the exact solution.

10. Using a step size $h = 0.05$ and the Euler method, but retaining only three digits throughout the computations, determine approximate values of the exact solution at $x = 0.05, 0.1, 0.15$, and 0.2 for each of the following initial value problems.

(a) $y' = 2y - 1$, $y(0) = 1$

(b) $y' = \frac{1}{2} - x + 2y$, $y(0) = 1$

(c) $y' = x^2 + y^2$, $y(0) = 1$

Compare your results with those using four digits which were obtained in the previous section. The small differences between some of those results rounded to three digits and the present results are due to round-off error. The round-off error would become important if the computation required many steps.

11. The following problem illustrates a danger which occurs because of round-off error when nearly equal numbers are subtracted, and the difference then multiplied by a large number. Evaluate the quantity

$$1000 \cdot \begin{vmatrix} 6.010 & 18.04 \\ 2.004 & 6.000 \end{vmatrix}$$

as follows.

(a) First round each entry in the determinant to two digits.
(b) First round each entry in the determinant to three digits.
(c) Retain all four digits. Compare the exact value with the results of parts (a) and (b).

12. The distributive law $a(b - c) = ab - ac$ does not hold, in general, if the products are rounded off to a smaller number of digits. To show this in a specific case take $a = 0.22$, $b = 3.19$, and $c = 2.17$. After each multiplication round off the last digit.

13. To obtain some idea of the possible dangers of small errors in the initial conditions, such as those due to round-off, consider the initial value problem

$$y' = x + y - 3, \qquad y(0) = 2.$$

(a) Show that the exact solution is $y = \phi_1(x) = 2 - x$.
(b) Suppose that in the initial condition a mistake is made and 2.001 is used instead of 2. Determine the solution $y = \phi_2(x)$ in this case, and compare the difference $\phi_2(x) - \phi_1(x)$ at $x = 1$ and as $x \to \infty$.

8.4 AN IMPROVED EULER METHOD

Consider the initial value problem

$$y' = f(x, y), \qquad y(x_0) = y_0. \tag{1}$$

Letting ϕ be the exact solution of the initial value problem (1), and integrating from x_n to x_{n+1}, as we did in Eq. (7) of Section 8.2, we obtain

$$\phi(x_{n+1}) = \phi(x_n) + \int_{x_n}^{x_{n+1}} f[x, \phi(x)] \, dx. \tag{2}$$

The Euler formula

$$y_{n+1} = y_n + hf(x_n, y_n) \tag{3}$$

was obtained by replacing $f[x, \phi(x)]$ in Eq. (2) by its approximate value $f(x_n, y_n)$ at the left-hand end point.

A more accurate formula can be obtained if the integrand in Eq. (2) is approximated by the average of its values at the two end points, namely,

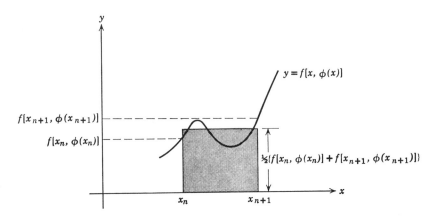

FIGURE 8.5

$\{f[x_n, \phi(x_n)] + f[x_{n+1}, \phi(x_{n+1})]\}/2$; see Figure 8.5. Further, we replace $\phi(x_n)$ and $\phi(x_{n+1})$ by their approximate values y_n and y_{n+1}. Then we obtain from Eq. (2)

$$y_{n+1} = y_n + \frac{f(x_n, y_n) + f(x_{n+1}, y_{n+1})}{2} h. \qquad (4)$$

Since the unknown y_{n+1} appears as one of the arguments of f on the right-hand side of Eq. (4), it will in general be fairly difficult to solve this equation for y_{n+1}. This difficulty can be overcome by replacing y_{n+1} on the right-hand side of Eq. (2) by the value obtained using the simple Euler formula (3). Thus

$$y_{n+1} = y_n + \frac{f(x_n, y_n) + f[x_n + h, y_n + hf(x_n, y_n)]}{2} h$$

$$= y_n + \frac{y_n' + f[x_n + h, y_n + hy_n']}{2} h, \qquad (5)$$

where x_{n+1} has been replaced by $x_n + h$.

Equation (5) gives a formula for computing y_{n+1}, the approximate value of $\phi(x_{n+1})$, in terms of the data at x_n. This formula is known as the *improved Euler formula* or the *Heun formula*. That Eq. (5) does represent an improvement over the Euler formula (2) rests on the fact that the local formula error in using Eq. (5) is proportional to h^3 while that for the Euler method is proportional to h^2. The error estimate for the improved Euler formula is established in Problem 4. It can also be shown that the accumulated formula error for the improved Euler formula is bounded by a constant times h^2. Note that this greater accuracy is achieved at the expense of more computational work, since it is now necessary to evaluate $f(x, y)$ twice in order to go from x_n to x_{n+1}.

TABLE 8.3 Numerical Solution of $y' = 1 - x + 4y$, $y(0) = 1$ Using the Improved Euler Method with $h = 0.1$

Table Instructions	A	B	$C = 1 - A + 4B$	$D = A + 0.1$	$E = B + 0.1C$	$F = 1 - D + 4E$	$G = C + F$	$H = (0.05)G$	$I = B + H$	
n	x_n	y_n	$y'_n = f(x_n, y_n)$	$x_n + h$	$y_n + hy'_n$	$f[x_n + h, y_n + hy'_n]$			y_{n+1}	$\phi(x_{n+1})$
0	0	1	5	0.1	1.5	6.9	11.9	0.595	1.595	1.6090418
1	0.1	1.595	7.280	0.2	2.323	10.092	17.372	0.8686	2.4636	2.5053299
2	0.2	2.4636	10.6544	0.3	3.52904	14.81616	25.47056	1.273528	3.737128	3.8301388
3	0.3									5.7942260
4	0.4									8.7120041
5										
6										

Example. To illustrate the use of the improved Euler formula (5) again consider the initial value problem

$$y' = 1 - x + 4y, \qquad y(0) = 1. \tag{6}$$

For the present problem $f(x, y) = 1 - x + 4y$; hence

$$y'_n = 1 - x_n + 4y_n,$$

and

$$f[x_n + h, y_n + hy'_n] = 1 - (x_n + h) + 4(y_n + hy'_n).$$

Using a step size $h = 0.1$ we set up Table 8.3. Note that a person who knows nothing about differential equations can complete this table simply by following the instructions in the row marked Table Instructions.*

A flow chart for the improved Euler method is similar to the one for the Euler method in Section 8.2. The main difference is that in the second and third boxes y'_n is replaced by $F(x_n, y_n)$, where $F(x_n, y_n) = \frac{1}{2}\{f(x_n, y_n) + f[x_n + h, y_n + hf(x_n, y_n)]\}$.

The results using the improved Euler method with $h = 0.1$ are not only better than those obtained with the Euler method for $h = 0.1$, but also better than those obtained with the Euler method for $h = 0.05$. This is clearly indicated by the results tabulated in Table 8.4. Thus even though more

TABLE 8.4 A Comparison of Results Using the Euler and Improved Euler Methods for $h = 0.1$ and $h = 0.05$ for the Initial Value Problem $y' = 1 - x + 4y$, $y(0) = 1$

	Euler		Improved Euler		
x	$h = 0.1$	$h = 0.05$	$h = 0.1$	$h = 0.05$	Exact
0	1.0000000	1.0000000	1.0000000	1.0000000	1.0000000
0.1	1.5000000	1.5475000	1.5950000	1.6049750	1.6090418
0.2	2.1900000	2.3249000	2.4636000	2.4932098	2.5053299
0.3	3.1460000	3.4333560	3.7371280	3.8030484	3.8301388
0.4	4.4744000	5.0185326	5.6099494	5.7404023	5.7942260
0.5	6.3241600	7.2901870	8.3697252	8.6117498	8.7120041
0.6	8.9038240	10.550369	12.442193	12.873253	13.052522
0.7	12.505354	15.234032	18.457446	19.203865	19.515518
0.8	17.537495	21.967506	27.348020	28.614138	29.144880
0.9	24.572493	31.652708	40.494070	42.608178	43.497903
1.0	34.411490	45.588400	59.938223	63.424698	64.897803

* An experienced person can reduce the number of entries since some results can be computed without recording the intermediate results. For example, it is not necessary to record G in computing H.

computations are required to use the improved Euler formula, substantially better results can be obtained with only half as many steps. The results using the improved Euler formula with $h = 0.05$ are also tabulated in Table 8.4. They are in fairly close agreement with the values of the exact solution, the percentage errors at $x = 0.5$ and $x = 1.0$ being 1.15% and 2.3% respectively.

PROBLEMS

In Problems 1 through 3 set up a table for use with the improved Euler method and determine approximate values of the exact solution at $x = 0.1, 0.2,$ and 0.3. Take $h = 0.1$. Compare your results with those obtained using the Euler method and the exact results (if available). Carry four digits in your computations.

1. $y' = 2y - 1,\qquad y(0) = 1$

2. $y' = \frac{1}{2} - x + 2y,\qquad y(0) = 1$

3. $y' = x^2 + y^2,\qquad y(0) = 1$

4. In this problem we will establish that the local formula error for the improved Euler formula is proportional to h^3. Assuming that the solution ϕ of the initial value problem $y' = f(x, y), y(x_0) = y_0$ has derivatives which are continuous through the third order (f has continuous second partial derivatives), it follows that

$$\phi(x_n + h) = \phi(x_n) + \phi'(x_n)h + \frac{\phi''(x_n)h^2}{2!} + \frac{\phi'''(\bar{x}_n)h^3}{3!},$$

where $x_n < \bar{x}_n < x_n + h$. Assume that $y_n = \phi(x_n)$.
   (a) Show that for y_{n+1} as given by Eq. (5)

$$e_{n+1} = \phi(x_{n+1}) - y_{n+1}$$

$$= \frac{\phi''(x_n)h - \{f[x_n + h, y_n + hf(x_n, y_n)] - f(x_n, y_n)\}}{2!}\, h + \frac{\phi'''(\bar{x}_n)h^3}{3!}. \qquad (i)$$

   (b) Making use of the fact that $\phi''(x) = f_x[x, \phi(x)] + f_y[x, \phi(x)]\phi'(x)$, and that the Taylor series with a remainder for a function of two variables (which we accept without proof) is

$$F(a + h, b + k) = F(a, b) + F_x(a, b)h + F_y(a, b)k$$

$$+ \frac{1}{2!}\,(h^2 F_{xx} + 2hk F_{xy} + k^2 F_{yy})\big|_{x=\xi, \, y=\eta},$$

where ξ lies between a and $a + h$ and η lies between b and $b + k$, show that the first term on the right-hand side of Eq. (i) is proportional to h^3 plus higher order terms. This is the desired result.
   (c) Show that if $f(x, y)$ is linear in x and y, then $e_{n+1} = \phi'''(\bar{x}_n)h^3/6$, where $x_n < \bar{x}_n < x_{n+1}$.
Hint: What are $f_{xx}, f_{xy},$ and f_{yy}?

5. Consider the improved Euler method for solving the initial value problem $y' = 1 - x + 4y$, $y(0) = 1$. Using the result of part (c) of Problem 4 and the exact solution of the initial value problem, determine e_{n+1} and a bound for the error at any step on $0 \le x \le 1$. Compare this error with the one obtained in the previous section, Eq. (15), using the Euler method. Also obtain a bound for e_1 for $h = 0.1$ and compare with Eq. (16) of the previous section.

6. Making use of the exact solution, determine e_{n+1} and a bound for e_{n+1} at any step on $0 \le x \le 1$ for the improved Euler method for each of the following initial value problems. Also obtain a bound for e_1 for $h = 0.1$ and compare with the similar estimate for the Euler method, and the actual error using the improved Euler method.

(a) $y' = 2y - 1$, $y(0) = 1$ (b) $y' = \frac{1}{2} - x + 2y$, $y(0) = 1$

7. The *modified Euler formula* for the initial value problem $y' = f(x, y)$, $y(x_0) = y_0$ is given by

$$y_{n+1} = y_n + hf[x_n + \tfrac{1}{2}h, y_n + \tfrac{1}{2}hf(x_n, y_n)].$$

Following the procedure outlined in Problem 4 show that the local formula error in the modified Euler formula is proportional to h^3.

8. Using the modified Euler formula with $h = 0.1$ compute approximate values of the exact solution at $x = 0.1, 0.2$, and 0.3 for each of the following initial value problems.

(a) $y' = 2y - 1$, $y(0) = 1$
(b) $y' = \frac{1}{2} - x + 2y$, $y(0) = 1$
(c) $y' = x^2 + y^2$, $y(0) = 1$

Where appropriate, compare your results with those obtained earlier.

8.5   THE THREE-TERM TAYLOR SERIES METHOD

We saw in Section 8.2 that the Euler formula $y_{n+1} = y_n + hf(x_n, y_n)$ for solving the initial value problem

$$y' = f(x, y) \tag{1}$$

and

$$y(x_0) = y_0 \tag{2}$$

can be derived by retaining the first two terms in the Taylor series for the solution $y = \phi(x)$ about the point $y = x_n$. A more accurate formula can be obtained by using the first three terms. Assuming that ϕ has at least three continuous derivatives in the interval of interest (f has continuous second partial derivatives) we have, using the Taylor series with a remainder,

$$\phi(x_n + h) = \phi(x_n) + \phi'(x_n)h + \phi''(x_n)\frac{h^2}{2!} + \phi'''(\bar{x}_n)\frac{h^3}{3!}, \tag{3}$$

where $\bar{x}_n$ is some point in the interval $x_n < \bar{x}_n < x_n + h$.

From Eq. (1)

$$\phi'(x_n) = f[x_n, \phi(x_n)]. \tag{4}$$

Further, $\phi''(x)$ can be computed from Eq. (1),

$$\phi''(x) = f_x[x, \phi(x)] + f_y[x, \phi(x)]\phi'(x). \tag{5}$$

Hence

$$\phi''(x_n) = f_x[x_n, \phi(x_n)] + f_y[x_n, \phi(x_n)]\phi'(x_n). \tag{6}$$

The three-term Taylor series formula is obtained by replacing $\phi(x_n)$ by its approximate value y_n in the formulas for $\phi'(x)$ and $\phi''(x)$ and then neglecting the term $\phi'''(\bar{x}_n)h^3/3!$ in Eq. (3). Thus we obtain

$$y_{n+1} = y_n + hy'_n + \frac{h^2}{2}\, y''_n, \tag{7}$$

where

$$y'_n = f(x_n, y_n), \tag{8}$$

and

$$y''_n = f_x(x_n, y_n) + f_y(x_n, y_n)y'_n. \tag{9}$$

It is trivial to show, assuming $\phi(x_n) = y_n$, that the local formula error e_{n+1} associated with formula (7) is

$$e_{n+1} = \phi(x_{n+1}) - y_{n+1} = \tfrac{1}{6}\phi'''(\bar{x}_n)h^3, \tag{10}$$

where $x_n < \bar{x}_n < x_n + h$. Thus the local formula error for the three-term Taylor series formula is proportional to h^3, just as for the improved Euler formula discussed in the previous section. Again it can also be shown that the accumulated formula error is no greater than a constant times h^2.

The three-term Taylor series formula requires the computation of $f_x(x, y)$ and $f_y(x, y)$, and then the evaluation of these functions as well as $f(x, y)$ at (x_n, y_n). In some problems it may be difficult, or fairly lengthy, to compute f_x and f_y. If this is the case, it is probably better to use a formula with comparable accuracy, such as the improved Euler formula, which does not require the partial derivatives f_x and f_y. In principle, four-term, or even higher, Taylor series formulas can be developed. However, such formulas involve even higher partial derivatives of f and are in general rather awkward to use.

Example.   For the illustrative example

$$y' = 1 - x + 4y, \qquad y(0) = 1$$

the three-term Taylor series method is fairly convenient. We have

$$f(x, y) = 1 - x + 4y,$$

$$f_x(x, y) = -1, \qquad f_y(x, y) = 4.$$

Hence

$$y'_n = 1 - x_n + 4y_n, \qquad y''_n = -1 + 4y'_n. \tag{11}$$

It follows from Eqs. (11) that $y_0' = 5$ and $y_0'' = 19$. Taking h equal to 0.1 and substituting in Eq. (7) gives

$$y_1 = 1 + (0.1)(5) + (0.005)(19)$$
$$= 1.595.$$

For the example problem the results using the three-term Taylor series method are identical, except for small differences due to round-off error, to those obtained using the improved Euler method. The reason for this is that when $f(x, y)$ is linear in x and y the two methods are identical. This can be shown by expanding the improved Euler formula about the point (x_n, y_n) and comparing with the three-term Taylor series formula. (See Problem 4 of Section 8.4. Note that the functions f_{xx}, f_{xy}, and f_{yy} are each zero.)

Thus the results given in Table 8.4 for the improved Euler method for $h = 0.1$ and $h = 0.05$ also apply for the three-term Taylor series method. On the other hand, if $f(x, y)$ is not linear in x and y the two methods will give slightly different results. For example, the results are different for the third of the exercise problems $y' = x^2 + y^2$, $y(0) = 1$.

PROBLEMS

In Problems 1 through 3 determine the three-term Taylor series formula for y_{n+1}. Set up an appropriate table and determine approximate values of the exact solution at $x = 0.1, 0.2$, and 0.3. Take $h = 0.1$. Compare your results with those obtained using the Euler method, the improved Euler method, and the exact results (if available). Carry four digits in your computations.

1. $y' = 2y - 1$, $y(0) = 1$
2. $y' = \frac{1}{2} - x + 2y$, $y(0) = 1$
3. $y' = x^2 + y^2$, $y(0) = 1$

4. For the illustrative problem $y' = 1 - x + 4y, y(0) = 1$, determine approximate values of the exact solution at $x = 0.2$ and 0.3, using the three-term Taylor series method. Take $h = 0.1$. Retain four digits. Check your results with those given in Table 8.4.

Problems 5, 6, and 7 deal with the initial value problem $y' = f(x, y), y(x_0) = y_0$. Let $y = \phi(x)$ be the exact solution.

5. Show that the local formula error e_{n+1} using the three-term Taylor series formula is given by $\phi'''(\bar{x}_n)h^3/6$, $x_n < \bar{x}_n < x_n + h$. Remember that in computing e_{n+1} it is assumed that $y_n = \phi(x_n)$.

6. Derive a four-term Taylor series formula for y_{n+1} in terms of $f(x, y)$ and its partial derivatives evaluated at (x_n, y_n). What is the local formula error?

7. Following the outline of Richardson's deferred approach to the limit (Problems 6 and 8 of Section 8.3) show that an estimate for $\phi(\bar{x})$, $\bar{x} = x_0 + nh$, in terms of $y_n(h)$ and $y_{2n}(h/2)$ computed using the three-term Taylor series method or

the improved Euler method is given by $y_{2n}(h/2) + [y_{2n}(h/2) - y_n(h)]/(2^2 - 1)$. For each of the following initial value problems compute approximate values of $\phi(0.2)$ using the three-term Taylor series formula with $h = 0.2$ and $h = 0.1$, and then use the above formula to determine a new estimate of $\phi(0.2)$. Compare with the exact result in (a) and (b). Also estimate the accuracy of the result using $h = 0.1$.

(a) $y' = 2y - 1$, $y(0) = 1$

(b) $y' = \frac{1}{2} - x + 2y$, $y(0) = 1$

(c) $y' = x^2 + y^2$, $y(0) = 1$

8. Consider the initial value problem $y' = 1 - x + 4y$, $y(0) = 1$. Using the approximate results for $\phi(1)$ obtained by the improved Euler method for $h = 0.1$ and $h = 0.05$ (see Table 8.4) and the procedure discussed in Problem 7 (or Problems 6 and 8 of Section 8.3), determine a new estimate of $\phi(1)$. Compare this result with the value of the exact solution.

8.6 THE RUNGE-KUTTA METHOD

Again consider the initial value problem

$$y' = f(x, y) \tag{1}$$

with

$$y(x_0) = y_0. \tag{2}$$

In the previous section we developed a three-term Taylor series formula which involved the functions f_x and f_y. Unfortunately, higher order Taylor series formulas rapidly become unwieldy because of the higher partial derivatives of f that must be computed.

However, it is possible to develop formulas which are equivalent to third, fourth, fifth, or even higher order Taylor series formulas and which do not involve partial derivatives of f. By equivalent numerical procedure we mean that the local formula errors are each proportional to the same power of h plus (possibly different) higher order terms. The development of these formulas started with the work of Runge (1856–1927) in 1895 and was continued by Kutta (1867–1944) in 1901. The classical Runge-Kutta formula is one which is equivalent to a five-term Taylor formula*

$$y_{n+1} = y_n + hy_n' + \frac{h^2}{2!} y_n'' + \frac{h^3}{3!} y_n''' + \frac{h^4}{4!} y_n^{iv}. \tag{3}$$

The Runge-Kutta formula involves a weighted average of values of $f(x, y)$ taken at different points in the interval $x_n \leq x \leq x_{n+1}$. It is given by

$$y_{n+1} = y_n + \frac{h}{6} (k_{n1} + 2k_{n2} + 2k_{n3} + k_{n4}), \tag{4}$$

*The numbers y_n'', y_n''', and y_n^{iv} are obtained by successively differentiating Eq. (1), and then evaluating at (x_n, y_n). See Eq. (9) of Section 8.5.

where

$$k_{n1} = f(x_n, y_n), \tag{5a}$$

$$k_{n2} = f(x_n + \tfrac{1}{2}h, y_n + \tfrac{1}{2}hk_{n1}), \tag{5b}$$

$$k_{n3} = f(x_n + \tfrac{1}{2}h, y_n + \tfrac{1}{2}hk_{n2}), \tag{5c}$$

$$k_{n4} = f(x_n + h, y_n + hk_{n3}). \tag{5d}$$

The sum $(k_{n1} + 2k_{n2} + 2k_{n3} + k_{n4})/6$ can be interpreted as an average slope. Note that k_{n1} is the slope at the left-hand end of the interval, k_{n2} is the slope at the midpoint using the Euler formula to go from x_n to $x_n + h/2$, k_{n3} is a second approximation to the slope at the midpoint, and finally k_{n4} is the slope at $x_n + h$ using the Euler formula and the slope k_{n3} to go from x_n to $x_n + h$.

While in principle it is not too difficult to show that Eqs. (3) and (4) differ by terms that are proportional to h^5, the algebra is extremely lengthy. Thus we will accept the fact that the local formula error in using Eq. (4) is proportional to h^5 and that the accumulated formula error is at most a constant times h^4. A derivation of a Runge-Kutta formula that is equivalent to the three-term Taylor series formula is given in Problem 5.

Clearly the Runge-Kutta formula, Eqs. (4) and (5), is more complicated than any of the formulas which have been discussed previously. On the other hand, it should be remembered that this is a very accurate formula (halving the step size reduces the local formula error by the factor $\tfrac{1}{32}$); and further, it is not necessary to compute any partial derivatives of f. We also note that if f does not depend on y, then

$$k_{n1} = f(x_n), \qquad k_{n2} = k_{n3} = f(x_n + \tfrac{1}{2}h), \qquad k_{n4} = f(x_n + h),$$

and Eq. (4) is identical with that obtained by using Simpson's (1710–1761) rule (see Problem 6) to evaluate the integral of $y' = f(x)$:

$$\int_{y_n}^{y_{n+1}} dy = \int_{x_n}^{x_n+h} f(x)\, dx$$

or

$$y_{n+1} - y_n = \frac{h}{6}\left[f(x_n) + 4f(x_n + \tfrac{1}{2}h) + f(x_n + h)\right].$$

The fact that Simpson's rule has an error which is proportional to h^5 is in agreement with the earlier comment concerning the error in the Runge-Kutta formula.

The Runge-Kutta formula, Eqs. (4) and (5), is one of the most widely used and most successful of all one-step formulas.

Example.   Using the Runge-Kutta method compute an approximate value of the exact solution $y = \phi(x)$ at $x = 0.2$ for the illustrative initial value problem

$$y' = 1 - x + 4y, \qquad y(0) = 1.$$

Taking $h = 0.2$ we have

$$k_{01} = f(0, 1) = 5; \qquad\qquad hk_{01} = 1.0$$
$$k_{02} = f(0 + 0.1, 1 + 0.5) = 6.9; \qquad hk_{02} = 1.38$$
$$k_{03} = f(0 + 0.1, 1 + 0.69) = 7.66; \qquad hk_{03} = 1.532$$
$$k_{04} = f(0 + 0.2, 1 + 1.532) = 10.928.$$

Thus

$$y_1 = 1 + \frac{0.2}{6} \, [5 + 2(6.9) + 2(7.66) + 10.928]$$

$$= 1 + 1.5016 = 2.5016.$$

The exact value of $\phi(0.2)$ is 2.5053299. Hence the Runge-Kutta method with a step size of $h = 0.2$ gives a better result than the Euler method (2.19) with $h = 0.1$, or the improved Euler method (2.4636) with $h = 0.1$.

A tabulation of the results for the illustrative example for the different methods which have been discussed is given in Table 8.5. The results for the three-term Taylor method are omitted since they are identical with those for the improved Euler method. The accuracy of the Runge-Kutta method for the present problem can be seen by comparing the approximate values of $\phi(1)$ using different methods and different step sizes. This is done in Table 8.6. Note that the results for the Runge-Kutta method with $h = 0.1$ are better than the results with either of the other methods with $h = 0.01$, a hundred steps compared to ten steps—actually a hundred evaluations of $f(x, y)$ compared to forty!

TABLE 8.5 Comparison of Results for the Numerical Solution of the Initial Value Problem $y' = 1 - x + 4y, y(0) = 1$

	Euler	Improved Euler	Runge-Kutta		Exact
x	$h = 0.1$	$h = 0.1$	$h = 0.2$	$h = 0.1$	
0	1.0000000	1.0000000	1.0000000	1.0000000	1.0000000
0.1	1.5000000	1.5950000		1.6089333	1.6090418
0.2	2.1900000	2.4636000	2.5016000	2.5050062	2.5053299
0.3	3.1460000	3.7371280		3.8294145	3.8301388
0.4	4.4774000	5.6099494	5.7776358	5.7927853	5.7942260
0.5	6.3241600	8.3697252		8.7093175	8.7120041
0.6	8.9038240	12.442193	12.997178	13.047713	13.052522
0.7	12.505354	18.457446		19.507148	19.515518
0.8	17.537495	27.348020	28.980768	29.130609	29.144880
0.9	24.572493	40.494070		43.473954	43.497903
1.0	34.411490	59.938223	64.441579	64.858107	64.897803

TABLE 8.6 Comparison of Results Using Different Numerical Procedures and Different Step Sizes for the Value at $x = 1$ of the Solution of the Initial Value Problem $y' = 1 - x + 4y, y(0) = 1$

h	Euler	Improved Euler	Runge-Kutta	Exact
0.2			64.441579	64.897803
0.1	34.411490	59.938223	64.858107	64.897803
0.05	45.588400	63.424698	64.894875	64.897803
0.025	53.807866	64.497931	64.897604	64.897803
0.01	60.037126	64.830722	64.897798	64.897803

PROBLEMS

In Problems 1 through 3 set up a table for use with the Runge-Kutta method and determine approximate values of the exact solution at $x = 0.2$ and 0.4. Take $h = 0.2$. Compare your results with those of other methods and the exact results (if available). Carry four digits in your computations.

1. $y' = 2y - 1$, $\qquad y(0) = 1$
2. $y' = \frac{1}{2} - x + 2y$, $\qquad y(0) = 1$
3. $y' = x^2 + y^2$, $\qquad y(0) = 1$

4. Compute an approximate value of the exact solution $y = \phi(x)$ at $x = 0.4$ for the illustrative example $y' = 1 - x + 4y$, $y(0) = 1$. Use $h = 0.2$, and the approximate value of $\phi(0.2)$ given in the example in the text. Compare your result with the value given in Table 8.5.

*5. Consider the initial value problem $y' = f(x, y)$, $y(x_0) = y_0$. The corresponding three-term Taylor series formula is

$$y_{n+1} = y_n + hu'_n + \frac{h^2}{2} y''_n. \tag{i}$$

For the moment consider the formula

$$y_{n+1} = y_n + h\{af(x_n, y_n) + bf[x_n + \alpha h, y_n + \beta h f(x_n, y_n)]\}, \tag{ii}$$

where a, b, α, and β are arbitrary.

(a) Show by expanding the right-hand side of this formula about the point (x_n, y_n) that for $a + b = 1$, $b\alpha = \frac{1}{2}$, and $b\beta = \frac{1}{2}$ the difference between formulas (i) and (ii) is proportional to h^3.
Hint: Use the Taylor series expansion for a function of two variables given in Problem 4 of Section 8.4.

(b) Show that the equations for a, b, α, and β have the infinity of solutions $a = 1 - \lambda$, $b = \lambda$, and $\alpha = \beta = 1/2\lambda$, $\lambda \neq 0$.

(c) For $\lambda = \frac{1}{2}$, show that Eq. (ii) reduces to the improved Euler formula given in Section 8.4.

(d) For $\lambda = 1$, show that Eq. (ii) reduces to the modified Euler formula given in Problem 7 of Section 8.4.

6. To derive Simpson's rule for the approximate value of the integral of $f(x)$ from $x = 0$ to $x = h$, first show that

$$\int_0^h (Ax^2 + Bx + C)\, dx = \frac{Ah^3}{3} + \frac{Bh^2}{2} + Ch.$$

Next choose the constants A, B, and C so that the parabola $Ax^2 + Bx + C$ passes through the points $[0, f(0)]$, $[h/2, f(h/2)]$, and $[h, f(h)]$. Using this polynomial to represent $f(x)$ approximately on the interval $0 \leq x \leq h$, substitute for A, B, and C in the above formula to obtain

$$\int_0^h f(x)\, dx \cong \frac{h}{6}\left[f(0) + 4f\left(\frac{h}{2}\right) + f(h)\right].$$

It can be shown that the error in using this formula is proportional to h^5.

7. Following the outline of Richardson's deferred approach to the limit (Problems 6 and 8 of Section 8.3), show that for the initial value problem $y' = f(x, y)$, $y(x_0) = y_0$ an estimate for $\phi(\bar{x})$, $\bar{x} = x_0 + nh$, in terms of $y_n(h)$ and $y_{2n}(h/2)$ for the Runge-Kutta method is given by $y_{2n}(h/2) + [y_{2n}(h/2) - y_n(h)]/(2^4 - 1)$. Consider the illustrative initial value problem, $y' = 1 - x + 4y$, $y(0) = 1$. Using the approximate values of $\phi(1)$ obtained by the Runge-Kutta method with $h = 0.2$ and $h = 0.1$ (Table 8.5) and the above formula, obtain a new estimate for $\phi(1)$. Compare your result with the exact solution.

8.7   SOME DIFFICULTIES WITH NUMERICAL METHODS

In Section 8.3 we discussed some ideas related to the errors that can occur in a numerical solution of the initial value problem

$$y' = f(x, y), \qquad y(x_0) = y_0. \tag{1}$$

In this section we will continue that discussion and also point out several more subtle difficulties that can arise. The points that we wish to make are fairly difficult to treat in detail at this level, and we will be content to illustrate them by means of examples.

First, recall that for the Euler method we showed that the local formula error is proportional to h^2 and that the accumulated formula error is at most a constant times h. Although we will not prove it, it is true in general that if the local formula error is proportional to h^p then the accumulated formula error is bounded by a constant times h^{p-1}. To achieve high accuracy we normally use a numerical procedure for which p is large (for the Runge-Kutta method $p = 5$). As p increases, the formula used in computing y_{n+1} normally becomes more complicated, and hence more calculations are required at each step; however, this is not a serious problem when using a high-speed computer unless $f(x, y)$ is very complicated.

If the step size h is decreased, the accumulated formula error is decreased by the same factor raised to the power $p - 1$. However, as we mentioned in Section 8.3, if h is too small, too many steps will be required to cover a fixed interval, and the accumulated round-off error may be larger than the accumulated formula error. This is illustrated by solving our example problem

$$y' = 1 - x + 4y, \qquad y(0) = 1 \tag{2}$$

on the interval $0 \leq x \leq 1$ using the Runge-Kutta method* with different step sizes h. In Table 8.7 the difference between the value of the exact solution and the computed value at $x = 1$ is shown for several values of h. Notice that initially the error decreases as h is decreased to about 0.025 to 0.02 (N, the number of steps is increased to about 40 to 50), but then begins to increase with decreasing h. This is the result of the accumulated round-off error. It is not possible to name an optimum value of N, since for values of N from about 40 to 55 both the accumulated formula error and the accumulated round-off error are probably affecting the last two significant digits and the small error is oscillatory.

TABLE 8.7 A Comparison of the Error at $x = 1$ Using Different Step Sizes and the Runge-Kutta Method for the Initial Value Problem $y' = 1 - x + 4y, y(0) = 1$

$N = 1/h$	h	$(-1) \times$ Error at $x = 1$
10	0.1	0.04008
20	0.05	0.00336
30	0.03333333	0.00114
40	0.025	0.00078
50	0.02	0.00089
60	0.01666667	0.00101
80	0.0125	0.00111
160	0.00625	0.00212
320	0.003125	0.00357
640	0.0015625	0.00731
1280	0.00078125	0.01567

As a second example of the types of difficulties that can arise when we use numerical procedures carelessly, consider the problem of determining the solution $y = \phi(x)$ of

$$y' = x^2 + y^2, \qquad y(0) = 1. \tag{3}$$

This is a nonlinear equation, and the existence and uniqueness theorem 2.2 guarantees only that there is a solution in *some* interval about $x = 0$. Suppose

* The calculations in this section were carried out on an I.B.M. 360-50 computer with seven-digit precision. To obtain all of the results given in Table 8.7 required a computing time of 55.72 seconds!

we try to compute a solution of the initial value problem on the interval $0 \leq x \leq 1$ using different numerical procedures.

If we use an Euler method with $h = 0.1$, 0.05, and 0.01, we find the following approximate values at $x = 1$: 7.189500, 12.32054, and 90.68743, respectively. The large differences among the computed values are convincing evidence that we should use a more accurate numerical procedure—the Runge-Kutta method, for example. Using the Runge-Kutta method with $h = 0.1$ we find the approximate value 735.0004 at $x = 1$, which is quite different from those obtained using the Euler method. If we were naive and stopped now, we would make a serious mistake. Repeating the calculations using step sizes of $h = 0.05$ and $h = 0.01$ we obtain the interesting information listed in Table 8.8.

TABLE 8.8 Calculation of the Solution of the Initial Value Problem $y' = x^2 + y^2$, $y(0) = 1$ Using the Runge-Kutta Method

h	$x = 0.90$	$x = 1.0$
0.1	14.02158	735.0004
0.05	14.27042	1.755613×10^4
0.01	14.30200	$> 10^{15}$

While the values at $x = 0.90$ are reasonable and we might well believe that the exact solution has a value of about 14.3 at $x = 0.90$, it is clear that something strange is happening between $x = 0.9$ and $x = 1.0$. To help determine what is happening let us turn to some analytical approximations to the solution of the initial value problem (3). Note that on $0 \leq x \leq 1$,

$$y^2 \leq x^2 + y^2 \leq 1 + y^2. \tag{4}$$

Thus the solution $y = \phi_1(x)$ of

$$y' = 1 + y^2, \qquad y(0) = 1 \tag{5}$$

and the solution $y = \phi_2(x)$ of

$$y' = y^2, \qquad y(0) = 1 \tag{6}$$

grow more rapidly and less rapidly, respectively, than the solution $y = \phi(x)$ of the original problem. Since all of these solutions pass through the same initial point, $\phi_2(x) \leq \phi(x) \leq \phi_1(x)$. The important thing to note is that we *can solve* Eqs. (5) and (6) for ϕ_1 and ϕ_2 by separation of variables. We find that

$$\phi_1(x) = \tan\left(x + \frac{\pi}{4}\right), \qquad \phi_2(x) = \frac{1}{1 - x}. \tag{7}$$

Thus $\phi_2(x) \to \infty$ as $x \to 1$ and $\phi_1(x) \to \infty$ as $x \to \pi/4 \cong 0.785$. These calculations show that the solution of the original initial value problem must become unbounded somewhere between $x \cong 0.785$ and $x = 1$. We now know that the problem (3) has no solution on the entire interval $0 \le x \le 1$.

However, our numerical calculations suggest that we can go beyond $x = 0.785$ and probably beyond $x = 0.9$. Assuming that the solution of the initial value problem exists at $x = 0.9$ and has the value 14.3, we can obtain a more accurate appraisal of what happens for larger x by considering the initial value problems (5) and (6) with $y(0) = 1$ replaced by $y(0.9) = 14.3$. Then we obtain

$$\phi_1(x) = \tan{(x + 0.6010)}, \qquad \phi_2(x) = \frac{1}{0.9699 - x} \qquad (8)$$

where only four decimal places have been kept. Thus $\phi_1(x) \to \infty$ as $x \to \pi/2 - 0.6010 \cong 0.9698$ and $\phi_2(x) \to \infty$ as $x \to 0.9699$. We conclude that the solution of the initial value problem (3) becomes unbounded near $x = 0.97$. We cannot be more precise than this because the initial condition $y(0.9) = 14.3$ is only approximate. This example illustrates the sort of information that can be obtained by a judicious combination of analytical and numerical work.

As a final example, consider the problem of determining two linearly independent solutions of the second order linear equation

$$y'' - 100y = 0 \qquad (9)$$

for $x > 0$. The generalization of numerical techniques for first order equations to higher order equations or to systems of equations is discussed in Section 8.9, but that is not needed for the present discussion. Two linearly independent solutions of Eq. (9) are $\phi_1(x) = \cosh{10x}$ and $\phi_2(x) = \sinh{10x}$. The solution $\phi_1(x) = \cosh{10x}$ is generated by the initial conditions $\phi_1(0) = 1$, $\phi_1'(0) = 0$; the solution $\phi_2(x) = \sinh{10x}$ is generated by the initial conditions $\phi_2(0) = 0$, $\phi_2'(0) = 10$. While analytically we can tell the difference between $\cosh{10x}$ and $\sinh{10x}$, for large x we have $\cosh{10x} \sim e^{10x}/2$ and $\sinh{10x} \sim e^{10x}/2$ and numerically these two functions look exactly the same if only a fixed number of digits are retained. For example, correct to eight significant figures,

$$\sinh 10 = \cosh 10 = 11{,}013.233.$$

If the calculations are carried out on a machine that carries only 7 digits the two solutions ϕ_1 and ϕ_2 are identical at $x = 1$ and indeed for all $x > 1$! Thus, while the solutions are linearly independent, because we can retain only a finite number of digits, their numerical tabulation would show that they are the same. We call this phenomenon *numerical dependence*. It is one of the important and difficult problems always encountered when we are solving a second or higher order equation which has at least one solution that grows very rapidly.

For the present problem we can partially circumvent this difficulty by computing instead of sinh $10x$ and cosh $10x$ the linearly independent solutions $\phi_3(x) = e^{10x}$ and $\phi_4(x) = e^{-10x}$ corresponding to the initial conditions $\phi_3(0) = 1$, $\phi_3'(0) = 10$ and $\phi_4(0) = 1$, $\phi_4'(0) = -10$, respectively. The solution ϕ_3 grows exponentially while ϕ_4 decays exponentially. Even so we will encounter difficulty in calculating ϕ_4 correctly if the interval is large. The reason is that at each step of the calculation for ϕ_4 we will introduce formula and round-off errors. Thus at any point x_n the data to be used in going to the next point are not precisely the values of $\phi_4(x_n)$ and $\phi_4'(x_n)$. The solution of the initial value problem with these data at x_n will involve not only e^{-10x} but also e^{10x}. Because the error in the data at x_n is small, the latter function will appear with a very small coefficient. Nevertheless, since e^{-10x} tends to zero and e^{10x} grows very rapidly, the latter will eventually dominate and the calculated solution will be simply a multiple of $e^{10x} = \phi_3(x)$.

Another problem that must be investigated for each numerical procedure is the convergence of the approximate solution to the exact solution as h tends to zero. While it does not occur for the one-step methods discussed in the previous sections there is the following danger when using multistep procedures, such as the Milne method discussed in the next section. It can happen that the numerical formula for y_n, which will involve y_{n-1} and y_{n-2}, etc., may have growing solutions that do not correspond to solutions of the original differential equation. Roughly speaking, the formula for y_n may admit extraneous solutions that are not really present in the original problem. If these solutions grow rather than decay they will cause difficulty.

Other practical problems, which the numerical analyst must often face, are how to compute solutions of a differential equation in the neighborhood of a regular singular point and how to calculate numerically the solution of a differential equation on an *unbounded* interval. Such problems generally require a combination of analytical and numerical work.

8.8 A MULTISTEP METHOD

In the previous sections we have considered one-step or starting methods for solving numerically the initial value problem

$$y' = f(x, y), \qquad y(x_0) = y_0. \tag{1}$$

Once approximate values of the exact solution $y = \phi(x)$ have been obtained at a few points beyond x_0, it is natural to ask whether we can make use of some of this information, rather than just the value at the last point, in order to obtain the value of ϕ at the next point. Specifically, if y_1 at x_1, y_2 at $x_2, \ldots, y_n$ at x_n are known, how can we use this information to determine y_{n+1} at x_{n+1}?

One of the best of the multistep or continuing methods is the Milne (1890–   ) method which makes use of information at the points x_n, x_{n-1},

x_{n-2}, and x_{n-3} in order to determine y_{n+1}. Before the Milne method can be used, it is necessary to compute y_1, y_2, and y_3 by some starting method such as the Runge-Kutta method—the starting method should be as accurate as the continuing method. We will briefly sketch the development of the Milne multistep method.

Suppose we integrate $\phi'(x)$ from x_{n-3} to x_{n+1}; then

$$\phi(x_{n+1}) - \phi(x_{n-3}) = \int_{x_{n-3}}^{x_{n+1}} \phi'(x)\, dx. \tag{2}$$

Assuming that $\phi(x_{n-3})$, $\phi(x_{n-2})$, $\phi(x_{n-1})$, and $\phi(x_n)$ are known, $\phi'(x_{n-3})$, ..., $\phi'(x_n)$ can be computed from Eq. (1). Next we approximate $\phi'(x)$ by a polynomial of degree three that passes through the four points $[x_{n-3}, \phi'(x_{n-3})]$, $[x_{n-2}, \phi'(x_{n-2})]$, $[x_{n-1}, \phi'(x_{n-1})]$, and $[x_n, \phi'(x_n)]$. It can be proved that this can always be done, and further that the polynomial is unique. This polynomial is called an *interpolation polynomial* since it provides us with an approximate formula* for $\phi'(x)$ at points other than the original points x_{n-3}, x_{n-2}, x_{n-1}, and x_n. Substituting this interpolation polynomial for $\phi'(x)$ in Eq. (2), evaluating the integral, and replacing $\phi(x_{n-3})$, ..., $\phi(x_{n+1})$ by their approximate values y_{n-3}, ..., y_{n+1} gives the multistep formula

$$y_{n+1} = y_{n-3} + \frac{4h}{3}(2y'_n - y'_{n-1} + 2y'_{n-2}). \tag{3}$$

The details of the derivation of Eq. (3) that have been omitted are the determination of the polynomial of degree three that passes through the points (x_{n-3}, y'_{n-3}), (x_{n-2}, y'_{n-2}), (x_{n-1}, y'_{n-1}), and (x_n, y'_n); and the integration of this polynomial from x_{n-3} to x_{n+1}. Some of these details are discussed in Problem 7. What is important at the present time is not these algebraic details, but the underlying general principle of all multistep methods.

1. A polynomial of degree p is fitted to the $p + 1$ points (x_{n-p}, y'_{n-p}), ..., (x_n, y'_n).

2. This interpolation polynomial is integrated from x_{n-p} to x_{n+1}, which gives an equation for y_{n+1}.

The method of constructing interpolation polynomials dates back to Newton and is thoroughly discussed (as are other multistep methods) in more advanced books on numerical methods.†

The Milne continuing method involves, in addition to the formula (3), a *correction formula* for improving the value of y_{n+1} computed from Eq. (3). The correction formula is derived by integrating $\phi'(x)$ from x_{n-1} to x_{n+1},

---

* Recall, for example, that we often use linear interpolation in determining the values of the trigonometric functions for arguments which lie between those given in a table.

† See, for example, Henrici [Chapter 5] or Milne [Chapters 3 and 4].

giving

$$\phi(x_{n+1}) = \phi(x_{n-1}) + \int_{x_{n-1}}^{x_{n+1}} \phi'(x) \, dx. \tag{4}$$

The integral in Eq. (4) can be evaluated approximately by using Simpson's rule* along with the approximate values y'_{n-1}, y'_n, and y'_{n+1} of $\phi'(x)$ at x_{n-1}, x_n, and x_{n+1}. Note that y'_{n+1} is determined by evaluating $f(x_{n+1}, y_{n+1})$ using the value of y_{n+1} determined from Eq. (3). Thus we obtain from Eq. (4) the formula

$$y_{n+1} = y_{n-1} + \frac{h}{3}(y'_{n-1} + 4y'_n + y'_{n+1}). \tag{5}$$

Once y_{n-3}, y_{n-2}, y_{n-1}, and y_n are known we compute y'_n, y'_{n-1}, and y'_{n-2} and then use Eq. (3) to obtain a first value for y_{n+1}. Then we compute y'_{n+1}, and use Eq. (5) to obtain a corrected value of y_{n+1}. Thus the formula (5) is referred to as a correction formula. With this idea in mind, it is natural to refer to Eq. (3) as a *predictor formula* and the method using both Eqs. (3) and (5) as a *predictor-corrector method*. We can, of course, continue to use the correction formula (5) if the change in y_{n+1} is too large. As a general rule, however, if it is necessary to use the corrector formula more than once it can be expected that the step size h is too large and should be made smaller. Note also that Eq. (5) serves as a check on the arithmetic in determining y_{n+1} from Eq. (3)—any substantial difference between the values of y_{n+1} from Eq. (3) and from Eq. (5) would indicate a definite possibility of an arithmetic error. Finally we mention that the local formula errors in the multistep formula (3) and the correction formula (5) are each proportional to h^5.

To summarize, we first compute y_1, y_2, and y_3 by a starting formula that has a local formula error that is no greater than h^5. We then switch to the Milne continuing method, using Eq. (3) to compute y_{n+1}, $n \geq 3$, and Eq. (5) to correct y_{n+1}. We continue to correct y_{n+1} until there is no longer any change, or until the change is less than the accuracy of the data or the numerical procedure. A more detailed discussion of the Milne continuing method as well as a discussion of the error and some practical hints can be found in Milne [Chapter 4].

Example.   Using the Milne predictor-corrector method with $h = 0.1$ determine an approximate value of the exact solution $y = \phi(x)$ at $x = 0.4$ for the initial value problem

$$y' = 1 - x + 4y, \qquad y(0) = 1. \tag{6}$$

For starting data we will use the values of y_1, y_2, and y_3 determined using the Runge-Kutta method. These are tabulated in Table 8.5. Then, using

---

* See Problem 6 of Section 8.6 for a brief derivation of Simpson's rule.

Eq. (6), we obtain

$$
\begin{array}{ll}
y_0 = 1 & y_0' = 5 \\
y_1 = 1.6089333 & y_1' = 7.3357332 \\
y_2 = 2.5050062 & y_2' = 10.820025 \\
y_3 = 3.8294145 & y_3' = 16.017658.
\end{array}
$$

From Eq. (3) we obtain

$$y_4 = 1 + \frac{0.4(35.886757)}{3} = 5.7849009.$$

Next we use the correction formula (5) to correct y_4. Corresponding to the predicted value of y_4 we obtain from Eq. (6) that $y_4' = 23.739604$. Hence, from Eq. (5), the corrected value of y_4 is

$$y_4 = 2.5050062 + \frac{0.1(98.630261)}{3} = 5.7926816.$$

The exact value, correct through eight digits, is 5.7942260. Note that using the correction formula once reduces the error in y_4 to approximately $\frac{1}{6}$ of the error before its use.

PROBLEMS

In Problems 1 through 3 determine an approximate value of the exact solution at $x = 0.4$ using the Milne continuing method. Take $h = 0.1$. The values for y_1, y_2, and y_3 are those computed by the Runge-Kutta method, rounded to six digits. Use the correction formula to compute one correction.

1. $y' = 2y - 1$; $y_0 = 1$, $y_1 = 1.11070$, $y_2 = 1.24591$, $y_3 = 1.41105$

2. $y' = \frac{1}{2} - x + 2y$; $y_0 = 1$, $y_1 = 1.27140$, $y_2 = 1.59182$, $y_3 = 1.97211$

3. $y' = x^2 + y^2$; $y_0 = 1$, $y_1 = 1.11146$, $y_2 = 1.25302$, $y_3 = 1.43967$

4. Given that the values of $\phi'(x)$ at x_{n-1} and x_n are y_{n-1}' and y_n', fit a first degree polynomial $ax + b$ to $\phi'(x)$ so that it passes through these two points. Using this result derive the following multistep formula for the equation $y' = f(x, y)$:

$$y_{n+1} = y_{n-1} + 2hy_n'.$$

5. Show that the multistep formula derived in Problem 4 has a local formula error that is proportional to h^3. Note that this formula is just as easy to use (after y_1 has been computed) as the Euler formula $y_{n+1} = y_n + hy_n'$ which has a local formula error proportional only to h^2.
Hint: Evaluate $\phi(x_n + h)$ and $\phi(x_n - h)$ by expanding $\phi(x)$ in a Taylor series about $x = x_n$.

6. Using the multistep formula of Problem 4 compute approximate values of the exact solution at $x = 0.2$ and 0.3 for the following initial value problems.

Take $h = 0.1$. The values of y_1 are those determined using the three-term Taylor series method or the improved Euler method.

(a) $y' = 2y - 1$; $y(0) = 1$, $y_1 = 1.110$

(b) $y' = \frac{1}{2} - x + 2y$; $y(0) = 1$, $y_1 = 1.270$

(c) $y' = x^2 + y^2$; $y(0) = 1$, $y_1 = 1.111$

Compare your results with previous computations.

*7. Let

$$\nabla y'_n = y'_n - y'_{n-1}, \qquad \nabla^2 y'_n = \nabla(\nabla y'_n) = \nabla(y'_n - y'_{n-1}) = y'_n - 2y'_{n-1} + y'_{n-2},$$

and so on.

(a) Verify that

$$y'_n + \frac{\nabla y'_n}{1! \, h}(x - x_n) + \frac{\nabla^2 y'_n}{2! \, h^2}(x - x_n)(x - x_{n-1})$$

$$+ \frac{\nabla^3 y'_n}{3! \, h^3}(x - x_n)(x - x_{n-1})(x - x_{n-2})$$

is a polynomial of third degree passing through the points (x_{n-3}, y'_{n-3}), (x_{n-2}, y'_{n-2}), (x_{n-1}, y'_{n-1}), and (x_n, y'_n).

(b) Using this polynomial for $\phi'(x)$ in Eq. (2) of this section derive Eq. (3).

8.9 SYSTEMS OF FIRST ORDER EQUATIONS

In the preceding sections we have discussed numerical methods for solving initial value problems associated with first order differential equations. These methods can also be applied to a system of first order equations or to equations of higher order. Recalling that a higher order equation such as $d^2x/dt^2 = f(t, x, dx/dt)$ can be reduced to the system of first order equations $dy/dt = f(t, x, y)$, $dx/dt = y$, we will only consider systems of first order equations.* We will use t to denote the independent variable, and $x, y, z, \ldots$ to denote the dependent variables. Primes will denote differentiation with respect to t. Further, for the purpose of simplicity, we will restrict our attention to a system of two first order equations

$$x' = f(t, x, y) \tag{1}$$

$$y' = g(t, x, y) \tag{2}$$

with the initial conditions

$$x(t_0) = x_0, \qquad y(t_0) = y_0. \tag{3}$$

---

* From the point of view of numerical accuracy there is some disagreement on whether a higher order equation should be reduced to a system of first order equations and solved by procedures of the type discussed in this section, or whether the higher order equation should be solved by procedures which are directly applicable. Such questions are well beyond the scope of an elementary text such as this, but are discussed in advanced books on numerical methods. See, for example, Henrici.

The functions f and g are assumed to satisfy the conditions of Theorem 7.1 so that the initial value problem (1), (2), and (3) has a unique solution in some interval of the t axis containing the point t_0. We wish to determine approximate values $x_1, x_2, x_3, \ldots, x_n, \ldots$ and $y_1, y_2, \ldots, y_n, \ldots$ of the exact solution $x = \phi(t)$, $y = \psi(t)$ at the points $t_n = t_0 + nh$.

As an example of how the methods of the previous sections can be generalized, consider the Euler method of Section 8.2. In this case we use the initial conditions (3) to determine $\phi'(t_0)$ and $\psi'(t_0)$, and then move along the tangent lines to the curves $x = \phi(t)$ and $y = \psi(t)$. Thus

$$x_1 = x_0 + hf(t_0, x_0, y_0), \qquad y_1 = y_0 + hg(t_0, x_0, y_0).$$

In general

$$x_{n+1} = x_n + hf(t_n, x_n, y_n) \qquad y_{n+1} = y_n + hg(t_n, x_n, y_n)$$
$$= x_n + hx'_n \qquad\qquad\qquad = y_n + hy'_n. \tag{4}$$

The other numerical methods can be generalized in a similar manner.

Example. Determine approximate values of $x = \phi(t)$, $y = \psi(t)$ at the points $t = 0.1$ and $t = 0.2$ using the Euler formula (4) for the initial value problem

$$x' = x - 4y, \qquad y' = -x + y \tag{5}$$

with

$$x(0) = 1, \qquad y(0) = 0. \tag{6}$$

Take $h = 0.1$.

For this problem $x'_n = x_n - 4y_n$ and $y'_n = -x_n + y_n$; hence

$$x'_0 = 1 - 4(0) \qquad\qquad y'_0 = -1 + 0$$
$$= 1 \qquad\qquad\qquad = -1.$$

Thus

$$x_1 = 1 + 0.1(1) \qquad\qquad y_1 = 0 + 0.1(-1)$$
$$= 1.1 \qquad\qquad\qquad = -0.1.$$

Similarly

$$x'_1 = 1.1 - 4(-0.1) \qquad\qquad y'_1 = -1.1 + (-0.1)$$
$$= 1.5 \qquad\qquad\qquad = -1.2;$$

and

$$x_2 = 1.1 + 0.1(1.5) \qquad\qquad y_2 = -0.1 + 0.1(-1.2)$$
$$= 1.25 \qquad\qquad\qquad = -0.22.$$

It is easily verified that the exact solution of the initial value problem (5) and (6) is

$$\phi(t) = \frac{e^{-t} + e^{3t}}{2}, \qquad \psi(t) = \frac{e^{-t} - e^{3t}}{4}. \tag{7}$$

The values of the exact solution, rounded to eight digits, at $t = 0.2$ are $\phi(0.2) = 1.3204248$ and $\psi(0.2) = -0.25084701$.

PROBLEMS

Some of the problems for this section will deal with the following initial value problems:

(a) $x' = x + y + t$, $y' = 4x - 2y$; $x(0) = 1$, $y(0) = 0$

(b) $x' = 2x + ty$, $y' = xy$; $x(0) = 1$, $y(0) = 1$

(c) $x' = -tx - y - 1$, $y' = x$; $x(0) = 1$, $y(0) = 1$

In all your computations carry four digits unless otherwise specified.

1. For each of initial value problems (a), (b), and (c), determine approximate values of the exact solution at $t = 0.1$ and $t = 0.2$ using the Euler method with $h = 0.1$.

2. Show that the generalization of the three-term Taylor formula of Section 8.5 for the initial value problem $x' = f(t, x, y)$, $y' = g(t, x, y)$, with $x(t_0) = x_0$, $y(x_0) = y_0$ is

$$x_{n+1} = x_n + hx'_n + \frac{h^2}{2} x''_n, \qquad y_{n+1} = y_n + hy'_n + \frac{h^2}{2} y''_n$$

where

$$x''_n = f_t(t_n, x_n, y_n) + f_x(t_n, x_n, y_n)x'_n + f_y(t_n, x_n, y_n)y'_n,$$

$$y''_n = g_t(t_n, x_n, y_n) + g_x(t_n, x_n, y_n)x'_n + g_y(t_n, x_n, y_n)y'_n.$$

Using these results determine an approximate value of the exact solution at $t = 0.2$ for the illustrative initial value problem in the text. Take $h = 0.2$ and compare your results with the exact values.

3. Using the three-term Taylor formula derived in Problem 2 determine an approximate value of the exact solution at $x = 0.2$ for each of the initial value problems (a), (b), and (c). Take $h = 0.2$.

4. Consider the initial value problem $x' = f(t, x, y)$ and $y' = g(t, x, y)$ with $x(t_0) = x_0$ and $y(t_0) = y_0$. The generalization of the Milne predictor-corrector method of Section 8.8 is

$$x_{n+1} = x_{n-3} + \frac{4h(2x'_n - x'_{n-1} + 2x'_{n-2})}{3},$$

$$y_{n+1} = y_{n-3} + \frac{4h(2y'_n - y'_{n-1} + 2y'_{n-2})}{3},$$

and

$$x_{n+1} = x_{n-1} + \frac{h(x'_{n+1} + 4x'_n + x'_{n-1})}{3},$$

$$y_{n+1} = y_{n-1} + \frac{h(y'_{n+1} + 4y'_n + y'_{n-1})}{3}.$$

Using this procedure determine an approximate value of the exact solution at $t = 0.4$ for the illustrative initial value problem $x' = x - 4y$, $y' = -x + y$ with $x(0) = 1$, $y(0) = 0$. Take $h = 0.1$. Correct the predicted value once. For the values of $x_1, \ldots, y_3$ use the values of the exact solutions rounded to six digits: $x_1 = 1.12883, x_2 = 1.32042, x_3 = 1.60021, y_1 = -0.110527, y_2 = -0.250847,$ and $y_3 = -0.429696.$

5. It is possible to construct an approximate solution of the initial value problem $x' = f(t, x, y), y' = g(t, x, y)$ with $x(t_0) = x_0$ and $y(t_0) = y_0$ by the iteration procedure discussed in Problem 8 of Section 8.2 (also see Section 2.11); thus

$$\phi_{n+1}(t) = x_0 + \int_{t_0}^{t} f[s, \phi_n(s), \psi_n(s)] \, ds,$$

$$\psi_{n+1}(t) = y_0 + \int_{t_0}^{t} g[s, \phi_n(s), \psi_n(s)] \, ds.$$

Using $\phi_0(t) = 1$ and $\psi_0(t) = 0$ determine $\phi_2(t)$ and $\psi_2(t)$ for the illustrative initial value problem $x' = x - 4y, y' = -x + y$ with $x(0) = 1, y(0) = 0$. Compare the approximate results at $t = 0.2$ and $t = 1.0$ with the exact results

$$\phi(0.2) = \quad 1.3042478 \qquad \phi(1) = \quad 10.226708,$$
$$\psi(0.2) = -0.25084701 \qquad \psi(1) = -4.9294144,$$

and with the values of $\phi_1(t)$ and $\psi_1(t)$.

6. Consider the initial value problem

$$x'' + t^2 x' + 3x = t, \qquad x(0) = 1, \qquad x'(0) = 2.$$

Reduce this problem to a system of two equations and determine approximate values of the exact solution at $t = 0.1$ and $t = 0.2$ using the Euler method with a step size $h = 0.1$.

REFERENCES

There are many books of varying degrees of sophistication dealing with numerical analysis in general, programming, and the numerical solution of ordinary differential equations and partial differential equations. The following books were mentioned in the text:

Henrici, Peter, *Discrete Variable Methods in Ordinary Differential Equations*, Wiley, New York, 1962.

Milne, W. E., *Numerical Solution of Differential Equations*, Wiley, New York, 1953.

The text by Henrici provides a wealth of theoretical information about numerical methods for solving ordinary differential equations; however, it is fairly advanced.

Two of the many elementary general texts with chapters on ordinary differential equations are:

Henrici, Peter, *Elements of Numerical Analysis*, Wiley, New York, 1964.

McCracken, Daniel D. and Dorn, William S., *Numerical Methods and Fortran Programming*, Wiley, New York, 1964.

Nonlinear Differential Equations and Stability

9.1 INTRODUCTION

Up to this point most of our discussion has dealt with methods for solving differential equations. Primarily, we have considered linear equations for which there is an elegant and extensive theory. However, some simple first order nonlinear equations were considered in Chapter 2, two special cases of second order nonlinear equations were discussed in the problems following Section 3.1, and the numerical methods of Chapter 8 apply equally well to nonlinear equations.

We must face the fact that it is usually very difficult, if not impossible, to find a solution of a given differential equation in a reasonably convenient and explicit form, especially if the equation is nonlinear. Therefore, it is important to consider what qualitative information can be obtained about the solutions of differential equations, particularly nonlinear ones, without actually solving the equations. The questions considered in this chapter are mainly associated with the idea of "stability" of a solution; this idea will be made more precise in Section 9.4. As an example, in applications such as automatic control theory, an important question (in its simplest form) is whether small changes in the initial conditions (input)* lead to small changes (stability) or to large changes (instability) in the solution (output). A second type of question arises when a nonlinear equation is approximated by a simpler linear one; for example, as mentioned in Section 1.1, when the nonlinear pendulum equation $d^2\theta/dt^2 + (g/l)\sin\theta = 0$ is replaced by $d^2\theta/dt^2 + (g/l)\theta = 0$ for θ small. If the solution of the linear equation is not a reasonable approximation to the solution of the original nonlinear equation, the linearization is of dubious value. Many of the arguments that we will present follow from geometric considerations and were developed by

---

* For purposes of discussion it may be helpful to think of the initial state as the input and the differential equation as an operation that starts once the input is given and gives an output, the solution.

the French mathematician H. Poincaré* and the Russian mathematician A. M. Liapounov.†

To illustrate some of the ideas in their simplest form, consider the nonlinear first order equation

$$\frac{dA}{dt} = \epsilon A - \sigma A^2, \tag{1}$$

with the initial condition

$$A(0) = A_0 \geq 0, \tag{2}$$

where ϵ and σ are given positive numbers. While negative values of A_0 are permissible mathematically, in physical applications A_0 will be nonnegative. Equations of the form (1) occur in many different applications. One example is population growth or decay; see Section 2.9. Another is in a study of the transition from laminar to turbulent fluid flow; there Eq. (1) is called the Landau‡ equation. Recall that if the nonlinear term σA^2 is neglected in Eq. (1), then the solution of Eq. (1) satisfying the initial condition (2) is $A = A_0 \exp(\epsilon t)$, and A grows exponentially with time.

The situation is entirely different if the nonlinear term is retained. Note that if $A = 0$ or if $A = \epsilon/\sigma$ the right-hand side of Eq. (1) vanishes. Thus we have the two constant solutions $A = \phi_1(t) = 0$ and $A = \phi_2(t) = \epsilon/\sigma$. As we shall see, these two solutions are of particular importance. Provided that $A \neq 0$ and $A \neq \epsilon/\sigma$, we can write Eq. (1) in the form

$$\frac{dA}{A(\epsilon - \sigma A)} = dt. \tag{3}$$

Using partial fractions we have

$$\left[\frac{1}{A} + \frac{\sigma}{\epsilon - \sigma A} \right] dA = \epsilon \, dt. \tag{4}$$

Integrating,

$$\ln |A| - \ln |\epsilon - \sigma A| = \epsilon t + K, \tag{5}$$

where K is a constant of integration to be chosen so that the initial condition $A(0) = A_0$ is satisfied. The cases $0 < A_0 < \epsilon/\sigma$, and $A_0 > \epsilon/\sigma$ must be considered separately since the sign of $(\epsilon - \sigma A)$ is different in the intervals

---

* H. Poincaré (1854–1912) was generally regarded as the outstanding mathematician in the world around 1900. He made many fundamental contributions in several different areas of mathematics. He founded the subject of topological dynamics and was the father of modern topology, which is one of the most active fields in mathematical research. He also obtained, independently of Einstein, many of the results of the theory of special relativity.
† A. M. Liapounov's (1857–1918) work on stability and nonlinear differential equations, which is now realized to be of great importance, was not fully appreciated during his lifetime.
‡ L. D. Landau (1908–1968) was a famous Russian physicist who received the Nobel prize for physics in 1962.

$0 < A < \epsilon/\sigma$ and $A > \epsilon/\sigma$. Nevertheless, the final result can be expressed in a single formula. Omitting several steps of algebra, we find that

$$A = \phi(t) = \frac{\epsilon}{\sigma + [(\epsilon - \sigma A_0)/A_0]e^{-\epsilon t}} \tag{6}$$

for $A_0 \neq 0$. While the formula (6) is not valid for $A_0 = 0$, it does contain the constant solution $A = \phi_2(t) = \epsilon/\sigma$ corresponding to $A_0 = \epsilon/\sigma$. Since $\epsilon > 0$, it follows that $\exp(-\epsilon t) \to 0$ as $t \to \infty$, and hence $A \to \epsilon/\sigma$ as $t \to \infty$. Several typical solutions for different values of A_0 as well as the solutions $A = \phi_1(t) = 0$ and $A = \phi_2(t) = \epsilon/\sigma$ are shown in Figure 9.1.

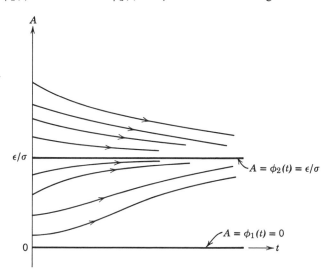

FIGURE 9.1 $dA/dt = \epsilon A - \sigma A^2$, $\epsilon > 0$, $\sigma > 0$.

Thus any solution of Eq. (1) which starts at an initial point $A_0 > 0$ ultimately approaches the solution $A = \phi_2(t) = \epsilon/\sigma$ as $t \to \infty$. This limiting behavior as $t \to \infty$ is an example of the type of qualitative information that is often of interest. Here we have obtained it by first solving the differential equation, but it is significant for more difficult problems that the limiting behavior can often be determined without a complete knowledge of the solutions. To show this for the present problem, let us plot dA/dt as a function of A as given by Eq. (1). The graph is a parabola with $dA/dt = 0$ at $A = 0$ and at $A = \epsilon/\sigma$. Furthermore, dA/dt is positive for A small; thus the graph must have the appearance indicated in Figure 9.2. If $0 < A < \epsilon/\sigma$, then $dA/dt > 0$ and A increases toward ϵ/σ. On the other hand, if $A > \epsilon/\sigma$, then $dA/dt < 0$ and A decreases toward ϵ/σ. As indicated, A always approaches the solution $A = \phi_2(t) = \epsilon/\sigma$ provided that the initial value $A_0 > 0$.

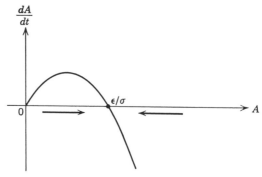

FIGURE 9.2 $dA/dt = \epsilon A - \sigma A^2$, $\epsilon > 0$, $\sigma > 0$.

Let us examine the solution $A = \phi_1(t) = 0$ in more detail. To emphasize the point we wish to make, suppose we think of Eq. (1) as representing a physical system, or black box, as depicted in Figure 9.3. If $A_0 = 0$ is the input, then the output is $A = 0$. But suppose a slight error is made, and a small but nonzero value of A_0 is the input. The question is whether the output remains close to $A = 0$. It is clear from Figure 9.1 that the answer is no. Instead, $A \to \epsilon/\sigma$ as $t \to \infty$. It is natural to say that the solution $A = \phi_1(t) = 0$ is an *unstable solution* of Eq. (1).

$$A_0 \longrightarrow \boxed{\dfrac{dA}{dt} = \epsilon A - \sigma A^2} \longrightarrow A = \phi(t; A_0)$$

FIGURE 9.3

Now consider the solution $A = \phi_2(t) = \epsilon/\sigma$. If the input is $A_0 = \epsilon/\sigma$, then the output of the black box is $A = \epsilon/\sigma$. If a small error is made in the input, the output will approach ϵ/σ asymptotically (in fact, exponentially) as $t \to \infty$. Hence we say that the solution $A = \phi_2(t) = \epsilon/\sigma$ is an *asymptotically stable* solution of Eq. (1). The terms asymptotically stable, stable, and unstable will be defined more precisely in Section 9.4.

As a second example consider again Eq. (1) with the initial condition (2), but suppose that $\epsilon < 0$ and $\sigma < 0$. Without computing the explicit solution of Eq. (1), let us consider what information can be obtained from the graph of dA/dt vs A shown in Figure 9.4. Since $dA/dt < 0$ for $0 < A < \epsilon/\sigma$ and $dA/dt > 0$ for $A > \epsilon/\sigma$ it is clear that if the initial value A_0 is in the interval $0 < A_0 < \epsilon/\sigma$, then A will approach the solution $A = \phi_1(t) = 0$ as $t \to \infty$. If $A_0 > \epsilon/\sigma$, then A will increase without bound as t increases. It also follows from Figure 9.4 that the solution $A = \phi_2(t) = \epsilon/\sigma$ is unstable to small changes in the initial condition from $A_0 = \epsilon/\sigma$; a small positive change causes A to increase without bound, and a small negative change causes A to approach zero with increasing t.

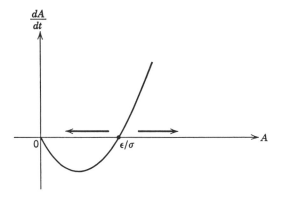

FIGURE 9.4 $dA/dt = \epsilon A - \sigma A^2$, $\epsilon < 0$, $\sigma < 0$.

On the other hand, the solution $A = \phi_1(t) = 0$ is asymptotically stable to small changes in the initial condition $A_0 = 0$, in the sense that the system causes a small initial deviation from the zero solution to decay. However, the solution $A = \phi_1(t) = 0$ is not stable to all initial deviations from $A_0 = 0$. If $A_0 > \epsilon/\sigma$, then rather than dying out, A will grow without bound. A sketch of the solutions of Eq. (1) with $\epsilon < 0$ and $\sigma < 0$ for different values of A_0 is shown in Figure 9.5.

Usually in applications where a mechanism is to deliver a certain output when a certain input (or something very close to that input) is provided, we

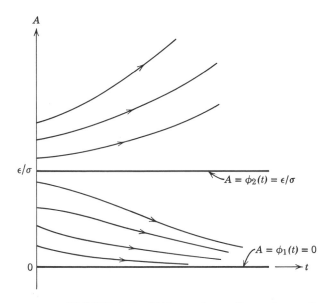

FIGURE 9.5 $dA/dt = \epsilon A - \sigma A^2$, $\epsilon < 0$, $\sigma < 0$.

are interested only in stability with respect to small disturbances. It is, of course, conceivable that large disturbances can occur. For example, suppose an automatic control is set to keep a flap on an airplane wing at a certain inclination. In the normal motion of the plane the changing aerodynamic forces on the flap will cause it to move from its set position, but then the automatic control (the black box) will come into action to damp out the small deviation and return the flap to its set position. (Mathematically, for Eq. (1) with $\epsilon < 0$ and $\sigma < 0$ the set position is $A = 0$.) However, if the airplane is caught in a high gust of wind the flap may be deflected so much that the automatic control cannot bring it back to the set position (this would correspond to a deviation greater than ϵ/σ). Presumably the pilot would then take control!

In concluding this introductory section let us consider the question of neglecting the nonlinear term σA^2 in Eq. (1). In the first case ($\epsilon > 0$, $\sigma > 0$) the linear equation does give the correct behavior of A for a small time interval if A is initially small. However, in studying the solution for all time it *is not* permissible to neglect the term σA^2. The reason is that even if A is initially very small, so that the term σA^2 is initially small compared to the term ϵA, A grows exponentially with t, and the term σA^2 eventually becomes important. In the second case ($\epsilon < 0$, $\sigma < 0$), it *is* permissible to neglect the quadratic term σA^2 provided that A is small. The solution of the linear equation, $A_0 \exp(\epsilon t)$, approaches zero for any value of A_0. The same result is obtained from the nonlinear equation provided that $A_0 < \epsilon/\sigma$, and this is what is meant by "small" in this particular example. Thus, in the first case, the solution of the linearized problem is not a good approximation (at least not for all time) to that of the nonlinear problem; in the second case it is, provided only that $A_0 < \epsilon/\sigma$.

In the following sections we will develop the ideas suggested here, and others, in greater depth. While many books dealing with nonlinear differential equations have appeared in recent years, almost all are at an advanced level and assume considerable mathematical sophistication. However, several texts, listed in the references at the end of this chapter, have chapters dealing with theory or applications which should be readable after completing the present chapter.

PROBLEMS

In Problems 1 through 6 determine the limiting behavior of the solution of each equation as $t \to \infty$ for different initial conditions $A(0) = A_0$ by plotting dA/dt vs A.

    1. $dA/dt = \epsilon A - \sigma A^2$, $\epsilon > 0$, $\sigma > 0$, $-\infty < A_0 < \infty$

    2. $dA/dt = \epsilon A - \sigma A^2$, $\epsilon < 0$, $\sigma < 0$, $-\infty < A_0 < \infty$

    3. $dA/dt = \epsilon A + \sigma A^2$, $\epsilon > 0$, $\sigma > 0$, $A_0 \geq 0$

4. $dA/dt = \epsilon A + \sigma A^2,$ $\epsilon > 0,$ $\sigma > 0,$ $-\infty < A_0 < \infty$

5. $dA/dt = A(A - 1)(A - 2),$ $A_0 \geq 0$

6. $dA/dt = A(1 - A)(A - 2),$ $A_0 \geq 0$

7. Show that all solutions of the linear equation $dA/dt = -\epsilon A$ with $\epsilon > 0$ approach the solution $A = \phi(t) = 0$ as $t \to \infty$ independent of the choice of the initial condition $A(0) = A_0,$ $-\infty < A_0 < \infty.$ The solution $A = \phi(t) = 0$ is said to be *globally asymptotically stable*, to emphasize that this solution is approached as $t \to \infty$ regardless of the initial state. This may be contrasted with the situation in Figure 9.4, where the solution $A = 0$ is approached as $t \to \infty$ only if $A_0 < \epsilon/\sigma.$

8. Derive Eq. (6) by choosing K in Eq. (5) so that the initial condition $A(0) = A_0$ is satisfied.

9. Determine the solution of the equation

$$dA/dt = \epsilon A - \sigma A^2,   \epsilon < 0,   \sigma < 0$$

with $A(0) = A_0,$ $0 \leq A_0 < \infty,$ and verify that the sketch shown in Figure 9.5 is correct.

9.2 SOLUTIONS AND TRAJECTORIES

Consider the two simultaneous differential equations

$$\frac{dx}{dt} = F(x, y),   \frac{dy}{dt} = G(x, y). \tag{1}$$

We will assume that the functions F and G are continuous and have continuous partial derivatives in some domain D in the xy plane. Then, by Theorem 7.1, if (x_0, y_0) is a point in this domain, there exists a unique solution $x = \phi(t),$ $y = \psi(t)$ of the system (1) satisfying the initial conditions

$$x(t_0) = x_0,   y(t_0) = y_0. \tag{2}$$

The solution is defined in some interval $\alpha < t < \beta$ which contains the point $t_0.$

It is very helpful to interpret a solution $x = \phi(t),$ $y = \psi(t)$ of the system (1) as the parametric representation of a curve in the xy plane, usually referred to as the *phase plane*. This is particularly true when the functions F and G do not depend upon $t,$ as is the case here. To illustrate the differences between the two cases, we will consider two simple examples. First, suppose that particles are being continuously emitted at the point $x = 1,$ $y = 2,$ and then move in the xy plane according to the law

$$\frac{dx}{dt} = x,   \frac{dy}{dt} = y. \tag{3}$$

The particle that is emitted at the time $t = s$ is specified by the initial conditions $x(s) = 1$, $y(s) = 2$. What is the path of the particle for $t \geq s$? The solution of Eq. (3) satisfying these initial conditions is

$$x = \phi(t; s) = e^{t-s}, \qquad y = \psi(t; s) = 2e^{t-s}, \qquad t \geq s. \qquad (4)$$

The paths followed by the particles emitted at different times s can be most readily visualized by eliminating t from Eqs. (4). This gives

$$y = 2x, \qquad (5)$$

where it is clear from Eqs. (4) that $x \geq 1$, $y \geq 2$. The straight line $y = 2x$ is sketched in Figure 9.6a. What is important is that the initial time s does not appear in Eq. (5); therefore, no matter when a particle is emitted from the point (1, 2), it always moves along the same curve.

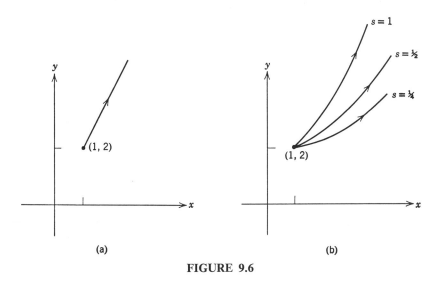

FIGURE 9.6

Now consider a similar problem in which the functions F and/or G depend on t; for example,

$$\frac{dx}{dt} = \frac{x}{t}, \qquad \frac{dy}{dt} = y. \qquad (6)$$

The solution of Eqs. (6) satisfying the initial conditions $x(s) = 1$, $y(s) = 2$ is

$$x = \phi(t; s) = \frac{t}{s}, \qquad y = \psi(t; s) = 2e^{t-s}, \qquad t \geq s. \qquad (7)$$

From the first of Eqs. (7), $t = sx$, and substituting in the second of Eqs. (7) gives

$$y = 2e^{s(x-1)}, \qquad (8)$$

where again $x \geq 1$. Since s appears in Eq. (8) the path that a particle follows will depend on the time at which it is emitted, that is, the time at which the initial condition is applied. The paths followed by particles emitted at several different times are sketched in Figure 9.6b.

In the first example, when we eliminated the parameter t we automatically eliminated s, since t and s appeared only in the combination $t - s$. In the second example this was not the case, and s remains in the final result (8).

In this chapter we shall only consider systems of equations of the form (1), in which the independent variable t does not appear explicitly. Such a system is said to be *autonomous*. Many of the results that will be obtained can be generalized to nonautonomous* systems, although the analysis is somewhat more complicated. Physically, an autonomous system is one in which the parameters of the system are not time-dependent. Autonomous systems occur frequently in practice; for example, the motion of an undamped pendulum of length l is governed by the differential equation

$$\frac{d^2\theta}{dt^2} + \frac{g}{l} \sin \theta = 0. \tag{9}$$

Letting $x = \theta$ and $y = d\theta/dt$, Eq. (9) can be rewritten as a nonlinear autonomous system of two equations:

$$\frac{dx}{dt} = y, \qquad \frac{dy}{dt} = -\left(\frac{g}{l}\right) \sin x. \tag{10}$$

We have already seen one property of autonomous systems: all particles passing through a given point follow the same curve in the phase plane. An equivalent, and the more usual, statement is the following. If $x = \phi(t)$, $y = \psi(t)$ is a solution of Eqs. (1) for t in some interval, say $\alpha < t < \beta$, then for any constant s, $x = \phi(t - s)$, $y = \psi(t - s)$ is a solution of Eqs. (1) for $t - s$ in the same interval, $\alpha < t - s < \beta$ or equivalently $\alpha + s < t < \beta + s$. This result is proved by direct substitution in Eqs. (1); it is explicitly illustrated by the solution (4) of the system (3).

A curve in the phase plane that is described parametrically by a solution of the system (1) is called a *trajectory* of the system. Different solutions may give precisely the same trajectory (curve). Indeed, according to the remarks of the preceding paragraph, if a given trajectory of an autonomous system is represented parametrically by the solution $x = \phi(t), y = \psi(t)$, for $\alpha < t < \beta$, the same trajectory is also represented by the family of solutions $x = \phi(t - s)$, $y = \psi(t - s)$, $\alpha + s < t < \beta + s$, for any fixed s. This is illustrated in Figure 9.6a, where every solution of the system (3) passing through the point $(1, 2)$ lies on the trajectory $y = 2x$. Also consider the following example.

---

* Formally, a nonautonomous system of n first order equations for $x_1(t), x_2(t), \ldots, x_n(t)$ can be written as an autonomous system of $n + 1$ equations by letting $t = x_{n+1}$ wherever t appears explicitly, and appending the equation $dx_{n+1}(t)/dt = 1$.

Example. Sketch the trajectories of the linearized pendulum equation, obtained by replacing $\sin x$ by x in Eqs. (10):

$$\frac{dx}{dt} = y, \qquad \frac{dy}{dt} = -\left(\frac{g}{l}\right)x. \tag{11}$$

It can be verified by direct substitution that for $-\infty < t < \infty$,

$$x = \phi(t; s) = C \sin\left(\sqrt{\frac{g}{l}}\, t - s\right),$$

$$y = \psi(t; s) = C\sqrt{\frac{g}{l}} \cos\left(\sqrt{\frac{g}{l}}\, t - s\right), \tag{12}$$

where C and s are arbitrary constants, is the general solution of Eqs. (11). Eliminating t by dividing the equation for y by $\sqrt{g/l}$ and then squaring and adding the equations for x and y shows that the trajectories of the system (11) lie on the ellipses

$$x^2 + \frac{y^2}{g/l} = C^2.$$

Several trajectories are sketched in Figure 9.7. The direction of motion with increasing t can be determined from the differential equations (11). For points in the first quadrant ($x > 0$, $y > 0$), Eqs. (11) imply that $dx/dt > 0$ and $dy/dt < 0$; therefore the motion is clockwise. Notice that the solution $x = \sqrt{l/g} \sin \sqrt{g/l}\, t$, $y = \cos\sqrt{g/l}\, t$, which satisfies the initial conditions $x = 0$, $y = 1$ at $t = 0$, describes the trajectory $(g/l)x^2 + y^2 = 1$. Similarly, the solution $x = \sqrt{l/g} \sin (\sqrt{g/l}\, t + \pi/2)$, $y = \cos (\sqrt{g/l}\, t + \pi/2)$, which satisfies the initial conditions $x = \sqrt{l/g}$, $y = 0$ at $t = 0$, also lies on the same trajectory. Clearly, infinitely many solutions follow the same trajectory.

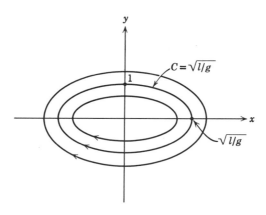

FIGURE 9.7

For this example, it is clear from Eqs. (12) that every solution of the linearized pendulum equations (11) is periodic with period $2\pi/\sqrt{g/l}$. More generally, a solution $x = \phi(t)$, $y = \psi(t)$ of Eqs. (1) is said to be *periodic* with period T if it exists for all t, and if $\phi(t + T) = \phi(t)$, $\psi(t + T) = \psi(t)$ for all t. The trajectory of a periodic solution is a closed curve, as illustrated by the elliptical trajectories in Figure 9.7.

In determining the trajectories of the system (1), it is often convenient to eliminate the parameter t from the solution $x = \phi(t)$, $y = \psi(t)$, obtaining a relation between x and y, as was just illustrated for Eqs. (12). Alternatively, in a region where $F(x, y) \neq 0$, we have from Eqs. (1)

$$\frac{dy}{dx} = \frac{dy/dt}{dx/dt} = \frac{G(x, y)}{F(x, y)}, \tag{13}$$

which is a first order differential equation* for $y = f(x)$. The one parameter family of solutions of Eq. (13) are the trajectories of the system (1). Equation (13) is particularly convenient for determining the slope at a point on a trajectory. Near a point where $F(x, y) = 0$, but $G(x, y) \neq 0$ one can consider in place of Eq. (13) the equation $dx/dy = F(x, y)/G(x, y)$.

A point (x_0, y_0) at which both F and G vanish, however, presents special difficulties and has a special significance. Such points are called *critical points*. If the point (x_0, y_0) is a critical point of the system (1), then $x = x_0$, $y = y_0$ is a solution of the system (1). Indeed, it follows from the existence and uniqueness theorem that the only solution of the system (1) passing through the point (x_0, y_0) is the constant solution itself. The trajectory of this solution is, of course, simply the single point (x_0, y_0). The particle at (x_0, y_0) is then often said to be at rest or in equilibrium. A trajectory, represented by the solution $x = \phi(t)$, $y = \psi(t)$, $t \geq \alpha$, is said to approach the critical point (x_0, y_0) as $t \to \infty$ if $\lim_{t \to \infty} \phi(t) = x_0$ and $\lim_{t \to \infty} \psi(t) = y_0$.

By determining the critical points of the system (1) and the behavior of the trajectories of the system in the neighborhood of the critical points, a great deal of information can be obtained about the solutions of the system. In this regard, there are several results about the trajectories of autonomous systems that are very helpful. The proofs follow from the existence and uniqueness theorem and are outlined in the problems.

1. Through any point (x_0, y_0) in the phase plane there is at most one trajectory of the system (1); see Problem 8.

2. A particle starting at a point that is not a critical point cannot reach a critical point in a finite time. Thus if (x_0, y_0) is a critical point, and a trajectory corresponding to a solution approaches (x_0, y_0), then necessarily $t \to \infty$; see Problem 9.

* The condition $F(x, y) \neq 0$ is needed so that we can divide by $F(x, y)$ to form Eq. (13), but also it then follows that $dx/dt \neq 0$ so that the solution $x = \phi(t)$ can be solved for t as a function of x and, in turn, y becomes a function of x.

3. A trajectory which passes through at least one point that is not a critical point cannot cross itself unless it is a closed curve. In this case the trajectory corresponds to a periodic solution of the system (1); see Problem 10.

The substance of these three results is the following. If a particle (solution) starts at a point that is not a critical point, then it moves on the same trajectory no matter at what time it starts, it can never come back to its initial point unless the motion is periodic, it can never cross another trajectory, and it can only "reach" a critical point in the limit as $t \to \infty$. This suggests that such a particle (solution) either approaches a critical point (x_0, y_0), moves on a closed trajectory or approaches a closed trajectory as $t \to \infty$, or else goes off to infinity. Thus for autonomous systems a study of the critical points and periodic solutions is of fundamental importance. These facts will be developed in greater detail in the next two sections.

PROBLEMS

1. Sketch the trajectory corresponding to the solution satisfying the specified initial conditions, and indicate the direction of motion for increasing t.

(a) $dx/dt = -x$, $dy/dt = -2y$; $x(0) = 4$, $y(0) = 2$

(b) $dx/dt = -x$, $dy/dt = 2y$;

$\qquad x(0) = 4$, $y(0) = 2$ and $x(0) = 4$, $y(0) = 0$

(c) $dx/dt = -y$, $dy/dt = x$;

$\qquad x(0) = 4$, $y(0) = 0$ and $x(0) = 0$, $y(0) = 4$

2. Determine the critical points for each of the following systems.

(a) $dx/dt = 2x - 3y$, $dy/dt = 2x - 2y$

(b) $dx/dt = x - xy$, $dy/dt = y + 2xy$

(c) $dx/dt = x - x^2 - xy$, $dy/dt = \frac{1}{2}y - \frac{1}{4}y^2 - \frac{3}{4}xy$

(d) $dx/dt = y$, $dy/dt = -(g/l)x - (c/ml)y$; $g, l, c, m > 0$

(e) $dx/dt = y$, $dy/dt = -(g/l)\sin x - (c/lm)y$; $g, l, c, m > 0$

(f) The van der Pol equation: $dx/dt = y$, $dy/dt = \mu(1 - x^2)y - x$, $\mu > 0$

3. Consider the linear system

$$dx/dt = ax + by, \qquad dy/dt = cx + dy,$$

where a, b, c, and d are real constants.

(a) Show that if $ad - bc \neq 0$, then the only critical point is $(0, 0)$.

(b) Show that if $ad - bc = 0$, then in addition to the critical point $(0, 0)$ there is a line through the origin for which every point is a critical point of the system. Thus in the latter case the critical point $(0, 0)$ is not "isolated" from the other critical points of the system.

4. Sketch the trajectories of the following system either by solving the system and then eliminating t to obtain a one-parameter family of curves, or by integrating the differential equation [Eq. (13)], which gives the slope of the tangent of a trajectory. Indicate the direction of motion with increasing t.

(a) $dx/dt = -x,$ $dy/dt = -2y$

(b) $dx/dt = -x,$ $dy/dt = 2y$

(c) $dx/dt = x,$ $dy/dt = -2y$

(d) $dx/dt = -x,$ $dy/dt = 3x + 2y$

5. Given that $x = \phi(t), y = \psi(t)$ is a solution of the autonomous system

$$dx/dt = F(x, y), \qquad dy/dt = G(x, y)$$

for $\alpha < t < \beta$, show that $x = \Phi(t) = \phi(t - s), y = \Psi(t) = \psi(t - s)$ is a solution for $\alpha + s < t < \beta + s$.

6. Show by direct integration that even though the right-hand side of the following system

$$\frac{dx}{dt} = \frac{x}{1 + t}, \qquad \frac{dy}{dt} = \frac{y}{1 + t}$$

depends upon t, the paths followed by particles emitted at (x_0, y_0) at $t = s$ are the same regardless of the value of s. Why is this so?
Hint: Consider Eq. (13) for this case.

7. Consider the system

$$dx/dt = F(x, y, t), \qquad dy/dt = G(x, y, t).$$

Show that if the functions $F/(F^2 + G^2)^{1/2}$ and $G/(F^2 + G^2)^{1/2}$ are independent of t, then the solutions corresponding to the initial conditions $x(s) = x_0, y(s) = y_0$ give the same trajectories regardless of the value of s.
Hint: Use Eq. (13).

8. Prove that for the system

$$dx/dt = F(x, y), \qquad dy/dt = G(x, y)$$

there is at most one trajectory which passes through a given point (x_0, y_0).
Hint: Let C_0 be the trajectory generated by the solution $x = \phi_0(t), y = \psi_0(t)$, with $\phi_0(t_0) = x_0, \psi_0(t_0) = y_0$, and let C_1 be the trajectory generated by the solution $x = \phi_1(t), y = \phi_1(t)$, with $\phi_1(t_1) = x_0, \psi_1(t_1) = y_0$. Use the fact that the system is autonomous and the existence and uniqueness theorem to show that C_0 and C_1 are the same.

9. Prove that if a trajectory starts at a noncritical point of the system then it

$$dx/dt = F(x, y), \qquad dy/dt = G(x, y)$$

cannot reach a critical point (x_0, y_0) in a finite length of time.
Hint: Assume the contrary, that is, assume that the solution $x = \phi(t), y = \psi(t)$ satisfies $\phi(a) = x_0, \psi(a) = y_0$. Then use the fact that $x = x_0, y = y_0$ is a solution of the given system satisfying the initial condition $x = x_0, y = y_0$ at $t = a$.

10. Assuming that the trajectory corresponding to a solution $x = \phi(t)$, $y = \psi(t)$, $-\infty < t < \infty$, of an autonomous system is closed, show that the solution is periodic.

Hint: Since the trajectory is closed there exists at least one point (x_0, y_0) such that $\phi(t_0) = x_0$, $\psi(t_0) = y_0$ and a number $T > 0$ such that $\phi(t_0 + T) = x_0$, $\psi(t_0 + T) = y_0$. Show that $x = \Phi(t) = \phi(t + T)$ and $y = \Psi(t) = \psi(t + T)$ is a solution and then use the existence and uniqueness theorem to show that $\Phi(t) = \phi(t)$ and $\Psi(t) = \psi(t)$ for all t.*

9.3 THE PHASE PLANE; THE LINEAR SYSTEM

In this section we will continue our discussion of the autonomous system

$$\frac{dx}{dt} = F(x, y), \qquad \frac{dy}{dt} = G(x, y). \tag{1}$$

In particular we will be concerned with the behavior of the trajectories of the system (1) in the neighborhood of a critical point (x_0, y_0) and the significance of this behavior. It is convenient to choose the critical point to be at the origin of the phase plane: $x_0 = 0, y_0 = 0$. This involves no loss of generality, since if $x_0 \neq 0, y_0 \neq 0$, it is always possible to make the substitution $x = x_0 + u$, $y = y_0 + v$ in Eqs. (1), so that u and v will satisfy an autonomous system of equations with a critical point at the origin.

We will further assume that the origin is an *isolated critical point* of the system (1); that is, we assume that there is some circle about the critical point, inside which there are no other critical points. Finally, we assume that in the neighborhood of $(0, 0)$, the functions F and G have the form

$$\begin{aligned}
F(x, y) &= ax + by + F_1(x, y), \\
G(x, y) &= cx + dy + G_1(x, y),
\end{aligned} \tag{2}$$

where $ad - bc \neq 0$, and the functions F_1 and G_1 are continuous, have continuous first partial derivatives, and are small in the sense† that

$$\frac{F_1(x, y)}{r} \to 0, \qquad \frac{G_1(x, y)}{r} \to 0 \qquad \text{as} \qquad r \to 0, \tag{3}$$

---

* If it is originally known only that the functions ϕ and ψ are defined on an interval containing t_0 and $t_0 + T$, the proof is more difficult. However, it can be shown that the interval of definition must be $-\infty < t < \infty$ and that the solution is periodic with period T.

† Actually, if the functions F and G are continuous and have continuous first partial derivatives, as we assumed in Section 9.2, then it can be shown that F and G have the form (2) in the neighborhood of the critical point $(0, 0)$ and that condition (3) is satisfied. The reason for the restriction $ad - bc \neq 0$ will be made clear after Eq. (7) of this section; also see Problem 3 of Section 9.2.

where $r = (x^2 + y^2)^{1/2}$. Such a system is often referred to as an *almost linear system* in the neighborhood of the critical point $(0, 0)$. While the conditions on F and G are somewhat restrictive, they are satisfied by many functions of two variables; for example, a polynomial in x and y with zero constant term.

As an example, the autonomous system for the undamped motion of a pendulum [Eqs. (10) of Section 9.2] can be written as

$$\frac{dx}{dt} = y,$$

$$\frac{dy}{dt} = -\frac{g}{l} x - \frac{g}{l} (\sin x - x).$$

(4)

Comparing the right hand side of Eqs. (4) with Eqs. (2), we find $a = 0$, $b = 1$, $c = -g/l$, $d = 0$, $F_1(x, y) = 0$, and

$$G_1(x, y) = -\frac{g}{l} (\sin x - x) = -\frac{g}{l} \left(-\frac{x^3}{3!} + \frac{x^5}{5!} + \cdots \right).$$

(5)

From Eq. (5), $\sin x - x$ is similar to $x^3/3! = (r^3 \cos^3 \theta)/3!$ for x very small and hence $(\sin x - x)/r \to 0$ as $r \to 0$. Consequently, the autonomous system (4) is almost linear.

A consequence of the assumption that $F_1(x, y)$ and $G_1(x, y)$ are small compared to the linear terms $ax + by$ and $cx + dy$ near the origin is that in many cases (but not all) the trajectories of the linear autonomous system

$$\frac{dx}{dt} = ax + by$$

$$\frac{dy}{dt} = cx + dy$$

(6)

are good approximations to those of the almost linear system, in the neighborhood of the critical point $(0, 0)$. Thus we first consider the linear system (6), and then in Section 9.4 we will relate our conclusions to the almost linear system.

It is possible to solve the system (6) by the methods of Chapter 7. The solutions are of the form $x = A \exp (rt)$, $y = B \exp (rt)$, where r is a root of the auxiliary equation

$$r^2 - (a + d)r + ad - bc = 0.$$

(7)

Notice that $r = 0$ cannot be a root of Eq. (7). If it were, then necessarily $ad - bc$ would be zero, implying that the equations $ax + by = 0$, $cx + dy = 0$ would have nontrivial solutions. These nontrivial solutions would be determined only up to a multiplicative constant and would lie on a line passing through the origin. Thus other critical points would be located arbitrarily close to the origin, violating the assumption that the origin is an isolated critical point.

There are a number of different cases that must be considered depending on whether the roots of Eq. (7) are both positive, both negative, one positive and one negative, complex with positive real parts, complex with negative real parts, or pure imaginary. We will consider each case in turn, illustrating the behavior of the trajectories by a specific example. We emphasize that the general situation for each case is similar to that for the corresponding example, since a suitable change of variables can be made which will transform a given system into a system having the form of the example for that case. Once the problem is solved in the new coordinate system, the solution can be transformed back to the original coordinate system and constitutes a solution of the original system. For example, a circle in the transformed coordinate system may be an ellipse in the original coordinate system with its major axis not necessarily parallel to one of the coordinate axes. Also for each case we will show a more "general" picture of a typical set of trajectories. It is important that the student become familiar with the type of behavior that the trajectories have for each case as these are the basic building blocks of the qualitative theory of differential equations.

Case 1. Real Unequal Roots of the Same Sign.   The general solution of Eqs. (6) is

$$x = A_1 e^{r_1 t} + A_2 e^{r_2 t}, \qquad y = B_1 e^{r_1 t} + B_2 e^{r_2 t}, \tag{8}$$

where only two of the four constants A_1, A_2, B_1, and B_2 are independent. Suppose first that r_1 and r_2 are negative; then both x and y will approach zero and the point (x, y) will approach the critical point $(0, 0)$ as t approaches infinity independent of the choice of the constants A_1, A_2, B_1, and B_2. Every solution of the system (6) approaches the solution $x = 0$, $y = 0$ exponentially as $t \to \infty$.

To illustrate this case consider the system

$$\frac{dx}{dt} = -x, \qquad \frac{dy}{dt} = -2y, \tag{9}$$

which has the general solution

$$x = A e^{-t}, \qquad y = B e^{-2t}, \tag{10}$$

where A and B are arbitrary. A few trajectories for this example are sketched in Figure 9.8a. If $A > 0$, $B = 0$, then $y = 0$ and $x \to 0$ through positive values as $t \to \infty$. The other halves of the coordinate axes correspond to the cases $A < 0$, $B = 0$; $A = 0$, $B > 0$; and $A = 0$, $B < 0$. If $A \neq 0$, $B \neq 0$, then $y = (B/A^2)x^2$, and we obtain the portions of the parabolas in the first, second, third, and fourth quadrants as indicated in Figure 9.8a.

This type of critical point is called a *node*, or sometimes an *improper node*, to distinguish it from another type of node to be mentioned later. The distinguishing feature is that all trajectories except one pair approach the critical

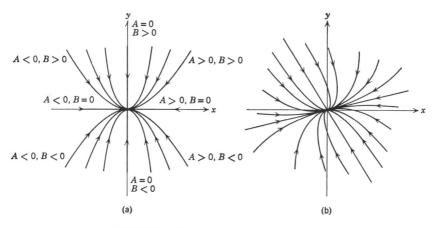

FIGURE 9.8 Improper node, $r_1 \neq r_2$.

point tangent to the same line, while the exceptional pair of trajectories approaches tangent to a different line. In the example all trajectories approach the origin tangent to the x axis except one pair, which approaches along the y axis. If the roots are real, unequal, and positive the situation is similar except that the direction of motion on the trajectories is away from the critical point $(0, 0)$. In this case every solution, except the solution $x = 0$, $y = 0$, even a solution started very near $(0, 0)$, recedes from the origin as $t \to \infty$. A more general sketch of trajectories near an improper node is shown in Figure 9.8b.

Case 2. Real Roots of Opposite Sign. The general solution of Eqs. (6) is still given by Eqs. (8), but with $r_1 > 0$ and $r_2 < 0$. It is now possible for the direction of motion to be toward the critical point on some trajectories and away from the critical point on other trajectories. Typical of this case is the system

$$\frac{dx}{dt} = -x, \qquad \frac{dy}{dt} = 2y, \tag{11}$$

which has the general solution

$$x = Ae^{-t}, \qquad y = Be^{2t}, \tag{12}$$

where A and B are arbitrary. For any initial point not on the x axis, $x \to 0$, $y \to \pm \infty$, depending on the sign of B, as $t \to \infty$; while for an initial point on the x axis, y stays zero and $x \to 0$ as $t \to \infty$. The trajectories are sketched in Figure 9.9a, where use has been made of the fact that for $A \neq 0$ and $B \neq 0$, the solution lies on a portion of the curve $y = BA^2/x^2$. In this case the critical point is called a *saddle point*.

It is important to note that only the trajectories on the x axis approach the critical point; all others approach infinity as t increases because of the

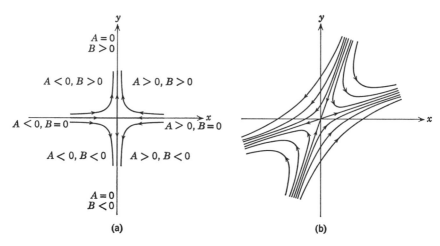

FIGURE 9.9   Saddle point.

presence of $y = B \exp(2t)$, $B \neq 0$. The situation is always similar for a saddle point. For example, if the general solution is

$$\begin{pmatrix} x \\ y \end{pmatrix} = A \begin{pmatrix} k_{11} \\ k_{21} \end{pmatrix} e^{r_1 t} + B \begin{pmatrix} k_{12} \\ k_{22} \end{pmatrix} e^{r_2 t},$$

where A and B are arbitrary constants, k_{11}, k_{21}, k_{12}, and k_{22} are known, and r_1 and r_2 are real but of opposite sign ($r_1 < 0$, $r_2 > 0$), then only the trajectories corresponding to solutions for which $B = 0$ will approach the critical point. Taking $A > 0$ gives one trajectory, $A < 0$ gives a second. A more general sketch of trajectories near a saddle point is shown in Figure 9.9b.

Case 3.   Equal Roots.   The general solution of Eqs. (6) is of the form

$$x = (A_1 + A_2 t)e^{rt}, \quad y = (B_1 + B_2 t)e^{rt}. \tag{13}$$

Regardless of the values of A_1, A_2, B_1, and B_2 it is clear that if $r < 0$, the direction of motion on all trajectories is toward the critical point and, if $r > 0$, it is away from the critical point. We will consider the case $r < 0$.

Depending on whether the term te^{rt} is present, the trajectories for this case are of two quite different types. The simpler case is when this term is not present; that is, when $A_2 = B_2 = 0$. Illustrative of this situation is the system

$$\frac{dx}{dt} = -x, \quad \frac{dy}{dt} = -y, \tag{14}$$

which has the general solution

$$x = Ae^{-t}, \quad y = Be^{-t}. \tag{15}$$

For $A \neq 0$, $B \neq 0$ the trajectories are the straight lines $y = (B/A)x$. The trajectories are sketched in Figure 9.10. Every trajectory has a different slope as it approaches (or recedes from, if r is greater than zero) the origin, and the critical point is called a *proper node*.

Typical of the situation when the term te^{rt} is present is the system

$$\frac{dx}{dt} = -2x, \qquad \frac{dy}{dt} = x - 2y, \tag{16}$$

which has the general solution

$$x = Ae^{-2t}, \qquad y = Be^{-2t} + Ate^{-2t}. \tag{17}$$

A detailed sketch of the trajectories represented by the solutions (17) is fairly complicated since, if t is eliminated between the equations for x and y, an

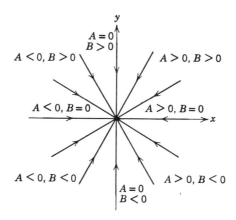

FIGURE 9.10   Proper node.

expression is obtained for y that involves both x and $\ln x$. Assuming that $A > 0$, it then follows from the first of Eqs. (17) that x is positive and $e^{-2t} = x/A$ so $t = -(\frac{1}{2}) \ln (x/A)$. Substituting this expression for t in the second of Eqs. (17) yields

$$y = \frac{Bx}{A} - \frac{x}{2} \ln \frac{x}{A}. \tag{18}$$

For assigned values of $A > 0$ and B, the trajectories can be obtained from Eq. (18). For $A < 0$ a similar equation can be derived.

It is clear from Eq. (17) that all of the trajectories approach the origin as $t \to \infty$. The slope at any point can be obtained from Eq. (18) for $A > 0$ or from a similar equation for $A < 0$, or by recalling that

$$\frac{dy}{dx} = \frac{dy/dt}{dx/dt} = \frac{-2Be^{-2t} - 2Ate^{-2t} + Ae^{-2t}}{-2Ae^{-2t}} = \frac{(-2B + A) - 2At}{-2A}. \tag{19}$$

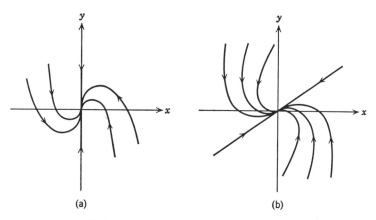

(a)   (b)

FIGURE 9.11   Improper node, $r_1 = r_2$.

For $t \to \infty$, $dy/dx \to \infty$; thus all of the trajectories enter the origin along the y axis. A qualitative picture of the trajectories is shown in Figure 9.11a. Again the critical point is called an *improper node*. A more general sketch is shown in Figure 9.11b.

    Case 4. Complex Roots.   In this case the general solution of Eqs. (6) is

$$x = e^{\lambda t}(A_1 \cos \mu t + A_2 \sin \mu t), \qquad y = e^{\lambda t}(B_1 \cos \mu t + B_2 \sin \mu t), \quad (20)$$

where the roots of Eq. (7) are $r = \lambda \pm i\mu$. If $\lambda < 0$ the motion on every trajectory is toward the critical point and, if $\lambda > 0$, it is away from the critical point. Consider the specific system

$$\frac{dx}{dt} = -x + 2y, \qquad \frac{dy}{dt} = -2x - y, \qquad (21)$$

which has the general solution

$$x = e^{-t}(A \cos 2t + B \sin 2t), \qquad y = e^{-t}(B \cos 2t - A \sin 2t). \quad (22)$$

The trajectories associated with the solutions (22) can best be visualized by introducing polar coordinates. Letting

$$x = r \cos \theta, \qquad y = r \sin \theta,$$

and

$$R = (A^2 + B^2)^{1/2}, \qquad R \cos \alpha = A, \qquad R \sin \alpha = B,$$

Eqs. (22) take the form

$$r \cos \theta = Re^{-t} \cos (2t - \alpha), \qquad r \sin \theta = -Re^{-t} \sin (2t - \alpha).$$

Thus $r = Re^{-t}$ and $\theta = -(2t - \alpha)$. Finally, eliminating t gives

$$r = Re^{(\theta - \alpha)/2},$$

which represents a family of spirals, one of which is sketched in Figure 9.12a.

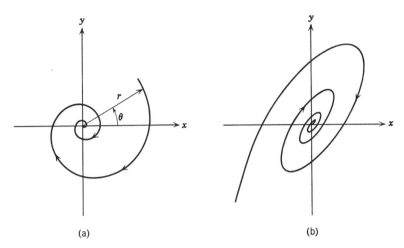

(a)   (b)

FIGURE 9.12 Spiral point.

Since $\lambda = -1 < 0$, the direction of motion is toward the critical point $(0, 0)$; since θ decreases with increasing t, the motion is clockwise. If λ were positive the spirals would be similar, but the direction of motion would be away from $(0, 0)$. The critical point is called a *spiral point*. A more general sketch of trajectories near a spiral point is shown in Figure 9.12*b*.

Case 5. Pure Imaginary Roots. While this is a special case of the previous one, it must be treated separately, since the trajectories are no longer spirals but rather closed curves. Typical of this case are the linearized undamped pendulum equations discussed as an example in Section 9.2. The trajectories, as shown in Figure 9.7 of the previous section, are ellipses centered at the origin. The origin is called a *center*. A typical case in which the major axes of the ellipses are inclined at an angle to the coordinate axes is shown in Figure 9.13.

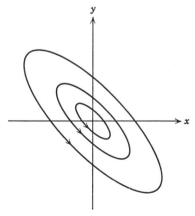

FIGURE 9.13 Center.

Of particular interest for this case is the fact that the smallest change in any one of the coefficients a, b, c, and d may change the trajectories from closed curves about the origin to spirals either directed toward the origin (real part of r_1, $r_2 < 0$) or away from the origin (real part of r_1, $r_2 > 0$).

In each of the cases we have discussed, the trajectories of the system exhibited one of the following three types of behavior.

(a) All of the trajectories approach the critical point as $t \to \infty$. This will be the case if the roots of the auxiliary equation (7) are real and negative or complex with negative real parts.

(b) The trajectories neither approach the critical point nor tend to infinity as $t \to \infty$. This will be the case if the roots of the auxiliary equation (7) are pure imaginary.

(c) At least one (possibly all) of the trajectories tends to infinity as $t \to \infty$. This will be the case if at least one of the roots of the auxiliary equation (7) is positive or if the roots have positive real parts.

The three possibilities (a), (b), and (c) illustrate the concepts of asymptotic stability, stability, and instability, respectively, of the critical point at the origin of the system (6). The precise definitions of these terms will be given in Section 9.4, but their basic meaning should be clear from the geometrical discussion above. Our analysis of the trajectories of the linear system (6) is summarized in Table 9.1.

In Section 9.4 we will discuss how these results may be used to investigate almost linear systems.

TABLE 9.1

$dx/dt = ax + by$	$r^2 - (a + d)r + (ad - bc) = 0$
$dy/dt = cx + dy$	$ad - bc \neq 0$

Roots of the Auxiliary Equation	Type of Critical Point	Stability
$r_1 > r_2 > 0$	Improper node	Unstable
$r_1 < r_2 < 0$		Asymptotically stable
$r_2 < 0 < r_1$	Saddle point	Unstable
$r_1 = r_2 > 0$	Proper or improper node	Unstable
$r_1 = r_2 < 0$		Asymptotically stable
$r_1, r_2 = \lambda \pm i\mu$	Spiral point	
$\lambda > 0$		Unstable
$\lambda < 0$		Asymptotically stable
$r_1 = i\mu, r_2 = -i\mu$	Center	Stable

PROBLEMS

In each of Problems 1 through 8 classify the critical point $(0, 0)$, and determine whether it is stable, asymptotically stable, or unstable.

1. $dx/dt = 3x - 2y$
   $dy/dt = 2x - 2y$

2. $dx/dt = 5x - y$
   $dy/dt = 3x + y$

3. $dx/dt = 2x - y$
   $dy/dt = 3x - 2y$

4. $dx/dt = x - 4y$
   $dy/dt = 4x - 7y$

5. $dx/dt = x - 5y$
   $dy/dt = x - 3y$

6. $dx/dt = 2x - 5y$
   $dy/dt = x - 2y$

7. $dx/dt = 3x - 2y$
   $dy/dt = 4x - y$

8. $dx/dt = -x - y$
   $dy/dt = -\frac{1}{4}y$

In each of Problems 9 through 11 determine the critical point (x_0, y_0), and then classify its type and examine its stability by making the transformation $x = x_0 + u$, $y = y_0 + v$.

9. $dx/dt = x + y - 2$
   $dy/dt = x - y$

10. $dx/dt = -2x + y - 2$
    $dy/dt = x - 2y + 1$

11. $dx/dt = -x - y - 1$
    $dy/dt = 2x - y + 5$

12. Consider the linear autonomous system

$$dx/dt = ax + by, \qquad dy/dt = cx + dy,$$

where a, b, c, and d are real constants. Let $p = a + d$, $q = ad - bc$, and $\Delta = p^2 - 4q$. Show that the critical point $(0, 0)$ is a

(a) node if $q > 0$ and $\Delta \geq 0$;
(b) saddle point if $q < 0$;
(c) spiral point if $p \neq 0$ and $\Delta < 0$;
(d) center if $p = 0$ and $q > 0$.

Hint: These conclusions can be obtained by studying the roots r_1 and r_2 of the auxiliary equation. It may also be helpful to show, and then use, the relations $r_1 r_2 = q$ and $r_1 + r_2 = p$.

13. Continuing Problem 12 show that the critical point $(0, 0)$ is

(a) asymptotically stable if $q > 0$ and $p < 0$;
(b) stable if $q > 0$ and $p = 0$;
(c) unstable if $q < 0$ or $p > 0$.

Notice that the results (a), (b), and (c) together with the fact that $q \neq 0$ show that the critical point is asymptotically stable if, and only if, $q > 0$ and $p < 0$.

14. The equation of motion of a spring-mass system with damping (see Section 3.7) is

$$m\frac{d^2u}{dt^2} + c\frac{du}{dt} + ku = 0,$$

where m, c, and k are positive. Write this second order equation as a system of two first order equations for $x = u$, $y = du/dt$. Show that $x = 0$, $y = 0$ is a critical point, and analyze the nature and stability of the critical point as a function of the parameters m, c, and k. A similar analysis can be applied to the electric circuit equation (see Section 3.8)

$$L\frac{d^2I}{dt^2} + R\frac{dI}{dt} + \frac{1}{C}I = 0.$$

9.4 STABILITY; ALMOST LINEAR SYSTEMS

In the previous sections of this chapter, we have on several occasions referred to the concepts of stability, asymptotic stability, and instability of a solution of the autonomous system

$$\frac{dx}{dt} = F(x, y), \qquad \frac{dy}{dt} = G(x, y). \tag{1}$$

In this section we will finally give a precise mathematical meaning to these concepts, discuss an important theorem dealing with the stability of an almost linear system, and explore its consequences by considering two illustrative examples.

A critical point $x = x_0$, $y = y_0$ (an equilibrium solution $x = x_0$, $y = y_0$) of the autonomous system (1) is said to be a *stable critical point* if, given any $\epsilon > 0$, it is possible to find a δ such that every solution $x = \phi(t)$, $y = \psi(t)$ of the system (1), which at $t = 0$ satisfies

$$\{[\phi(0) - x_0]^2 + [\psi(0) - y_0]^2\}^{1/2} < \delta, \tag{2}$$

exists and satisfies

$$\{[\phi(t) - x_0]^2 + [\psi(t) - y_0]^2\}^{1/2} < \epsilon \tag{3}$$

for all $t \geq 0$. This is illustrated geometrically in Figures 9.14a and 9.14b. These mathematical statements say that all solutions that start "sufficiently

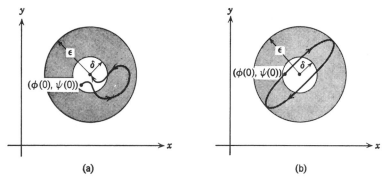

(a)   (b)

FIGURE 9.14

close" to (x_0, y_0) stay "close" to (x_0, y_0). Note that in Figure 9.14a the trajectory is within the circle $(x - x_0)^2 + (y - y_0)^2 = \delta^2$ at $t = 0$ and, while it soon passes outside of this circle, it remains within the circle $(x - x_0)^2 + (y - y_0)^2 = \epsilon^2$ for all $t \geq 0$. However, the trajectory of the solution does not have to approach the critical point (x_0, y_0), as is illustrated in Figure 9.14b.

A critical point (x_0, y_0) is said to be *asymptotically stable*, if it is stable and if there exists a δ_0, $0 < \delta_0 < \delta$, such that if a solution $x = \phi(t), y = \psi(t)$ satisfies

$$\{[\phi(0) - x_0]^2 + [\psi(0) - y_0]^2\}^{1/2} < \delta_0 \tag{4}$$

then

$$\lim_{t \to \infty} \phi(t) = x_0, \qquad \lim_{t \to \infty} \psi(t) = y_0. \tag{5}$$

Trajectories that start "sufficiently close" to (x_0, y_0) must not only stay "close" but must eventually approach (x_0, y_0) as t approaches infinity. This is the case for the trajectory in Figure 9.14a but not for the one in Figure 9.14b. Note that asymptotic stability is a stronger requirement than stability, since a critical point must be stable before we can even talk about whether it is asymptotically stable. On the other hand, the limit condition (5) which is an essential feature of asymptotic stability, does not by itself imply even ordinary stability. Indeed, examples can be constructed in which all of the trajectories approach (x_0, y_0) as $t \to \infty$, but for which (x_0, y_0) is not a stable critical point. Geometrically, all that is needed is a family of trajectories having members that start arbitrarily close to (x_0, y_0), then recede an arbitrarily large distance before eventually approaching (x_0, y_0) as t approaches infinity.*

A critical point that is not stable is said to be *unstable*.

For the linear system

$$\frac{dx}{dt} = ax + by, \qquad \frac{dy}{dt} = cx + dy, \tag{6}$$

with $ad - bc \neq 0$, the type and stability characteristics of the critical point $(0, 0)$ as a function of the roots $r_1 \neq 0$ and $r_2 \neq 0$ of the auxiliary equation

$$r^2 - (a + d)r + ad - bc = 0 \tag{7}$$

were listed in Table 9.1 of the preceding section. The stability characteristics are summarized in the following theorem.

Theorem 9.1. *The critical point $(0, 0)$ of the linear system (6) is asymptotically stable if the roots of the auxiliary equation (7) are real and negative or have negative real parts. It is stable, but not asymptotically stable, if the roots are pure imaginary. If either of the roots is real and positive or if they have positive real parts, it is unstable.*

---

* Such examples are fairly complicated and not often encountered in practice (see Cesari, page 96).

This theorem was established by intuitive arguments in the preceding section. For a rigorous proof, it is necessary to show how to compute δ for a given ϵ so that Eq. (3) is satisfied and how to compute δ_0 (for asymptotic stability) so that Eq. (5) is true. We will not take up this type of detailed analysis; however, the necessary arguments for a typical case are discussed in Problem 16.

Notice that if a critical point of the linear system (6) is asymptotically stable, then not only do trajectories which start close to the critical point approach the critical point but in fact, since every solution is a linear combination of $e^{r_1 t}$ and $e^{r_2 t}$, *every* trajectory approaches the critical point. In this case the critical point is said to be *globally asymptotically stable*. This property of linear systems is not, in general, true for nonlinear systems. This was illustrated by the example $dA/dt = \epsilon A - \sigma A^2$ with $\epsilon < 0$ and $\sigma < 0$, whose solutions are sketched in Figure 9.5 in Section 9.1. The critical point $A = 0$ is asymptotically stable but not globally asymptotically stable. Often an important practical problem in considering an asymptotically stable critical point of a nonlinear problem is to estimate the set of initial conditions for which the critical point is asymptotically stable. This set of initial points is called the *region of asymptotic stability* for the critical point. Alternatively, we may wish to determine whether the critical point is asymptotically stable for a given set of initial conditions. Again for the example sketched in Figure 9.5 the critical point $A = 0$ is asymptotically stable for all initial conditions $A(0)$ such that $A(0) < \epsilon/\sigma$.

We now want to relate these results for the linear system (6) to the nonlinear system

$$\frac{dx}{dt} = ax + by + F_1(x, y),$$

$$\frac{dy}{dt} = cx + dy + G_1(x, y),$$

(8)

mentioned at the beginning of Section 9.3. We assume that $(0, 0)$ is a critical point of the system (8) and that $ad - bc \neq 0$. Also we assume that F_1 and G_1 have continuous first partial derivatives and are small near the origin in the sense that $F_1(x, y)/r \to 0$ and $G_1(x, y)/r \to 0$ as $r \to 0$, where $r = (x^2 + y^2)^{1/2}$. Recall that such a system is said to be almost linear in the neighborhood of the origin. In our discussion we will usually not mention the phrase "near the origin," since it will be clear that we are talking about the neighborhood of the critical point $(0, 0)$.

As an example, the system

$$\frac{dx}{dt} = x - x^2 - xy$$

$$\frac{dy}{dt} = \tfrac{1}{2}y - \tfrac{1}{4}y^2 - \tfrac{3}{4}xy$$

(9)

satisfies the stated conditions. Here $a = 1$, $b = 0$, $c = 0$, $d = \frac{1}{2}$, $F_1(x, y) =$ $-x^2 - xy$, and $G_1(x, y) = -\frac{1}{4}y^2 - \frac{3}{4}xy$. To show that $F_1(x, y)/r \to 0$ as $r \to 0$, let $x = r \cos \theta$, $y = r \sin \theta$. Then

$$\frac{F_1(x, y)}{r} = \frac{-r^2 \cos^2 \theta - r^2 \sin \theta \cos \theta}{r} = -r(\cos^2 \theta + \cos \theta \sin \theta) \to 0$$

$$(10)$$

as $r \to 0$. The argument that $G_1(x, y)/r \to 0$ as $r \to 0$ is similar.

The question of the stability of the critical point $(0, 0)$ of the nonlinear system (8) is answered by the following theorem, which is due to Liapounov.

Theorem 9.2. *If the critical point $(0, 0)$ of the almost linear system (8) is an asymptotically stable critical point of the linear system (6), then it is an asymptotically stable critical point of the almost linear system (8). If it is an unstable critical point of the linear system (6), then it is an unstable critical point of the almost linear system (8).*

At this stage, the proof of this theorem is too difficult to give, and we will accept Theorem 9.2 without proof. The theorem does follow as a consequence of a result discussed in Section 9.5, and a proof is sketched in Problems 7 and 8 of Section 9.5. Essentially Theorem 9.2 says that for x and y near zero the nonlinear terms $F_1(x, y)$ and $G_1(x, y)$ are small and do not affect the asymptotic stability or instability of the critical point as determined by the linear terms. While it is not really correct to do so, we can think of the nonlinear terms as changing the roots of the auxiliary equation of the associated linear system by a small amount,* which gets smaller as x and y are restricted to smaller and smaller domains containing the origin. If r_1 and r_2 are real and nonzero, then a small change will not change the sign of the roots, and hence the stability or instability will not be changed; the situation is similar if r_1 and r_2 are complex with real parts not equal to zero. The case *not covered* by Theorem 9.2 is that of a critical point which is a center of the linear system (6). Then r_1 and r_2 are pure imaginary, and the "small" changes introduced by the nonlinear terms may lead to complex values for r_1 and r_2, with nonzero real parts. Depending on the real parts of r_1 and r_2 the center of the linear system may become a stable or an unstable spiral point, or it may even remain a center of the almost linear system (see Problem 15).

Furthermore, it can be shown that the critical point of the almost linear system (8) is of the same type (node, saddle point, spiral point) as that of the linear system (6) if

(a) r_1, r_2 are real, unequal, and of the same sign (improper node);
(b) r_1, r_2 are real and of opposite sign (saddle point);
(c) r_1, r_2 are complex with real parts not equal to zero (spiral point).

---

* In general the nonlinear system will not have simple solutions of the form exp (rt).

The two cases not mentioned are r_1 and r_2 pure imaginary and r_1 and r_2 real and equal. For the former, as mentioned earlier, nothing can be inferred about the critical point of the almost linear system. For the latter $(r_1 = r_2)$, while the asymptotic stability or instability does not change, the nature of the critical point for the almost linear system may be altered. The reason is that if the coefficients in an auxiliary equation that has equal roots are slightly perturbed, it is possible that (1) r_1 and r_2 remain equal, (2) r_1 and r_2 remain real but become unequal (improper node), or (3) r_1 and r_2 split apart to form two complex roots whose real parts are only slightly changed from the original value of $r_1 = r_2$ but with small nonzero imaginary parts (spiral point). The latter case is illustrated schematically in Figure 9.15.

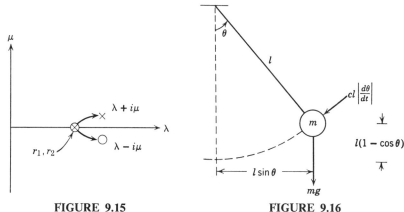

FIGURE 9.15   FIGURE 9.16

Even though the critical point is of the same type in cases (a), (b), and (c) as that of the linear system, the trajectories of the almost linear system may be considerably different in appearance from those of the corresponding linear system. This is illustrated in Problems 13 and 14. However, it can be shown that the slope at which trajectories "enter" or "leave" the critical point is given correctly by the linear equations.

Let us illustrate some of these ideas by considering two examples. First, consider the motion of a damped pendulum for which the damping is proportional to the speed; see Figure 9.16. It is not difficult to show, by reasoning similar to that used in the derivation of the spring-mass equation (Section 3.7), that the governing equation is

$$ml^2 \frac{d^2\theta}{dt^2} + cl \frac{d\theta}{dt} + mgl \sin \theta = 0, \tag{11}$$

where the damping constant $c > 0$. Letting $x = \theta$ and $y = d\theta/dt$ gives the system

$$\frac{dx}{dt} = y, \qquad \frac{dy}{dt} = -\frac{g}{l} \sin x - \frac{c}{ml} y. \tag{12}$$

The point $x = 0$, $y = 0$ is a critical point of the system (12). Because of the damping mechanism, we expect any small motion about $\theta = 0$ to decay in amplitude. Thus intuitively the equilibrium point $(0, 0)$ should be asymptotically stable. To show this we rewrite the system (12) as

$$\frac{dx}{dt} = y,$$

$$\frac{dy}{dt} = -\frac{g}{l}x - \frac{c}{ml}y - \frac{g}{l}(\sin x - x). \tag{13}$$

It was shown in Section 9.3 [see Eq. (5)] that $(\sin x - x)/r \to 0$ as $r \to 0$, so the system (13) is an almost linear system; hence Theorem 9.2 is applicable. The roots of the auxiliary equation associated with the corresponding linear system

$$\frac{dx}{dt} = y, \qquad \frac{dy}{dt} = -\frac{g}{l}x - \frac{c}{ml}y \tag{14}$$

are

$$r_1, r_2 = \frac{-c/ml \pm \sqrt{(c/ml)^2 - 4g/l}}{2}. \tag{15}$$

1. If $(c/ml)^2 - 4g/l > 0$ the roots are real, unequal, and negative. The critical point $(0, 0)$ is an asymptotically stable improper node of the linear system (14) and of the almost linear system (13).

2. If $(c/ml)^2 - 4g/l = 0$ the roots are real, equal, and negative. The critical point $(0, 0)$ is an asymptotically stable node of the linear system (14). It may be either an asymptotically stable node or an asymptotically stable spiral point of the almost linear system (13).

3. If $(c/ml)^2 - 4g/l < 0$ the roots are complex with negative real parts. The critical point $(0, 0)$ is an asymptotically stable spiral point of the linear system (14) and of the almost linear system (13).

In addition to the critical point $(0, 0)$, the almost linear system (13) has the critical points $x = n\pi$, $y = 0$, $n = \pm1, \pm2, \pm3, \ldots$ corresponding to $\theta = \pm\pi, \pm2\pi, \pm3\pi, \ldots$, $d\theta/dt = 0$. Again we expect (from Figure 9.16) that the points corresponding to $\theta = \pm2\pi, \pm4\pi, \ldots$ are asymptotically stable, and the points corresponding to $\theta = \pm\pi, \pm3\pi, \ldots$ are unstable. Consider the critical point $x = \pi$, $y = 0$. To examine the stability of this point, let

$$x = \pi + u, \qquad y = 0 + v. \tag{16}$$

Substituting for x and y in Eqs. (13) gives

$$\frac{du}{dt} = v,$$

$$\frac{dv}{dt} = -\frac{g}{l}(\pi + u) - \frac{c}{ml}v - \frac{g}{l}[\sin(\pi + u) - (\pi + u)]. \tag{17}$$

We are interested in studying the critical point $u = v = 0$ of the system (17). Noting that $\sin(\pi + u) = -\sin u$, the second of Eqs. (17) can be written as

$$\frac{dv}{dt} = -\frac{c}{ml}v + \frac{g}{l}\sin u$$

$$= \frac{g}{l}u - \frac{c}{ml}v + \frac{g}{l}(\sin u - u). \tag{18}$$

It is clear that the first of Eqs. (17) and Eq. (18) are the same as the system (13), except that $-g/l$ is replaced by g/l. The system is almost linear and the roots of the auxiliary equation of the corresponding linear system are given by

$$r_1, r_2 = \frac{-c/ml \pm \sqrt{(c/ml)^2 + 4g/l}}{2}.$$

One root will be positive, the other negative. Therefore, the critical point $x = \pi,\ y = 0$ is an unstable saddle point of both the linear system and the almost linear system, as expected.

As a final example, consider the system (9). Restricting x and y to be positive, we can think of these equations as a mathematical model of the interaction of two bacteria cultures with x and y denoting the population of each culture at time t. We ask whether there are equilibrium states that might be reached, or whether a periodic growth and decay will be observed, and how such possibilities depend on the initial state of the two cultures?

The critical points of the system (9) are the solutions of the nonlinear algebraic equations

$$x - x^2 - xy = x(1 - x - y) = 0$$

and $$\tag{19}$$

$$\tfrac{1}{2}y - \tfrac{1}{4}y^2 - \tfrac{3}{4}xy = y(\tfrac{1}{2} - \tfrac{1}{4}y - \tfrac{3}{4}x) = 0.$$

Clearly one solution is $x = y = 0$; a second solution is $x = 1,\ y = 0$; a third is $x = 0,\ y = 2$. Finally, if $x \neq 0,\ y \neq 0$ we obtain from Eqs. (19) the system

$$x + y = 1$$
$$3x + y = 2 \tag{20}$$

which has the solution $x = \tfrac{1}{2},\ y = \tfrac{1}{2}$. These four points in the xy plane are the only critical points of the system (9). We will consider each separately.

$x = 0,\ y = 0$. This corresponds to a state in which the two bacteria have destroyed each other. For this case the corresponding linear system, from Eqs. (9), is

$$\frac{dx}{dt} = x, \qquad \frac{dy}{dt} = \tfrac{1}{2}y, \tag{21}$$

and the roots of the auxiliary equation are 1 and $\frac{1}{2}$. Thus the origin is an unstable improper node: the solution $x = 0$, $y = 0$ of the interaction problem will not occur in practice.

$x = 1, y = 0.$ Clearly this corresponds to a state in which bacteria "x" has won the "war," having destroyed all of bacteria "y." To examine this critical point, it is convenient to translate it to the origin by letting $x = 1 + u$, $y = 0 + v$. Substituting for x and y in Eqs. (9) and simplifying we obtain

$$\frac{du}{dt} = -u - v - u^2 - uv,$$

$$\frac{dv}{dt} = -\tfrac{1}{4}v - \tfrac{1}{4}v^2 - \tfrac{3}{4}uv. \tag{22}$$

It is not difficult to show that the system (22) is an almost linear system. The corresponding linear system is $du/dt = -u - v$, $dv/dt = -v/4$, the roots of the auxiliary equation are $-\frac{1}{4}$ and -1, and the general solution is

$$u = -\tfrac{4}{3}Ae^{-t/4} + Be^{-t}, \qquad v = Ae^{-t/4}.$$

Thus $x = 1$, $y = 0$ is an asymptotically stable improper node. If the initial values of x and y are sufficiently close to $x = 1, y = 0$ the interaction will lead finally to that state.

For this critical point we will indicate how the trajectories of the linear system behave in the neighborhood of $x = 1$, $y = 0$. If $A = 0$, then $x = 1 + u = 1 + Be^{-t}$ and $y = v = 0$ so one pair of trajectories "enters" along the x axis. If $A \neq 0$ then

$$\frac{dy}{dx} = \frac{dv/dt}{d(1 + u)/dt} = \frac{-\tfrac{1}{4}Ae^{-t/4}}{\tfrac{1}{3}Ae^{-t/4} - Be^{-t}}$$

$$= \frac{-\tfrac{1}{4}A}{\tfrac{1}{3}A - Be^{-3t/4}} \to -\frac{3}{4}$$

as $t \to \infty$. Thus all other trajectories enter along a line with slope $-\frac{3}{4}$.

$x = 0, y = 2.$ The analysis is exactly similar to that for the critical point $x = 1, y = 0$. The critical point $x = 0, y = 2$ is also an asymptotically stable improper node. In this case bacteria y has won the war.

$x = 1/2, y = 1/2.$ This critical point corresponds to a possible mixed equilibrium state; a stand-off, so to speak, in the war between the two bacteria cultures. To examine the nature of this critical point we let $x = \frac{1}{2} + u$, $y = \frac{1}{2} + v$. Substituting for x and y in Eqs. (9) we obtain

$$\frac{du}{dt} = -\tfrac{1}{2}u - \tfrac{1}{2}v - u^2 - uv,$$

$$\frac{dv}{dt} = -\tfrac{3}{8}u - \tfrac{1}{8}v - \tfrac{1}{4}v^2 - \tfrac{3}{4}uv. \tag{23}$$

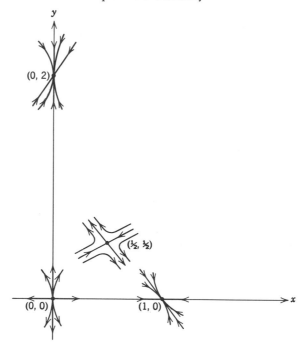

FIGURE 9.17(a)

The system (23) is an almost linear system, and the roots of the auxiliary equation of the corresponding linear system are $(-5 \pm \sqrt{57})/16$. Since these roots are real and of opposite sign, the critical point $(\frac{1}{2}, \frac{1}{2})$ is a saddle point. One pair of trajectories will enter the critical point; the others will recede from it. It can be shown by considering the general solution of the corresponding linear system that the slope of the pair of entering trajectories as $(x, y) \to (\frac{1}{2}, \frac{1}{2})$ is $(\sqrt{57} - 3)/8 \simeq 0.57$.

A *schematic* sketch of what the trajectories might look like in the neighborhood of each critical point is shown in Figure 9.17a. With a little detective work it is possible to extend the local pictures and obtain a global picture of the trajectories in the phase plane. First, we are only interested in x and y positive and, since the x and y axes are trajectories, it follows (trajectories cannot cross each other) that a trajectory that starts in the first quadrant must stay in the first quadrant, and a trajectory that starts in any other quadrant cannot enter the first quadrant. Second, we will accept the fact, which can be shown by advanced theory, that the system (9) does not have any trajectories that are closed curves (periodic solutions). Also we will accept without proof the fact that a trajectory cannot wander forever in the finite part of the plane—it must either enter a critical point or go off to infinity. But consider what is happening for x and y large. The nonlinear terms $-(x^2 + xy)$ and $-\frac{1}{4}(y^2 + 3xy)$ in the first and second of Eqs. (9), respectively, will outweigh the linear terms. Since they are negative, dx/dt

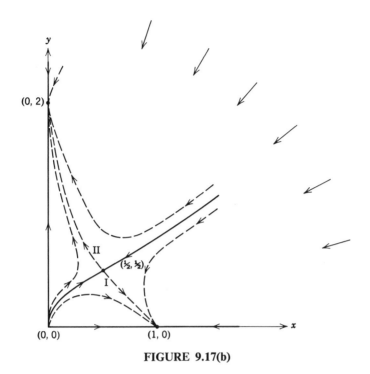

FIGURE 9.17(b)

and dy/dt will be negative for x and y large. Thus for x and y large the direction of motion on any trajectory is inward. The trajectories cannot escape to infinity! Eventually they must head toward one or the other of the two stable nodes. The *schematic* sketch shown in Figure 9.17b is not an unreasonable representation* of what must be happening in the first quadrant. If the initial values of x, y are in region I of Figure 9.17b, then x wins the war; if the initial values are in region II, then y wins—"peaceful coexistence" is not possible unless the initial point lies exactly on the dividing trajectory. Of particular interest would be the determination of the dividing trajectories that enter the saddle point $(\frac{1}{2}, \frac{1}{2})$.

PROBLEMS

In each of Problems 1 through 10, verify that $(0, 0)$ is a critical point, show that the system is almost linear, and discuss the type and stability of the critical point $(0, 0)$.

1. $dx/dt = x - y + xy$
   $dy/dt = 3x - 2y - xy$

2. $dx/dt = x + x^2 + y^2$
   $dy/dt = y - xy$

* The dotted trajectories that appear to go, for example, from $(0, 0)$ to $(1, 0)$ actually correspond to trajectories through particular initial points. As $t \to \infty$, they approach the stable node $(1, 0)$; as $t \to -\infty$ they approach the unstable node $(0, 0)$.

3. $dx/dt = -2x - y - x(x^2 + y^2)$
   $dy/dt = x - y + y(x^2 + y^2)$

4. $dx/dt = y + x(1 - x^2 - y^2)$
   $dy/dt = -x + y(1 - x^2 - y^2)$

5. $dx/dt = 2x + y + xy^3$
   $dy/dt = x - 2y - xy$

6. $dx/dt = x + 2x^2 - y^2$
   $dy/dt = x - 2y + x^3$

7. $dx/dt = y$
   $dy/dt = -x + \mu y(1 - x^2), \ \mu > 0$

8. $dx/dt = 1 + y - e^{-x}$
   $dy/dt = y - \sin x$

9. $dx/dt = (1 + x) \sin y$
   $dy/dt = 1 - x - \cos y$

10. $dx/dt = e^{-x+y} - \cos x$
    $dy/dt = \sin (x - 3y)$

11. Determine all real critical points of each of the following systems of equations and discuss their type and stability.

(a) $dx/dt = x + y^2$
    $dy/dt = x + y$

(b) $dx/dt = 1 - xy$
    $dy/dt = x - y^3$

(c) $dx/dt = x - x^2 - xy$
    $dy/dt = 3y - xy - 2y^2$

(d) $dx/dt = 1 - y$
    $dy/dt = x^2 - y^2$

12. For the undamped pendulum equation, $d^2\theta/dt^2 + (g/l) \sin \theta = 0$, show that Theorem 9.2 is not applicable for the critical point corresponding to $\theta = 0$, but does apply for the critical point corresponding to $\theta = \pi$.

13. Consider the autonomous system

$$dx/dt = y, \qquad dy/dt = x + 2x^3.$$

(a) Show that the critical point $(0, 0)$ is a saddle point.

(b) Sketch the trajectories for the corresponding linear system by integrating the equation for dy/dx. Show from the parametric form of the solution that the only trajectory on which $x \to 0$, $y \to 0$ as $t \to \infty$ is $y = -x$.

(c) Determine the trajectories for the nonlinear system by integrating the equation for dy/dx. Sketch the trajectories for the nonlinear system that correspond to $y = -x$ and $y = x$ for the linear system.

14. Consider the autonomous system

$$dx/dt = x, \qquad dy/dt = -2y + x^3.$$

(a) Show that the critical point $(0, 0)$ is a saddle point.

(b) Sketch the trajectories for the corresponding linear system (Problem 4(c) of Section 9.2), and show that the trajectory for which $x \to 0$, $y \to 0$ as $t \to \infty$ is given by $x = 0$.

(c) Determine the trajectories for the nonlinear system for $x \neq 0$ by integrating the equation for dy/dx. Show that the trajectory corresponding to $x = 0$ for the linear system is unaltered, but that the one corresponding to $y = 0$ is $y = x^5/5$. Sketch several of the trajectories for the nonlinear system.

15. Theorem 9.2 provides no information about the stability of a critical point of an almost linear system if that point is a center of the corresponding linear system. That this must be the case is illustrated by the following two systems

(i) $\begin{cases} dx/dt = y + x(x^2 + y^2) \\ dy/dt = -x + y(x^2 + y^2) \end{cases}$

(ii) $\begin{cases} dx/dt = y - x(x^2 + y^2) \\ dy/dt = -x - y(x^2 + y^2). \end{cases}$

(a) Show that $(0, 0)$ is a critical point of each system and, furthermore, is a center of the corresponding linear system.

(b) Show that each system is almost linear.

(c) Let $r^2 = x^2 + y^2$, and note that $x\,dx/dt + y\,dy/dt = r\,dr/dt$. For system (ii) show that $dr/dt < 0$ and that $r \to 0$ as $t \to \infty$, and hence the critical point is asymptotically stable. For system (i) show that the solution of the initial value problem for r with $r = r_0$ at $t = 0$ becomes unbounded as $t \to 1/2r_0^2$, and hence the critical point is unstable.

16. In this problem we will prove that if the roots of the auxiliary equation associated with the linear system $dx/dt = ax + by$, $dy/dt = cx + dy$ are real, negative, and unequal, then the critical point $(0, 0)$ is asymptotically stable. For simplicity, assume that the general solution is $x = A \exp\,(-r_1 t)$, $y = B \exp\,(-r_2 t)$ with $0 < r_1 < r_2$. It is necessary to show that given any $\epsilon > 0$, there exists a δ such that if

$$\{[x(0) - 0]^2 + [y(0) - 0]^2\}^{1/2} = (A^2 + B^2)^{1/2} < \delta,$$

then

$$\{[x - 0]^2 + [y - 0]^2\}^{1/2} = (A^2 e^{-2r_1 t} + B^2 e^{-2r_2 t})^{1/2} < \epsilon$$

for $t \geq 0$, and further $x \to 0$, $y \to 0$ as $t \to \infty$. The latter requirement is clearly true, so we consider the inequalities. Show that

$$A^2 e^{-2r_1 t} + B^2 e^{-2r_2 t} \leq A^2 + B^2$$

for $t \geq 0$. Hence δ may be taken equal to ϵ, and the desired conclusion follows. For other cases the arguments will be more complicated, but the result is the same: δ may be taken equal to ϵ.

9.5 LIAPOUNOV'S SECOND METHOD

In Section 9.4 we showed how the stability of a critical point of an almost linear system can usually be determined from a study of the corresponding linear system. However, no conclusion can be drawn when the critical point is a center of the corresponding linear system. Furthermore, for example, for an asymptotically stable critical point it may be important to investigate the region of asymptotic stability, that is, the domain such that all solutions which start within that domain approach the critical point. Since the theory of almost linear systems is a local theory, it provides no information about this question.

In this section we will discuss another approach, known as Liapounov's second method or direct method. This is a very powerful technique, which will provide a more global type of information, for example, an estimate of the extent of the region of asymptotic stability of a critical point. In addition, Liapounov's second method can also be used to study systems of equations that are not almost linear; however, we will not discuss such problems.

Basically Liapounov's second method is a generalization of the physical principles that for a conservative system (i) a rest position is stable if the potential energy is a local minimum, otherwise it is unstable; and (ii) the total energy is a constant during any motion. To illustrate these concepts, again consider the undamped pendulum (a conservative mechanical system), which is governed by the equation

$$\frac{d^2\theta}{dt^2} + \frac{g}{l}\sin\theta = 0. \tag{1}$$

The corresponding system of first order equations is

$$\frac{dx}{dt} = y, \qquad \frac{dy}{dt} = -\frac{g}{l}\sin x, \tag{2}$$

where $x = \theta$ and $y = d\theta/dt$. Omitting an arbitrary constant, the potential energy U is the work done in lifting the pendulum above its lowest position, namely $mgl(1 - \cos\theta)$; see Figure 9.16 in the previous section. Hence

$$U(x, y) = mgl(1 - \cos x). \tag{3}$$

The critical points of the system (2) are $x = \pm n\pi, y = 0, n = 0, 1, 2, 3, \ldots$, corresponding to $\theta = \pm n\pi, d\theta/dt = 0$. Physically, we expect that the points $x = 0, y = 0$; $x = \pm 2\pi, y = 0$; $\ldots$ corresponding to $\theta = 0, \pm 2\pi, \ldots$ for which the pendulum bob is vertical with the weight down will be stable; and that the points $x = \pm\pi, y = 0$; $x = \pm 3\pi, y = 0$; $\ldots$ corresponding to $\theta = \pm\pi, \pm 3\pi, \ldots$ for which the pendulum bob is vertical with the weight up will be unstable. This agrees with statement (i), for at the former points U is a minimum equal to zero, and at the latter points U is a maximum equal to $2\,mgl$.

Next consider the total energy V, which is the sum of the potential energy U and the kinetic energy $\frac{1}{2}ml^2(d\theta/dt)^2$. In terms of x and y

$$V(x, y) = mgl(1 - \cos x) + \frac{1}{2}ml^2y^2. \tag{4}$$

On a trajectory corresponding to a solution $x = \phi(t), y = \psi(t)$ of Eqs. (2), V can be considered as a function of t. The derivative of $V[\phi(t), \psi(t)]$ is called the rate of change of V following the trajectory. By the chain rule

$$\frac{dV[\phi(t), \psi(t)]}{dt} = V_x[\phi(t), \psi(t)]\frac{d\phi(t)}{dt} + V_y[\phi(t), \psi(t)]\frac{d\psi(t)}{dt}$$

$$= (mgl\sin x)\frac{dx}{dt} + ml^2y\frac{dy}{dt}, \tag{5}$$

where it is understood that $x = \phi(t), y = \psi(t)$. But dx/dt and dy/dt can be obtained in terms of x and y from Eqs. (2) Thus at any point (x, y) the rate of change of V along the trajectory passing through that point can be computed *without actually solving* the system (2). It is precisely this fact that allows us to use Liapounov's second method for systems whose solutions we do not know, and hence makes it such an important technique. Substituting in Eqs. (5) for dx/dt and dy/dt from Eqs. (2) yields $dV/dt = 0$.

Hence V is a constant along any trajectory of the system (2), which is in agreement with our earlier remark (ii) that the total energy is constant during any motion of a conservative system.

At the stable critical points, $x = \pm 2n\pi$, $y = 0$, $n = 0, 1, 2, \ldots$, the energy V is zero. If the initial state, say (x_1, y_1), of the pendulum is sufficiently near a stable critical point the trajectory in the phase plane of the motion will stay near the critical point. Since V is constant the trajectory lies on the curve given by $V(x, y) = V(x_1, y_1)$, the initial value of the energy. It is not difficult to show that if $V(x_1, y_1)$ is sufficiently small, which will be the case if (x_1, y_1) is sufficiently near a stable critical point, then the curve will be closed and will contain the critical point. Physically, this corresponds to a solution that is periodic in time—the motion is a small oscillation about the equilibrium point. If damping is present, however, it is natural to expect that the amplitude of the motion decays in time and that the stable critical point becomes an asymptotically stable critical point. This can almost be argued from a consideration of dV/dt. For the damped pendulum, the total energy is still given by Eq. (4); but now from Eqs. (12) of Section 9.4 $dx/dt = y$ and $dy/dt = -(g/l)\sin x - (c/lm)y$. Substituting for dx/dt and dy/dt in Eq. (5) gives $dV/dt = -cly^2 \leq 0$. Thus the energy is nonincreasing along any trajectory and, except for the line $y = 0$, the motion is such that the energy decreases, and hence each trajectory must approach a point of minimum energy—a stable equilibrium point. If $dV/dt < 0$ instead of $dV/dt \leq 0$ it is reasonable to expect that this would be true for all trajectories that start sufficiently close to the origin.

To pursue these ideas further, consider the autonomous system

$$\frac{dx}{dt} = F(x, y), \qquad \frac{dy}{dt} = G(x, y), \tag{6}$$

and suppose that the point $x = 0$, $y = 0$ is an asymptotically stable critical point. Then there exists some domain D containing $(0, 0)$ such that every trajectory which starts in D must approach the origin as $t \to \infty$. Suppose that there exists an "energy" function V such that $V(x, y) \geq 0$ for (x, y) in D with $V = 0$ only at the origin. Since each trajectory in D approaches the origin as $t \to \infty$, then following any particular trajectory, V decreases to zero as t approaches infinity. The type of result we want to prove is essentially the converse: if, on every trajectory, V decreases as t increases, then the trajectories must approach the origin as $t \to \infty$, and hence the origin is asymptotically stable. First, however, it is necessary to make several definitions.

Let V be defined on some domain D containing the origin. Then V is said to be *positive definite* on D if $V(0, 0) = 0$ and $V(x, y) > 0$ for all other points in D. Similarly, V is said to be *negative definite* on D if $V(0, 0) = 0$ and $V(x, y) < 0$ for all other points in D. If the inequalities $>$ and $<$ are replaced by $\geq$ and $\leq$, then V is said to be *positive semidefinite* and *negative semidefinite*, respectively. We emphasize that in speaking of a positive definite (negative definite, . . .) function on a domain D containing the origin, the function must be zero at the origin in addition to satisfying the proper inequality at all other points in D.

Example 1.   The function

$$V(x, y) = \sin (x^2 + y^2)$$

is positive definite on $x^2 + y^2 < \pi^2/4$ since $V(0, 0) = 0$ and $V(x, y) > 0$ for $0 < x^2 + y^2 < \pi^2/4$. However, the function

$$V(x, y) = (x + y)^2$$

is only positive semidefinite since $V(x, y) = 0$ on the line $y = -x$.

We will also want to consider the function

$$\dot{V}(x, y) = V_x(x, y)F(x, y) + V_y(x, y)G(x, y). \tag{7}$$

The reason that we choose this notation is because $\dot{V}(x, y)$ can be identified as the rate of change of V along the trajectory of the system (6) that passes through the point (x, y). That is, if $x = \phi(t)$, $y = \psi(t)$ is a solution of the system (6), then

$$\frac{dV[\phi(t), \psi(t)]}{dt} = V_x[\phi(t), \psi(t)] \frac{d\phi(t)}{dt} + V_y[\phi(t), \psi(t)] \frac{d\psi(t)}{dt}$$

$$= V_x(x, y)F(x, y) + V_y(x, y)G(x, y)$$

$$= \dot{V}(x, y). \tag{8}$$

The function $\dot{V}$ is sometimes referred to as the derivative of V with respect to the system (6).

We now state two Liapounov theorems, the first dealing with stability, the second with instability.

Theorem 9.3.   *Suppose that the autonomous system* (6) *has an isolated critical point at the origin. If there exists a function V that is continuous and has continuous first partial derivatives, is positive definite, and for which the function $\dot{V}$ given by Eq.* (7) *is negative definite on some domain D in the xy plane containing* $(0, 0)$, *then the origin is an asymptotically stable critical point. If $\dot{V}$ is negative semidefinite, then the origin is a stable critical point.*

Theorem 9.4.   *Let the origin be an isolated critical point of the autonomous system* (6). *Let V be a function that is continuous and has continuous first partial derivatives. Suppose that $V(0, 0) = 0$ and that in every neighborhood of the origin there is at least one point at which V is positive (negative). Then if there exists a domain D containing the origin such that the function $\dot{V}$ as given by Eq.* (7) *is positive definite (negative definite) on D, then the origin is c unstable critical point.*

Before sketching a geometric proof of Theorem 9.3, we note that the difficulty is using Theorems 9.3 and 9.4 is that they tell us nothing about how to construct the function V, called a *Liapounov function*, assuming that one exists. In cases where the autonomous system (6) represents a physical problem it is natural first to consider the actual total energy function of the system as a possible Liapounov function. However, we emphasize that Theorems 9.3 and 9.4 are applicable in cases where there is no physical energy. In such cases a judicious trial and error approach may be necessary.

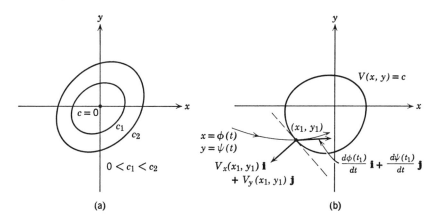

FIGURE 9.18

Now consider the second part of Theorem 9.3, that is, the case $\dot{V}(x, y) \leq 0$. Let $c \geq 0$ be a constant and consider the curve in the xy plane given by the equation $V(x, y) = c$. For $c = 0$ the curve reduces to the single point $x = 0$, $y = 0$. However, for $c > 0$ and sufficiently small, it can be shown by using the continuity of V that we will obtain a closed curve containing the origin as illustrated in Figure 9.18a. There may, of course, be other curves in the xy plane corresponding to the same value of c, but these are not of interest. Further, again by continuity, as c gets smaller and smaller the closed curves $V(x, y) = c$ enclosing the origin shrink to the origin. We will show that a trajectory that starts inside of a closed curve $V(x, y) = c$ cannot cross to the outside. Thus given a circle of radius ϵ about the origin, we can by taking c sufficiently small ensure that every trajectory that starts inside of the closed curve $V(x, y) = c$ stays within the circle of radius ϵ; indeed it will stay within the closed curve $V(x, y) = c$ itself. Thus the origin will be a stable critical point.

It is shown in calculus books that the vector*

$$V_x(x, y)\mathbf{i} + V_y(x, y)\mathbf{j}, \tag{9}$$

---

* The vector $V_x(x, y)\mathbf{i} + V_y(x, y)\mathbf{j}$ is known as the gradient of V or grad V.

where $\mathbf{i}$ and $\mathbf{j}$ are unit vectors in the positive x and y directions, is normal to the curve $V(x, y) = c$. Furthermore, since $V(x, y)$ increases outward from the origin, the vector (9) will point away from the origin as indicated in Figure 9.18b. Next consider the angle of intersection of a trajectory corresponding to a solution $x = \phi(t)$, $y = \psi(t)$ of the system (6) and a closed curve $V(x, y) = c$. Suppose that the point of intersection is $x_1 = \phi(t_1)$, $y_1 = \psi(t_1)$. From Eq. (7) and the fact that $d\phi(t_1)/dt = F(x_1, y_1)$, $d\psi(t_1)/dt = G(x_1, y_1)$ we have

$$\dot{V}(x_1, y_1) = V_x(x_1, y_1)\frac{d\phi(t_1)}{dt} + V_y(x_1, y_1)\frac{d\psi(t_1)}{dt}$$

$$= [V_x(x_1, y_1)\mathbf{i} + V_y(x_1, y_1)\mathbf{j}] \cdot \left[\frac{d\phi(t_1)}{dt}\mathbf{i} + \frac{d\psi(t_1)}{dt}\mathbf{j}\right],$$

where $[d\phi(t_1)/dt]\mathbf{i} + [d\psi(t_1)/dt]\mathbf{j}$ is the tangent vector to the trajectory $x = \phi(t)$, $y = \psi(t)$ at the point (x_1, y_1); see Figure 9.18b. Since, by hypothesis, $\dot{V}(x_1, y_1) \leq 0$, it follows that the angle between these two vectors is greater than or equal to 90°. Hence the direction of motion on the trajectory must be inward or, at worst, tangent to the curve. Trajectories that start inside a closed curve $V(x, y) = c$ (no matter how small c is) cannot escape, so the origin is a stable point. If $\dot{V}(x, y) < 0$ then the trajectories passing through points on the curve are actually pointed inward. As a consequence, it can be shown that trajectories which start sufficiently close to the origin must approach the origin, and hence the origin will be asymptotically stable.

A geometric proof of Theorem 9.4 follows by somewhat similar arguments. Briefly, suppose that $\dot{V}$ is positive definite, and suppose that given any circle about the origin there is an interior point (x_1, y_1) at which $V(x_1, y_1) > 0$. Consider a trajectory that starts at (x_1, y_1). Along this trajectory it follows from Eq. (8) that V must increase, since $\dot{V}(x, y) > 0$; furthermore, since $V(x_1, y_1) > 0$ the trajectory cannot approach the origin because $V(0, 0) = 0$. This shows that the origin cannot be asymptotically stable. By further exploiting the fact that $\dot{V}(x, y) > 0$, it is possible to show that the origin is an unstable point; however, we will not pursue such an argument.

To illustrate the use of Theorem 9.3 we consider the question of the stability of the critical point $(0, 0)$ of the undamped pendulum equations (2). While the system (2) is almost linear, the point $(0, 0)$ is a center of the corresponding linear system, so no conclusion can be drawn from Theorem 9.2. Since the mechanical system is conservative, it is natural to suspect that the total energy function V given by Eq. (4) will be a Liapounov function. For example, if we take D to be the domain $-\pi/2 < x < \pi/2$, $-\infty < y < \infty$, then V is positive definite. As we have seen $\dot{V}(x, y) = 0$, so it follows from the second part of Theorem 9.3 that the critical point $(0, 0)$ of Eqs. (2) is a stable critical point.

From a practical point of view one is usually interested more in asymptotic stability than stability. For example, for the automatic control for the wing flap mentioned in Section 9.1, it is not sufficient that the control keep the flap close to a certain setting—rather, it must damp out deviations from the correct setting. Clearly it is desirable to know the allowable deviations from the set position that the automatic control can damp out; that is, to know the region of asymptotic stability. One of the simplest results, dealing with this question, is given by the following theorem.

Theorem 9.5.   *Let the origin be an isolated critical point of the autonomous system (6). Let the function V be continuous and have continuous first partial derivatives. If there is a bounded domain D_K containing the origin such that $V(x, y) < K$, V is positive definite, and $\dot{V}$ is negative definite in D_K, then every solution of Eqs. (6) that starts in D_K approaches the origin as t approaches infinity.*

This theorem is proved by showing that there are no periodic solutions of the system (6) in D_K, nor are there any other critical points in D_K. It then follows that trajectories that start in D_K cannot escape and, hence, must tend to the origin as t tends to infinity.

Liapounov's second method is a *direct method* in that no knowledge of the solution of the system of differential equations is required; rather, conclusions about the stability or instability of a critical point are obtained by constructing a suitable Liapounov function. Theorems 9.3 and 9.4 give sufficient conditions for stability and instability, respectively. However, these conditions are not necessary, nor does our failure to determine a suitable Liapounov function mean that there is not one. Unfortunately, there are no general methods for the construction of Liapounov functions; however, there has been extensive work on the construction of Liapounov functions for special classes of equations. One simple result from elementary algebra, which is often useful in constructing positive definite or negative definite functions, is stated without proof in the following theorem.

Theorem 9.6.   *The function*

$$V(x, y) = ax^2 + bxy + cy^2 \tag{10}$$

is positive definite if, and only if,

$$a > 0 \qquad and \qquad 4ac - b^2 > 0, \tag{11}$$

and is negative definite if, and only if,

$$a < 0 \qquad and \qquad 4ac - b^2 > 0. \tag{12}$$

The use of Theorem 9.6 is illustrated in the following example.

Example 2.   Show that the critical point (0, 0) of the autonomous system

$$\frac{dx}{dt} = -x - xy^2, \qquad \frac{dy}{dt} = -y - yx^2 \tag{13}$$

is asymptotically stable.

We try to construct a Liapounov function of the form (10). Then
$V_x(x, y) = 2ax + by$, $V_y(x, y) = bx + 2cy$, so

$$\dot{V}(x, y) = (2ax + by)(-x - xy^2) + (bx + 2cy)(-y - yx^2)$$
$$= -[2a(x^2 + x^2y^2) + b(2xy + xy^3 + yx^3) + 2c(y^2 + x^2y^2)].$$

If we choose $b = 0$, and a and c to be any positive numbers, then $\dot{V}$ is
negative definite and V is positive definite by Theorem 9.6. Thus by Theorem
9.3 the origin is an asymptotically stable critical point.

PROBLEMS

1. By constructing suitable Liapounov functions of the form $ax^2 + cy^2$, where
a and c are to be determined, show that for each of the following systems the
critical point at the origin is of the indicated type.

(a) $dx/dt = -x^3 + xy^2$, $dy/dt = -2x^2y - y^3$;   asymptotically stable
(b) $dx/dt = -\frac{1}{2}x^3 + 2xy^2$, $dy/dt = -y^3$;   asymptotically stable
(c) $dx/dt = -x^3 + 2y^3$, $dy/dt = -2xy^2$;   stable (at least)
(d) $dx/dt = x^3 - y^3$, $dy/dt = 2xy^2 + 4x^2y + 2y^3$;   unstable

2. For the system of equations

$$\frac{dx}{dt} = y - xf(x, y), \qquad \frac{dy}{dt} = -x - yf(x, y),$$

where f is continuous and has continuous first partial derivatives, show that if
$f(x, y) > 0$ in some neighborhood of the origin, then the origin is an asymptotically
stable critical point, and if $f(x, y) < 0$ in some neighborhood of the origin then the
origin is an unstable critical point.
Hint: Construct a Liapounov function of the form $c(x^2 + y^2)$.

3. A generalization of the undamped pendulum equation is

$$\frac{d^2u}{dt^2} + g(u) = 0, \tag{i}$$

where $g(0) = 0$, $g(u) > 0$ for $0 < u < k$, and $g(u) < 0$ for $-k < u < 0$; that
is, $ug(u) > 0$ for $u \neq 0$, $-k < u < k$. (Notice that $g(u) = \sin u$ has this property
for $-\pi/2 < u < \pi/2$.)
(a) Letting $x = u$, $y = du/dt$, write Eq. (i) as a system of two equations, and
show that $x = 0$, $y = 0$ is a critical point.
(b) Show that

$$V(x, y) = \frac{1}{2}y^2 + \int_0^x g(s)\, ds, \qquad -k < x < k, \tag{ii}$$

is positive definite, and use this result to show that the critical point $(0, 0)$ is stable.
Note that the Liapounov function V given by Eq. (ii) corresponds to the energy
function $V(x, y) = \frac{1}{2}y^2 + (1 - \cos x)$ for $g(u) = \sin u$.

4. By introducing suitable dimensionless variables, the system of nonlinear equations for the damped pendulum (Eqs. (12) of Section 9.4) can be written as

$$\frac{dx}{dt} = y, \qquad \frac{dy}{dt} = -y - \sin x.$$

(a) Show that the origin is a critical point.

*(b) Show that while $V(x, y) = x^2 + y^2$ is positive definite, $\dot{V}(x, y)$ takes on both positive and negative values in any domain containing the origin, so that V is not a Liapounov function.

Hint: $x - \sin x > 0$ for $x > 0$ and $x - \sin x < 0$ for $x < 0$. Consider these cases with y positive but y so small that y^2 can be ignored compared to y.

(c) Show using the energy function $V(x, y) = \frac{1}{2}y^2 + (1 - \cos x)$, obtained from Eq. (ii) of Problem 3, that the origin is a stable critical point. Note, however, that even though there is damping and we can expect that the origin is asymptotically stable, it is not possible to draw this conclusion using the present Liapounov function.

*(d) To show asymptotic stability it is necessary to construct a better Liapounov function than the one used in Part (c). Show that $V(x, y) = \frac{1}{2}(x + y)^2 + x^2 + \frac{1}{2}y^2$ is such a Liapounov function, and conclude that the origin is an asymptotically stable critical point.

Hint: Using Taylor's formula with a remainder, it follows that $\sin x = x - \alpha x^3/3!$ where α depends on x but $0 < \alpha < 1$ for $-\pi/2 < x < \pi/2$; then letting $x = r \cos \theta$, $y = r \sin \theta$ show that $\dot{V}(r, \theta) = -r^2[1 + h(r, \theta)]$ where $|h(r, \theta)| < 1$ if r is sufficiently small.

5. (a) A generalization of the damped pendulum problem, or a damped mass spring system where the spring force may be nonlinear, is the Liénard equation

$$\frac{d^2u}{dt^2} + \frac{du}{dt} + g(u) = 0,$$

where the function g satisfies the conditions of Problem 3. Letting $x = u, y = du/dt$, show that the origin is a critical point of the resulting system. Using the Liapounov function of Problem 3, show that the origin is a stable critical point, but note that even with damping we cannot conclude asymptotic stability using this Liapounov function.

*(b) Asymptotic stability of the critical point $(0, 0)$ can be shown by constructing a better Liapounov function as was done in part (d) of Problem 4. However, the analysis for a general function g is somewhat sophisticated and we will only mention that V will have the form

$$V(x, y) = \frac{1}{2}y^2 + Ayg(x) + \int_0^x g(s)\, ds,$$

where A is a positive constant to be chosen so that V is positive definite and $\dot{V}$ is negative definite. For the pendulum problem [$g(x) = \sin x$] use V as given by the above equation with $A = \frac{1}{2}$ to show that the origin is asymptotically stable.

Hint: Use $\sin x = x - \alpha x^3/3!$ and $\cos x = 1 - \beta x^2/2!$ where α and β depend on x, but $0 < \alpha < 1$ and $0 < \beta < 1$ for $-\pi/2 < x < \pi/2$; let $x = r \cos \theta, y = r \sin \theta$, and show that $\dot{V}(r, \theta) = -\frac{1}{2}r^2[1 + \frac{1}{2}\sin 2\theta + h(r, \theta)]$ where $|h(r, \theta)| < \frac{1}{2}$ if r is sufficiently small. To show that V is positive definite use $\cos x = 1 - x^2/2 + \gamma x^4/4$ where γ depends on x, but $0 < \gamma < 1$ for $-\pi/2 < x < \pi/2$.

6. A further generalization of the Liénard equation of Problem 5 is the equation

$$\frac{d^2u}{dt^2} + c(u)\frac{du}{dt} + g(u) = 0,$$

where the function g satisfies the conditions of Problem 3 and $c(u) \geq 0$. Show that the point $u = 0$, $du/dt = 0$ is a stable critical point.

In Problems 7 and 8 we will prove the first part of Theorem 9.2: if the critical point at $(0, 0)$ of the almost linear system

$$\frac{dx}{dt} = ax + by + F_1(x, y), \qquad \frac{dy}{dt} = cx + dy + G_1(x, y) \tag{i}$$

is an asymptotically stable critical point of the corresponding linear system

$$\frac{dx}{dt} = ax + by, \qquad \frac{dy}{dt} = cx + dy, \tag{ii}$$

then it is an asymptotically stable critical point of the almost linear system (i).

7. Consider the linear system (ii).
(a) Since $(0, 0)$ is an asymptotically stable point, show that $a + d < 0$ and $ad - bc > 0$. (See Problem 13 of Section 9.3.)
(b) Construct a Liapounov function $V(x, y) = Ax^2 + Bxy + Cy^2$, such that V is positive definite and $\dot{V}$ is negative definite. One way to insure that $\dot{V}$ is negative definite is to choose A, B, and C so that $\dot{V}(x, y) = -x^2 - y^2$. Show that this leads to the result

$$A = -\frac{c^2 + d^2 + (ad - bc)}{2\Delta}, \qquad B = \frac{bd + ac}{\Delta}, \qquad C = -\frac{a^2 + b^2 + (ad - bc)}{2\Delta},$$

where $\Delta = (a + d)(ad - bc)$.
(c) Using the result of part (a) show that $A > 0$, and then show (several steps of algebra are required) that

$$4AC - B^2 = \frac{(a^2 + b^2 + c^2 + d^2)(ad - bc) + 2(ad - bc)^2}{\Delta^2} > 0.$$

Thus by Theorem 9.6, V is positive definite.

8. In this problem we will show that the Liapounov function constructed in the previous problem is also a Liapounov function for the almost linear system (i). We must show that there is some region containing the origin for which $\dot{V}$ is negative definite.
(a) Show that

$$\dot{V}(x, y) = -(x^2 + y^2) + (2Ax + By)F_1(x, y) + (Bx + 2Cy)G_1(x, y).$$

(b) Recall that $F_1(x, y)/r \to 0$ and $G_1(x, y)/r \to 0$ as $r = (x^2 + y^2)^{1/2} \to 0$. This means that given any $\epsilon > 0$ there exists a circle $r = R$ about the origin such that for $0 \leq r < R$, $|F_1(x, y)| < \epsilon r$ and $|G_1(x, y)| < \epsilon r$. Letting M be the maximum of $|2A|$, $|B|$, and $|C|$, show by introducing polar coordinates that R can be chosen so that $\dot{V}(x, y) < 0$ for $r < R$.
Hint: Choose ϵ sufficiently small in terms of M.

*9.6 PERIODIC SOLUTIONS AND LIMIT CYCLES

On several occasions we have mentioned the possible existence of periodic solutions of nonlinear autonomous systems. Such solutions, whose trajectories form *closed curves* in the phase plane, play an important role in many physical phenomena. A periodic solution often represents a sort of "final state" toward which all "neighboring" solutions tend as the transients due to the initial conditions die out. In some cases, for example an electronic oscillator, even though resistance is present the flow of current is periodic. The existence of these periodic solutions can only be explained by a consideration of the nonlinear terms in the governing equations—no linearized mathematical model with a resistance term can predict a periodic solution.

A special case of a periodic solution is a constant solution $x = x_0$, $y = y_0$, corresponding to a critical point of the autonomous system. Such a solution is clearly periodic with any period. In this section when we speak of a periodic solution we will mean a nonconstant periodic solution.

Recall that the solutions of the linear autonomous system

$$\frac{dx}{dt} = ax + by, \qquad \frac{dy}{dt} = cx + dy \tag{1}$$

are periodic if and only if the roots of the auxiliary equation

$$r^2 - (a + d)r + (ad - bc) = 0 \tag{2}$$

are pure imaginary. In this case the critical point at the origin will necessarily be a stable critical point as discussed in Section 9.3. We emphasize that if the roots of Eq. (2) are pure imaginary, then *every* solution of the linear system (1) is periodic, and if the roots are not pure imaginary then Eqs. (1) have *no* periodic solutions.

The situation can be quite different for a nonlinear autonomous system. A standard example is the system

$$\frac{dx}{dt} = y + x - x(x^2 + y^2), \qquad \frac{dy}{dt} = -x + y - y(x^2 + y^2). \tag{3}$$

It is not difficult to show that $x = 0$, $y = 0$ is the only critical point of the system (3), and also that the system is almost linear in the neighborhood of the origin. Further, from a consideration of the corresponding linear system [$a = 1$, $b = 1$, $c = -1$, $d = 1$ in Eq. (1)], it follows that the origin is an unstable spiral point for the system (3). Thus any solution that starts near the origin in the phase plane will spiral away from the origin. Since there are no other critical points, our first thought might be that all solutions of Eqs. (3) have trajectories which spiral out to infinity. However, we will now show that far away from the origin the trajectories are directed inward, so that something else must be happening.

It is convenient to introduce the polar coordinates r and θ where

$$x = r \cos \theta, \qquad y = r \sin \theta. \tag{4}$$

Multiplying the first of Eqs. (3) by x, the second by y, and adding gives

$$x \frac{dx}{dt} + y \frac{dy}{dt} = (x^2 + y^2) - (x^2 + y^2)^2. \tag{5}$$

Since $r^2 = x^2 + y^2$ and $r\, dr/dt = x\, dx/dt + y\, dy/dt$, we obtain

$$r \frac{dr}{dt} = r^2(1 - r^2). \tag{6}$$

Thus if $r > 1$, then $dr/dt < 0$, and the direction of motion on a trajectory is inward. Similarly, if $r < 1$, then the direction of motion is outward. Clearly, the circle $r = 1$ in the phase plane has a special significance for this system.

To obtain an equation for θ, we multiply the first of Eqs. (3) by y, the second by x, and subtract, obtaining

$$y \frac{dx}{dt} - x \frac{dy}{dt} = x^2 + y^2. \tag{7}$$

Upon computing dx/dt and dy/dt from Eqs. (4), we find that the left-hand side of Eq. (7) is $-r^2\, d\theta/dt$, so Eq. (7) reduces to

$$\frac{d\theta}{dt} = -1. \tag{8}$$

The system of equations (6) and (8) for r and θ is equivalent to the original system (3). One solution of the system (6) and (8) is

$$r = 1, \qquad \theta = -t + t_0, \tag{9}$$

where t_0 is an arbitrary constant. As t increases, a point satisfying Eqs. (9) moves clockwise around the unit circle. Thus the autonomous system (3) has a periodic solution. Other solutions can be obtained by solving Eq. (6) by separation of variables; for $r \neq 0$ and $r \neq 1$,

$$\frac{dr}{r(1 - r^2)} = dt. \tag{10}$$

Equation (10) can be integrated by using partial fractions to rewrite the left-hand side. Omitting these algebraic calculations, the solution of Eqs. (8) and (10) is

$$r = \frac{1}{\sqrt{1 + c_0 e^{-2t}}}, \qquad \theta = -t + t_0, \tag{11}$$

where c_0 and t_0 are arbitrary constants. In this case the solution (11) also contains the solution (9), which is obtained by setting $c_0 = 0$ in Eq. (11).

The solution satisfying the initial conditions $r = \rho$, $\theta = \alpha$ at $t = 0$ is given by

$$r = \frac{1}{\sqrt{1 + [(1/\rho^2) - 1]e^{-2t}}}, \qquad \theta = -(t - \alpha). \qquad (12)$$

If $0 < \rho < 1$, $r \to 1$ from the inside as $t \to \infty$; if $\rho > 1$, $r \to 1$ from the outside as $t \to \infty$. Thus the trajectories spiral toward the circle $r = 1$ as $t \to \infty$. A schematic sketch of the trajectories is shown in Figure 9.19.

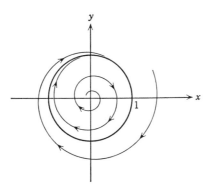

FIGURE 9.19

Not only does the circle $r = 1$ correspond to a periodic solution of the autonomous system (3), but also nonclosed trajectories spiral toward it as $t \to \infty$. A closed curve in the phase plane which has nonclosed curves spiraling toward it, either from the inside or outside, as $t \to \infty$ is called a *limit cycle*.* Thus the circle $r = 1$ is a limit cycle of the autonomous system (3). If all trajectories that start near a closed trajectory (both inside and outside) spiral toward the closed trajectory as $t \to \infty$, we say that the limit cycle is *stable*. This type of stability is sometimes referred to as *orbital stability*. If the trajectories on one side spiral toward the closed trajectory, while on the other side they spiral away as $t \to \infty$, we say that the limit cycle is *semistable*. If the trajectories on both sides of the closed trajectory spiral away as $t \to \infty$, we say that the closed trajectory is *unstable*. It is also possible to have closed trajectories that are neither approached nor receded from; for example, the family of periodic solutions of a linear autonomous system. In this case we say the closed trajectory is *neutrally stable*.

For the example just considered the existence of a stable limit cycle was established by direct calculation; in most cases this is not possible. However, there are several general theorems concerning the existence or nonexistence of limit cycles of a nonlinear autonomous system. While proofs of these theorems are too advanced for a book of this level, we can state these theorems

* Slightly different definitions are also used; the present one is sufficient for our purposes.

and illustrate how they may be used. We consider the autonomous system

$$\frac{dx}{dt} = F(x, y), \qquad \frac{dy}{dt} = G(x, y). \tag{13}$$

Theorem 9.7 (*Poincaré-Bendixson Theorem*). *Let the functions F and G have continuous first partial derivatives in a domain D in the xy plane. Let D_1 be a bounded subdomain in D, and let R be the region that consists of D_1 plus its boundary (all points in R are in D). Suppose that R contains no critical point of the system* (13). *If there exists a constant t_0 such that $x = \phi(t)$, $y = \psi(t)$ is a solution of the system* (13) *which exists and stays in R for $t \geq t_0$, then either*

(1) $x = \phi(t)$, $y = \psi(t)$ *is a periodic solution (closed trajectory)*

or

(2) $x = \phi(t)$, $y = \psi(t)$ *spirals toward a closed trajectory as $t \to \infty$.*

In either case, the system (13) *has a periodic solution in R.*

As an application of the Poincaré-Bendixson theorem, consider the system (3) again. Since the origin is a critical point, it must be excluded. For example, we might consider the region R defined by $\frac{1}{2} \leq r \leq 2$. Next we must show that there is a solution whose trajectory stays in R for all t greater than or equal to some t_0. But this follows immediately from Eq. (6). For $r = \frac{1}{2}$, $dr/dt > 0$, so r increases and for $r = 2$, $dr/dt < 0$, so r decreases. Thus any solution of Eqs. (3) which starts (the t_0 of Theorem 9.7 can be taken as the initial time) in the region $\frac{1}{2} \leq r \leq 2$ must stay in that region. Hence, by Theorem 9.7, there is a periodic solution of the system (3) whose trajectory is a closed curve in the region $\frac{1}{2} \leq r \leq 2$. For this simple example, we found from Eq. (6) that there are periodic solutions whose trajectories lie on the circle $r = 1$; however, in general we will not be able to solve the autonomous system. The difficulty in using the Poincaré-Bendixson theorem is the determination of a region R not containing critical points and for which a trajectory stays inside.

A result about the nonexistence of periodic solutions (closed trajectories) is given by the following theorem.*

Theorem 9.8. *Let the functions F and G have continuous first partial derivatives in a simply connected domain D in the xy plane. If $F_x + G_y$ has the same sign throughout D, then there is no periodic solution of Eqs.* (13) *which is entirely in D.*

Simply connected domains are discussed on page 39; briefly, such a domain is one which has no holes. Note that if $F_x + G_y$ changes sign in

---

* For students who have had Green's theorem in the plane, which relates line integrals over closed curves to double integrals over the area inside the curve, the proof of Theorem 9.8 is not difficult (see Problem 7).

D, no conclusion is possible; there may or may not be periodic solutions in D. For the example problem (3), a simple calculation shows that

$$F_x(x, y) + G_y(x, y) = 2 - 4(x^2 + y^2). \tag{14}$$

Thus we can conclude that there are no periodic solutions of Eqs. (3) in the domain $0 \leq r < \frac{1}{2}$. In fact, however, we know that there are none in the domain $0 \leq r < 1$.

In Problem 6 of Section 9.5 we introduced the generalized Liénard equation

$$\frac{d^2u}{dt^2} + f(u)\frac{du}{dt} + g(u) = 0, \tag{15}$$

which can be thought of as describing a spring-mass system with a damping term $f(u)\,du/dt$ which is nonlinear unless f is a constant function, and with a spring force $g(u)$, which is nonlinear unless $g(u)$ is proportional to u. A particularly important special case of Eq. (15) is the van der Pol (1889–1959) equation, which governs the flow of current u in a triode oscillator,

$$\frac{d^2u}{dt^2} - \mu(1 - u^2)\frac{du}{dt} + u = 0, \tag{16}$$

where μ is a positive constant. Experimentally it is observed that the flow of current is periodic. This periodic flow can only be explained by a consideration of the nonlinear equation. If we consider the linearized form of Eq. (16) obtained by neglecting u^2 in comparison to 1 we have

$$\frac{d^2u}{dt^2} - \mu\frac{du}{dt} + u = 0. \tag{17}$$

Because of the term $-\mu\,du/dt$, Eq. (17) has no periodic solutions. Indeed, since $\mu > 0$, all solutions of Eq. (17) *grow* with increasing time. However, for the nonlinear equation (16) if u becomes greater than one then the coefficient $-\mu(1 - u^2)$ of du/dt becomes *positive*, and this term damps the current. Thus in the nonlinear equation (16) the "resistance" term $-\mu(1 - u^2)\,du/dt$ amplifies the current if $u < 1$ and damps it if $u > 1$. This alternate action of the resistance term explains how the van der Pol equation can have a periodic solution.

Liénard established the existence of periodic solutions of Eq. (15) for certain types of functions f and g, which included the case of the van der Pol equation. A more general result, proved by Levinson* and Smith in 1942, is the following.

Theorem 9.9. *Let f be even $[f(-u) = f(u)]$ and continuous for all u. Let g be odd $[g(-u) = -g(u)]$, with $g(u) > 0$ for all $u > 0$, and have a continuous*

---

* Professor N. Levinson (1912–   ) is a prominent American mathematician who received the Bôcher prize from the American Mathematical Society in 1954 for his contributions to the theory of linear, nonlinear, ordinary, and partial differential equations.

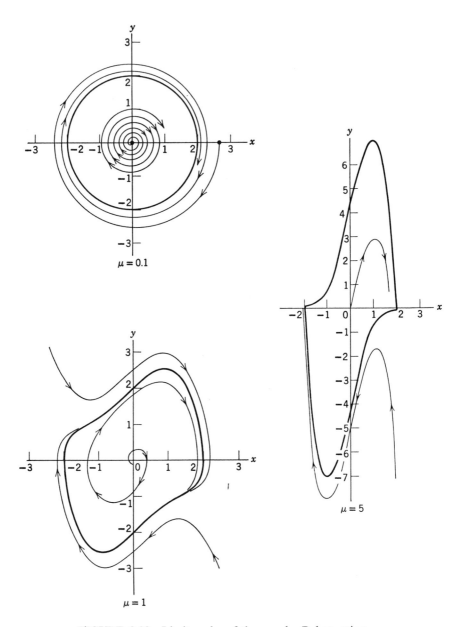

FIGURE 9.20   Limit cycles of the van der Pol equation.

first derivative for all u. Let

$$F(u) = \int_0^u f(s)\, ds, \qquad G(u) = \int_0^u g(s)\, ds. \tag{18}$$

If

(a) $G(u) \to \infty$ *as* $u \to \infty$;

(b) *there exists a positive number u_0 such that $F(u) < 0$ for $0 < u < u_0$, $F(u) > 0$ for $u > u_0$, and $F(u)$ is monotonically increasing for $u > u_0$ with $F(u) \to \infty$ as $u \to \infty$;*

then

(a) *the generalized Liénard equation (15) has a unique periodic solution (unique in the sense that there are no other closed trajectories);*

(b) *the corresponding trajectory is a closed curve encircling the origin in the phase plane $x = u$, $y = du/dt$;*

(c) *all other trajectories in the phase plane, except that corresponding to the critical point $(0, 0)$, spiral toward the closed trajectory as $t \to \infty$.*

It is a straightforward calculation to show that the conditions of Theorem 9.9 are satisfied for the van der Pol equation (16). For example, the function F satisfies hypothesis (b):

$$F(u) = -\mu \int_0^u (1 - s^2)\, ds = -\mu \left(u - \frac{u^3}{3} \right)$$

is less than zero for $0 < u < \sqrt{3}$, is greater than zero for $u > \sqrt{3}$, and increases monotonically to infinity as u increases to infinity. Thus the van der Pol equation *has* a periodic solution.

In Figure 9.20 a few of the trajectories in the phase plane $x = u$, $y = du/dt$ are sketched for the van der Pol equation for the cases $\mu = 0.1$, 1, and 5, respectively. The limit cycle is shown by a heavy line. For μ small the limit cycle is nearly a circle of radius 2 (the trajectories of the linear equation obtained by setting $\mu = 0$ are circles), but for μ large the limit cycle is considerably different.

PROBLEMS

1. For each of the following autonomous systems, expressed in polar coordinates, determine all periodic solutions, all limit cycles, and discuss their stability.

(a) $dr/dt = r^2(1 - r^2)$, $\qquad d\theta/dt = 1$

(b) $dr/dt = r(1 - r)^2$, $\qquad d\theta/dt = -1$

(c) $dr/dt = r(r - 1)(r - 3)$, $\qquad d\theta/dt = 1$

(d) $dr/dt = r(1 - r)(r - 2)$, $\qquad d\theta/dt = -1$

(e) $dr/dt = \sin \pi r$, $\qquad d\theta/dt = 1$

(f) $dr/dt = r\, |r - 2|\, (r - 3)$, $\qquad d\theta/dt = -1$

2. Show that if $x = r \cos \theta$, $y = r \sin \theta$, then $y \, dx/dt - x \, dy/dt = -r^2 \, d\theta/dt$.

3. (a) Show that the system

$$dx/dt = -y + xf(r)/r, \qquad dy/dt = x + yf(r)/r$$

has periodic solutions corresponding to the zeros of $f(r)$. What is the direction of motion on these closed curves?

(b) Determine all periodic solutions of the above system and discuss their stability if $f(r) = r(r - 2)^2(r^2 - 4r + 3)$.

4. Determine the periodic solutions, if any, of the system

$$\frac{dx}{dt} = y + \frac{x}{\sqrt{x^2 + y^2}} (x^2 + y^2 - 2)$$

$$\frac{dy}{dt} = -x + \frac{y}{\sqrt{x^2 + y^2}} (x^2 + y^2 - 2).$$

5. Using Theorem 9.8 show that a sufficient condition for the linear autonomous system

$$dx/dt = ax + by, \qquad dy/dt = cx + dy$$

not to have a periodic solution, other than $x = 0$, $y = 0$, is $a + d \neq 0$.

6. Show that each of the following systems has no periodic solutions other than constant solutions.

(a) $dx/dt = x + y + x^3 - y^2$, $\qquad dy/dt = -x + 2y + yx^2 + \frac{1}{3}y^3$

(b) $dx/dt = -2x - 3y - xy^2$, $\qquad dy/dt = y + x^3 - x^2y$

7. Prove Theorem 9.8 by completing the following argument. According to Green's theorem in the plane if C is a closed curve which is sufficiently "smooth" and if F and G are continuous and have continuous first partial derivatives, then

$$\oint_C [F(x, y) \, dy - G(x, y) \, dx] = \iint_R [F_x(x, y) + G_y(x, y)] \, dA,$$

where R is the region enclosed by C. Assume that $x = \phi(t)$, $y = \psi(t)$ is a solution of the system (13) which is periodic with period T. Let C be the closed curve given by $x = \phi(t)$, $y = \psi(t)$ for $0 \leq t \leq T$. Show that for this curve the line integral is zero.

8. Show that each of the following differential equations or systems of equations has a periodic solution.

(a) $\dfrac{d^2u}{dt^2} + (u^2 - 1)\dfrac{du}{dt} + u^3 = 0$

(b) $\dfrac{d^2u}{dt^2} + (3u^4 - 4u^2)\dfrac{du}{dt} + u = 0$

(c) $\dfrac{d^2u}{dt^2} - (2 - u^2)\dfrac{du}{dt} + u^3 + \sin u = 0$

(d) $\dfrac{d^2u}{dt^2} + \alpha(u^{2m} - k)\dfrac{du}{dt} + \beta u^{2n-1} = 0$

(α, β, and k positive constants; n, m positive integers)

(e) $\dfrac{dx}{dt} = y, \qquad \dfrac{dy}{dt} = -x + y - x^5 - 2x^2y$

REFERENCES

Several books on nonlinear differential equations present a number of applications in addition to theory. A few of these are:

LaSalle, J., and Lefschetz, S., *Stability by Liapunov's Direct Method with Applications*, Academic Press, New York, 1961.

Minorsky, N., *Introduction to Nonlinear Mechanics*, J. W. Edwards, Ann Arbor, Michigan, 1947.

Stoker, J. J., *Nonlinear Vibrations*, Interscience, New York, 1950.

A few of the more theoretically oriented books are:

Cesari, L., *Asymptotic Behavior and Stability Problems in Ordinary Differential Equations*, Springer-Verlag, Berlin, 1959.

Birkhoff, G., and Rota, G. C., *Ordinary Differential Equations*, Ginn, Boston, 1962.

Coddington, E. A. and Levinson, N., *Theory of Ordinary Differential Equations*, McGraw-Hill, New York, 1955.

Hurewicz, W., *Lectures on Ordinary Differential Equations*, Wiley, New York, 1958.

Kaplan, W., *Ordinary Differential Equations*, Addison-Wesley, Reading, Mass., 1958.

Struble, R. A., *Nonlinear Differential Equations*, McGraw-Hill, New York, 1962.

Of these books, the ones by Kaplan and Struble are the more elementary.

Partial Differential Equations and Fourier Series

10.1 INTRODUCTION

In this chapter we will consider a number of problems involving partial differential equations. No effort will be made to present a general theory of such equations; rather, we will limit our discussion to the basic partial differential equations of heat conduction, wave propagation, and potential theory. These equations are linear, of second order, and in rectangular coordinates have constant coefficients. Despite their somewhat special character, these equations are of fundamental importance in many branches of physics, and have been the subject of intense study since the eighteenth century. A variety of methods have been advanced for their solution. Among these we will deal with only one, a technique known as the method of *separation of variables.*

Historically, the method of separation of variables is perhaps the oldest systematic method for solving partial differential equations, having been used by D'Alembert, D. Bernoulli, and Euler about 1750 in their treatments of the wave equation. It has been considerably refined and generalized in the meantime, and remains a method of great importance today. The essential features of this method are the replacement of the partial differential equation by a set of ordinary differential equations, and the representation of the solution by a series of sine and/or cosine functions, known as a Fourier series. Experience shows that many significant problems in partial differential equations can be solved by the method of separation of variables; this method is one of the classical techniques of mathematical physics.

In Section 10.2 we show how the method of separation of variables can be used to solve a basic problem arising in the study of heat conduction and other diffusion processes. In solving this problem it is eventually necessary to consider the question of whether an essentially arbitrary function can be expressed as an infinite series of sine and cosine functions. Series of this kind are called Fourier series, and Sections 10.3 to 10.5 are devoted to a development of their elementary properties. Then, in Sections 10.6 to 10.8 we return to some typical problems in heat conduction, wave propagation, and potential theory, solving them by means of separation of variables and Fourier series.

10.2   HEAT CONDUCTION AND SEPARATION OF VARIABLES

One of the classical partial differential equations of mathematical physics is the equation describing the conduction of heat in a solid body. The study of this equation originated in the eighteenth century, and it continues to command the attention of modern scientists. For example, one important aspect of the reentry problem for a space vehicle is the analysis of the transfer and dissipation of the heat generated by friction with the earth's atmosphere.

FIGURE 10.1

Let us now consider a heat conduction problem for a straight bar of uniform cross-section and homogeneous material. Let the x axis be chosen to lie along the axis of the bar, and let $x = 0$ and $x = l$ denote the ends of the bar; see Figure 10.1. Suppose further that the sides of the bar are perfectly insulated so that no heat passes through them. We also assume that the cross-sectional dimensions are so small that the temperature u can be considered as constant on any given cross-section. Then u is a function only of the axial coordinate x and the time t.

The variation of temperature in the bar is governed by a partial differential equation whose derivation appears in Appendix A at the end of the chapter. This equation is called the *heat conduction equation*, and is

$$\alpha^2 u_{xx} = u_t, \qquad 0 < x < l, \qquad t > 0, \tag{1}$$

where α^2 is a constant known as the *thermal diffusivity*. The parameter α^2 depends only on the material from which the bar is made, and is defined by

$$\alpha^2 = \frac{\kappa}{\rho s}, \tag{2}$$

where κ is the thermal conductivity, ρ is the density, and s is the specific heat of the material in the bar. The dimensions of α^2 are (length)^2/time. Typical values of α^2 are given in Table 10.1.

In addition, we will assume that the ends of the bar are held at temperature zero; thus u is always zero when $x = 0$ or $x = l$:

$$u(0, t) = 0, \qquad u(l, t) = 0, \qquad t > 0. \tag{3}$$

TABLE 10.1   Values of the Thermal Diffusivity for Some Common Materials

Material	$\alpha^2 (\text{cm}^2/\text{sec})$
Silver	1.71
Copper	1.14
Aluminum	0.86
Cast iron	0.12
Granite	0.011
Brick	0.0038
Water	0.00144

Finally, the initial distribution of temperature in the bar is assumed to be given; thus

$$u(x, 0) = f(x), \qquad 0 \le x \le l, \tag{4}$$

where f is a given function. The fundamental problem of heat conduction is to find $u(x, t)$ which satisfies the differential equation (1) and also satisfies the boundary conditions (3) and the initial condition (4).

Because of the rather special nature of the boundary conditions (3) it may appear that this so-called fundamental problem will be of limited interest. However, this is not the case since other problems having more general boundary conditions can be reduced to it. Thus, upon solving the fundamental problem (1), (3), (4), we will in effect have solved a much larger class of problems. This is discussed in Section 10.6.

The problem described by Eqs. (1), (3), and (4) is an initial value problem in the time variable t; an initial condition is given and the differential equation governs what happens later. However, with respect to the space variable x, the problem is of a different type known as a boundary value problem. The solution of the differential equation is desired in a certain interval, and conditions (called boundary conditions) are imposed at the ends of the interval. Alternatively, we can consider the problem as a boundary value problem in the xt plane; see Figure 10.2. The solution $u(x, t)$ of Eq. (1) is sought in the semiinfinite strip $0 < x < l, t > 0$ subject to the requirement that $u(x, t)$ must assume a prescribed value at each point on the boundary of this strip.

The mathematical solution of Eqs. (1), (3), and (4) can be carried out by a technique known as the method of separation of variables. This method is based on the idea of finding certain solutions of the differential equation (1) which are of the form

$$u(x, t) = X(x)T(t). \tag{5}$$

Substituting Eq. (5) for u in the differential equation (1) yields

$$\alpha^2 X''T = XT', \tag{6}$$

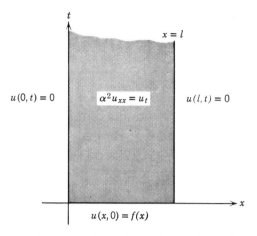

FIGURE 10.2   Boundary value problem for
the heat conduction equation.

where primes refer to ordinary differentiation with respect to the independent
variable, whether x or t. Equation (6) is equivalent to

$$\frac{X''}{X} = \frac{1}{\alpha^2}\frac{T'}{T}, \tag{7}$$

in which the variables are separated; that is, the left-hand side depends only
on x and the right-hand side only on t. In order for Eq. (7) to be valid for
$0 < x < l$, $t > 0$, it is necessary that both sides of Eq. (7) be equal to the
same constant. Otherwise, by keeping one independent variable (say x)
fixed and varying the other, one side (the left in this case) of Eq. (7) would
remain unchanged while the other varied, thus violating the equality. If we
call this separation constant σ, then Eq. (7) becomes

$$\frac{X''}{X} = \frac{1}{\alpha^2}\frac{T'}{T} = \sigma. \tag{8}$$

Hence we obtain the following two ordinary differential equations for $X(x)$
and $T(t)$:

$$X'' - \sigma X = 0, \tag{9}$$

$$T' - \alpha^2 \sigma T = 0. \tag{10}$$

The partial differential equation (1) has thus been replaced by two ordinary
differential equations. This is the essence of the method of separation of
variables.

However, the reduction of the partial differential equation (1) to the
ordinary differential equations (9) and (10) has been accomplished at the
cost of introducing the unknown separation constant σ. Before determining
allowable values for σ, it is helpful to consider briefly the effect of the

hypothesis (5) upon the boundary conditions (3). The boundary condition at $x = 0$ yields

$$u(0, t) = T(t)X(0) = 0. \tag{11}$$

If Eq. (11) is satisfied by choosing $T(t)$ to be zero for all t, then $u(x, t)$ will be identically zero. This is unacceptable, since it does not satisfy the initial condition (4). Therefore Eq. (11) must be satisfied by requiring that

$$X(0) = 0. \tag{12}$$

Similarly, the boundary condition at $x = l$ requires that

$$X(l) = 0. \tag{13}$$

We now want to consider Eq. (9) subject to the boundary conditions (12) and (13). Two cases must be distinguished, depending upon whether $\sigma = 0$ or $\sigma \neq 0$.

If $\sigma = 0$, then the general solution of Eq. (9) is

$$X(x) = k_1 x + k_2. \tag{14}$$

In order to satisfy the boundary condition (12) we must choose $k_2 = 0$ and, in order to satisfy the second boundary condition, we must have $k_1 = 0$. Hence $X(x)$ is identically zero, and therefore $u(x, t)$ is also identically zero. As before, this is unacceptable, and we conclude that σ must be nonzero.

If $\sigma \neq 0$, it is convenient to replace it by $-\lambda^2$, where λ is a new parameter, not necessarily real. Then Eq. (9) becomes

$$X'' + \lambda^2 X = 0, \tag{15}$$

and its general solution is

$$X(x) = k_1 e^{i\lambda x} + k_2 e^{-i\lambda x}. \tag{16}$$

Applying the boundary conditions (12) and (13), we obtain

$$k_1 + k_2 = 0,$$
$$k_1 e^{i\lambda l} + k_2 e^{-i\lambda l} = 0. \tag{17}$$

The system of equations (17) always has the trivial solution $k_1 = 0$, $k_2 = 0$; as before, this leads to the unacceptable conclusion that $u(x, t)$ is identically zero. Nontrivial solutions of Eqs. (17) exist if and only if the determinant of coefficients is zero, that is,

$$\begin{vmatrix} 1 & 1 \\ e^{i\lambda l} & e^{-i\lambda l} \end{vmatrix} = e^{-i\lambda l} - e^{i\lambda l} = 0. \tag{18}$$

If we now write $\lambda = \mu + i\nu$, where μ and ν are real, Eq. (18) reduces to

$$e^{-i\mu l} e^{\nu l} - e^{i\mu l} e^{-\nu l} = 0. \tag{19}$$

Using Euler's relation

$$e^{i\mu l} = \cos \mu l + i \sin \mu l, \tag{20}$$

and separating Eq. (19) into real and imaginary parts, we find that

$$(e^{\nu l} - e^{-\nu l}) \cos \mu l - i(e^{\nu l} + e^{-\nu l}) \sin \mu l = 0. \tag{21}$$

Equation (21) will be satisfied only if the real and imaginary parts of the left-hand side are separately zero; thus

$$(e^{\nu l} - e^{-\nu l}) \cos \mu l = 0, \tag{22a}$$

$$(e^{\nu l} + e^{-\nu l}) \sin \mu l = 0. \tag{22b}$$

Since $e^{\nu l} + e^{-\nu l} > 0$ for all values of ν and l, Eq. (22b) requires that $\sin \mu l = 0$. Hence μ must be chosen so that μl is a multiple of π, that is, $\mu = n\pi/l$, where n is a positive or negative integer. For this choice of μ, $\cos \mu l \neq 0$, and Eq. (22a) reduces to

$$e^{\nu l} - e^{-\nu l} = 2 \sinh \nu l = 0;$$

consequently $\nu = 0$. Hence

$$\lambda = \mu = \frac{n\pi}{l}, \tag{23}$$

where n is a nonzero integer.

Returning to Eqs. (17) we see that $k_2 = -k_1$, and hence from Eq. (16)

$$X(x) = k_1(e^{i\mu x} - e^{-i\mu x}), \tag{24}$$

On using Euler's relation (20) again we find that $X(x)$ is proportional to $\sin \mu x$.

Summarizing our results to this point: we have shown that all of the allowable values for the separation constant σ in Eq. (8) are real and negative, and are given by

$$\sigma = -\lambda^2 = -n^2\pi^2/l^2, \tag{25}$$

where n is an integer. The corresponding functions X are proportional to $\sin (n\pi x/l)$. Upon introducing the values of σ given by Eq. (25) into Eq. (10), it follows that $T(t)$ is proportional to $\exp [-n^2\pi^2\alpha^2t/l^2]$. Hence the functions

$$u_n(x, t) = c_n e^{-n^2\pi^2\alpha^2t/l^2} \sin \frac{n\pi x}{l}, \qquad n = 1, 2, 3, \ldots, \tag{26}$$

where c_n is an arbitrary constant, satisfy the boundary conditions (3) as well as the differential equation (1). It is sufficient to consider only positive values of n because if n assumes negative values the same functions as given by Eq. (26) are generated a second time. The functions u_n are sometimes called fundamental solutions of the heat conduction problem (1), (3), and (4).

It only remains to satisfy the initial condition (4),

$$u(x, 0) = f(x), \qquad 0 \le x \le l.$$

To do this we will make use of the principle of superposition. Since the differential equation (1) and boundary conditions (3) are *linear* and *homogeneous*, any finite sum of functions that satisfy these equations will also satisfy them. Thus any finite sum of the u_n will satisfy Eqs. (1) and (3). We wish to investigate whether an appropriate sum can be chosen, so that the initial condition (4) is also satisfied. Let us first consider two simple examples.

Example 1.   Let

$$f(x) = 3 \sin \frac{4\pi x}{l}.$$

Then

$$u_n(x, 0) = c_n \sin \frac{n\pi x}{l} = f(x)$$

provided $n = 4$ and $c_4 = 3$. The solution to the complete boundary value problem is

$$u(x, t) = 3e^{-16\pi^2 \alpha^2 t/l^2} \sin \frac{4\pi x}{l}. \tag{27}$$

Example 2.   Let

$$f(x) = b_1 \sin \frac{\pi x}{l} + \cdots + b_m \sin \frac{m\pi x}{l}, \tag{28}$$

where $b_1, \ldots, b_m$ are given constants. We will use the principle of superposition to solve this more complicated problem. If we choose c_n equal to b_n in Eq. (26), then we obtain a function that assumes the initial value $b_n \sin (n\pi x/l)$ and also satisfies the differential equation (1) and boundary conditions (3). By adding the solutions corresponding to $n = 1, 2, \ldots, m$ we obtain the solution

$$u(x, t) = \sum_{n=1}^{m} b_n e^{-n^2 \pi^2 \alpha^2 t/l^2} \sin \frac{n\pi x}{l}, \tag{29}$$

which satisfies the desired initial condition.

Let us return to the general problem of Eqs. (1), (3), and (4) with f an arbitrary function. Unless $f(x)$ takes the form given in Eq. (28), it is not possible to satisfy the initial condition (4) by means of a finite sum of terms of the form (26). This suggests that we formally extend the principle of superposition to include *infinite series;* that is, we assume that

$$u(x, t) = \sum_{n=1}^{\infty} c_n e^{-n^2 \pi^2 \alpha^2 t/l^2} \sin \frac{n\pi x}{l}. \tag{30}$$

It is clear that the individual terms in Eq. (30) satisfy the partial differential equation (1) and boundary conditions (3) and that any finite sum of such terms will do so as well (since for a finite sum the operations of differentiation and summation can be interchanged). We will assume that the infinite series of Eq. (30) also satisfies Eqs. (1) and (3). In order to satisfy the initial condition (4) we must have

$$u(x, 0) = \sum_{n=1}^{\infty} c_n \sin \frac{n\pi x}{l} = f(x). \tag{31}$$

Now let us suppose that it is possible to express $f(x)$ by means of an infinite series of sine terms,

$$f(x) = \sum_{n=1}^{\infty} b_n \sin \frac{n\pi x}{l}, \tag{32}$$

and that we know how to compute the coefficients b_n in this infinite series. Then, just as in Example 2, we can satisfy Eq. (31) by choosing c_n equal to b_n for each n. With the coefficients c_n selected in this manner, Eq. (30) gives the solution of the boundary value problem (1), (3), and (4).

Thus, in order to solve the given heat conduction problem for a fairly arbitrary initial temperature distribution by the method of separation of variables, it is necessary to express the initial temperature distribution $f(x)$ as a series of the form (32). In the next three sections we will show how a large class of functions can be represented by series similar to that in Eq. (32); furthermore, we will show that the coefficients in these series can be determined in a very simple manner.

PROBLEMS

1. State exactly the boundary value problem which determines the temperature in a copper bar 1 meter in length if the entire bar is originally at 20°C, and one end is then suddenly heated to 60°C and held at that temperature while the other end is held at 20°C.

2. State exactly the boundary value problem that determines the temperature in a silver rod 2 meters long if the ends are held at the temperatures 30°C and 50°C, respectively. Assume that the initial temperature in the bar is given by a quadratic function of distance along the bar consistent with the above boundary conditions, and with the condition that the temperature at the center of the rod is 60°C.

3. Suppose that $u_n(x, t)$ is given by Eq. (26). Show that $b_1 u_1(x, t) + \cdots + b_m u_m(x, t)$, where $b_1, \ldots, b_m$ are constants, satisfies the differential equation (1) and the boundary conditions (3).

4. Find the solution of the heat conduction problem

$$100u_{xx} = u_t, \qquad 0 < x < 1, \qquad t > 0$$
$$u(0, t) = 0, \qquad u(1, t) = 0, \qquad t > 0$$
$$u(x, 0) = \sin 2\pi x - 2 \sin 5\pi x, \qquad 0 \le x \le 1.$$

5. Find the solution of the heat conduction problem

$$u_{xx} = 4u_t, \qquad 0 < x < 2, \qquad t > 0$$

$$u(0, t) = 0, \qquad u(2, t) = 0, \qquad t > 0$$

$$u(x, 0) = 2 \sin \frac{\pi x}{2} - \sin \pi x + 4 \sin 2\pi x, \qquad 0 \le x \le 2.$$

6. If the temperature distribution in a rod does not depend on time, a *steady state* is said to exist. Show that such a steady state distribution must be a linear function of the space variable x. Find the steady state temperature distribution if $u(0, t) = T_1$ and $u(l, t) = T_2$, where T_1 and T_2 are constants.

7. Determine whether the method of separation of variables can be used to replace each of the following partial differential equations by pairs of ordinary differential equations. If so, find the equations.

(a) $xu_{xx} + u_t = 0$

(b) $tu_{xx} + xu_t = 0$

(c) $u_{xx} + u_{xt} + u_t = 0$

(d) $[p(x)u_x]_x - r(x)u_{tt} = 0$

(e) $u_{xx} + (x + y)u_{yy} = 0$

*8. In solving differential equations the computations can almost always be simplified by the use of *dimensionless variables*. Show that if the dimensionless variable ξ defined by $\xi = x/l$ is introduced, the heat conduction equation becomes

$$\frac{\partial^2 u}{\partial \xi^2} = \frac{l^2}{\alpha^2} \frac{\partial u}{\partial t}, \qquad 0 < \xi < 1, \qquad t > 0.$$

Since l^2/α^2 has the dimensions of time, it is convenient to use this quantity as the unit on the time scale. Defining a dimensionless time variable $\tau = (\alpha^2/l^2)t$, show that the heat conduction equation reduces to

$$\frac{\partial^2 u}{\partial \xi^2} = \frac{\partial u}{\partial \tau}, \qquad 0 < \xi < 1, \qquad \tau > 0.$$

*9. The heat conduction equation in two space dimensions is

$$\alpha^2(u_{xx} + u_{yy}) = u_t.$$

Assuming that $u(x, y, t) = X(x)Y(y)T(t)$, find ordinary differential equations satisfied by $X(x)$, $Y(y)$, and $T(t)$.

*10. The heat conduction equation in two space dimensions may be expressed in terms of polar coordinates as

$$\alpha^2 \left(u_{rr} + \frac{1}{r} u_r + \frac{1}{r^2} u_{\theta\theta} \right) = u_t.$$

Assuming that $u(r, \theta, t) = R(r)\Theta(\theta)T(t)$, find ordinary differential equations satisfied by $R(r)$, $\Theta(\theta)$, and $T(t)$.

10.3 FOURIER SERIES

In the last section we showed how to solve the fundamental boundary value problem of heat conduction provided that it is possible to express a given function defined on $0 \le x \le l$ as a series of sines, $\sum b_m \sin (m\pi x/l)$. We will now begin to consider somewhat more general series of the form

$$\frac{a_0}{2} + \sum_{m=1}^{\infty} \left(a_m \cos \frac{m\pi x}{l} + b_m \sin \frac{m\pi x}{l} \right). \tag{1}$$

On the set of points for which the series (1) converges, it defines a function f, whose value at each point is the sum of the series for that value of x. In this case the series (1) is said to be the *Fourier series** for f. Our immediate object is to determine what functions can be represented as a sum of a Fourier series and to find some means of computing the coefficients in the series. We note in passing that the first term in the series (1) is written as $a_0/2$ rather than as a_0 in order to simplify a formula for the coefficients that we will derive below. Besides their association with the method of separation of variables, Fourier series are also useful in various other ways, such as in the analysis of mechanical or electrical systems acted upon by periodic external forces.

In order to discuss Fourier series it is necessary to develop certain properties of the trigonometric functions $\sin (m\pi x/l)$ and $\cos (n\pi x/l)$, where m and n are positive integers. The first is their periodic character. A function f is said to be *periodic with period T* if the domain of f contains $x + T$ whenever it contains x, and if

$$f(x + T) = f(x) \tag{2}$$

for every value of x. An example of a periodic function is shown in Figure 10.3. It follows immediately from the definition that if T is a period of f, then $2T$ is also a period, and so indeed is any integral multiple of T.

The definition of period given by Eq. (2) admits the possibility of negative periods. However, in most applications the period represents either a length or an interval of time and is thus intrinsically positive. In any case the sign of negative periods can be changed by reversing the direction of the axis of the independent variable. With no loss of generality we will therefore consider T as positive. The smallest positive value of T for which Eq. (2) holds is called the *fundamental period* of f. In this connection it should be

---

* Fourier series are named in honor of the French scientist, J. B. Fourier (1768–1830), who made the first systematic use, although not a rigorous investigation, of them in 1807 and 1811. According to Riemann, when Fourier presented his first paper to the Paris Academy in 1807, stating that a completely arbitrary function could be expressed as a series of the form (1), the famous mathematician Lagrange was so surprised that he denied the possibility in the most definite terms. See Carslaw [Historical Introduction] for a detailed history of Fourier series.

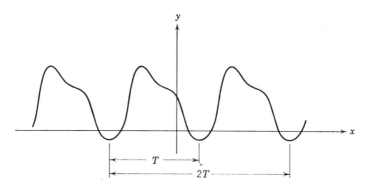

FIGURE 10.3 A periodic function.

noted that a constant may be thought of as a periodic function with an arbitrary period, but no fundamental period. For any nonconstant periodic function the fundamental period is uniquely defined and all other periods are multiples of it.

If f and g are two periodic functions with common period T, then their sum $f + g$ is also periodic with period T. To prove this, let $F(x) = f(x) + g(x)$; then

$$F(x + T) = f(x + T) + g(x + T) = f(x) + g(x) = F(x).$$

Moreover, it can be shown that the sum of any finite number, or even the sum of a convergent infinite series, of functions of period T is also periodic with period T.

Now let us apply these facts to the trigonometric functions $\sin(m\pi x/l)$ and $\cos(m\pi x/l)$. We will prove the following theorem.

Theorem 10.1.   *The functions* $\sin(m\pi x/l)$ *and* $\cos(m\pi x/l)$, $m = 1, 2, 3, \ldots$, *are periodic with fundamental period* $T = 2l/m$. *Further, every such function has the period* $2l$.

We must show that there are values of T for which

$$\sin \frac{m\pi(x + T)}{l} = \sin \frac{m\pi x}{l} \tag{3}$$

for all x, and that the minimum such value of T is $2l/m$. Expanding the left side of Eq. (3) gives

$$\sin \frac{m\pi x}{l} \cos \frac{m\pi T}{l} + \cos \frac{m\pi x}{l} \sin \frac{m\pi T}{l} = \sin \frac{m\pi x}{l}, \tag{4}$$

which is true for all x provided that $m\pi T/l = 0,\ \pm 2\pi,\ \pm 4\pi,\ \ldots$. To show that there are no other values of T for which Eq. (3) is satisfied, assume that there is such a T, and choose x so that $\cos (m\pi x/l) = 0$. Then Eq. (4) becomes

$$\sin \frac{m\pi x}{l} \cos \frac{m\pi T}{l} = \sin \frac{m\pi x}{l},$$

which is true only for the values of $m\pi T/l$ given above. The fundamental period of $\sin (m\pi x/l)$ is then

$$T = \frac{2\pi l}{m\pi} = \frac{2l}{m}. \tag{5}$$

Since any integral multiple of a period is also a period, it follows that $\sin (m\pi x/l)$ has the period $2l$ for any m. A similar argument applies to $\cos (m\pi x/l)$.

A second essential property of the functions $\sin (m\pi x/l)$ and $\cos (m\pi x/l)$ is contained in the following theorem.

Theorem 10.2. *The functions* $\sin (m\pi x/l)$ *and* $\cos (m\pi x/l)$ *satisfy the following integral relations, known as orthogonality* relations:*

$$\int_{-l}^{l} \cos \frac{m\pi x}{l} \cos \frac{n\pi x}{l} \, dx = \begin{cases} 0, & m \neq n, \\ l, & m = n; \end{cases} \tag{6}$$

$$\int_{-l}^{l} \cos \frac{m\pi x}{l} \sin \frac{n\pi x}{l} \, dx = 0, \quad \text{all } m, n; \tag{7}$$

$$\int_{-l}^{l} \sin \frac{m\pi x}{l} \sin \frac{n\pi x}{l} \, dx = \begin{cases} 0, & m \neq n, \\ l, & m = n. \end{cases} \tag{8}$$

These results can be obtained by direct integration. For example,

$$\int_{-l}^{l} \sin \frac{m\pi x}{l} \sin \frac{n\pi x}{l} \, dx = \frac{1}{2} \int_{-l}^{l} \left[\cos \frac{(m-n)\pi x}{l} - \cos \frac{(m+n)\pi x}{l} \right] dx$$

$$= \frac{1}{2} \frac{l}{\pi} \left\{ \frac{\sin [(m-n)\pi x/l]}{m-n} - \frac{\sin [(m+n)\pi x/l]}{m+n} \right\} \Big|_{-l}^{l}$$

$$= 0,$$

as long as $m + n$ and $m - n$ are not zero. Since m and n are positive, $m + n \neq 0$. On the other hand, if $m - n = 0$, then $m = n$, and the integral

---

* The use of the word orthogonal in this connection is a generalization of its use with respect to vectors. Here the ordinary scalar product is replaced by an integral. The real-valued functions u and v are said to be orthogonal on the interval $\alpha \leq x \leq \beta$ if
$$\int_{\alpha}^{\beta} u(x)v(x) \, dx = 0.$$

must be evaluated in a different way. In this case

$$\int_{-l}^{l} \sin \frac{m\pi x}{l} \sin \frac{n\pi x}{l}\, dx = \int_{-l}^{l} \left(\sin \frac{m\pi x}{l}\right)^2 dx$$

$$= \frac{1}{2}\int_{-l}^{l}\left[1 - \cos \frac{2m\pi x}{l}\right] dx$$

$$= \frac{1}{2}\left\{x - \frac{\sin (2m\pi x/l)}{2m\pi/l}\right\}\Big|_{-l}^{l}$$

$$= l.$$

This establishes Eq. (8); Eqs. (6) and (7) can be verified by similar computations.

Now let us suppose that a series of the form (1) converges, and let us call its sum $f(x)$:

$$f(x) = \frac{a_0}{2} + \sum_{m=1}^{\infty} \left(a_m \cos \frac{m\pi x}{l} + b_m \sin \frac{m\pi x}{l}\right). \tag{9}$$

The coefficients a_m and b_m can be related very simply to $f(x)$ as a consequence of the orthogonality conditions (6), (7), and (8). First multiply Eq. (9) by $\cos (n\pi x/l)$, where n is a *fixed* positive integer $(n > 0)$, and integrate with respect to x from $-l$ to l. Assuming that the integration can be legitimately carried out term by term,* we obtain

$$\int_{-l}^{l} f(x) \cos \frac{n\pi x}{l}\, dx = \frac{a_0}{2}\int_{-l}^{l} \cos \frac{n\pi x}{l}\, dx + \sum_{m=1}^{\infty} a_m \int_{-l}^{l} \cos \frac{m\pi x}{l} \cos \frac{n\pi x}{l}\, dx$$

$$+ \sum_{m=1}^{\infty} b_m \int_{-l}^{l} \sin \frac{m\pi x}{l} \cos \frac{n\pi x}{l}\, dx. \tag{10}$$

Keeping in mind that n is fixed whereas m ranges over the positive integers, it follows from the orthogonality relations (Theorem 10.2) that the only nonvanishing term on the right side of Eq. (10) is the one for which $m = n$ in the first summation. Hence

$$\int_{-l}^{l} f(x) \cos \frac{n\pi x}{l}\, dx = la_n, \qquad n = 1, 2, \dots. \tag{11}$$

To determine a_0 we can integrate Eq. (9) from $-l$ to l, obtaining

$$\int_{-l}^{l} f(x)\, dx = \frac{a_0}{2}\int_{-l}^{l} dx + \sum_{m=1}^{\infty} a_m \int_{-l}^{l} \cos \frac{m\pi x}{l}\, dx + \sum_{m=1}^{\infty} b_m \int_{-l}^{l} \sin \frac{m\pi x}{l}\, dx$$

$$= la_0, \tag{12}$$

* This is a nontrivial assumption, since not all convergent series with variable terms can be so integrated. For the special case of Fourier series, however, term by term integration can always be justified.

since all of the integrals involving trigonometric functions vanish. Thus for all values of n we have the formula

$$a_n = \frac{1}{l} \int_{-l}^{l} f(x) \cos \frac{n\pi x}{l} \, dx, \qquad n = 0, 1, 2, \ldots. \tag{13}$$

By writing the constant term in Eq. (9) as $a_0/2$ it is possible to compute all of the a_n from Eq. (13). Otherwise a separate formula would have to be used for a_0.

A similar expression for b_n may be obtained by multiplying Eq. (9) by $\sin(n\pi x/l)$, integrating termwise from $-l$ to l, and using the orthogonality relations; thus

$$b_n = \frac{1}{l} \int_{-l}^{l} f(x) \sin \frac{n\pi x}{l} \, dx, \qquad n = 1, 2, 3, \ldots. \tag{14}$$

Equations (13) and (14) are known as the Euler-Fourier formulas for the coefficients in a Fourier series. Hence, if the series (9) converges to $f(x)$, and if the series can be integrated term by term, then the coefficients *must be given* by Eqs. (13) and (14).

Note that the formulas (13) and (14) depend only upon the values of $f(x)$ in the interval $-l \le x \le l$. Since each of the terms in the Fourier series (9) is periodic with period $2l$, the series converges for all x whenever it converges in $-l \le x \le l$, and its sum is also a periodic function with period $2l$. Hence $f(x)$ is determined for all x by its values in the interval $-l \le x \le l$.

It is possible to show (see Problem 2) that if g is periodic with period T, then every integral of g over an interval of length T has the same value. Applying this result to the Euler-Fourier formulas (13) and (14), it follows that the interval of integration, $-l \le x \le l$, can be replaced, if it is more convenient to do so, by any other interval of length $2l$.

Example 1. Assume that there is a Fourier series which converges to the function f defined by

$$f(x) = \begin{cases} -x, & -l \le x < 0, \\ x, & 0 \le x < l; \end{cases} \tag{15}$$

$$f(x + 2l) = f(x).$$

Determine the coefficients in this Fourier series.

This function represents a triangular wave (see Figure 10.4) and is periodic with period $2l$. Thus the Fourier series is of the form

$$f(x) = \frac{a_0}{2} + \sum_{m=1}^{\infty} \left(a_m \cos \frac{m\pi x}{l} + b_m \sin \frac{m\pi x}{l} \right),$$

where the coefficients are computed from Eqs. (13) and (14). Substituting for

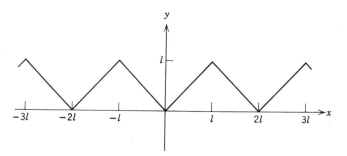

FIGURE 10.4 Triangular wave.

$f(x)$ in these equations and carrying out the indicated integrations, we obtain

$$a_0 = l;$$

$$a_m = \frac{2l}{(m\pi)^2}(\cos m\pi - 1), \qquad m = 1, 2, \ldots;$$

$$b_m = 0, \qquad\qquad\qquad\quad m = 1, 2, \ldots.$$

Thus the Fourier series for f is

$$f(x) = \frac{l}{2} - \frac{4l}{\pi^2}\left(\cos\frac{\pi x}{l} + \frac{1}{3^2}\cos\frac{3\pi x}{l} + \frac{1}{5^2}\cos\frac{5\pi x}{l} + \cdots\right)$$

$$= \frac{l}{2} - \frac{4l}{\pi^2}\sum_{n=1}^{\infty}\frac{1}{(2n-1)^2}\cos\frac{(2n-1)\pi x}{l}. \tag{16}$$

Example 2. Using the same function f as in Example 1, compute the coefficients in its Fourier series by integrating over the interval $[0, 2l]$.

Since the integrands are periodic with period $2l$, it is only necessary to change the limits of integration in Eqs. (13) and (14):

$$a_n = \frac{1}{l}\int_0^{2l} f(x)\cos\frac{n\pi x}{l}\,dx, \qquad b_n = \frac{1}{l}\int_0^{2l} f(x)\sin\frac{n\pi x}{l}\,dx. \tag{17}$$

The only problem is to determine the correct formulas for $f(x)$ in this interval. According to Eq. (15) we have $f(x) = x$ for $0 \le x < l$. To determine $f(x)$ in the interval $l \le x \le 2l$, we make use of the fact that $f(x + 2l) = f(x)$. Hence in this interval $f(x) = 2l - x$. To compute a_n we substitute for $f(x)$ in the first of Eqs. (17):

$$a_n = \frac{1}{l}\int_0^{2l} f(x)\cos\frac{n\pi x}{l}\,dx$$

$$= \frac{1}{l}\left\{\int_0^l x\cos\frac{n\pi x}{l}\,dx + \int_l^{2l}(2l - x)\cos\frac{n\pi x}{l}\,dx\right\}. \tag{18}$$

Carrying out the indicated integrations yields again the results obtained in Example 1. The computation of b_n from the second of Eqs. (17) is similar.

PROBLEMS

1. Determine whether or not each of the following functions is periodic. If so, find its fundamental period.

(a) $\sin \pi x/l$ (b) $\cos 2\pi x$ (c) $\sinh 2x$ (d) $\tan \pi x$

(e) x^2 (f) $\sin 5x$ (g) $\sin mx$ (h) e^x

(i) $f(x) = \begin{cases} 0, & 2n - 1 \le x < 2n, \\ 1, & 2n \le x < 2n + 1; \end{cases} \quad n = 0, \pm1, \pm2, \ldots$

(j) $f(x) = \begin{cases} (-1)^n, & 2n - 1 \le x < 2n, \\ 1, & 2n \le x < 2n + 1; \end{cases} \quad n = 0, \pm1, \pm2, \ldots$

2. Suppose that g is an integrable periodic function with period T.
(a) If $0 \le a \le T$, show that

$$\int_0^T g(x)\, dx = \int_a^{a+T} g(x)\, dx.$$

Hint: Show first that $\int_0^a g(x)\, dx = \int_T^{a+T} g(x)\, dx$. Consider the change of variable $s = x - T$ in the second integral.

(b) Show that for any value of a, not necessarily in $0 \le a \le T$,

$$\int_0^T g(x)\, dx = \int_a^{a+T} g(x)\, dx.$$

(c) Show that for any values of a and b,

$$\int_a^{a+T} g(x)\, dx = \int_b^{b+T} g(x)\, dx.$$

3. If f is differentiable and is periodic with period T, show that f' is also periodic with period T. Determine whether

$$F(x) = \int_0^x f(t)\, dt$$

is always periodic.

4. Verify Eqs. (6) and (7) of the text by direct integration.

In each of Problems 5 through 10 find the Fourier series corresponding to the given function.

5. $f(x) = -x$, $-l \le x < l$; $f(x + 2l) = f(x)$

6. $f(x) = \begin{cases} 1, & -l \le x < 0, \\ 0, & 0 \le x < l; \end{cases} \quad f(x + 2l) = f(x)$

7. $f(x) = \begin{cases} -l - x, & -l \le x < 0, \\ l - x, & 0 \le x < l; \end{cases} \quad f(x + 2l) = f(x)$

8. $f(x) = x$, $-1 \le x < 1$; $f(x + 2) = f(x)$

9. $f(x) = \begin{cases} x + 1, & -1 \leq x < 0, \\ x, & 0 \leq x < 1; \end{cases}$ $f(x + 2) = f(x)$

10. $f(x) = \begin{cases} -1, & -2 \leq x < 0, \\ 1, & 0 \leq x < 2; \end{cases}$ $f(x + 4) = f(x)$

11. If $f(x) = -x$ for $-l < x < l$, and $f(x + 2l) = f(x)$, find a formula for $f(x)$ in the interval $l < x < 2l$; in the interval $-3l < x < -2l$.

12. If $f(x) = \begin{cases} x + 1, & -1 < x < 0, \\ x, & 0 < x < 1, \end{cases}$

and $f(x + 2) = f(x)$, find a formula for $f(x)$ in the interval $1 < x < 2$; in the interval $8 < x < 9$.

13. If $f(x) = l - x$ for $0 < x < 2l$, and $f(x + 2l) = f(x)$, find a formula for $f(x)$ in the interval $-l < x < 0$.

14. If $f(x) = \begin{cases} 1, & -l \leq x < 0, \\ 0, & 0 \leq x < l, \end{cases}$

and $f(x + 2l) = f(x)$, find the coefficients in the Fourier series corresponding to f by integrating over the interval $0 \leq x \leq 2l$. Compare your result with that of Problem 6.

15. If $f(x) = x$ for $-1 \leq x < 1$, and $f(x + 2) = f(x)$, find the coefficients in the Fourier series corresponding to f by integrating over the interval $0 \leq x \leq 2$. Compare your result with that of Problem 8.

10.4 THE FOURIER THEOREM

In the last section we showed that if the Fourier series

$$\frac{a_0}{2} + \sum_{m=1}^{\infty} \left(a_m \cos \frac{m\pi x}{l} + b_m \sin \frac{m\pi x}{l} \right) \tag{1}$$

converges and thereby defines a function f, then f is periodic with period $2l$, and the coefficients a_m and b_m are related to $f(x)$ by the Euler-Fourier formulas:

$$a_m = \frac{1}{l} \int_{-l}^{l} f(x) \cos \frac{m\pi x}{l} \, dx, \qquad m = 0, 1, 2, \ldots; \tag{2}$$

$$b_m = \frac{1}{l} \int_{-l}^{l} f(x) \sin \frac{m\pi x}{l} \, dx, \qquad m = 1, 2, \ldots. \tag{3}$$

In this section we will adopt a somewhat different point of view. Suppose that a function f is given. If this function is periodic with period $2l$ and integrable on the interval $[-l, l]$, then a set of coefficients a_m and b_m can be computed from Eqs. (2) and (3), and a series of the form (1) can be formally constructed.

The question is whether this series converges for each value of x and, if so, whether its sum is $f(x)$. Examples have been discovered which show that the Fourier series corresponding to a function f may not converge to $f(x)$, or may not even converge at all. Functions whose Fourier series do not converge to the value of the function at isolated points are easily constructed, and examples will appear later in this section. Functions whose Fourier series do not converge at all are more pathological, and we will not consider them in this book. Until the question of convergence is settled it is customary to use the symbol $\sim$ instead of the equality sign; thus

$$f(x) \sim \frac{a_0}{2} + \sum_{m=1}^{\infty} \left(a_m \cos \frac{m\pi x}{l} + b_m \sin \frac{m\pi x}{l} \right) \tag{4}$$

means that the coefficients have been computed according to the formulas (2) and (3), but that it is not yet known whether the series converges to $f(x)$.

To guarantee convergence of a Fourier series to the function from which its coefficients were computed it is essential to place additional conditions on the function. From a practical point of view such conditions should be broad enough to cover all situations of interest, yet simple enough to be easily checked for particular functions. Through the years several sets of conditions have been devised to serve this purpose.

Before stating a convergence theorem for Fourier series, we will define a term which appears in the theorem. A function f is said to be *piecewise continuous* on an interval $a \leq x \leq b$, or $a < x < b$, if the interval can be partitioned by a finite number of points $a = x_0 < x_1 < \cdots < x_n = b$ so that

(i) f is continuous on each open subinterval $x_{i-1} < x < x_i$;

(ii) f approaches a finite limit as the end points of each subinterval are approached from within the subinterval.

The notation $f(c + 0)$ is used to denote the right-hand limit of $f(x)$ as $x \to c$ from above, that is,

$$f(c + 0) = \lim_{x \to c+} f(x).$$

Similarly, $f(c - 0) = \lim_{x \to c-} f(x)$ denotes the limit of $f(x)$ as x approaches c from below.

Theorem 10.3. *Suppose that f and f' are piecewise continuous on the interval $-l \leq x < l$. Further, suppose that f is defined outside the interval $-l \leq x < l$ so that it is periodic with period $2l$. Then f has a Fourier series*

$$f(x) = \frac{a_0}{2} + \sum_{m=1}^{\infty} \left(a_m \cos \frac{m\pi x}{l} + b_m \sin \frac{m\pi x}{l} \right), \tag{5}$$

whose coefficients are given by Eqs. (2) and (3). The Fourier series converges to $f(x)$ at all points where f is continuous, and to $[f(x + 0) + f(x - 0)]/2$ at all points where f is discontinuous.

Note that $[f(x + 0) + f(x - 0)]/2$ is the mean value of the right- and left-hand limits at the point x. At any point where f is continuous, $f(x + 0) = f(x - 0) = f(x)$. Thus it is correct to say that the Fourier series converges to $[f(x + 0) + f(x - 0)]/2$ at all points. Whenever we say that a Fourier series converges to a function f, we will always mean that it converges in this sense.

It should be emphasized that the conditions given in this theorem are only sufficient for the convergence of a Fourier series; they are by no means necessary. Neither are they the most general sufficient conditions that have been discovered. In spite of this the proof of the theorem is fairly difficult and will not be given here.*

To obtain a better understanding of the content of the theorem it is helpful to consider some classes of functions which fail to satisfy the assumed conditions. Functions which are not considered in the theorem are primarily those with infinite discontinuities in the interval $[-l, l]$, such as $1/x^2$ or $\ln |x|$, or functions having an infinite number of jump discontinuities in this interval. Functions of the latter type are seldom encountered; however, an example of such a function is

$$f(x) = \begin{cases} 1, & \dfrac{1}{2n + 1} \leq x < \dfrac{1}{2n}, & n = 1, 2, \ldots \\[2ex] 0, & \dfrac{1}{2n} \leq x < \dfrac{1}{2n - 1}, & n = 1, 2, \ldots. \end{cases}$$

It is noteworthy that a Fourier series may converge to a sum which is not differentiable, or even continuous, in spite of the fact that each term in the series (5) is continuous, and even differentiable infinitely many times. The example below is an illustration of this.

Example.   Let

$$f(x) = \begin{cases} 0, & -l < x < 0, \\ l, & 0 < x < l, \end{cases} \tag{6}$$

and let f be defined outside this interval so that $f(x + 2l) = f(x)$ for all x. We will temporarily leave open the definition of f at the points $x = 0$, $\pm l$, except that its values must be finite. Then the equation $y = f(x)$ has the graph shown in Figure 10.5, extended to infinity in both directions. It can be thought of as representing a square wave. The interval $[-l, l]$ can be partitioned to give the two open subintervals $(-l, 0)$ and $(0, l)$. In $(0, l)$, $f(x) = l$ and $f'(x) = 0$. Clearly, both f and f' are continuous and, furthermore, have limits as $x \to 0$ from above and as $x \to l$ from below. The

---

* Proofs of the convergence of a Fourier series can be found in most books on advanced calculus. See, for example, Widder [Chapter 12] or Kaplan [Chapter 7].

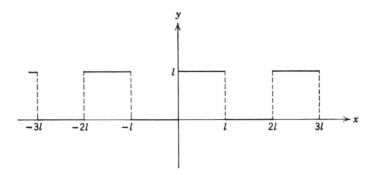

FIGURE 10.5   Square wave.

situation in $(-l, 0)$ is similar. Consequently, both f and f' are piecewise continuous on $[-l, l)$, so f satisfies the conditions of Theorem 10.3. If the coefficients a_m and b_m are computed from Eqs. (2) and (3) the convergence of the resulting Fourier series to $f(x)$ is assured at all points where f is continuous. Note that the values of a_m and b_m are the same regardless of the definition of f at its points of discontinuity. This is true because the value of an integral is unaffected by the values of the integrand at a finite number of points. From Eq. (2)

$$a_0 = \frac{1}{l} \int_{-l}^{l} f(x)\,dx = \int_{0}^{l} dx = l;$$

$$a_m = \frac{1}{l} \int_{-l}^{l} f(x) \cos \frac{m\pi x}{l}\,dx = \int_{0}^{l} \cos \frac{m\pi x}{l}\,dx$$

$$= 0, \qquad m \ne 0.$$

Similarly, from Eq. (3),

$$b_m = \frac{1}{l} \int_{-l}^{l} f(x) \sin \frac{m\pi x}{l}\,dx = \int_{0}^{l} \sin \frac{m\pi x}{l}\,dx$$

$$= \frac{l}{m\pi} (1 - \cos m\pi)$$

$$= \begin{cases} 0, & m \text{ even;} \\ \dfrac{2l}{m\pi}, & m \text{ odd.} \end{cases}$$

Hence

$$f(x) = \frac{l}{2} + \frac{2l}{\pi}\left(\sin \frac{\pi x}{l} + \frac{1}{3}\sin \frac{3\pi x}{l} + \frac{1}{5}\sin \frac{5\pi x}{l} + \cdots\right)$$

$$= \frac{l}{2} + \frac{2l}{\pi} \sum_{m=1}^{\infty} \frac{\sin\left[(2m-1)\pi x/l\right]}{2m-1}.$$

At the points $x = 0$, $\pm nl$, where the function f in the example is not continuous, all terms in the series after the first vanish and the sum is $l/2$. This is the mean value of the limits from the right and left, as it should be. Thus we might as well define f at these points to have the value $l/2$. If we choose to define it otherwise the series will still give the value $l/2$ at these points since none of the preceding calculations will be altered in any detail; it will simply not converge to the function at those points unless f is defined to have this value. This illustrates the possibility that the Fourier series corresponding to a function may not converge to it at points of discontinuity unless the function is properly defined at such points.

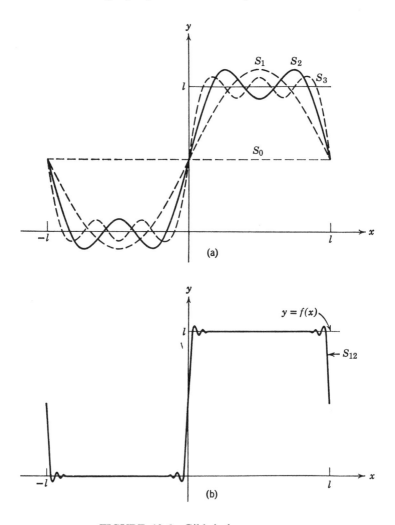

FIGURE 10.6 Gibbs' phenomenon.

The manner in which the partial sums

$$S_0(x) = \frac{l}{2},$$

$$S_1(x) = \frac{l}{2} + \frac{2l}{\pi} \sin \frac{\pi x}{l},$$

.
.
.

$$S_n(x) = \frac{l}{2} + \frac{2l}{\pi} \left(\sin \frac{\pi x}{l} + \cdots + \frac{1}{2n-1} \sin \frac{(2n-1)\pi x}{l} \right),$$

of the Fourier series (7) converge to $f(x)$ is sketched in Figure 10.6. The figure shows that at points where f is continuous the partial sums do approach $f(x)$ as n increases. However, in the neighborhood of points of discontinuity, such as $x = 0$ and $x = l$, the partial sums do not converge smoothly to the mean value. Instead they tend to overshoot the mark at each end of the jump, as though they cannot quite accommodate themselves to the sharp turn required at this point. This behavior is typical of Fourier series at points of discontinuity, and is known as the Gibbs* phenomenon.

PROBLEMS

Find the Fourier series for each of the functions in Problems 1 through 8. Assume that the functions are periodically extended outside the original interval. Sketch the function to which each series converges for several periods.

1. $f(x) = \begin{cases} -1, & -1 \le x < 0 \\ 1, & 0 \le x < 1 \end{cases}$
   $\qquad$ 2. $f(x) = \begin{cases} 0, & -\pi \le x < 0 \\ x, & 0 \le x < \pi \end{cases}$

3. $f(x) = \sin^2 x, \qquad -\pi \le x \le \pi$

4. $f(x) = \begin{cases} 1, & 0 \le x < t \\ 0, & t \le x < 2 - t \\ 1, & 2 - t \le x < 2 \end{cases}$
   $\qquad$ 5. $f(x) = \begin{cases} l + x, & -l \le x < 0 \\ l - x, & 0 \le x < l \end{cases}$

6. $f(x) = 1 - x^2, \qquad -1 \le x \le 1$

7. $f(x) = \begin{cases} 0, & -\pi \le x < -\pi/2 \\ 1, & -\pi/2 \le x < \pi/2 \\ 0, & \pi/2 \le x < \pi \end{cases}$
   $\qquad$ 8. $f(x) = \begin{cases} 0, & -1 \le x < 0 \\ x^2, & 0 \le x < 1 \end{cases}$

* The Gibbs phenomenon is named after Josiah Willard Gibbs (1839–1903), who is better known for his work on vector analysis and statistical mechanics. Gibbs was one of the first American mathematicians to achieve an international reputation. Gibbs' phenomenon is discussed in more detail by Guillemin [Chapter 7] and Carslaw [Chapter 9].

9. Find the solution of the initial value problem

$$\frac{d^2x}{dt^2} + \omega^2 x = \sin nt, \qquad x(0) = 0, \qquad \frac{dx}{dt}(0) = 0,$$

where $n \neq \omega$ is a positive integer. What happens if $\omega^2 = n^2$?

In each of Problems 10 through 12 solve the given initial value problem by assuming that the solution can be expanded in a Fourier series, and then determining the coefficients in this expansion.

10. Find the formal solution of the initial value problem

$$\frac{d^2x}{dt^2} + \omega^2 x = \sum_{n=1}^{\infty} b_n \sin nt, \qquad x(0) = 0, \qquad \frac{dx}{dt}(0) = 0.$$

11. Find the formal solution of the initial value problem

$$\frac{d^2x}{dt^2} + \omega^2 x = f(t), \qquad x(0) = 0, \qquad \frac{dx}{dt}(0) = 0,$$

where f is periodic with period 2π and

$$f(t) = \begin{cases} 1, & 0 < t < \pi, \\ 0, & t = 0, \pi, 2\pi, \\ -1, & \pi < t < 2\pi. \end{cases}$$

12. Find the formal solution of the initial value problem

$$\frac{d^2x}{dt^2} + \omega^2 x = f(t), \qquad x(0) = 1, \qquad \frac{dx}{dt}(0) = 0,$$

where f is periodic with period 2 and

$$f(t) = \begin{cases} 1 - t, & 0 \le t < 1, \\ -1 + t, & 1 \le t < 2. \end{cases}$$

13. Find the general solution of the differential equation

$$y'' + 3y' + 2y = \sum_{n=1}^{\infty} a_n \cos nx.$$

14. Assuming that

$$f(x) = \frac{a_0}{2} + \sum_{n=1}^{\infty} \left(a_n \cos \frac{n\pi x}{l} + b_n \sin \frac{n\pi x}{l} \right),$$

show formally by squaring and integrating term by term from $-l$ to l that

$$\frac{1}{l} \int_{-l}^{l} [f(x)]^2 \, dx = \frac{a_0^2}{2} + \sum_{n=1}^{\infty} (a_n^2 + b_n^2).$$

This relation between a function f and its Fourier coefficients is known as Parseval's equation. Parseval's equation is very important in the theory of Fourier series, and is discussed further in Section 11.7.

15. (a) If f and f' are piecewise continuous on $-l \le x < l$, and if f is periodic with period $2l$, show that na_n and nb_n have finite limits as $n \to \infty$.

(b) If f is continuous on $-l \le x \le l$ and periodic with period $2l$, and if f' and f'' are piecewise continuous on $-l \le x < l$, show that n^2a_n and n^2b_n have finite limits as $n \to \infty$. Use this fact to show that the Fourier series for f converges at each point in $-l \le x \le l$. Why must f be continuous on the *closed* interval? *Hint:* Use integration by parts.

10.5 EVEN AND ODD FUNCTIONS

Before looking at further examples of Fourier series it is useful to distinguish two classes of functions for which the Euler-Fourier formulas can be simplified. These are even and odd functions, which are characterized geometrically by the property of symmetry with respect to the y axis and the origin, respectively; see Figure 10.7.

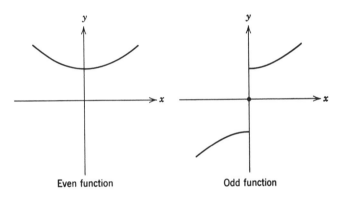

Even function   Odd function

FIGURE 10.7 Even and odd functions.

Analytically, f is an *even function* if its domain contains the point $-x$ whenever it contains the point x, and if

$$f(-x) = f(x) \tag{1}$$

for each x in the domain of f. Similarly, f is an *odd function* if its domain contains $-x$ whenever it contains x, and if

$$f(-x) = -f(x) \tag{2}$$

for each x in the domain of f. Note that according to Eq. (2), $f(0)$ must be zero if f is an odd function whose domain contains the origin. Examples of even functions are 1, x^2, $\cos nx$, $|x|$, and x^{2n}. The functions x, x^3, $\sin nx$, and x^{2n+1} are examples of odd functions. Most functions are neither even nor odd; for instance, e^x. Only one function, f identically zero, is both even and odd.

Elementary properties of even and odd functions include the following:

(1) The sum (difference) and product (quotient) of two even functions are even.

(2) The sum (difference) of two odd functions is odd; the product (quotient) of two odd functions is even.

(3) The sum (difference) of an odd function and an even function is neither even nor odd; the product (quotient) of two such functions is odd.*

The proofs of all these assertions are trivial, and follow directly from the definitions. For example, if both f_1 and f_2 are odd, and if $g(x) = f_1(x) + f_2(x)$, then

$$
\begin{aligned}
g(-x) = f_1(-x) + f_2(-x) &= -f_1(x) - f_2(x) \\
&= -[f_1(x) + f_2(x)] = -g(x),
\end{aligned}
\tag{3}
$$

so $f_1 + f_2$ is an odd function also. Similarly, if $h(x) = f_1(x)f_2(x)$, then

$$
h(-x) = f_1(-x)f_2(-x) = [-f_1(x)][-f_2(x)] = f_1(x)f_2(x) = h(x), \tag{4}
$$

so that $f_1 f_2$ is even.

Also of importance are the following two integral properties of even and odd functions:

(4) If f is an even function, then

$$
\int_{-l}^{l} f(x)\,dx = 2\int_{0}^{l} f(x)\,dx. \tag{5}
$$

(5) If f is an odd function, then

$$
\int_{-l}^{l} f(x)\,dx = 0. \tag{6}
$$

These properties are intuitively clear from the interpretation of an integral in terms of area under a curve, and also follow immediately from the definitions. For example, if f is even, then

$$
\int_{-l}^{l} f(x)\,dx = \int_{-l}^{0} f(x)\,dx + \int_{0}^{l} f(x)\,dx.
$$

Letting x equal $-u$ in the first term on the right side, and using Eq. (1), gives

$$
\int_{-l}^{l} f(x)\,dx = -\int_{l}^{0} f(u)\,du + \int_{0}^{l} f(x)\,dx = 2\int_{0}^{l} f(x)\,dx.
$$

The proof of the corresponding property for odd functions is similar.

Even and odd functions are particularly important in the theory of Fourier series since their Fourier series are of a special form.

---

* These statements may need to be modified slightly if either function vanishes identically.

Cosine Series. Suppose that f is an even periodic function with period $2l$. Let $g(x) = f(x) \cos (n\pi x/l)$ and $h(x) = f(x) \sin (n\pi x/l)$. It then follows from properties (1) and (3) that g is even and h is odd. As a consequence of Eqs. (5) and (6), the Fourier coefficients of f are then given by

$$a_n = \frac{2}{l} \int_0^l f(x) \cos \frac{n\pi x}{l} \, dx, \qquad n = 0, 1, 2, \ldots ;$$

$$b_n = 0, \qquad\qquad\qquad n = 1, 2, \ldots . \tag{7}$$

Thus f has the Fourier series

$$f(x) \sim \frac{a_0}{2} + \sum_{n=1}^{\infty} a_n \cos \frac{n\pi x}{l} ;$$

since no sine terms are present, such a series is called a *Fourier cosine series*.

Sine Series. If f is an odd periodic function of period $2l$, and if g and h are defined as above, then it follows from properties (2) and (3) that g is odd and h is even.

In this case the Fourier coefficients of f are

$$a_n = 0, \qquad\qquad\qquad n = 0, 1, 2, \ldots ;$$

$$b_n = \frac{2}{l} \int_0^l f(x) \sin \frac{n\pi x}{l} \, dx, \qquad n = 1, 2, \ldots ; \tag{8}$$

and the Fourier series for f is of the form

$$f(x) \sim \sum_{n=1}^{\infty} b_n \sin \frac{n\pi x}{l} .$$

Such a series is called a *Fourier sine series*.

Example. Let $f(x) = x$, $-l < x < l$, and let $f(-l) = f(l) = 0$. Let f be defined elsewhere so that it is periodic of period $2l$; see Figure 10.8.

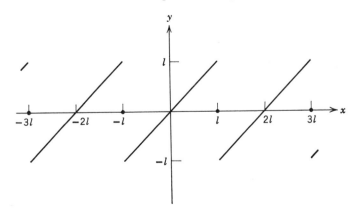

FIGURE 10.8 Sawtooth wave.

The function defined in this manner is known as a sawtooth wave. Since f is an odd function, its Fourier coefficients are, according to Eq. (8):

$$a_n = 0, \qquad n = 0, 1, \ldots ;$$

$$b_n = \frac{2}{l} \int_0^l x \sin \frac{n\pi x}{l} \, dx$$

$$= \frac{2}{l} \left(\frac{l}{n\pi}\right)^2 \left\{ \sin \frac{n\pi x}{l} - \frac{n\pi x}{l} \cos \frac{n\pi x}{l} \right\} \Big|_0^l$$

$$= \frac{2l}{n\pi}(-1)^{n+1}, \qquad n = 1, 2, \ldots .$$

Hence the Fourier series for f, the sawtooth wave, is

$$f(x) = \frac{2l}{\pi} \sum_{n=1}^{\infty} \frac{(-1)^{n+1}}{n} \sin \frac{n\pi x}{l}. \tag{9}$$

Note that the series (9) converges to the value zero at the points $x = 0$, $\pm l, \ldots$. This is also indicated in Figure 10.8.

Note that in this example $f(-l) = f(l) = 0$, as well as $f(0) = 0$. This is required if the function f is to be both odd and periodic with period $2l$. When we speak of constructing a sine series for a function defined on $0 \leq x \leq l$, it is understood that, if necessary, we must first redefine the function to be zero at $x = 0$ and $x = l$.

It is worthwhile to observe that the triangular wave function (Example 1 of Section 10.3) and the sawtooth wave function just considered are identical on the interval $0 \leq x < l$. Therefore, their Fourier series converge to the same function, $f(x) = x$, on this interval. Thus, if it is required to represent the function $f(x) = x$ on $0 \leq x < l$ by a Fourier series, it is possible to do this by *either a cosine series or a sine series*. In the former case f is extended as an *even* function into the interval $-l < x < 0$ and elsewhere periodically (the triangular wave). In the latter case f is extended into $-l < x < 0$ as an *odd* function, and elsewhere periodically (the sawtooth wave). If f is extended in any other way, the resulting Fourier series will still converge to x in $0 \leq x < l$ but will involve both sine and cosine terms.

In solving problems in differential equations it is often useful to expand in a Fourier series a function f originally defined only on the interval $[0, l]$. As indicated above for the function $f(x) = x$ several alternatives are available. Explicitly, we can:

(a) Define a function g of period $2l$ so that

$$g(x) = \begin{cases} f(x), & 0 \leq x \leq l, \\ f(-x), & -l < x < 0. \end{cases} \tag{10}$$

The function g is thus the even periodic extension of f. Its Fourier series, which is a cosine series, represents f on $[0, l]$.

(b) Define a function h of period $2l$ so that

$$h(x) = \begin{cases} f(x), & 0 < x < l, \\ 0, & x = 0, l, \\ -f(-x), & -l < x < 0. \end{cases} \tag{11}$$

The function h is thus the odd periodic extension of f. Its Fourier series, which is a sine series, also represents f on $[0, l]$.

(c) Define a function k of period $2l$ so that

$$k(x) = f(x), \qquad 0 \leq x \leq l, \tag{12}$$

and let $k(x)$ be defined for $(-l, 0)$ in any way consistent with the conditions of Theorem 10.3. Sometimes it is convenient to define $k(x)$ to be zero for $-l < x < 0$. The Fourier series for k, which involves both sine and cosine terms, also represents f on $[0, l]$ regardless of the manner in which $k(x)$ is defined in $(-l, 0)$. Thus there are infinitely many such series, all of which converge to $f(x)$ in the original interval.

Usually, the form of the expansion to be used will be dictated (or at least suggested) by the purpose for which it is needed. If, however, there is a choice as to the kind of Fourier series to be used, the selection can sometimes be based on the rapidity of convergence. For example, the cosine series for the triangular wave [Eq. (16) of Section 10.3] converges more rapidly than the sine series for the sawtooth wave [Eq. (9) of Section 10.5], although both converge to the same function for $0 \leq x < l$. This is due to the fact that the triangular wave is a smoother function than the sawtooth wave and is therefore easier to approximate. In general, the more continuous derivatives possessed by a function over the entire interval $-\infty < x < \infty$, the faster its Fourier series will converge. See Problem 15 of Section 10.4.

PROBLEMS

1. Determine whether the following functions are even, odd, or neither.

(a) x^3

(b) $x^3 - 2x$

(c) $x^3 - 2x + 1$

(d) $\tan 2x$

(e) $\sec x$

(f) $|x|^3$

(g) e^{-x}

(h) $\ln|\sin x|$

(i) $\ln|\cos x|$

(j) $(2x - x^3)^4$

(k) the function of Problem 1(i), Section 10.3

(l) the function of Problem 1(j), Section 10.3

2. Using the properties of even and odd functions, evaluate the following integrals.

(a) $\displaystyle\int_{-1}^{1} x\,dx$

(b) $\displaystyle\int_{-1}^{1} x^4\,dx$

(c) $\displaystyle\int_{-\pi}^{\pi} x\sin nx\,dx$

(d) $\displaystyle\int_{-l}^{l} \sin\frac{n\pi x}{l}\cos\frac{n\pi x}{l}\,dx$

(e) $\displaystyle\int_{-\pi}^{\pi} x^4\sin nx\,dx$

(f) $\displaystyle\int_{-\pi}^{\pi} x\cos nx\,dx$

3. Prove that any function can be expressed as the sum of two other functions, one of which is even and the other odd. That is, for any function f, whose domain contains $-x$ whenever it contains x, show that there is an even function g and an odd function h such that $f(x) = g(x) + h(x)$.
Hint: Assuming $f(x) = g(x) + h(x)$, what is $f(-x)$?

In each of Problems 4 through 11 find the required Fourier series for the given function; sketch the graph of the function to which the series converges over two periods.

4. $f(x) = \begin{cases} 1, & 0 < x < 1, \\ 0, & 1 < x < 2; \end{cases}$ cosine series, period 4

Compare with the example and Problems 4 and 7 of Section 10.4.

5. $f(x) = \begin{cases} x, & 0 \le x < 1, \\ 1, & 1 \le x < 2; \end{cases}$ sine series, period 4

6. $f(x) = 1,$ $0 \le x \le \pi;$ cosine series, period 2π

7. $f(x) = 1,$ $0 < x < \pi;$ sine series, period 2π

8. $f(x) = \begin{cases} 0, & 0 < x < \pi, \\ 1, & \pi < x < 2\pi, \\ 2, & 2\pi < x < 3\pi; \end{cases}$ sine series, period 6π

9. $f(x) = x,$ $0 \le x < 1;$ series of period 1

10. $f(x) = 1 - x,$ $0 \le x \le l;$ cosine series, period $2l$

Compare with Example 1 of Section 10.3.

11. $f(x) = 1 - x,$ $0 < x < l;$ sine series, period $2l$

12. Prove that if f is an odd function, then

$$\int_{-l}^{l} f(x)\,dx = 0.$$

13. Prove properties (2) and (3) on page 446.

14. Prove that the derivative of an even function is odd, and that the derivative of an odd function is even.

15. Let $F(x) = \int_0^x f(t)\, dt$. Show that if f is even, then F is odd, and that if f is odd, then F is even.

16. From the Fourier series for the square wave (Section 10.4), show that

$$\frac{\pi}{4} = 1 - \frac{1}{3} + \frac{1}{5} - \frac{1}{7} + \cdots = \sum_{n=0}^{\infty} \frac{(-1)^n}{2n + 1}.$$

This relation between π and the odd positive integers was discovered by Leibniz in 1673. Compute an approximate value of π by using the first four terms of this series.

17. (a) From the Fourier series for the triangular wave (Example 1 of Section 10.3), show that

$$\frac{\pi^2}{8} = 1 + \frac{1}{3^2} + \frac{1}{5^2} + \cdots = \sum_{n=0}^{\infty} \frac{1}{(2n + 1)^2}.$$

(b) Compute an approximate value of π by using the first four terms of the series in (a).

18. Let f represent the sawtooth wave, Figure 10.8, and let

$$k(x) = \frac{1}{2}\left\{ -f\left[2\left(x + \frac{l}{2}\right)\right] + l \right\}.$$

Graph $y = k(x)$. Obtain the Fourier series for k by substituting in the definition of $k(x)$ the Fourier series for f, Eq. (9). Note that the sum of f and k is the square wave function. Obtain the Fourier series for the square wave, Eq. (7) of Section 10.4, by adding those for f and k.

19. Let f represent the sawtooth wave, Figure 10.8, and let g represent the triangular wave, Figure 10.4. Show that

$$g(x) = \frac{2}{l} \int_{-l}^{x}\left[f(u) - \frac{l}{2}\right] du + l.$$

Verify that the Fourier series for g is obtained by substituting the Fourier series for f in this equation.

20. Assuming that f has a Fourier sine series

$$f(x) = \sum_{n=1}^{\infty} b_n \sin \frac{n\pi x}{l}$$

for $0 \leq x \leq l$, show formally that

$$\frac{2}{l} \int_0^l [f(x)]^2\, dx = \sum_{n=1}^{\infty} b_n^2.$$

Compare this result with that of Problem 14 of Section 10.4. What is the corresponding result if f has a cosine series?

Let f be a function originally defined on $0 \le x \le l$. In this section we have shown that it is possible to represent f either by a sine series or by a cosine series by constructing odd or even periodic extensions of f, respectively. Problems 21 to 24 concern some other specialized Fourier series which converge to the given function f at least on $(0, l)$.

21. Let f be extended into $(l, 2l]$ in an arbitrary manner. Then extend the resulting function into $(-2l, 0)$ as an odd function and elsewhere as a periodic

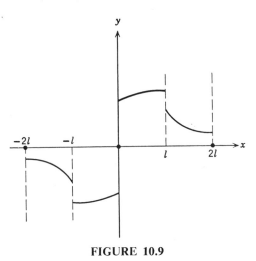

FIGURE 10.9

function of period $4l$; see Figure 10.9. Show that this function has a Fourier sine series in terms of the functions $\sin(n\pi x/2l)$, $n = 1, 2, 3, \ldots$, that is,

$$f(x) = \sum_{n=1}^{\infty} b_n \sin \frac{n\pi x}{2l},$$

where

$$b_n = \frac{1}{l} \int_0^{2l} f(x) \sin \frac{n\pi x}{2l}\, dx,$$

and that this series converges to the original function on $(0, l)$.

22. Let f first be extended into $(l, 2l]$ so that it is symmetric about $x = l$, that is, so as to satisfy $f(2l - x) = f(x)$ for $0 \le x < l$. Let the resulting function be extended into $(-2l, 0)$ as an odd function and elsewhere (see Figure 10.10) as a periodic function of period $4l$. Show that this function has a Fourier series in terms of the functions $\sin(\pi x/2l)$, $\sin(3\pi x/2l)$, $\sin(5\pi x/2l)$, $\ldots$; that is,

$$f(x) = \sum_{n=1}^{\infty} b_n \sin \frac{(2n - 1)\pi x}{2l},$$

where

$$b_n = \frac{2}{l} \int_0^l f(x) \sin \frac{(2n - 1)\pi x}{2l}\, dx.$$

This series converges to the original function on $(0, l)$.

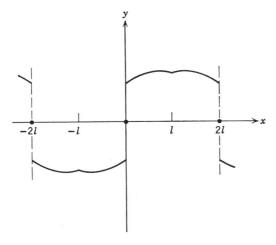

FIGURE 10.10

23. Let f be extended into $(l, 2l]$ as a function symmetric about $x = l$, that is, so that $f(2l - x) = f(x)$. Let the resulting function be extended into the interval $(-2l, 0)$ as an even function and elsewhere as a periodic function of period $4l$. Show that f has a Fourier series of the form

$$f(x) = \frac{a_0}{2} + \sum_{n=1}^{\infty} a_n \cos \frac{n\pi x}{l},$$

where

$$a_n = \frac{2}{l} \int_0^l f(x) \cos \frac{n\pi x}{l} \, dx,$$

and that this series converges to the original function on $[0, l]$. Note that this series is the same as that obtained by simply extending f into $(-l, 0)$ as an even function and elsewhere as a periodic function of period $2l$.

24. How should f, originally defined on $[0, l]$, be extended so as to obtain a Fourier series involving the functions $\cos (\pi x/2l)$, $\cos (3\pi x/2l)$, $\cos (5\pi x/2l)$, ... ? If $f(x) = x$ for $0 \le x \le l$, sketch the function to which the Fourier series converges for $-4l \le x \le 4l$.

10.6 SOLUTION OF OTHER HEAT CONDUCTION PROBLEMS

In Section 10.2 we considered the problem consisting of the heat conduction equation

$$\alpha^2 u_{xx} = u_t, \qquad 0 < x < l, \qquad t > 0, \tag{1}$$

the boundary conditions

$$u(0, t) = 0, \qquad u(l, t) = 0, \qquad t > 0, \tag{2}$$

and the initial condition

$$u(x, 0) = f(x), \qquad 0 \le x \le l. \tag{3}$$

We found the solution to be

$$u(x, t) = \sum_{n=1}^{\infty} b_n e^{-n^2 \pi^2 \alpha^2 t / l^2} \sin \frac{n \pi x}{l}, \tag{4}$$

where the coefficients b_n are the same as in the series

$$f(x) = \sum_{n=1}^{\infty} b_n \sin \frac{n \pi x}{l}. \tag{5}$$

The series in Eq. (5) is just the Fourier sine series for f; according to Section 10.5 its coefficients are given by

$$b_n = \frac{2}{l} \int_0^l f(x) \sin \frac{n \pi x}{l} \, dx. \tag{6}$$

Hence the solution of the heat conduction problem, Eqs. (1) to (3), is given by the series in Eq. (4) with the coefficients computed from Eq. (6).

We emphasize that, at this stage, the solution (4) must be regarded as a *formal* solution; that is, we obtained it without rigorous justification of the limiting processes involved. Such a justification is beyond the scope of this book. However, once the series (4) has been obtained, it is possible to show that in $0 < x < l$, $t > 0$ it converges to a continuous function, that the derivatives u_{xx} and u_t can be computed by differentiating the series (4) term by term, and that the heat equation (1) is indeed satisfied. The argument rests heavily upon the fact that each term of the series (4) contains a negative exponential factor, and this results in relatively rapid convergence of the series. A further argument establishes that the function u given by Eq. (4) also satisfies the boundary and initial conditions; this completes the justification of the formal solution. It is interesting to note that the initial temperature distribution $u(x, 0) = f(x)$ may have points of discontinuity, although f must satisfy the conditions of the Fourier Convergence Theorem (Section 10.4). Nevertheless, the solution $u(x, t)$ is continuous for arbitrarily small values of t. Thus, heat conduction is a diffusive process which instantly smooths out any discontinuities that may be present in the initial temperature distribution. Finally, since f is bounded it follows from Eq. (6) that the coefficients b_n are also bounded. Consequently, the presence of the negative exponential factor in each term of the series (4) guarantees that

$$\lim_{t \to \infty} u(x, t) = 0 \tag{7}$$

for all x regardless of the initial condition. This is in accord with the result expected from physical intuition.

We will now consider two other problems of one dimensional heat conduction which can be handled by the method developed in Section 10.2.

Nonhomogeneous Boundary Conditions.   Suppose now that one end of the bar is held at a constant temperature T_1 and the other is maintained at a constant temperature T_2. Then the boundary conditions are

$$u(0, t) = T_1, \qquad u(l, t) = T_2, \qquad t > 0. \tag{8}$$

The differential equation (1) and the initial condition (3) remain unchanged.

This problem is somewhat more difficult, because of the nonhomogeneous boundary conditions, than the one in Section 10.2. Nevertheless, if appropriate modifications are made, the problem can be solved directly by the method of separation of variables. In particular, the solution corresponding to the zero value of the separation constant [Eq. (14) of Section 10.2] must be retained and used to satisfy the boundary conditions (8). We can reach the same result in a slightly different way by *reducing the present problem to one having homogeneous boundary conditions*, which can then be solved as in Section 10.2. The technique for doing this is suggested by the following physical argument.

After a long time, that is, as $t \to \infty$, we anticipate that a steady state temperature distribution $v(x)$ will be reached, which is independent of the time t and the initial conditions. Since $v(x)$ must satisfy the equation of heat conduction (1), then

$$v''(x) = 0, \qquad 0 < x < l. \tag{9}$$

Further, $v(x)$ must satisfy the boundary conditions

$$v(0) = T_1, \qquad v(l) = T_2, \tag{10}$$

which apply even as $t \to \infty$. The solution of Eq. (9) satisfying Eqs. (10) is

$$v(x) = (T_2 - T_1)\frac{x}{l} + T_1. \tag{11}$$

Hence the steady state temperature distribution is a linear function of x.

Returning to the original problem, Eqs. (1), (3), and (8), we will try to express $u(x, t)$ as the sum of the steady state temperature distribution $v(x)$ and another (transient) temperature distribution $w(x, t)$; thus

$$u(x, t) = v(x) + w(x, t). \tag{12}$$

Since $v(x)$ is given by Eq. (11), the problem will be solved provided we can determine $w(x, t)$. The boundary value problem for $w(x, t)$ is found by substituting the expression in Eq. (12) for $u(x, t)$ in Eqs. (1), (3), and (8).

From Eq. (1) we have

$$\alpha^2(v + w)_{xx} = (v + w)_t;$$

it follows that

$$\alpha^2 w_{xx} = w_t, \tag{13}$$

since $v_{xx} = 0$ and $v_t = 0$. Similarly, from Eqs. (12), (8), and (10),

$$w(0, t) = u(0, t) - v(0) = T_1 - T_1 = 0,$$
$$w(l, t) = u(l, t) - v(l) = T_2 - T_2 = 0. \tag{14}$$

Finally, from Eqs. (12) and (3),

$$w(x, 0) = u(x, 0) - v(x) = f(x) - v(x), \tag{15}$$

where $v(x)$ is given by Eq. (11). Thus the transient part of the solution to the original problem is found by solving the problem consisting of Eqs. (13), (14), and (15). This latter problem is precisely the one solved in Section 10.2 provided that $f(x) - v(x)$ is now regarded as the initial temperature distribution. Hence

$$u(x, t) = (T_2 - T_1)\frac{x}{l} + T_1 + \sum_{n=1}^{\infty} b_n e^{-n^2\pi^2\alpha^2 t/l^2} \sin\frac{n\pi x}{l}, \tag{16}$$

where

$$b_n = \frac{2}{l}\int_0^l \left[f(x) - (T_2 - T_1)\frac{x}{l} - T_1\right]\sin\frac{n\pi x}{l}\,dx. \tag{17}$$

This is another case in which a more difficult problem is solved by reducing it to a simpler problem that has already been solved. The technique of reducing a problem with nonhomogeneous boundary conditions to one with homogeneous boundary conditions by subtracting the steady state solution is capable of wide application.

Bar with Insulated Ends. A slightly different problem occurs if the ends of the bar are insulated so that there is no passage of heat through them. It is shown in Appendix A that in this case the boundary conditions are

$$u_x(0, t) = 0, \qquad u_x(l, t) = 0, \qquad t > 0. \tag{18}$$

The problem posed by Eqs. (1), (3), and (18) can also be solved by the method of separation of variables. Letting

$$u(x, t) = X(x)T(t), \tag{19}$$

it follows as in Section 10.2 that if $u(x, t)$ satisfies Eq. (1), then

$$\frac{X''}{X} = \frac{1}{\alpha^2}\frac{T'}{T} = \sigma. \tag{20}$$

It is also true once again that the separation constant σ must be real. We will omit the proof of this fact, however, since in Section 11.3 it will be established for a much more general class of problems. Assuming that σ is real, then it can be either positive, negative, or zero, and we will examine each of these possibilities in turn.

If $\sigma > 0$, it is convenient to let $\sigma = \lambda^2$, where λ is also real and positive. It is sufficient to consider $\lambda > 0$ since every positive value of σ can be obtained by using only positive values of λ. Then from Eq. (20) we have $X'' - \lambda^2 X = 0$, $T' - \alpha^2 \lambda^2 T = 0$, and solutions of the differential equation (1) must be of the form

$$u(x, t) = e^{\alpha^2 \lambda^2 t}(k_1 \sinh \lambda x + k_2 \cosh \lambda x). \tag{21}$$

In this case the boundary conditions can be satisfied only by choosing $k_1 = k_2 = 0$. Since this is unacceptable, the separation constant σ cannot be positive.

If $\sigma = 0$, then Eq. (20) gives $X'' = 0$, $T' = 0$, and solutions of Eq. (1) are of the form

$$u(x, t) = k_1 x + k_2. \tag{22}$$

The boundary conditions (18) require that $k_1 = 0$, and hence corresponding to $\sigma = 0$, we have the constant solution $u(x, t) = k_2$.

Finally, if $\sigma < 0$, let $\sigma = -\lambda^2$, where λ is real and positive. It is again sufficient to consider $\lambda > 0$ only, since all negative values of σ are obtained from positive values of λ. Then the separated equations are $X'' + \lambda^2 X = 0$ and $T' + \alpha^2 \lambda^2 T = 0$; solutions of Eq. (1) now are of the form

$$u(x, t) = e^{-\alpha^2 \lambda^2 t}(k_1 \sin \lambda x + k_2 \cos \lambda x). \tag{23}$$

The boundary condition at $x = 0$ requires that $k_1 = 0$, and the boundary condition at $x = l$ requires that $\lambda = n\pi/l$ for $n = 1, 2, 3, \ldots$. Thus there are nontrivial solutions of Eq. (1) whenever $\sigma = -(n\pi/l)^2$, where n is a positive integer.

Combining all of these results we have the following fundamental solutions for the problem (1), (3), and (18):

$$u_0(x, t) = \frac{c_0}{2},$$
$$u_n(x, t) = c_n e^{-n^2 \pi^2 \alpha^2 t/l^2} \cos \frac{n\pi x}{l}, \qquad n = 1, 2, \ldots, \tag{24}$$

where the constants have been relabeled in a convenient way. These functions satisfy the differential equation (1) and the boundary conditions (18) for any values of the constants c_n. Because both the differential equation and boundary conditions are linear and homogeneous, any finite sum of the fundamental solutions will also satisfy them. We will assume that this is also true for convergent infinite sums of fundamental solutions as well. Thus, in order to satisfy the initial condition (3), we assume that $u(x, t)$ has the form

$$u(x, t) = \sum_{n=0}^{\infty} u_n(x, t) = \frac{c_0}{2} + \sum_{n=1}^{\infty} c_n e^{-n^2 \pi^2 \alpha^2 t/l^2} \cos \frac{n\pi x}{l}. \tag{25}$$

The c_n are determined by the requirement that

$$u(x, 0) = \frac{c_0}{2} + \sum_{n=1}^{\infty} c_n \cos \frac{n\pi x}{l} = f(x). \tag{26}$$

Thus the unknown coefficients in Eq. (25) must be the coefficients in the Fourier cosine series of period $2l$ for f. Hence

$$c_n = \frac{2}{l} \int_0^l f(x) \cos \frac{n\pi x}{l}\, dx, \qquad n = 0, 1, 2, \ldots. \qquad (27)$$

With this choice of the coefficients $c_0, c_1, c_2, \ldots$ the series (25) provides the solution to the heat conduction problem for a rod with insulated ends, Eqs. (1), (3), and (18).

It is worth observing that the solution (25) can also be thought of as the sum of a steady state temperature distribution (given by the constant $c_0/2$) which is independent of time t, and a transient distribution (given by the rest of the infinite series) which vanishes in the limit as t approaches infinity. That the steady state is a constant is consistent with the expectation that the process of heat conduction will gradually smooth out the temperature distribution in the bar as long as no heat is allowed to escape to the outside. The physical interpretation of the constant is the mean or average value of the original temperature distribution.

The problem in which one end of the bar is insulated and the other held at a constant temperature can be treated in essentially the same manner. However, the extension of f outside of the interval $[0, l]$ is somewhat different from that in any case considered so far. See Problems 9 and 10.

PROBLEMS

1. Consider the conduction of heat in a copper rod 100 cm in length whose ends are maintained at $0°$ C for all $t > 0$. Find an expression for the temperature $u(x, t)$ if the initial temperature distribution in the rod is given by

(a) $u(x, 0) = 50,$ $0 \le x \le 100;$

(b) $u(x, 0) = \begin{cases} x, & 0 \le x < 50, \\ 100 - x, & 50 \le x \le 100; \end{cases}$

(c) $u(x, 0) = \begin{cases} 0, & 0 \le x < 25, \\ 50, & 25 \le x \le 75, \\ 0, & 75 < x \le 100. \end{cases}$

2. Let a metallic rod 20 cm long be heated to a uniform temperature of $100°$ C. Suppose that at $t = 0$ the ends of the bar are plunged into an ice bath at $0°$ C, and thereafter maintained at this temperature, but that no heat is allowed to escape through the lateral surface. Find an expression for the temperature at any point in the bar at any later time. Use two terms in the series expansion for the temperature to determine approximately the temperature at the center of the bar at time $t = 30$ sec if the bar is made of (a) silver; (b) aluminum; (c) cast iron.

3. For the situation of Problem 2 find the time that will elapse before the center of the bar cools to a temperature of $25°$ C if the bar is made of (a) silver; (b) aluminum; (c) cast iron. Use only one term in the series expansion for $u(x, t)$.

4. Let an aluminum rod of length l be initially at the uniform temperature of $25°$ C. Suppose that at time $t = 0$ the end $x = 0$ is cooled to $0°$ C while the end $x = l$ is heated to $60°$ C, and both are thereafter maintained at those temperatures.
   (a) Find the temperature distribution in the rod at any time t.
Assume in the remaining parts of this problem that $l = 20$ cm.
   (b) Use only the first term in the series for the temperature $u(x, t)$ to find the approximate temperature at $x = 5$ cm when $t = 30$ sec; when $t = 60$ sec.
   (c) Use the first two terms of the series for $u(x, t)$ to find an approximate value of $u(5, 30)$. What is the percentage difference between the one and two term approximations? Does the third term in the series have any appreciable effect for this value of t?
   (d) Use the first term in the series for $u(x, t)$ to estimate the time interval that must elapse before the temperature at $x = 5$ cm comes within 1 percent of its steady state value.

5. (a) Let the ends of a copper rod 100 cm long be maintained at $0°$ C. Suppose the center of the bar is heated to $100°$ C by an external heat source and that this situation is maintained until a steady state results. Find this steady state temperature distribution.
   (b) At a time $t = 0$ [after the steady state of part (a) has been reached] let the heat source be removed. At the same instant let the end $x = 0$ be placed in thermal contact with a reservoir at $20°$ C while the other remains at $0°$ C. Find the temperature as a function of position and time.

6. Consider a uniform rod of length l having an initial temperature given by $\sin(\pi x/l)$, $0 \le x \le l$. Assume that both ends of the bar are insulated. Find a formal series expansion for the temperature $u(x, t)$. What is the steady state temperature as $t \to \infty$?

Problems 7 through 10 deal with the heat conduction problem in a rod that is insulated at one end and held at a constant temperature at the other end.

7. Find the steady state temperature in a bar that is insulated at the end $x = 0$ and held at the constant temperature $0°$ C at the end $x = l$.

8. Find the steady state temperature in a bar that is insulated at the end $x = 0$ and held at the constant temperature T at the end $x = l$.

9. Consider a uniform rod of length l having an initial temperature distribution given by $f(x)$, $0 \le x \le l$. Assume that the temperature at the end $x = 0$ is held at $0°$ C, while the end $x = l$ is insulated so that no heat passes through it.
   (a) Show that the fundamental solutions of the partial differential equation and boundary conditions are

$$u_n(x, t) = c_n e^{-(2n-1)^2 \pi^2 \alpha^2 t/4l^2} \sin \frac{(2n - 1)\pi x}{2l}, \qquad n = 1, 2, 3, \ldots.$$

(b) Find a formal series expansion for the temperature $u(x, t)$,

$$u(x, t) = \sum_{n=1}^{\infty} u_n(x, t),$$

which also satisfies the initial condition $u(x, 0) = f(x)$.
Hint: Even though the fundamental solutions involve only the odd sines, it is still possible to represent f by a Fourier series involving only these functions. See Problem 22 of Section 10.5.

10. Consider the rod of Problem 9, but assume that the temperature of the end $x = 0$ is held at the constant value T. Find a formal series expansion for the temperature $u(x, t)$ at any point in the bar at any time.

11. Solve the problem

$$\alpha^2 u_{xx} = u_t, \qquad 0 < x < l, \quad t > 0$$

$$u(0, t) = T_1, \qquad u(l, t) = T_2, \quad t > 0$$

$$u(x, 0) = f(x), \qquad 0 \le x \le l$$

directly by the method of separation of variables without introducing the steady state solution. The solution of the separated equations corresponding to $\sigma = 0$ must be retained and used to satisfy the nonhomogeneous boundary conditions. Homogeneous boundary conditions are again prescribed for solutions of the separated equations for other values of σ. Then superpose these solutions and choose the coefficients to satisfy the initial condition. Note that this solution is identical to that obtained in the text.

10.7 THE WAVE EQUATION; VIBRATIONS OF AN ELASTIC STRING

A second partial differential equation occurring frequently in applied mathematics is the wave equation. Some form of this equation, or a generalization of it, almost inevitably arises in any mathematical analysis of phenomena involving the propagation of waves in a continuous medium. For example, the studies of acoustic waves, water waves, and electromagnetic waves are all based on this equation. Perhaps the easiest situation to visualize occurs in the study of mechanical vibrations. Suppose that an elastic string of length l is tightly stretched between two supports at the same horizontal level, so that the x axis lies along the string; see Figure 10.11. The elastic string may be thought of as a violin string, a guy wire, or possibly an electric power line. Suppose that the string is set in motion (by plucking, for example) so that it vibrates in a vertical plane, and let $u(x, t)$ denote the vertical displacement experienced by the string at the point x at time t. If damping effects, such as air resistance, are neglected, and if the amplitude of the motion is not too large, then $u(x, t)$ will satisfy the partial differential equation

$$a^2 u_{xx} = u_{tt} \tag{1}$$

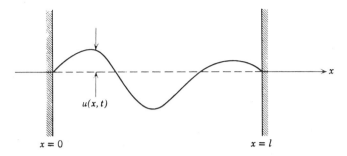

FIGURE 10.11

in the domain $0 < x < l,\, t > 0$. Equation (1) is known as the *wave equation* and is derived in Appendix B at the end of the chapter. The constant coefficient a^2 appearing in Eq. (1) is given by

$$a^2 = \frac{H}{\rho}, \tag{2}$$

where H is the horizontal component of the tension in the string, and ρ is the mass per unit length of the string material.

   In order to describe the motion of the string completely it is necessary also to specify suitable initial and boundary conditions for the displacement $u(x, t)$. The ends are assumed to remain fixed, and therefore the boundary conditions are

$$u(0, t) = 0, \qquad u(l, t) = 0, \qquad t \geq 0. \tag{3}$$

Since the differential equation (1) is of second order with respect to t as well as x, it is plausible that two initial conditions must be prescribed. These are the initial position of the string

$$u(x, 0) = f(x), \qquad 0 \leq x \leq l, \tag{4}$$

and its initial velocity

$$u_t(x, 0) = g(x), \qquad 0 \leq x \leq l, \tag{5}$$

where f and g are given functions. In order that Eqs. (3), (4), and (5) be consistent it is also necessary to require that

$$f(0) = f(l) = 0, \qquad g(0) = g(l) = 0. \tag{6}$$

   The mathematical problem then is to determine the solution of the wave equation (1) which also satisfies the boundary conditions (3) and the initial conditions (4) and (5). Like the heat conduction problem of Sections 10.2 and 10.6, this problem is an initial value problem in the time variable t, and a boundary value problem in the space variable x. Alternatively, it can be considered as a boundary value problem in the semiinfinite strip $0 < x < l$,

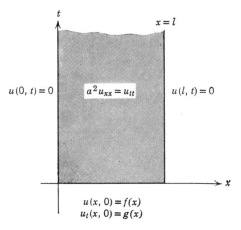

FIGURE 10.12 Boundary value problem
for the wave equation.

$t > 0$ of the xt plane; see Figure 10.12. One condition is imposed at each point on the semiinfinite sides, and two are imposed at each point on the finite base. In contrast, the heat conduction problem, being first order in time, required only one condition on the initial line $t = 0$.

It is important to realize that Eq. (1) governs a large number of other wave problems besides the transverse vibrations of an elastic string. For example, it is only necessary to interpret the function u and the constant a appropriately to have problems dealing with water waves in an ocean, acoustic or electromagnetic waves in the atmosphere, or elastic waves in a solid body. If more than one space dimension is significant, then Eq. (1) must be slightly generalized. The two-dimensional wave equation is

$$a^2(u_{xx} + u_{yy}) = u_{tt}. \tag{7}$$

This equation would arise, for example, if we considered the motion of a thin elastic sheet, such as a drumhead. Similarly, in three dimensions the wave equation is

$$a^2(u_{xx} + u_{yy} + u_{zz}) = u_{tt}. \tag{8}$$

In connection with the latter two equations, the boundary and initial conditions must also be suitably generalized.

We will now solve some typical boundary value problems involving the one dimensional wave equation.

Elastic String with Nonzero Initial Displacement.   First suppose that the string is disturbed from its equilibrium position, and then released with zero velocity at time $t = 0$ to vibrate freely. Then the vertical displacement $u(x, t)$ must satisfy the wave equation (1)

$$a^2 u_{xx} - u_{tt} = 0, \qquad 0 < x < l, \qquad t > 0;$$

the boundary conditions (3)

$$u(0, t) = 0, \qquad u(l, t) = 0, \qquad t \geq 0;$$

and the initial conditions

$$u(x, 0) = f(x), \qquad u_t(x, 0) = 0, \qquad 0 \leq x \leq l; \tag{9}$$

where f is a given function describing the configuration of the string at $t = 0$.

The method of separation of variables can be used to obtain the solution of Eqs. (1), (3), and (9). Assuming that

$$u(x, t) = X(x)T(t) \tag{10}$$

and substituting for u in Eq. (1) yields

$$\frac{X''}{X} = \frac{1}{a^2} \frac{T''}{T} = \sigma. \tag{11}$$

As in the cases considered previously it is possible to show that the separation constant σ must be real, but we will again omit any discussion of this matter for the present; see Section 11.3. Further, if $\sigma = 0$, then $X'' = 0$, and

$$X(x) = k_1 x + k_2; \tag{12}$$

if $\sigma > 0$, then $X'' - \lambda^2 X = 0$, and

$$X(x) = k_1 \sinh \lambda x + k_2 \cosh \lambda x, \tag{13}$$

where $\lambda = \sqrt{\sigma}$. In either case the boundary conditions (3) can be satisfied only by choosing $k_1 = k_2 = 0$. Thus we conclude that the separation constant must be negative; it is then convenient to write $\sigma = -\lambda^2$, where λ is real and positive.

Hence, from Eq. (11), $X(x)$ and $T(t)$ satisfy the equations

$$X'' + \lambda^2 X = 0 \tag{14}$$

and

$$T'' + \lambda^2 a^2 T = 0, \tag{15}$$

respectively. Therefore, $X(x) = k_1 \sin \lambda x + k_2 \cos \lambda x$ and $T(t) = k_3 \sin \lambda a t + k_4 \cos \lambda a t$. The product

$$u(x, t) = (k_1 \sin \lambda x + k_2 \cos \lambda x)(k_3 \sin \lambda a t + k_4 \cos \lambda a t) \tag{16}$$

satisfies Eq. (1) for all values of k_1, k_2, k_3, and k_4, and for any $\lambda > 0$.

From this infinity of solutions of the partial differential equation (1) we will now choose those which also satisfy the boundary conditions (3). In order that $u(0, t) = 0$ it is necessary that $k_2 = 0$. The second boundary condition $u(l, t) = 0$ then requires that

$$(k_1 \sin \lambda l)(k_3 \sin \lambda a t + k_4 \cos \lambda a t) = 0. \tag{17}$$

In order to obtain a nontrivial solution $u(x, t)$ of the boundary value problem it is necessary to satisfy Eq. (17) by choosing λ so that $\sin \lambda l = 0$. Thus

$$\lambda = \frac{n\pi}{l}, \qquad n = 1, 2, \ldots . \tag{18}$$

Hence functions which satisfy the homogeneous boundary conditions (3) as well as the partial differential equation (1) are of the form

$$u_n(x, t) = \sin \frac{n\pi x}{l} \left(c_n \sin \frac{n\pi at}{l} + k_n \cos \frac{n\pi at}{l} \right), \qquad n = 1, 2, \ldots, \tag{19}$$

where the c_n and k_n are arbitrary constant multipliers. These functions may be considered as fundamental solutions of the present problem.

We will now seek a suitable superposition of the fundamental solutions (19) which also satisfies the initial conditions (9). Thus let us assume that $u(x, t)$ can be written in the form

$$u(x, t) = \sum_{n=1}^{\infty} u_n(x, t) = \sum_{n=1}^{\infty} \sin \frac{n\pi x}{l} \left(c_n \sin \frac{n\pi at}{l} + k_n \cos \frac{n\pi at}{l} \right). \tag{20}$$

If we further assume that this series can be differentiated term by term with respect to t the condition $u_t(x, 0) = 0$ yields

$$u_t(x, 0) = \sum_{n=1}^{\infty} c_n \frac{n\pi a}{l} \sin \frac{n\pi x}{l} = 0.$$

Hence $c_n = 0$ for all values of n. The other initial condition $u(x, 0) = f(x)$ gives

$$u(x, 0) = \sum_{n=1}^{\infty} k_n \sin \frac{n\pi x}{l} = f(x).$$

Consequently the k_n must be the coefficients in the Fourier sine series of period $2l$ for f, and are given by

$$k_n = \frac{2}{l} \int_0^l f(x) \sin \frac{n\pi x}{l} \, dx, \qquad n = 1, 2, \ldots . \tag{21}$$

Thus the formal solution of the problem of Eqs. (1), (3), and (9) is

$$u(x, t) = \sum_{n=1}^{\infty} k_n \sin \frac{n\pi x}{l} \cos \frac{n\pi at}{l}, \tag{22}$$

with the coefficients k_n given by Eq. (21).

For a fixed value of n the expression $\sin (n\pi x/l) \cos (n\pi at/l)$ in Eq. (22) is periodic in time t with the period $2l/na$; it therefore represents a vibratory motion of the string having this period, or having the frequency $n\pi a/l$. The quantities $\lambda a = n\pi a/l$ for $n = 1, 2, \ldots$, are the *natural frequencies* of the string, that is, the frequencies at which the string will freely vibrate. The factor $k_n \sin (n\pi x/l)$ represents the displacement pattern occurring in the string when it is executing vibrations of the given frequency. The total motion of the string, given by the function $u(x, t)$ of Eq. (22), is thus a combination of the fundamental modes of vibration, and is also a periodic function of time with period $2l/a$.

Justification of the Solution. As in the heat conduction problem considered earlier, Eq. (22) with the coefficients k_n given by Eq. (21) is only a *formal* solution of Eqs. (1), (3), and (9). To ascertain whether Eq. (22) *actually* represents the solution of the given problem requires some further investigation. As in the heat conduction problem, it is tempting to try to show this by directly substituting Eq. (22) for $u(x, t)$ in Eqs. (1), (3), and (9). However, on formally computing u_{xx}, for example, we obtain

$$u_{xx}(x, t) = -\sum_{n=1}^{\infty} k_n \left(\frac{n\pi}{l}\right)^2 \sin \frac{n\pi x}{l} \cos \frac{n\pi at}{l} ;$$

due to the presence of the n^2 factor in the numerator this series may not converge. Thus it may not be possible to substitute Eq. (22) for $u(x, t)$ in the differential equation (1). The basic difference between solutions of the wave equation and those of the heat conduction equation is that the latter contain negative exponential terms which approach zero very rapidly with increasing n. In contrast, series solutions of the wave equation contain sinusoidal terms which are oscillatory in nature.

However, there is an alternative way to establish the validity of Eq. (22) indirectly. At the same time we will gain additional information about the structure of the solution. First we will show that Eq. (22) is equivalent to

$$u(x, t) = \tfrac{1}{2}[h(x - at) + h(x + at)], \tag{23}$$

where h is the function obtained by extending the initial data f into $(-l, 0)$ as an odd function, and to other values of x as a periodic function of period $2l$. That is,

$$h(x) = \begin{cases} f(x), & 0 \le x \le l, \\ -f(-x), & -l < x < 0; \end{cases} \tag{24}$$
$$h(x + 2l) = h(x).$$

To establish Eq. (23) note that h has the Fourier series

$$h(x) = \sum_{n=1}^{\infty} k_n \sin \frac{n\pi x}{l} . \tag{25}$$

Then

$$h(x - at) = \sum_{n=1}^{\infty} k_n \left(\sin \frac{n\pi x}{l} \cos \frac{n\pi at}{l} - \cos \frac{n\pi x}{l} \sin \frac{n\pi at}{l}\right),$$

$$h(x + at) = \sum_{n=1}^{\infty} k_n \left(\sin \frac{n\pi x}{l} \cos \frac{n\pi at}{l} + \cos \frac{n\pi x}{l} \sin \frac{n\pi at}{l}\right),$$

and Eq. (23) follows immediately upon adding the last two equations. From Eq. (23) we see that $u(x, t)$ is continuous for $0 < x < l$, $t > 0$ provided that h is continuous on the interval $(-\infty, \infty)$. This requires that f be continuous on the original interval $[0, l]$ and, since h is the odd periodic extension of f, that f be zero at $x = 0$ and $x = l$. Similarly, u is twice continuously differentiable with respect to either variable in $0 < x < l, t > 0$, provided that h is twice continuously differentiable on $(-\infty, \infty)$. This requires that f' and f'' be continuous on $[0, l]$. Furthermore, since h'' is the odd extension of f'', we must also have $f''(0) = f''(l) = 0$. However, since h' is the even extension of f', no further conditions are required on f'. Provided that these conditions are met, u_{xx} and u_{tt} can be computed from Eq. (23), and it is an elementary exercise to show that these derivatives satisfy the wave equation. Some of the details of the argument indicated above are given in Problems 12 and 13.

If some of the continuity requirements stated in the last paragraph are not met, then u will fail to be differentiable at some points in the semiinfinite strip $0 < x < l, t > 0$, and thus will be a solution of the wave equation only in a somewhat restricted sense. An important physical consequence of this observation is that any discontinuities present in the initial data f will be preserved in the solution $u(x, t)$ for all time; in contrast, in heat conduction problems initial discontinuities are instantly damped out (Section 10.6). Suppose that the initial displacement f has a jump discontinuity at $x = x_0$, $0 \le x_0 \le l$. Since h is a periodic extension of f, the same discontinuity is present in $h(\xi)$ at $\xi = x_0 + 2nl$ and at $\xi = -x_0 + 2nl$, where n is any integer. Thus $h(x - at)$ is discontinuous when $x - at = x_0 + 2nl$, or when $x - at = -x_0 + 2nl$. For a fixed x in $[0, l]$ the discontinuity which was originally at x_0 will reappear in $h(x - at)$ at the times $t = (x \pm x_0 - 2nl)/a$. Similarly, $h(x + at)$ is discontinuous at the point x at the times $t = (-x \pm x_0 + 2ml)/a$, where m is any integer. Referring to Eq. (23), it then follows that the solution $u(x, t)$ is also discontinuous at the given point x at these times. Since the physical problem is posed for $t > 0$, only those values of m and n yielding positive values of t are of interest.

General Problem for the Elastic String. Let us suppose that the string is set in motion from a specified initial position with a given velocity. Then the vertical displacement $u(x, t)$ must satisfy the wave equation (1),

$$a^2 u_{xx} - u_{tt} = 0, \qquad 0 < x < l, \qquad t > 0;$$

the boundary conditions (3),

$$u(0, t) = 0, \qquad u(l, t) = 0, \qquad t \ge 0;$$

and the initial conditions

$$u(x, 0) = f(x), \qquad u_t(x, 0) = g(x), \qquad 0 \le x \le l; \qquad (26)$$

where f and g are given functions defining the initial position and velocity of the string, respectively.

Applying the method of separation of variables, we find in the same way as before that the fundamental solutions, which satisfy the partial differential equation and boundary conditions, are

$$u_n(x, t) = \sin \frac{n\pi x}{l} \left(c_n \sin \frac{n\pi at}{l} + k_n \cos \frac{n\pi at}{l} \right), \qquad n = 1, 2, \ldots . \quad (27)$$

where c_n and k_n are two sets of arbitrary constant coefficients. Again we assume that it is possible to express the solution $u(x, t)$ as a linear combination of the fundamental solutions, that is,

$$u(x, t) = \sum_{n=1}^{\infty} u_n(x, t) = \sum_{n=1}^{\infty} \sin \frac{n\pi x}{l} \left(c_n \sin \frac{n\pi at}{l} + k_n \cos \frac{n\pi at}{l} \right). \quad (28)$$

The coefficients in Eq. (28) are to be determined by the initial conditions. Applying the condition $u(x, 0) = f(x)$ yields

$$u(x, 0) = \sum_{n=1}^{\infty} k_n \sin \frac{n\pi x}{l} = f(x). \quad (29)$$

Hence the coefficients k_n are again the coefficients in the Fourier sine series of period $2l$ for f, and are thus given by Eq. (21),

$$k_n = \frac{2}{l} \int_0^l f(x) \sin \frac{n\pi x}{l} \, dx, \qquad n = 1, 2, \ldots .$$

Differentiating Eq. (28) with respect to t, and applying the second initial condition $u_t(x, 0) = g(x)$ now yields

$$u_t(x, 0) = \sum_{n=1}^{\infty} \frac{n\pi a}{l} c_n \sin \frac{n\pi x}{l} = g(x). \quad (30)$$

Hence the quantities $(n\pi a/l)c_n$ are the coefficients in the Fourier sine series of period $2l$ for g; therefore

$$\frac{n\pi a}{l} c_n = \frac{2}{l} \int_0^l g(x) \sin \frac{n\pi x}{l} \, dx, \qquad n = 1, 2, \ldots . \quad (31)$$

Thus Eq. (28), with the coefficients given by Eqs. (21) and (31), constitutes a formal solution to the problem of Eqs. (1), (3), and (26). The validity of this formal solution can be established by arguments similar to those previously indicated for the solution of Eqs. (1), (3), and (9).

PROBLEMS

1. Find the displacement $u(x, t)$ in an elastic string which is fixed at its ends and is set in motion by plucking it at its center. In this case $u(x, t)$ satisfies Eqs.

(1), (3), and (9) with $f(x)$ defined by

$$f(x) = \begin{cases} Ax, & 0 \le x \le l/2, \\ A(l - x), & l/2 < x \le l. \end{cases}$$

2. Find the displacement $u(x, t)$ in an elastic string, fixed at both ends, which is set in motion with no initial velocity from the initial position $u(x, 0) = f(x)$, where

$$f(x) = \begin{cases} Ax, & 0 \le x \le l/4, \\ Al/4, & l/4 < x < 3l/4, \\ A(l - x), & 3l/4 \le x \le l. \end{cases}$$

3. Find the displacement $u(x, t)$ in an elastic string, held fixed at the ends, which is set in motion from its equilibrium position, $u(x, 0) = 0$, with an initial velocity $u_t(x, 0) = g(x)$, where g is a given function.

4. Find the displacement $u(x, t)$ in an elastic string of length l, fixed at both ends, which is set in motion from its straight equilibrium position with the initial velocity g defined by

$$g(x) = \begin{cases} Ax, & 0 \le x \le l/2, \\ A(l - x), & l/2 < x \le l. \end{cases}$$

5. Show that the solution $u(x, t)$ of the problem

$$a^2 u_{xx} - u_{tt} = 0,$$

$$u(0, t) = 0, \qquad u(l, t) = 0, \qquad u(x, 0) = f(x), \qquad u_t(x, 0) = g(x),$$

can be written as

$$u(x, t) = v(x, t) + w(x, t),$$

where $v(x, t)$ is the solution of the same problem with $g(x) = 0$ and $w(x, t)$ is the solution of the same problem with $f(x) = 0$. Thus $v(x, t)$ represents the motion of a string started from rest with initial displacement $f(x)$, and $w(x, t)$ represents the motion of a string set in motion from its equilibrium position with initial velocity $g(x)$. The solution of the general problem can therefore be obtained by solving two subsidiary problems.

6. If an elastic string is free at one end, the boundary condition to be satisfied there is that $u_x = 0$. Find the displacement $u(x, t)$ in an elastic string of length l, fixed at $x = 0$ and free at $x = l$, set in motion with no initial velocity from the initial position $u(x, 0) = f(x)$, where f is a given function.
Hint: Show that the fundamental solutions for this problem, satisfying all conditions except the nonhomogeneous initial condition, must be of the form

$$u_n(x, t) = c_n \sin \lambda_n x \cos \lambda_n a t,$$

where $\lambda_n = (2n - 1)\pi/2l$, $n = 1, 2, \ldots$. Compare this problem with Problems 9 and 10 of Section 10.6; pay particular attention to the extension of the initial data out of the original interval $[0, l]$.

7. Dimensionless variables can be introduced into the wave equation (1) in the following manner. Letting $s = x/l$, show that the wave equation becomes

$$a^2 u_{ss} = l^2 u_{tt}.$$

Then show that l/a has the dimension of time, and thus can be used as the unit on the time scale. Finally, let $\tau = at/l$ and show that the wave equation then reduces to

$$u_{ss} = u_{\tau\tau}.$$

Problems 8 to 10 indicate the form of the general solution of the wave equation and the physical significance of the constant a.

8. Show that the wave equation

$$a^2 u_{xx} = u_{tt}$$

can be reduced to the form

$$u_{\xi\eta} = 0$$

by the change of variables

$$\xi = x - at, \qquad \eta = x + at.$$

Show that $u(x, t)$ must be of the form

$$u(x, t) = \phi(x - at) + \psi(x + at),$$

where ϕ and ψ are arbitrary functions.

9. Plot the value of $\phi(x - at)$ for $t = 0$, $1/a$, $2/a$, t_0/a if $\phi(u) = \sin u$. Note that for any $t \neq 0$ the graph of $y = \phi(x - at)$ is the same as that of $y = \phi(x)$ when $t = 0$, but displaced a distance at in the positive x direction. Thus a represents the velocity at which a disturbance moves along the string. What is the interpretation of $\phi(x + at)$?

10. A certain steel wire 5 ft in length is stretched by a tensile force of 50 lb. The wire has a linear density of 0.026 lb/ft. Find the velocity of propagation of transverse waves in the wire.

11. Show that the solution of the wave equation

$$a^2 u_{xx} = u_{tt}$$

which also satisfies the initial conditions

$$u(x, 0) = f(x), \qquad -\infty < x < \infty$$
$$u_t(x, 0) = 0, \qquad -\infty < x < \infty$$

is given by

$$u(x, t) = \tfrac{1}{2}[f(x - at) + f(x + at)].$$

Hint: Consider the form of the solution of the wave equation given in Problem 8.

Problems 12 and 13 indicate how the formal solution (22) of Eqs. (1), (3), and (9) can be shown to constitute the actual solution of that problem.

*12. By using the trigonometric identity $\sin A \cos B = \frac{1}{2}[\sin (A + B) + \sin (A - B)]$ show that the solution of the problem of Eqs. (1), (3), and (9) can be written in the form (23).

*13. Let $h(\xi)$ represent the initial displacement in $[0, l]$, extended into $(-l, 0)$ as an odd function and extended elsewhere as a periodic function of period $2l$. Assuming that h, h', and h'' are all continuous, show by direct differentiation that $u(x,t)$ as given in Eq. (23) satisfies the wave equation (1) and also the initial conditions (9). Note also that since Eq. (22) clearly satisfies the boundary conditions (3), the same is true of Eq. (23). Comparing Eq. (23) with the solution of the corresponding problem for the infinite string (Problem 11), we see that they have the same form provided that the initial data for the finite string, defined originally only on the interval $0 \leq x \leq l$, is extended in the given manner over the entire x axis. Provided that this is done, the solution for the infinite string is also applicable to the finite one.

14. The motion of an elastic membrane, such as a thin rubber sheet, is governed by the two dimensional wave equation

$$a^2(u_{xx} + u_{yy}) - u_{tt} = 0.$$

Assuming that $u(x, y, t) = X(x)Y(y)T(t)$, find ordinary differential equations that determine $X(x)$, $Y(y)$, and $T(t)$. Solve these equations, and determine the general form of $u(x, y, t)$ if u is to be periodic in x and in t.

15. The motion of a circular elastic membrane is governed by the two dimensional wave equation in polar coordinates

$$\frac{\partial^2 u}{\partial r^2} + \frac{1}{r}\frac{\partial u}{\partial r} + \frac{1}{r^2}\frac{\partial^2 u}{\partial \theta^2} - \frac{1}{a^2}\frac{\partial^2 u}{\partial t^2} = 0.$$

Assuming that $u(r, \theta, t) = R(r)\Theta(\theta)T(t)$, find ordinary differential equations satisfied by $R(r)$, $\Theta(\theta)$, and $T(t)$.

10.8 LAPLACE'S EQUATION

One of the most important of all the partial differential equations occurring in applied mathematics is that associated with the name of Laplace: in two dimensions

$$u_{xx} + u_{yy} = 0, \tag{1}$$

and in three dimensions

$$u_{xx} + u_{yy} + u_{zz} = 0. \tag{2}$$

For example, in a two dimensional heat conduction problem, the temperature $u(x, y, t)$ must satisfy the differential equation

$$\alpha^2(u_{xx} + u_{yy}) = u_t, \tag{3}$$

where α^2 is the thermal diffusivity. If a steady state exists, u is a function of x and y only, and the time derivative vanishes; in this case Eq. (3) reduces to Eq. (1). Similarly, for the steady state heat conduction problem in three dimensions, the temperature must satisfy the three dimensional form of Laplace's equation. Equations (1) and (2) also occur in other branches of mathematical physics. In the consideration of electrostatic fields the electric potential function in a dielectric medium containing no electric charges must satisfy either Eq. (1) or Eq. (2), depending on the number of space dimensions involved. Similarly, the potential energy function of a particle in free space acted on only by gravitational forces satisfies the same equations. Consequently, Laplace's equation is often referred to as the *potential equation.* Another example arises in the study of the steady (time-independent), two dimensional, inviscid, irrotational motion of an incompressible fluid, which centers about two functions, known as the velocity potential function and the stream function, both of which satisfy Eq. (1). In elasticity the displacements that occur when a perfectly elastic bar is twisted are described in terms of the so-called warping function, which also satisfies Eq. (1).

Since there is no time dependence in any of the problems mentioned above, there are no initial conditions to be satisfied by the solutions of Eq. (1) or (2). They must, however, satisfy certain boundary conditions on the bounding curve or surface of the region in which the differential equation is to be solved. Since Laplace's equation is of second order it would be plausible to expect that two boundary conditions would be required to determine the solution completely. This, however, is not the case. Recall that in the heat conduction problem for the finite bar (Sections 10.2 and 10.6) it was necessary to prescribe one condition at each end of the bar, that is, *one condition at each point of the boundary.* Generalizing this observation to multidimensional problems, it is then natural to prescribe one condition on the function u at each point on the boundary of the region in which a solution of Eq. (1) or (2) is sought. The most common boundary condition occurs when the value of u is specified at each boundary point; in terms of the heat conduction problem this corresponds to prescribing the temperature on the boundary. In some problems the value of the derivative, or rate of change, of u in the direction normal to the boundary is specified instead; the condition on the boundary of a thermally insulated body, for example, is of this type. It is entirely possible for more complicated boundary conditions to occur; for example, u might be prescribed on part of the boundary, and its normal derivative specified on the remainder. The problem of finding a solution of Laplace's equation which takes on given boundary values is known as a *Dirichlet problem,* in honor of P. G. L. Dirichlet (1805–1859). In contrast, if the values of the normal derivative are prescribed on the boundary, the problem is said to be a *Neumann problem,* in honor of Karl Gottfried Neumann (1832–1925). Dirichlet's and Neumann's problems are also known as the first and second boundary value problems of potential theory.

Physically, it is plausible to expect that the types of boundary conditions just mentioned will be sufficient to completely determine the solution. Indeed, it is possible to establish the existence and uniqueness of the solution to Laplace's equation under the boundary conditions mentioned, provided the shape of the boundary and the functions appearing in the boundary conditions satisfy certain very mild requirements. However, the proofs of these theorems, and even their accurate statement, are beyond the scope of the present book. We will be concerned only with the solution of some typical problems by means of separation of variables and Fourier series.

While the problems chosen as examples are capable of interesting physical interpretations (in terms of electrostatic potentials or steady state temperature distributions, for instance), our purpose here is primarily to point out some of the features which may occur during their mathematical solution. It is also worth noting again that more complicated problems can sometimes be solved by expressing the solution as the sum of solutions of several simpler problems (see Problems 3 and 4).

Dirichlet Problem for a Rectangle.   Consider the mathematical problem of finding the function u which satisfies Laplace's equation (1),

$$u_{xx} + u_{yy} = 0$$

in the rectangle $0 < x < a, 0 < y < b$, and which also satisfies the boundary conditions

$$u(x, 0) = 0, \qquad u(x, b) = 0, \qquad 0 < x < a,$$
$$u(0, y) = 0, \qquad u(a, y) = f(y), \qquad 0 \le y \le b, \tag{4}$$

where f is a given function on $0 \le y \le b$; see Figure 10.13.

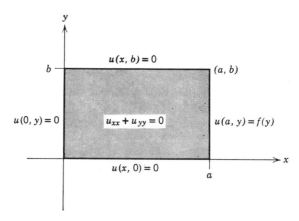

FIGURE 10.13   Dirichlet problem for a rectangle.

To solve this problem assume that

$$u(x, y) = X(x) Y(y),   (5)$$

and substitute for u in Eq. (1). This yields

$$\frac{X''}{X} = -\frac{Y''}{Y},   (6)$$

in which the variables are separated, and each side of Eq. (6) must be equal to a constant. As in the cases considered previously, this constant must be real if $u(x, y)$ is to be not identically zero. The argument is similar to that in Section 10.2 and will be omitted here; see also Section 11.3.

If the separation constant is zero, then $X'' = 0$, $Y'' = 0$, and

$$u(x, y) = (k_1 x + k_2)(c_1 y + c_2).   (7)$$

The homogeneous boundary conditions at $y = 0$ and $y = b$ can only be satisfied if $c_1 = c_2 = 0$; hence $u(x, y)$ is identically zero. Similarly, if the separation constant is negative, we may denote it by $-\lambda^2$, where $\lambda > 0$, Then $X'' + \lambda^2 X = 0$, $Y'' - \lambda^2 Y = 0$, and

$$u(x, y) = (k_1 \sin \lambda x + k_2 \cos \lambda x)(c_1 \sinh \lambda y + c_2 \cosh \lambda y).   (8)$$

Again the boundary conditions at $y = 0$ and $y = b$ lead to $c_1 = c_2 = 0$, so again $u(x, y)$ is zero everywhere. Hence we can eliminate both of these cases and need consider only a positive separation constant. Denoting it by λ^2, where $\lambda > 0$, we find that $X'' - \lambda^2 X = 0$, $Y'' + \lambda^2 Y = 0$, and thus

$$u(x, y) = (k_1 \sinh \lambda x + k_2 \cosh \lambda x)(c_1 \sin \lambda y + c_2 \cos \lambda y).   (9)$$

In order to satisfy the boundary conditions on the sides $x = 0$ and $y = 0$ of the rectangle it is necessary to take $k_2 = c_2 = 0$. Then the condition at $y = b$ becomes

$$k_1 c_1 \sinh \lambda x \sin \lambda b = 0,$$

and it follows that $\sin \lambda b = 0$, or

$$\lambda b = n\pi,   n = 1, 2, 3, \ldots .   (10)$$

Thus solutions of the differential equation and homogeneous boundary conditions must be of the form

$$u_n(x, y) = c_n \sinh \frac{n\pi x}{b} \sin \frac{n\pi y}{b},   n = 1, 2, 3, \ldots .   (11)$$

These functions serve as fundamental solutions for the present problem. As usual, we will assume that we can represent the solution $u(x, y)$ in the form

$$u(x, y) = \sum_{n=1}^{\infty} u_n(x, y) = \sum_{n=1}^{\infty} c_n \sinh \frac{n\pi x}{b} \sin \frac{n\pi y}{b}.   (12)$$

The coefficients c_n are determined by the boundary condition

$$u(a, y) = \sum_{n=1}^{\infty} c_n \sinh \frac{n\pi a}{b} \sin \frac{n\pi y}{b} = f(y). \tag{13}$$

Therefore the quantities $c_n \sinh (n\pi a/b)$ must be the coefficients in the Fourier sine series of period $2b$ for f and are given by

$$c_n \sinh \frac{n\pi a}{b} = \frac{2}{b} \int_0^b f(y) \sin \frac{n\pi y}{b} \, dy. \tag{14}$$

Thus the solution of the partial differential equation (1) satisfying the boundary conditions (4) is given by Eq. (12) with the coefficients c_n computed from Eq. (14).

Dirichlet Problem for a Circle.   Consider the problem of solving Laplace's equation in the circular region $r < a$ subject to the boundary condition

$$u(a, \theta) = f(\theta), \tag{15}$$

where f is a given function on $0 \le \theta < 2\pi$; see Figure 10.14.   In polar coordinates Laplace's equation takes the form

$$u_{rr} + \frac{1}{r} u_r + \frac{1}{r^2} u_{\theta\theta} = 0. \tag{16}$$

Moreover, in order that $u(r, \theta)$ be single valued, it is necessary that, as a function of θ, u be periodic with period 2π.

To apply the method of separation of variables to this problem we assume that

$$u(r, \theta) = R(r)\Theta(\theta), \tag{17}$$

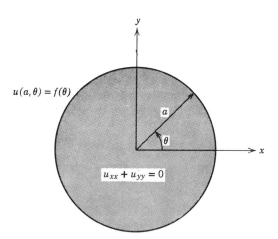

FIGURE 10.14   Dirichlet problem for a circle.

and substitute for u in the differential equation (16). This yields

$$R''\Theta + \frac{1}{r} R'\Theta + \frac{1}{r^2} R\Theta'' = 0,$$

or

$$r^2 \frac{R''}{R} + r \frac{R'}{R} = -\frac{\Theta''}{\Theta}, \tag{18}$$

in which the variables r and θ are separated. Again we will assume that the separation constant must be real, although this can be established by an argument similar to that in Section 10.2. First let us suppose that the separation constant is zero. Then Eq. (18) becomes

$$r^2 R'' + rR' = 0, \qquad \Theta'' = 0. \tag{19}$$

The first of these equations is of the Euler type, and has the solution

$$R(r) = k_1 + k_2 \ln r; \tag{20}$$

the equation in θ yields

$$\Theta(\theta) = c_1 + c_2\theta. \tag{21}$$

Thus, if the separation constant is zero, $u(r, \theta)$ is of the form

$$u(r, \theta) = (k_1 + k_2 \ln r)(c_1 + c_2\theta). \tag{22}$$

The condition that u be a periodic function of θ requires that $c_2 = 0$. Further, the term $\ln r$ becomes unbounded as $r \to 0$. This behavior is unacceptable physically; therefore we will place an additional restriction on the solution u, namely, that u remain finite at all points in the circle. Hence, we must take $k_2 = 0$. Thus, when the separation constant is zero the only allowable form for $u(r, \theta)$ is a constant, which for convenience we will write as

$$u_0(r, \theta) = \frac{c_0}{2}. \tag{23}$$

If the separation constant in Eq. (18) is negative, then we may denote it by $-\lambda^2$, and we obtain

$$\Theta'' - \lambda^2\Theta = 0 \tag{24}$$

as the equation in Θ. Equation (24), however, has the solution

$$\Theta(\theta) = c_1 e^{\lambda\theta} + c_2 e^{-\lambda\theta},$$

which can be periodic only if $c_1 = c_2 = 0$. Hence we must eliminate this choice of the separation constant.

Finally, if the separation constant is positive, we may denote it by λ^2, where $\lambda > 0$, and Eq. (18) yields

$$r^2 R'' + rR' - \lambda^2 R = 0, \tag{25}$$

and

$$\Theta'' + \lambda^2\Theta = 0. \tag{26}$$

Equation (25) is an Euler equation, and has the solution

$$R(r) = k_1 r^\lambda + k_2 r^{-\lambda}, \tag{27}$$

while Eq. (26) has the solution

$$\Theta(\theta) = c_1 \sin \lambda\theta + c_2 \cos \lambda\theta. \tag{28}$$

In order that Θ be periodic with period 2π it is necessary that λ be a positive integer n. Moreover, the solution $r^{-\lambda}$ of Eq. (25) must be discarded since it becomes unbounded as $r \to 0$. Consequently $k_2 = 0$ and the appropriate solutions of Eq. (16) are

$$u_n(r, \theta) = r^n(c_n \cos n\theta + k_n \sin n\theta), \qquad n = 1, 2, 3, \ldots. \tag{29}$$

These functions, together with that of Eq. (23), serve as fundamental solutions of the present problem.

In the usual way we now assume that u can be expressed as a linear combination of the fundamental solutions, that is,

$$u(r, \theta) = \frac{c_0}{2} + \sum_{n=1}^{\infty} r^n(c_n \cos n\theta + k_n \sin n\theta). \tag{30}$$

The boundary condition (15) then requires that

$$u(a, \theta) = \frac{c_0}{2} + \sum_{n=1}^{\infty} a^n(c_n \cos n\theta + k_n \sin n\theta) = f(\theta) \tag{31}$$

for $0 \le \theta < 2\pi$. The function f may be extended outside of this interval so that it is periodic of period 2π, and hence has a Fourier series of the form (31). Since the extended function has period 2π, we may compute its Fourier coefficients by integrating over any period of the function. In particular, it is convenient to use the original interval $(0, 2\pi)$; then

$$a^n c_n = \frac{1}{\pi} \int_0^{2\pi} f(\theta) \cos n\theta \, d\theta, \qquad n = 0, 1, 2, \ldots; \tag{32}$$

$$a^n k_n = \frac{1}{\pi} \int_0^{2\pi} f(\theta) \sin n\theta \, d\theta, \qquad n = 1, 2, \ldots. \tag{33}$$

With this choice of the coefficients, Eq. (30) represents the solution of the boundary value problem of Eqs. (15) and (16).

PROBLEMS

1. (a) Find the solution $u(x, y)$ of Laplace's equation in the rectangle $0 < x < a, 0 < y < b$, which also satisfies the following boundary conditions:

$$u(0, y) = 0, \qquad u(a, y) = 0, \qquad 0 < y < b$$
$$u(x, 0) = 0, \qquad u(x, b) = g(x), \qquad 0 \le x \le a.$$

(b) Find the solution if $g(x)$ is given by the formula

$$g(x) = \begin{cases} x, & 0 \le x < a/2, \\ a - x, & a/2 \le x \le a. \end{cases}$$

2. Find the solution $u(x, y)$ of Laplace's equation in the rectangle $0 < x < a$, $0 < y < b$, which also satisfies the following boundary conditions:

$$u(0, y) = 0, \qquad u(a, y) = 0, \qquad 0 < y < b,$$
$$u(x, b) = 0, \qquad u(x, 0) = h(x), \qquad 0 \le x \le a.$$

3. Find the solution $u(x, y)$ of Laplace's equation in the rectangle $0 < x < a$, $0 < y < b$, which also satisfies the following boundary conditions:

$$u(0, y) = 0, \qquad u(a, y) = f(y), \qquad 0 < y < b,$$
$$u(x, 0) = h(x), \qquad u(x, b) = 0, \qquad 0 \le x \le a.$$

Hint: Consider the possibility of adding the solutions of two problems, one with homogeneous boundary conditions except for $u(a, y) = f(y)$, and the other with homogeneous boundary conditions except for $u(x, 0) = h(x)$.

*4. Show how to find the solution $u(x, y)$ of Laplace's equation in the rectangle $0 < x < a$, $0 < y < b$, which also satisfies the following boundary conditions:

$$u(0, y) = k(y), \qquad u(a, y) = f(y), \qquad 0 < y < b,$$
$$u(x, 0) = h(x), \qquad u(x, b) = g(x), \qquad 0 \le x \le a.$$

Hint: See Problem 3.

5. Find the solution $u(r, \theta)$ of Laplace's equation

$$u_{rr} + \frac{1}{r} u_r + \frac{1}{r^2} u_{\theta\theta} = 0$$

outside the circle $r = a$, and satisfying the boundary condition

$$u(a, \theta) = f(\theta), \qquad 0 \le \theta < 2\pi,$$

on the circle. Assume further that $u(r, \theta)$ is single valued and remains finite for $r > a$.

6. Find the solution $u(r, \theta)$ of Laplace's equation in the semicircular region $r < a$, $0 < \theta < \pi$, which also satisfies the following boundary conditions:

$$u(r, 0) = 0, \qquad u(r, \pi) = 0, \qquad 0 \le r < a,$$
$$u(a, \theta) = f(\theta), \qquad 0 \le \theta \le \pi.$$

Assume that u is single valued and finite in the given region.

7. Consider the problem of finding a solution $u(x, y)$ of Laplace's equation in the rectangle $0 < x < a$, $0 < y < b$, which also satisfies the boundary conditions

$$u_x(0, y) = 0, \qquad u_x(a, y) = f(y), \qquad 0 < y < b,$$
$$u_y(x, 0) = 0, \qquad u_y(x, b) = 0, \qquad 0 \le x \le a.$$

This is an example of a Neumann problem.

(a) Show that Laplace's equation and the homogeneous boundary conditions determine the fundamental set of solutions

$$u_0(x, y) = c_0,$$

$$u_n(x, y) = c_n \cosh \frac{n\pi x}{b} \cos \frac{n\pi y}{b} ; \qquad n = 1, 2, 3, \dots .$$

(b) By superposing the fundamental solutions of part (a), formally determine a function u which also satisfies the nonhomogeneous boundary condition $u_x(a, y) = f(y)$. Note that when $u_x(a, y)$ is calculated, the constant term in $u(x, y)$ is eliminated, and there is no condition from which to determine c_0. Furthermore, it must be possible to express f by means of a Fourier cosine series of period $2b$ which does not have a constant term. This means that

$$\int_0^b f(y)\, dy = 0$$

is a necessary condition for the given problem to be solvable. Finally, note that c_0 remains arbitrary, and hence the solution is only determined up to this additive constant. This is a property of all Neumann problems.

8. Find a solution $u(r, \theta)$ of Laplace's equation inside the circle $r = a$, which also satisfies the boundary condition on the circle

$$u_r(a, \theta) = g(\theta), \qquad 0 \le \theta < 2\pi.$$

Note that this is a Neumann problem, and that its solution is determined only up to an arbitrary additive constant. State a necessary condition on $g(\theta)$ for this problem to be solvable by the method of separation of variables.

9. Laplace's equation in three dimensions is

$$u_{xx} + u_{yy} + u_{zz} = 0.$$

Assuming that $u(x, y, z) = X(x) Y(y) Z(z)$, find ordinary differential equations which are satisfied by X, Y, and Z. Find the set of fundamental solutions which satisfy the following homogeneous boundary conditions on the surface of a rectangular parallelepiped of sides a, b, and c.

$$u(0, y, z) = 0, \qquad u(a, y, z) = 0,$$
$$u(x, 0, z) = 0, \qquad u(x, b, z) = 0,$$
$$u(x, y, 0) = 0.$$

APPENDIX A

Derivation of the Heat Conduction Equation. In this section we will derive the differential equation which, to a first approximation at least, governs the conduction of heat in solids. It is important to understand that the mathematical analysis of a physical situation or process such as this ultimately rests on a foundation of empirical knowledge of the phenomenon involved. The mathematician must have a place to start, so to speak, and this place is furnished by experience. In the case of heat conduction it has been demonstrated many times that if two parallel plates of the same area A and different constant temperatures T_1 and T_2, respectively, are separated by a small distance d, an amount of heat per unit time will pass from the warmer to the cooler. Moreover, to a high degree of approximation, this amount of heat is proportional to the area A, the temperature difference $|T_2 - T_1|$, and inversely proportional to the separation distance d. Thus

$$\text{amount of heat per unit time} = \frac{\kappa A \, |T_2 - T_1|}{d}, \tag{1}$$

where the positive proportionality factor κ is called the thermal conductivity and depends only on the material* between the two plates. The physical law expressed by Eq. (1) is known as Newton's law of cooling. We repeat that Eq. (1) is an empirical, not a theoretical, result, and that it can be, and has often been, verified by careful experiment. It is the basis of the mathematical theory of heat conduction.

Now consider a straight rod of uniform cross section and homogeneous material, oriented so that the x axis lies along the axis of the rod; see Figure 10.15. Let $x = 0$ and $x = l$ designate the ends of the bar.

$$x = x_0 \qquad x = x_0 + \Delta x$$

FIGURE 10.15

We will assume that the sides of the bar are perfectly insulated so that there is no passage of heat through them. We will also assume that the temperature u depends only on the axial position x and the time t, and not on the lateral coordinates y and z. In other words, we assume that the temperature remains constant on any cross-section of the bar. This assumption is usually satisfactory when the lateral dimensions of the rod are small compared to its length. The differential equation which is satisfied by the temperature in the bar can be found in the following way.

Consider an element of the bar lying between the cross-sections $x = x_0$ and $x = x_0 + \Delta x$, where x_0 is arbitrary and Δx is small. The instantaneous rate of heat transfer $H(x_0, t)$ from left to right across the cross-section $x = x_0$ is given by

$$H(x_0, t) = -\lim_{d \to 0} \kappa A \, \frac{u(x_0 + d/2, t) - u(x_0 - d/2, t)}{d}$$

or

$$H(x_0, t) = -\kappa A u_x(x_0, t). \tag{2}$$

The minus sign appears in this equation since there will be a positive flow of heat from left to right only if the temperature is greater to the left of $x = x_0$ than to the right; in this case $u_x(x_0, t)$ is negative. In a similar manner the rate at which heat

---

* Actually, κ also depends on the temperature, but if the temperature range is not too great, it is satisfactory to assume that κ is independent of temperature.

passes from left to right through the cross-section $x = x_0 + \Delta x$ is given by

$$H(x_0 + \Delta x, t) = -\kappa A u_x(x_0 + \Delta x, t). \tag{3}$$

The net rate at which heat flows into the segment of the bar between $x = x_0$ and $x = x_0 + \Delta x$ is thus given by

$$Q = H(x_0, t) - H(x_0 + \Delta x, t) = \kappa A[u_x(x_0 + \Delta x, t) - u_x(x_0, t)]. \tag{4}$$

The average change in temperature Δu, in the time interval Δt, is proportional to the amount of heat $Q \, \Delta t$ introduced, and inversely proportional to the mass Δm of the element. Thus

$$\Delta u = \frac{1}{s} \frac{Q \, \Delta t}{\Delta m} = \frac{Q \, \Delta t}{s \rho A \, \Delta x}, \tag{5}$$

where the constant of proportionality s is known as the specific heat of the material of the bar, and ρ is its density.* The average temperature change Δu in the bar element under consideration is the actual temperature change at some intermediate point $x = x_0 + \theta \, \Delta x$, where $0 < \theta < 1$. Thus Eq. (5) can be written as

$$u(x_0 + \theta \, \Delta x, t + \Delta t) - u(x_0 + \theta \, \Delta x, t) = \frac{Q \, \Delta t}{s \rho A \, \Delta x}. \tag{6}$$

Solving Eq. (6) for Q and equating the resulting expression with that given by Eq. (4) yields

$$\kappa A \frac{u_x(x_0 + \Delta x, t) - u_x(x_0, t)}{\Delta x}$$
$$= s \rho A \frac{u(x_0 + \theta \, \Delta x, t + \Delta t) - u(x_0 + \theta \, \Delta x, t)}{\Delta t}. \tag{7}$$

If we let Δx and Δt approach zero in Eq. (7), we obtain the *heat conduction* or *diffusion* equation

$$\alpha^2 u_{xx} = u_t. \tag{8}$$

The quantity α^2 defined by

$$\alpha^2 = \frac{\kappa}{\rho s} \tag{9}$$

is called the *thermal diffusivity*, and is a parameter depending only on the material of the bar. The dimensions of α^2 are (length)^2/time. Typical values of α^2 are given in Table 10.1 on page 424.

Several relatively simple conditions may be imposed at the ends of the bar. For example, the temperature at an end may be maintained at some constant value T. This might be accomplished by placing the end of the bar in thermal contact with some reservoir of sufficient size that any heat which may flow between the bar and reservoir does not appreciably alter the temperature of the reservoir. At an end where this is done the boundary condition is

$$u = T. \tag{10}$$

* The dependence of the density and specific heat on temperature is relatively small, and will be neglected. Thus both ρ and s will be considered as constants.

Another simple boundary condition occurs if the end is insulated so that no heat passes through it. Recalling the expression (2) for the amount of heat crossing any cross-section of the bar, the condition for insulation is clearly that this quantity vanish. Thus

$$u_x = 0 \tag{11}$$

is the boundary condition at an insulated end.

More complicated boundary conditions, including radiation effects, for example, are discussed in more advanced works on heat conduction.

Finally, to determine completely the flow of heat in the bar it is necessary to state the temperature distribution at one fixed instant, usually taken as the initial time $t = 0$. This initial condition is of the form

$$u(x, 0) = f(x), \qquad 0 \le x \le l. \tag{12}$$

The problem then is to determine the solution of the partial differential equation (8)

$$\alpha^2 u_{xx} = u_t,$$

subject to one or the other of the boundary conditions (10) and (11)

$$u = T, \qquad u_x = 0$$

at each end, and the initial condition (12)

$$u = f(x)$$

at time $t = 0$.

A generalization of Eq. (8) is worth noting at this point. If the solid body has more than one significant space dimension, so that the temperature depends on two or three space coordinates rather than on x alone, then considerations similar to those leading to Eq. (8) can be employed to derive the heat conduction equation in two dimensions

$$\alpha^2(u_{xx} + u_{yy}) = u_t, \tag{13}$$

or in three dimensions

$$\alpha^2(u_{xx} + u_{yy} + u_{zz}) = u_t. \tag{14}$$

The boundary conditions corresponding to Eqs. (10) and (11) in the multidimensional problems correspond to a prescribed temperature distribution on the boundary, or to an insulated boundary. Similarly the initial temperature distribution will in general be a function of x and y for Eq. (13), and a function of x, y, and z for Eq. (14).

APPENDIX B

Derivation of the Wave Equation. In this section we will derive the wave equation in one space dimension as it applies to the transverse vibrations of an elastic string, or cable; the elastic string may be thought of as a violin string, a guy wire, or possibly an electric power line. The same equation, however, with the variables properly interpreted, occurs in many other wave problems having only one significant space variable. The wave equation for an elastic string was first derived in 1746 by D'Alembert.

Consider a perfectly flexible elastic string stretched tightly between supports fixed at the same horizontal level; see Figure 10.16a. Let the x axis lie along the string with the end points located at $x = 0$ and $x = l$. If the string is set in motion at some initial time $t = 0$ (by plucking, for example) and is thereafter left undisturbed, it will vibrate freely in a vertical plane provided damping effects, such as air

(a)

(b)

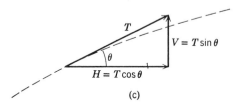

(c)

FIGURE 10.16

resistance, are neglected. To determine the differential equation governing this motion we will consider the forces acting on a small element of the string of length Δx lying between the points x and $x + \Delta x$; see Figure 10.16b. We assume that each point on the string moves solely on a vertical line, and will denote by $u(x, t)$ the vertical displacement of the point x at the time t. Let the tension in the string, which always acts in the tangential direction, be denoted by $T(x, t)$, and let ρ denote the mass per unit length of the string.

Newton's law, as it applies to the element Δx of the string, states that the net external force, due to the tension at the ends of the element, must be equal to the product of the mass of the element and the acceleration of its mass center. Since there is no horizontal acceleration, the horizontal components must satisfy

$$T(x + \Delta x, t) \cos (\theta + \Delta \theta) - T(x, t) \cos \theta = 0. \tag{1}$$

Denoting the horizontal component of the tension (see Figure 10.16c) by H, Eq. (1) states that H is independent of x. On the other hand, the vertical components satisfy

$$T(x + \Delta x, t) \sin (\theta + \Delta \theta) - T(x, t) \sin \theta = \rho \, \Delta x \, u_{tt}(\bar{x}, t), \tag{2}$$

where $\bar{x}$ is the coordinate of the center of gravity of the element of the string under consideration. Clearly $\bar{x}$ lies in the interval $x < \bar{x} < x + \Delta x$. The weight of the string, which acts vertically downward, is assumed to be negligible, and has been neglected in Eq. (2).

If the vertical component of T is denoted by V, then Eq. (2) can be written as

$$\frac{V(x + \Delta x, t) - V(x, t)}{\Delta x} = \rho u_{tt}(\bar{x}, t).$$

Passing to the limit as $\Delta x \to 0$ gives

$$V_x(x, t) = \rho u_{tt}(x, t). \tag{3}$$

To express Eq. (3) entirely in terms of u we note that

$$V(x, t) = H(t) \tan \theta = H(t) u_x(x, t).$$

Hence Eq. (3) becomes

$$(H u_x)_x = \rho u_{tt},$$

or, since H is independent of x,

$$H u_{xx} = \rho u_{tt}. \tag{4}$$

It is customary to write Eq. (4) in the form

$$a^2 u_{xx} = u_{tt}, \tag{5}$$

where

$$a^2 = \frac{H}{\rho}. \tag{6}$$

In this derivation it is possible for H to depend on t, and for ρ to depend on both x and t; in this event a^2 would be a function of both x and t. We will assume, however, that a^2 is a constant. Equation (5) is called the wave equation for one space dimension. Since H has the dimension of force, and ρ that of mass/length, it follows that the constant a has the dimension of velocity. It is possible to identify a as the velocity with which a small disturbance (wave) moves along the string. According to Eq. (6) the wave velocity a varies directly with the tension in the string, but inversely with the density of the string material. These facts are in agreement with experience.

REFERENCES

The following books contain additional information on Fourier series.

Carslaw, H. S., *Introduction to the Theory of Fourier's Series and Integrals*, 3rd ed., Cambridge University, Cambridge, 1930.

Courant R. and John, F., *Introduction to Calculus and Analysis*, Wiley (Interscience), New York, 1965.

Guillemin, E. A., *The Mathematics of Circuit Analysis*, Wiley, New York, 1949.

Kaplan, W., *Advanced Calculus*, Addison-Wesley, Reading, Mass., 1952.

Widder, D. V., *Advanced Calculus*, 2nd ed., Prentice-Hall, Englewood Cliffs, N.J., 1961.

Useful references on partial differential equations and the method of separation of variables include the following:

Berg P. W. and McGregor, J. L., *Elementary Partial Differential Equations*, Holden-Day, San Francisco, 1956.

Churchill, R. V., *Fourier Series and Boundary Value Problems*, McGraw-Hill, New York, 1941.

Duff, G. F. D. and Naylor, D., *Differential Equations of Applied Mathematics*, Wiley, New York, 1966.

Sagan, H., *Boundary and Eigenvalue Problems in Mathematical Physics*, Wiley, New York, 1961.

Weinberger, H. F., *A First Course in Partial Differential Equations*, Blaisdell, New York, 1965.

Boundary Value Problems and Sturm-Liouville Theory

11.1 INTRODUCTION

In Chapter 10 several problems involving partial differential equations were solved by the method of separation of variables. This method consisted of two principal steps: (i) the reduction of the partial differential equation to two (or more) ordinary differential equations and (ii) the expansion of certain functions in Fourier series. The ordinary differential equation in the space variable was typically of the form

$$X'' + \lambda X = 0, \tag{1}$$

subject to additional conditions such as

$$X(0) = 0, \qquad X(1) = 0 \tag{2}$$

or

$$X'(0) = 0, \qquad X'(1) = 0. \tag{3}$$

The solution of Eq. (1) is sought in the interval $0 < x < 1$, and the conditions (2) or (3) prescribe values of X or X' at each end of this interval. Such conditions are called *boundary conditions*, and problems of this kind are known as two-point *boundary value problems*. In contrast, in an initial value problem values of the unknown function and its derivatives are prescribed at a single point, and the solution of the differential equation is usually sought in the semiinfinite interval beginning at this initial point. Although these differences may seem superficial, there are in fact striking dissimilarities in the nature of the solutions and in the theory associated with the two kinds of problems. In this chapter we will discuss some of the properties of boundary value problems for linear second order equations. At the end of the chapter we will use these results to extend the method of separation of variables to somewhat more general problems in partial differential equations than those considered in the last chapter.

It is useful to distinguish at the outset between two types of linear boundary value problems, namely, homogeneous and nonhomogeneous problems. Linear second order differential equations

$$P(x)y'' + Q(x)y' + R(x)y = g(x) \tag{4}$$

were classified in Chapter 3 as homogeneous if $g(x)$ is identically zero, and nonhomogeneous otherwise. Similarly, a linear boundary condition

$$a_1 y(0) + a_2 y'(0) = c \tag{5}$$

is said to be homogeneous if c is zero, and nonhomogeneous if it is not. A boundary value problem is homogeneous if both the differential equation and all boundary conditions are homogeneous; if not, then the problem is nonhomogeneous. A typical linear homogeneous second order boundary value problem is of the form

$$P(x)y'' + Q(x)y' + R(x)y = 0, \qquad 0 < x < 1, \tag{6}$$

$$a_1 y(0) + a_2 y'(0) = 0, \tag{7}$$

$$b_1 y(1) + b_2 y'(1) = 0. \tag{8}$$

Nonhomogeneous boundary value problems are easily identified by the presence in the differential equation or a boundary condition of at least one nonzero term that is independent of y and its derivatives. The choice of the interval $0 \le x \le 1$ involves no loss of generality. If the interval were originally $\alpha \le s \le \beta$, it could be reduced to $0 \le x \le 1$ by the transformation $x = (s - \alpha)/(\beta - \alpha)$.

Higher order problems can also occur; in them the number of boundary conditions must equal the order of the differential equation. As a rule, the order of the differential equation is even, and half of the boundary conditions are given at each end of the basic interval. It is also possible for a single boundary condition to involve values of the solution and/or its derivatives at both boundary points; for example,

$$y(0) - y(1) = 0. \tag{9}$$

However, most of the problems we will consider are of the form given by Eqs. (6) to (8).

11.2 LINEAR HOMOGENEOUS BOUNDARY VALUE PROBLEMS; EIGENVALUES AND EIGENFUNCTIONS

Consider the boundary value problem consisting of the differential equation

$$y'' + p(x)y' + q(x)y = 0, \qquad 0 < x < 1, \tag{1}$$

and the boundary conditions

$$a_1 y(0) + a_2 y'(0) = 0, \tag{2a}$$

$$b_1 y(1) + b_2 y'(1) = 0. \tag{2b}$$

According to the definitions in Section 11.1, the boundary value problem (1), (2) is linear and homogeneous. It was stated in Section 3.1 that an initial value problem for the differential equation (1) has a unique solution on any interval about the initial point in which the functions p and q are continuous. No such sweeping statement can be made about the boundary value problem (1), (2). In the first place, all homogeneous problems have the solution $y = 0$. This trivial solution is usually devoid of interest, and the significant question is whether there are other, nontrivial, solutions. Assuming that $y = \phi(x)$ is such a solution, then it follows from the linear homogeneous nature of the problem that $y = k\phi(x)$ is also a solution for any value of the constant k. Thus, corresponding to a nontrivial solution ϕ there is an infinite family of solutions, each member of which is proportional to ϕ. For problems of the form (1), (2) it is possible to show that there is at most one such family of nontrivial solutions; see Section 11.3. However, for more general second order boundary value problems there may be two families of solutions corresponding to two linearly independent solutions ϕ_1 and ϕ_2. All three possibilities are illustrated by the following examples.

Example 1. Find $y = \phi(x)$ satisfying

$$
\begin{aligned}
y'' + y &= 0, \\
y(0) = 0, \quad y(1) &= 0.
\end{aligned}
\tag{3}
$$

The general solution of the differential equation is

$$y = c_1 \sin x + c_2 \cos x.$$

Since $y(0) = c_2$, the first boundary condition requires that $c_2 = 0$. Then $y = c_1 \sin x$, and $y(1) = c_1 \sin 1$. Since $\sin 1 \neq 0$, the second boundary condition requires that $c_1 = 0$. Hence the only solution is $\phi(x) = 0$, the trivial solution.

Example 2. Find $y = \phi(x)$ satisfying

$$
\begin{aligned}
y'' + \pi^2 y &= 0, \\
y(0) = 0, \quad y(1) &= 0.
\end{aligned}
\tag{4}
$$

The general solution of the differential equation is now

$$y = c_1 \sin \pi x + c_2 \cos \pi x,$$

and the first boundary condition is satisfied if $c_2 = 0$. The function $y = c_1 \sin \pi x$ also satisfies the second boundary condition for any constant c_1

inasmuch as $\sin \pi = 0$. Hence $\phi(x) = c_1 \sin \pi x$, where c_1 is arbitrary. The given problem thus has a single infinite family of solutions, each of which is a multiple of $\sin \pi x$.

Example 3.   Find $y = \phi(x)$ satisfying

$$y'' + \pi^2 y = 0,$$
$$y(0) + y(1) = 0, \qquad y'(0) + y'(1) = 0. \tag{5}$$

Again the general solution of the differential equation is

$$y = c_1 \sin \pi x + c_2 \cos \pi x. \tag{6}$$

However, in this example the boundary conditions impose no restrictions at all upon the arbitrary constants c_1 and c_2, and thus the function $y = \phi(x)$ given by Eq. (6) is also the most general solution of the boundary value problem. In this case there are two infinite families of solutions, one proportional to $\phi_1(x) = \sin \pi x$, the other proportional to $\phi_2(x) = \cos \pi x$, and ϕ itself is a linear combination of them. Note also that the boundary conditions are not of the form (2), since each involves both boundary points.

Somewhat more generally we often wish to consider a boundary value problem in which the differential equation contains an arbitrary parameter λ; for example,

$$y'' + \lambda y = 0, \tag{7}$$
$$y(0) = 0, \qquad y(1) = 0. \tag{8}$$

If $\lambda = 1$ or $\lambda = \pi^2$, we obtain the problems occurring in Examples 1 and 2, respectively. In these examples we found that if $\lambda = 1$, the problem (7), (8) has only the trivial solution, whereas if $\lambda = \pi^2$, then the problem has nontrivial solutions. This raises the question of what happens when λ takes on some other value.

The boundary value problem (7), (8) was considered in detail in Section 10.2. It was shown there that nontrivial solutions of this problem exist only for certain real values of λ, namely,

$$\lambda = \pi^2, 4\pi^2, 9\pi^2, \ldots, n^2\pi^2, \ldots. \tag{9}$$

For other values of λ there is only the trivial solution. The values given by Eq. (9) are called *eigenvalues* of the boundary value problem (7), (8). The corresponding nontrivial solutions $\phi_n(x) = \sin n\pi x$ are called *eigenfunctions*. The existence of such values and functions is typical of linear homogeneous boundary value problems containing a parameter.

In problems arising from physics, the eigenvalues and eigenfunctions usually have important physical interpretations. For example, the problem (7), (8) occurs in the study of the vibrating elastic string (Section 10.7). There the eigenvalues are proportional to the squares of the natural frequencies of vibration of the string, and the eigenfunctions describe the configuration of the string when it is vibrating in one of its natural modes.

Now let us take up the question of existence of eigenvalues and eigenfunctions for a more general problem. Consider the differential equation

$$y'' + p(x, \lambda)y' + q(x, \lambda)y = 0, \qquad 0 < x < 1, \tag{10}$$

whose coefficients depend on a parameter λ, and the boundary conditions (2). For which values of λ, if any, do there exist nontrivial solutions of the given boundary value problem? We will assume that the functions p and q are continuous for $0 \le x \le 1$ and for all values λ.

Clearly the general solution of Eq. (10) must depend on both x and λ, and can be written in the form

$$y = c_1 y_1(x, \lambda) + c_2 y_2(x, \lambda), \tag{11}$$

where y_1 and y_2 are a fundamental set of solutions of Eq. (10). Substituting for y in the boundary conditions (2) yields

$$c_1[a_1 y_1(0, \lambda) + a_2 y_1'(0, \lambda)] + c_2[a_1 y_2(0, \lambda) + a_2 y_2'(0, \lambda)] = 0,$$
$$c_1[b_1 y_1(1, \lambda) + b_2 y_1'(1, \lambda)] + c_2[b_1 y_2(1, \lambda) + b_2 y_2'(1, \lambda)] = 0, \tag{12}$$

a set of two linear homogeneous algebraic equations for the constants c_1 and c_2. Such a set of equations has solutions (other than $c_1 = c_2 = 0$) if and only if the determinant of coefficients $D(\lambda)$ vanishes, that is, if and only if

$$D(\lambda) = \begin{vmatrix} a_1 y_1(0, \lambda) + a_2 y_1'(0, \lambda) & a_1 y_2(0, \lambda) + a_2 y_2'(0, \lambda) \\ b_1 y_1(1, \lambda) + b_2 y_1'(1, \lambda) & b_1 y_2(1, \lambda) + b_2 y_2'(1, \lambda) \end{vmatrix} = 0. \tag{13}$$

Values of λ, if any, satisfying this determinantal equation are the eigenvalues of the boundary value problem (10), (2). Corresponding to each eigenvalue is at least one nontrivial solution, an eigenfunction, which is determined at most to within an arbitrary multiplicative constant.

Example 4. Find the eigenvalues and the corresponding eigenfunctions of the boundary value problem

$$y'' + \lambda y = 0, \tag{14}$$

$$y(0) + y'(0) = 0, \qquad y(1) = 0. \tag{15}$$

First, if $\lambda = 0$, the general solution of the differential equation is

$$y = c_1 x + c_2.$$

The first boundary condition requires that

$$c_1 + c_2 = 0,$$

and the same relation also results from the second boundary condition.

Hence $c_2 = -c_1$, and the boundary value problem has the eigenfunction

$$y = \phi_0(x) = c_1(x - 1)$$

corresponding to the eigenvalue $\lambda_0 = 0$.

On the other hand, if $\lambda > 0$, then the general solution of the differential equation is

$$y = c_1 \sin \sqrt{\lambda}\, x + c_2 \cos \sqrt{\lambda}\, x,$$

where $\sqrt{\lambda} > 0$. Substituting for y in the boundary conditions (15) yields

$$c_1 \sqrt{\lambda} \quad + c_2 \qquad = 0,$$

$$c_1 \sin \sqrt{\lambda} + c_2 \cos \sqrt{\lambda} = 0.$$

The determinantal equation for the calculation of the eigenvalues is

$$D(\lambda) = \begin{vmatrix} \sqrt{\lambda} & 1 \\ \sin \sqrt{\lambda} & \cos \sqrt{\lambda} \end{vmatrix} = 0,$$

or

$$\sqrt{\lambda} \cos \sqrt{\lambda} - \sin \sqrt{\lambda} = 0,$$

or

$$\sqrt{\lambda} = \tan \sqrt{\lambda}. \tag{16}$$

The solutions of this equation can be determined approximately by plotting $f(\sqrt{\lambda}) = \sqrt{\lambda}$ and $g(\sqrt{\lambda}) = \tan \sqrt{\lambda}$ for $\sqrt{\lambda} > 0$, and identifying the points of intersection of the two curves; see Figure 11.1. The point $\lambda = 0$ is specifically excluded from this argument; we have already shown, however, that it is an eigenvalue. The first positive solution of Eq. (16) is $\sqrt{\lambda_1} \simeq 4.49$. As can be seen from Figure 11.1, the other roots are given with reasonable accuracy by $\sqrt{\lambda_n} \simeq (2n + 1)\pi/2$ for $n = 2, 3, \ldots$, the precision of this estimate increasing with n. Hence the eigenvalues are

$$\lambda_0 = 0, \qquad \lambda_1 \simeq 20.2, \qquad \lambda_n \simeq \frac{(2n + 1)^2 \pi^2}{4} \qquad \text{for} \qquad n = 2, 3, \ldots . \tag{17}$$

Finally, it follows from the first boundary condition that $c_2 = -\sqrt{\lambda}\, c_1$. Hence the eigenfunction corresponding to λ_n is

$$\phi_n(x, \lambda_n) = c_1(\sin \sqrt{\lambda_n}\, x - \sqrt{\lambda_n} \cos \sqrt{\lambda_n}\, x), \qquad n \geq 1, \tag{18}$$

where the constant c_1 remains arbitrary.

It can also be shown that there are no nontrivial solutions of the boundary value problem for $\lambda < 0$ or for complex values of λ. However, we will not discuss these possibilities. Assuming that this is true, then all of the eigenvalues and eigenfunctions of the given problem are included in Eqs. (17) and (18).

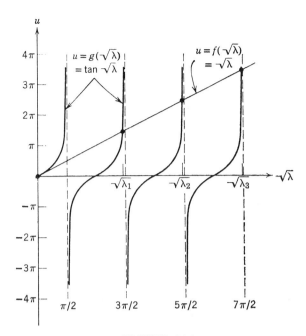

FIGURE 11.1

In conclusion, the existence of eigenvalues and eigenfunctions of the linear homogeneous boundary value problem (10), (2) depends on whether the determinantal equation (13) has solutions. In specific cases this determinantal equation is usually transcendental and not algebraic in character; hence the number and kind of its roots, if any, may be difficult to determine. In particular, the possibility of complex roots must always be borne in mind. In this book, however, we will consider almost exclusively problems having only real eigenvalues.

PROBLEMS

In each of Problems 1 through 4 find the real eigenvalues and eigenfunctions of the given boundary value problem.

1. $y'' + \lambda y = 0$

   $y(0) = 0, \qquad y'(l) = 0$

2. $y'' + \lambda y = 0$

   $y'(0) = 0, \qquad y(\pi) = 0$

3. $y'' + \lambda y = 0$

   $y'(0) = 0, \qquad y'(1) = 0$

4. $y'' - \lambda y = 0$

   $y(0) = 0, \qquad y'(1) = 0$

In each of Problems 5 through 8 determine the form of the eigenfunctions and the determinantal equation satisfied by the eigenvalues. Find an approximate value for λ_1, the eigenvalue of smallest absolute value. Estimate λ_n for large values of n. Assume that all eigenvalues are real.

5. $y'' - \lambda y = 0$
   $y(0) + y'(0) = 0, \qquad y(1) = 0$

6. $y'' + \lambda y = 0$
   $y(0) = 0, \qquad y(\pi) + y'(\pi) = 0$

7. $y'' + \lambda y = 0$
   $y'(0) = 0, \qquad y(1) + y'(1) = 0$

8. $y'' + \lambda y = 0$
   $y(0) - y'(0) = 0, \qquad y(1) + y'(1) = 0$

Determine, at least approximately, the real eigenvalues in each of Problems 9 through 12. Also find the corresponding eigenfunctions.

9. $y'' - 2y' + (1 + \lambda)y = 0$
   $y(0) = 0, \qquad y(1) = 0$

10. $y'' + 4y' + (4 + 9\lambda)y = 0$
    $y(0) = 0, \qquad y'(l) = 0$

11. $y'' + (1 + \lambda)y' + \lambda y = 0$
    $y'(0) = 0, \qquad y(1) = 0$

*12. $x^2 y'' - \lambda x y' + \lambda y = 0$
    $y(1) = 0, \qquad y(2) - y'(2) = 0$

*13. Consider the problem

$$y'' + \lambda y = 0$$

$$y(0) = 0, \qquad y'(l) = 0.$$

Show that if ϕ_m and ϕ_n are eigenfunctions, corresponding to the eigenvalues λ_m and λ_n, respectively, then

$$\int_0^l \phi_m(x)\phi_n(x)\,dx = 0,$$

provided that $\lambda_m \neq \lambda_n$.
Hint: Note that

$$\phi_m'' + \lambda_m \phi_m = 0, \qquad \phi_n'' + \lambda_n \phi_n = 0.$$

Multiply the first of these equations by ϕ_n, the second by ϕ_m, and integrate from 0 to l, using integration by parts.

*14. In the study of transverse vibrations of a uniform elastic bar one is led to the differential equation

$$\frac{d^4 y}{dx^4} - \lambda y = 0,$$

where y is the transverse displacement and $\lambda = m\omega^2/EI$; m is the mass per unit length in the rod, E is Young's (1773–1829) modulus (a constant characteristic of the material), I is the moment of inertia of the cross-section about an axis through the centroid perpendicular to the plane of vibration, and ω is the frequency of vibration. Thus for a bar whose material and geometrical properties are given, the eigenvalues determine the natural frequencies of vibration. Boundary conditions at each end are usually one of the following types:

$$y = y' = 0 \quad \text{(clamped end)},$$
$$y = y'' = 0 \quad \text{(simply supported or hinged end)},$$
$$y'' = y''' = 0 \quad \text{(free end)}.$$

For each of the following three cases find the form of the eigenfunctions and the equation satisfied by the eigenvalues of this fourth order boundary value problem. Assume that the eigenvalues are real and positive.

(a) $y(0) = y''(0) = 0,$ \qquad $y(l) = y''(l) = 0$

(b) $y(0) = y''(0) = 0,$ \qquad $y(l) = y'(l) = 0$

(c) $y(0) = y'(0) = 0,$ \qquad $y''(l) = y'''(l) = 0$ \qquad (cantilevered bar)

11.3   STURM-LIOUVILLE BOUNDARY VALUE PROBLEMS

In Chapter 10 several problems in partial differential equations were solved by the method of separation of variables. The last step in this process of solution was to expand a certain function (or functions) in a Fourier series, that is, as the sum of an infinite series of sine and/or cosine functions. In each particular problem, we used the trigonometric functions that arose naturally during the process of solution, that is, as solutions of the ordinary differential equation $y'' + \lambda y = 0$ subject to various sets of boundary conditions. The question of whether the required function could be represented by such a series was resolved by Theorem 10.3.

It is of fundamental importance that the eigenfunctions of a more general class of boundary value problems can be used as the basis for series expansions, which have properties very similar to Fourier series. Such eigenfunction series are useful in extending the method of separation of variables to a larger class of problems in partial differential equations. We will be especially interested in solving the heat conduction equation, the wave equation, and the potential equation in different geometrical regions than those in Chapter 10.

The class of boundary value problems we will discuss is associated with the names of Sturm (1803–1855) and Liouville (1809–1882). We first define the linear homogeneous differential operator L:

$$L[y] = -[p(x)y']' + q(x)y. \tag{1}$$

Then a second order Sturm-Liouville problem consists of the differential equation

$$L[y] = \lambda r(x)y, \tag{2}$$

or

$$[p(x)y']' - q(x)y + \lambda r(x)y = 0, \tag{3}$$

on the interval $0 < x < 1$, together with the boundary conditions

$$a_1 y(0) + a_2 y'(0) = 0,$$
$$b_1 y(1) + b_2 y'(1) = 0,$$

(4)

at the end points. We will assume that the functions p, p', q, and r are continuous on the interval $0 \le x \le 1$ and, further, that $p(x) > 0$ and $r(x) > 0$ at all points in $0 \le x \le 1$. These assumptions are necessary to render the theory as simple as possible while retaining considerable generality. It turns out that these conditions are satisfied in many significant problems in mathematical physics. For example, the equation $y'' + \lambda y = 0$, which arose repeatedly in the previous chapter, is of the form (3) with $p(x) = 1$, $q(x) = 0$, and $r(x) = 1$. The boundary conditions (4) are said to be *separated*; that is, each involves only one of the boundary points. No more general separated boundary conditions are possible for a second order differential equation.

Before proceeding to establish some of the properties of the Sturm-Liouville problem (3), (4), it is necessary to derive an identity, known as *Lagrange's identity*, which is basic to the study of linear boundary value problems. Let u and v be functions having continuous second derivatives on the interval $0 \le x \le 1$. Then*

$$\int_0^1 v L[u] \, dx = \int_0^1 \{ -v(pu')' + vqu \} \, dx.$$

Integrating the first term on the right-hand side twice by parts, we obtain

$$\int_0^1 v L[u] \, dx = -v(x)p(x)u'(x) \Big|_0^1 + v'(x)p(x)u(x) \Big|_0^1.$$
$$+ \int_0^1 \{ -u(pv')' + uqv \} \, dx$$
$$= -p(x)[u'(x)v(x) - u(x)v'(x)] \Big|_0^1 + \int_0^1 u L[v] \, dx.$$

Hence

$$\int_0^1 \{ v L[u] - u L[v] \} \, dx = -p(x)[u'(x)v(x) - u(x)v'(x)] \Big|_0^1,$$

(5)

which is Lagrange's identity.

Now let us suppose that both of the functions u and v in Eq. (5) also satisfy the boundary conditions (4). Then, assuming that $a_2 \ne 0$ and $b_2 \ne 0$,

* For brevity we will sometimes use the notation $\int_0^1 f \, dx$ rather than $\int_0^1 f(x) \, dx$ in this chapter.

the right-hand side of Eq. (5) becomes

$$-p(x)[u'(x)v(x) - u(x)v'(x)]\Big|_0^1$$

$$= -p(1)[u'(1)v(1) - u(1)v'(1)] + p(0)[u'(0)v(0) - u(0)v'(0)]$$

$$= -p(1)\left[-\frac{b_1}{b_2}u(1)v(1) + \frac{b_1}{b_2}u(1)v(1)\right]$$

$$+ p(0)\left[-\frac{a_1}{a_2}u(0)v(0) + \frac{a_1}{a_2}u(0)v(0)\right]$$

$$= 0.$$

The same result holds if either a_2 or b_2 is zero; the proof in this case is even simpler, and is left to the reader. Thus, for the differential operator L defined by Eq. (1), and if the functions u and v satisfy the boundary conditions (4), Lagrange's identity reduces to

$$\int_0^1 \{vL[u] - uL[v]\}\,dx = 0. \tag{6}$$

In proving Theorems 11.1 and 11.2 below, it is important to know that Eqs. (5) and (6) remain valid under the stated conditions even if the functions u and v are complex-valued. To establish this, one can retrace the derivation given above, assuming that u and v are complex-valued, and separating each term into its real and imaginary parts. The calculations are straightforward but somewhat tedious, and will be omitted.

We will now consider some of the implications of Eq. (6) for the Sturm-Liouville boundary value problem (3), (4). We will assume without proof* that this problem actually has eigenvalues and eigenfunctions. In Theorems 11.1 to 11.3 below, we will state several of their important, but relatively elementary, properties. Each of these properties is illustrated by the very simple Sturm-Liouville problem

$$y'' + \lambda y = 0, \tag{7}$$

$$y(0) = 0, \qquad y(1) = 0, \tag{8}$$

whose eigenvalues are $\lambda_n = n^2\pi^2$, with the corresponding eigenfunctions $\phi_n(x) = \sin n\pi x$.

Theorem 11.1. *All of the eigenvalues of the Sturm-Liouville problem* (3), (4) *are real.*

The proof of this theorem is by contradiction. Let us suppose that there exists a complex eigenvalue $\lambda = \mu + i\nu$ with $\nu \neq 0$, and a corresponding

---

* The proof may be found, for example, in the references by Sagan [Chapter 5] or Birkhoff and Rota [Chapter 10].

eigenfunction ϕ which may also be complex-valued, $\phi(x) = U(x) + iV(x)$, where at least one of $U(x)$ and $V(x)$ is not identically zero. Then ϕ satisfies the differential equation

$$(p\phi')' - q\phi + \lambda r\phi = 0, \tag{9a}$$

or

$$L[\phi] = \lambda r\phi. \tag{9b}$$

Upon taking the complex conjugate of each term in Eq. (9a) we obtain

$$(p\bar{\phi}')' - q\bar{\phi} + \bar{\lambda}r\bar{\phi} = 0 \tag{10a}$$

or

$$L[\bar{\phi}] = \bar{\lambda}r\bar{\phi}, \tag{10b}$$

where we have used the fact that p, q, and r are real-valued functions. Similarly, upon taking the conjugate of each of the boundary conditions (4), we find that $\bar{\phi}$ satisfies the same boundary conditions as ϕ. Hence $\bar{\phi}$ is also an eigenfunction of the problem (3), (4) and $\bar{\lambda}$ is the corresponding eigenvalue.

We now turn to Eq. (6), letting $u = \phi$ and $v = \bar{\phi}$. Then

$$\int_0^1 \{\bar{\phi}L[\phi] - \phi L[\bar{\phi}]\}\, dx = 0$$

or, making use of Eqs. (9b) and (10b),

$$(\lambda - \bar{\lambda}) \int_0^1 r(x)\phi(x)\bar{\phi}(x)\, dx = 0.$$

Hence

$$2\nu \int_0^1 r(x)[U^2(x) + V^2(x)]\, dx = 0. \tag{11}$$

Since $r(x) > 0$ for all x in $0 \leq x \leq 1$, Eq. (11) can be satisfied only if $\nu = 0$. This contradicts the original hypothesis and thus establishes the theorem.

An important consequence of Theorem 11.1 is that in finding eigenvalues and eigenfunctions of a Sturm-Liouville boundary value problem, one can ignore the possibility of complex eigenvalues. This is particularly helpful since, if a boundary value problem does have complex eigenvalues, they are likely to be awkward to determine.

Theorem 11.2. *If ϕ_1 and ϕ_2 are two eigenfunctions of the Sturm-Liouville problem (3), (4) corresponding to eigenvalues λ_1 and λ_2, respectively, and if $\lambda_1 \neq \lambda_2$, then*

$$\int_0^1 r(x)\phi_1(x)\phi_2(x)\, dx = 0. \tag{12}$$

This theorem expresses the property of *orthogonality* of the eigenfunctions with respect to the weight function r. To prove the theorem we note that ϕ_1 and ϕ_2 satisfy the differential equations

$$L[\phi_1] = \lambda_1 r \phi_1 \tag{13}$$

and

$$L[\phi_2] = \lambda_2 r \phi_2, \tag{14}$$

respectively. If we let $u = \phi_1$, $v = \phi_2$, and substitute for $L[u]$ and $L[v]$ in Eq. (6), we obtain

$$(\lambda_1 - \lambda_2) \int_0^1 r(x)\phi_1(x)\phi_2(x) \, dx = 0. \tag{15}$$

Since by hypothesis $\lambda_1 \neq \lambda_2$, it follows that ϕ_1 and ϕ_2 must satisfy Eq. (12), and the theorem is proved.

Theorem 11.3.   *The eigenvalues of the Sturm-Liouville problem* (3), (4) *are all simple; that is, to each eigenvalue there corresponds only one linearly independent eigenfunction. Further, the eigenvalues form an infinite sequence, and can be ordered according to increasing magnitude so that*

$$\lambda_1 < \lambda_2 < \lambda_3 < \cdots < \lambda_n < \cdots.$$

Moreover, $\lambda_n \to \infty$ *as* $n \to \infty$.

The proof of this theorem is somewhat more advanced than those of the two previous theorems, and will be omitted. Part of the proof is indicated, however, in Problem 4.

Again we note that all of the properties stated in Theorems 11.1 to 11.3 are exemplified by the eigenvalues $\lambda_n = n^2\pi^2$ and eigenfunctions $\phi_n(x) = \sin n\pi x$ of the example problem (7), (8). The eigenfunctions satisfy the orthogonality relation

$$\int_0^1 \phi_m(x)\phi_n(x) \, dx = \int_0^1 \sin m\pi x \sin n\pi x \, dx = 0, \qquad m \neq n, \tag{16}$$

which was established in Section 10.3 by another method. Further, it is clear that the eigenvalues are real, that they can be ordered so that $\lambda_1 < \lambda_2 < \cdots$, and that $\lambda_n \to \infty$ as $n \to \infty$. Finally, to each eigenvalue there corresponds a single linearly independent eigenfunction.

Let us now consider briefly a much more general boundary value problem for the differential equation

$$L[y] = \lambda M[y], \qquad 0 < x < 1, \tag{17}$$

where L and M are linear homogeneous differential operators of orders n and m, respectively:

$$L[y] = p_0(x)y^{(n)} + p_1(x)y^{(n-1)} + \cdots + p_{n-1}(x)y' + p_n(x)y, \tag{18}$$

$$M[y] = r_0(x)y^{(m)} + r_1(x)y^{(m-1)} + \cdots + r_{m-1}(x)y' + r_m(x)y, \tag{19}$$

with $n > m$. In addition to the differential equation a set of n linear homogeneous boundary conditions at $x = 0$ and $x = 1$ is also prescribed. If the relations

$$\int_0^1 (vL[u] - uL[v]) \, dx = 0, \qquad \int_0^1 (vM[u] - uM[v]) \, dx = 0 \qquad (20)$$

are valid for every pair of functions u and v, which are n-times continuously differentiable on $[0, 1]$ and which satisfy the given boundary conditions, then the given boundary value problem is said to be *self-adjoint*. We emphasize that Eq. (20) imposes certain restrictions both on the differential operators L and M and on the associated boundary conditions. The operator L must be such that when the expression $vL[u]$ is integrated by parts, the effect is to transfer L from u to v, and similarly for the operator M. Further, the boundary conditions must be such as to eliminate the boundary terms arising during the integration.

For the Sturm-Liouville boundary value problem (3), (4), $L[y]$ is given by Eq. (1), and $M[y] = r(x)y$. The second of Eqs. (20) is clearly satisfied, and consequently in deriving Eq. (6) we have shown that the Sturm-Liouville boundary value problem is self-adjoint. However, the class of self-adjoint boundary value problems is much larger than this, containing many problems for differential equations of higher than second order, as well as some second order problems with nonseparated boundary conditions.

Self-adjoint problems are of particular interest physically because they occur frequently in applications, and are of interest mathematically because their theory is especially well-developed and elegant. Some of the properties of Sturm-Liouville problems can be extended to more general self-adjoint boundary value problems, provided that the differential operators L and M satisfy certain further requirements. However, in general, the eigenvalues of a self-adjoint problem may be complex or (as the following example shows) repeated. This example also shows how the functions 1, $\cos (n\pi x/l)$, $\sin (n\pi x/l)$, $n = 1, 2, \ldots$, which appeared in the Fourier series

$$f(x) = \frac{a_0}{2} + \sum_{n=1}^{\infty} \left(a_n \cos \frac{n\pi x}{l} + b_n \sin \frac{n\pi x}{l} \right)$$

studied in Sections 10.3 to 10.5, can arise as eigenfunctions of a certain boundary value problem.

Consider the problem

$$y'' + \lambda y = 0, \qquad (21)$$

$$y(-l) - y(l) = 0, \qquad y'(-l) - y'(l) = 0. \qquad (22)$$

Since the boundary conditions (22) are not separated, this is not a Sturm-Liouville problem. However, the problem (21), (22) is self-adjoint, and we leave it to the reader to verify this fact. The boundary conditions (22) are called *periodic boundary conditions*, since they require that y and y' assume the same values at $x = l$ as at $x = -l$.

It is straightforward to show that $\lambda_0 = 0$ is an eigenvalue and that the corresponding eigenfunction is $\phi_0(x) = 1$. Further, there are additional eigenvalues $\lambda_1 = (\pi/l)^2$, $\lambda_2 = (2\pi/l)^2$, ..., $\lambda_n = (n\pi/l)^2$, ... To each of these nonzero eigenvalues there correspond *two* linearly independent eigenfunctions; for example, corresponding to λ_n are the two eigenfunctions $\phi_n(x) = \cos(n\pi x/l)$ and $\psi_n(x) = \sin(n\pi x/l)$. This does not contradict the first part of Theorem 11.3, since the boundary conditions (22) are not of the form (4).

PROBLEMS

1. Determine whether each of the following boundary value problems is self-adjoint.

(a) $y'' + y' + 2y = 0$, $y(0) = 0$, $y(1) = 0$

(b) $(1 + x^2)y'' + 2xy' + y = 0$, $y'(0) = 0$, $y(1) + 2y'(1) = 0$

(c) $y'' + y = \lambda y$, $y(0) - y'(1) = 0$, $y'(0) - y(1) = 0$

(d) $(1 + x^2)y'' + 2xy' + y = \lambda(1 + x^2)y$, $y(0) - y'(1) = 0$,

$y'(0) + 2y(1) = 0$

2. Show that if the functions u and v satisfy Eqs. (4), and either $a_2 = 0$ or $b_2 = 0$, or both, then

$$p(x)[u'(x)v(x) - u(x)v'(x)]\Big|_0^1 = 0.$$

This completes the proof, begun in the text, that a Sturm-Liouville problem is self-adjoint.

3. Consider the differential equation

$$y'' + \lambda y = 0$$

with the boundary conditions

$$y(0) - y(1) = 0, \qquad y'(0) - y'(1) = 0.$$

Note that the boundary conditions are not separated since both end points appear in each boundary condition.

(a) Show that the problem is self-adjoint, even though it is not a Sturm-Liouville problem.

(b) Find all eigenvalues and eigenfunctions of the given problem. Note that the nonzero eigenvalues are double eigenvalues; to each one there correspond two linearly independent eigenfunctions.

4. In this problem we outline a proof of the first part of Theorem 11.3: that the eigenvalues of the Sturm-Liouville problem (3), (4) are simple.

For a given λ suppose that ϕ_1 and ϕ_2 are two linearly independent eigenfunctions. Compute the Wronskian $W(\phi_1, \phi_2)(x)$ and use the boundary conditions (4) to show that $W(\phi_1, \phi_2)(0) = 0$. Then use Theorem 3.8, which actually holds on the closed interval $0 \leq x \leq 1$, to conclude that ϕ_1 and ϕ_2 cannot be linearly independent as assumed.

5. Consider the Sturm-Liouville problem

$$-[p(x)y']' + q(x)y = \lambda r(x)y,$$

$$a_1 y(0) + a_2 y'(0) = 0, \qquad b_1 y(1) + b_2 y'(1) = 0,$$

where p, q, and r satisfy the conditions stated in the text.

(a) Show that if λ is an eigenvalue and ϕ a corresponding eigenfunction, then

$$\lambda \int_0^1 r\phi^2 \, dx = \int_0^1 (p\phi'^2 + q\phi^2) \, dx + \frac{b_1}{b_2} p(1)\phi^2(1) - \frac{a_1}{a_2} p(0)\phi^2(0)$$

provided that $a_2 \neq 0$ and $b_2 \neq 0$. How must this result be modified if $a_2 = 0$ or $b_2 = 0$?

(b) Show that if $q(x) \geq 0$ and if b_1/b_2 and $-a_1/a_2$ are nonnegative, then the eigenvalue λ is nonnegative.

(c) Show that the eigenvalue λ is strictly positive unless $q(x) = 0$ for each x in $0 \leq x \leq 1$.

6. Consider the problem (Problem 9 of Section 11.2)

$$y'' - 2y' + (1 + \lambda)y = 0,$$

$$y(0) = 0, \qquad y(1) = 0.$$

(a) Show that this problem is not self-adjoint.

(b) Show that, nevertheless, all eigenvalues are real. Thus the conclusion of Theorem 11.1 is also true for certain nonself-adjoint problems.

(c) Show that the eigenfunctions are not orthogonal (with respect to the weight function arising from the coefficient of λ in the differential equation).

7. Consider the problem

$$x^2 y'' = \lambda(xy' - y), \qquad 1 < x < 2,$$

$$y(1) = 0, \qquad y(2) = 0.$$

(a) Show that this problem is not self-adjoint.

(b) Show that this problem has eigenvalues, but that none of them are real. This shows that in general nonself-adjoint problems have eigenvalues that are not real.

Problems 8 through 10 are concerned with the concept of a differential operator which is the adjoint of a given operator.

8. Consider the linear differential operator L defined by

$$L[y] = P_0(x)y'' + P_1(x)y' + P_2(x)y. \tag{i}$$

Show that, if u and v are any twice differentiable functions, then

$$\int_0^1 vL[u]\, dx = P_0 vu' \Big|_0^1 - (P_0 v)'u \Big|_0^1 + P_1 vu \Big|_0^1 + \int_0^1 u\{(P_0 v)'' - (P_1 v)' + P_2 v\}\, dx. \quad \text{(ii)}$$

The operator $M[v] = (P_0 v)'' - (P_1 v)' + P_2 v$ is known as the *adjoint of L*. Equation (ii) is a more general form of Lagrange's identity than Eq. (5) of the text. If $M[u] = L[u]$ for all u, then L is said to be a *self-adjoint operator*. Show that a necessary and sufficient condition for L to be self-adjoint is that $P_1 = P_0'$. Thus the most general self-adjoint differential operator of second order is $L[u] = (P_0 u')' + P_2 u$. A self-adjoint boundary value problem requires that the differential operator be self-adjoint, and also that the boundary conditions be such that the boundary terms in Eq. (ii) are eliminated when these conditions are satisfied by both u and v. See also Problems 18 to 20 of Section 3.2.

9. Consider the linear differential operators of third and fourth orders,

$$L_3[u] = P_0(x)u''' + P_1(x)u'' + P_2(x)u' + P_3(x)u,$$

$$L_4[u] = P_0(x)u^{\text{iv}} + P_1(x)u''' + P_2(x)u'' + P_3(x)u' + P_4(x)u,$$

respectively. Find the adjoint operators of L_3 and L_4. Show that there is no self-adjoint third order operator. Find necessary and sufficient conditions that L_4 be a self-adjoint operator.

10. Consider the differential equation

$$P_0(x)y'' + P_1(x)y' + P_2(x)y = \lambda r(x)y.$$

(a) Show that the differential operator on the left can be made self-adjoint through multiplication by a properly chosen function μ.

(b) Determine whether it is also possible to do this for a fourth order equation. See Problems 8 and 9.

11. Let

$$u^{\text{iv}} - \lambda u = 0,$$

$$u'(0) = 0, \qquad u''(0) = 0, \qquad u''(1) = 0, \qquad u'''(1) = 0.$$

Show that this problem is not self-adjoint even though the differential operator itself is self-adjoint (see Problem 9), and the boundary conditions are separated.

12. Determine whether the following problem is self-adjoint:

$$u^{\text{iv}} + \lambda u'' = 0,$$

$$u(0) = 0, \qquad u'(0) = 0, \qquad u''(1) = 0, \qquad u'''(1) = 0.$$

11.4 SOLUTION OF NONHOMOGENEOUS BOUNDARY VALUE PROBLEMS

In this section we will again consider the Sturm-Liouville boundary value problem consisting of the differential equation

$$L[y] = -[p(x)y']' + q(x)y = \lambda r(x)y, \qquad 0 < x < 1, \qquad (1)$$

and the boundary conditions

$$a_1 y(0) + a_2 y'(0) = 0, \qquad (2a)$$

$$b_1 y(1) + b_2 y'(1) = 0. \qquad (2b)$$

Under the conditions on p, q, and r given in Section 11.3, the boundary value problem (1), (2) has an infinite sequence of real eigenvalues $\lambda_1 < \lambda_2 < \cdots < \lambda_n < \cdots$. Associated with each eigenvalue λ_i is a corresponding eigenfunction ϕ_i, determined up to a multiplicative constant. Further, the eigenfunctions ϕ_i and ϕ_j corresponding to different eigenvalues λ_i and λ_j, respectively, satisfy the orthogonality relation

$$\int_0^1 r(x) \phi_i(x) \phi_j(x)\, dx = 0, \qquad i \neq j. \qquad (3)$$

It is convenient to choose the arbitrary constant multiplying each eigenfunction so as to satisfy the condition

$$\int_0^1 r(x) \phi_i^2(x)\, dx = 1, \qquad i = 1, 2, \ldots. \qquad (4)$$

Equation (4) is called a normalization condition, and eigenfunctions satisfying this equation are said to be *normalized*. Indeed, when the eigenfunctions are chosen to satisfy Eq. (4) as well as Eq. (3), they are said to form an *orthonormal set* with respect to the weight function r. It is sometimes useful to combine Eqs. (3) and (4) into a single equation. To this end we define the symbol δ_{ij}, known as the Kronecker (1823–1891) delta, so that

$$\delta_{ij} = \begin{cases} 0, & \text{if } i \neq j, \\ 1, & \text{if } i = j. \end{cases} \qquad (5)$$

Making use of the Kronecker delta, we can write Eqs. (3) and (4) as

$$\int_0^1 r(x) \phi_i(x) \phi_j(x)\, dx = \delta_{ij}. \qquad (6)$$

Example. Determine the normalized eigenfunctions of the problem

$$y'' + \lambda y = 0, \qquad y(0) = 0, \qquad y(1) = 0. \qquad (7)$$

The eigenvalues of this problem are $\lambda_1 = \pi^2, \lambda_2 = 4\pi^2, \ldots, \lambda_n = n^2 \pi^2, \ldots$, and the corresponding eigenfunctions are $c_1 \sin \pi x, c_2 \sin 2\pi x, \ldots, c_n \sin n\pi x, \ldots$, respectively. In this case the weight function is $r(x) = 1$. In order to satisfy Eq. (4) we must choose c_n so that

$$\int_0^1 (c_n \sin n\pi x)^2\, dx = 1 \qquad (8)$$

for each value of n. Since

$$\int_0^1 \sin^2 n\pi x\, dx = \int_0^1 (\tfrac{1}{2} - \tfrac{1}{2}\cos 2n\pi x)\, dx$$

$$= \tfrac{1}{2},$$

Eq. (8) will be satisfied if c_n is chosen to be $\sqrt{2}$ for each value of n. Hence the normalized eigenfunctions of the boundary value problem (7) are

$$\phi_n(x) = \sqrt{2}\sin n\pi x, \qquad n = 1, 2, 3, \ldots. \tag{9}$$

Now consider a given function f which is continuous and has a piecewise continuous derivative on $0 \le x \le 1$, and satisfies the boundary conditions $f(0) = 0$, $f(1) = 0$. It was shown in Sections 10.4 and 10.5 that such a function can be expanded in a Fourier sine series,

$$f(x) = \sum_{n=1}^{\infty} b_n \sin n\pi x, \tag{10}$$

which converges at each point in the interval $0 \le x \le 1$. Alternatively, we can use the functions ϕ_n defined by Eq. (9), which differ from $\sin n\pi x$ by the factor $\sqrt{2}$, and write

$$f(x) = \sum_{n=1}^{\infty} \beta_n \phi_n(x). \tag{11}$$

From Eq. (8) of Section 10.5 we obtain the formula for the coefficients in Eq. (11):

$$\beta_n = \int_0^1 f(x)\phi_n(x)\, dx, \qquad n = 1, 2, 3, \ldots. \tag{12}$$

Thus we see that the Fourier sine series for f on $0 \le x \le 1$ obtained in Chapter 10 can be regarded as an expansion of f in terms of the eigenfunctions of the boundary value problem (7).

In a very similar way a given function f, which satisfies certain conditions, can be expanded in an infinite series of eigenfunctions of the more general Sturm-Liouville problem (1), (2). If this can be done, we have

$$f(x) = \sum_{i=1}^{\infty} \alpha_i \phi_i(x), \tag{13}$$

where the $\phi_i(x)$ satisfy Eqs. (1), (2), and also the orthonormality condition (6). To compute the coefficients in the series (13) we multiply Eq. (13) by $r(x)\phi_j(x)$ and integrate from $x = 0$ to $x = 1$. Assuming that the series can be integrated term by term we obtain

$$\int_0^1 r(x)f(x)\phi_j(x)\, dx = \sum_{i=1}^{\infty} \alpha_i \int_0^1 r(x)\phi_i(x)\phi_j(x)\, dx$$

$$= \sum_{i=1}^{\infty} \alpha_i \delta_{ij}, \tag{14}$$

where Eq. (6) has also been used. Since $\delta_{ij} = 0$ whenever $i \neq j$, the sum in Eq. (14) reduces to a single term, and we obtain

$$\alpha_j = \int_0^1 r(x)f(x)\phi_j(x)\,dx, \qquad j = 1, 2, 3, \ldots . \tag{15}$$

The coefficients in the series (13) have thus been formally determined. Equation (15) has much the same structure as the Euler-Fourier formulas for the coefficients in a Fourier series, and the eigenfunction series (13) also has convergence properties similar to those of Fourier series. The following theorem* gives sufficient conditions for the convergence of the series (13).

Theorem 11.4. *Let $\phi_1, \phi_2, \ldots, \phi_n, \ldots$ be the normalized eigenfunctions of the Sturm-Liouville problem (1), (2). Let f be continuous and let f' be piecewise continuous on the interval $0 \leq x \leq 1$. If $a_2 = 0$ in Eq. (2a) [so that $\phi_i(0) = 0$], then let $f(0) = 0$. Similarly, if $b_2 = 0$ in Eq. (2b), let $f(1) = 0$. Otherwise, no boundary conditions need be prescribed for f. Then the series (13) whose coefficients are given by Eq. (15) converges to $f(x)$ at each point in the interval $0 \leq x \leq 1$.*

Eigenfunction expansions are very useful in solving boundary value problems for nonhomogeneous differential equations. Consider the differential equation

$$L[y] = -[p(x)y']' + q(x)y = \mu r(x)y + f(x), \tag{16}$$

where μ is a given constant and f is a given function on $0 \leq x \leq 1$, together with the boundary conditions (2). We will solve this problem by making use of the eigenfunctions ϕ_i of the corresponding homogeneous boundary value problem (1), (2). We assume that the solution $y = \phi(x)$ can be expressed as a series of the form (13):

$$\phi(x) = \sum_{i=1}^{\infty} b_i \phi_i(x), \tag{17}$$

whose coefficients are to be determined so as to satisfy the differential equation (16). If ϕ is given by Eq. (17), then formally

$$L[\phi](x) = L\left[\sum_{i=1}^{\infty} b_i \phi_i\right](x)$$

$$= \sum_{i=1}^{\infty} b_i L[\phi_i](x)$$

$$= \sum_{i=1}^{\infty} b_i \lambda_i r(x) \phi_i(x). \tag{18}$$

---

* The proof of Theorem 11.4 can be found, for example, in Weinberger [Chapter 7]. Actually, the conditions of the theorem are sufficient to guarantee a stronger form of convergence, known as uniform convergence.

Note that the function r appears in Eq. (18) and also in the term $\mu r(x)y$ in Eq. (16). This suggests that we rewrite the nonhomogeneous term in Eq. (16) as $r(x)[f(x)/r(x)]$. If the function f/r satisfies the conditions of Theorem 11.4, then

$$\frac{f(x)}{r(x)} = \sum_{i=1}^{\infty} c_i \phi_i(x), \tag{19}$$

where, according to Eq. (15),

$$c_i = \int_0^1 r(x)\frac{f(x)}{r(x)} \phi_i(x) \, dx = \int_0^1 f(x)\phi_i(x) \, dx, \qquad i = 1, 2, \ldots. \tag{20}$$

Upon substituting for $\phi(x)$, $L[\phi](x)$, and $f(x)$ in Eq. (16) from Eqs. (17), (18), and (19), respectively, we find that

$$\sum_{i=1}^{\infty} b_i \lambda_i r(x)\phi_i(x) = \mu r(x) \sum_{i=1}^{\infty} b_i \phi_i(x) + r(x) \sum_{i=1}^{\infty} c_i \phi_i(x). \tag{21}$$

After collecting terms we have

$$\sum_{i=1}^{\infty} [(\lambda_i - \mu)b_i - c_i]r(x)\phi_i(x) = 0. \tag{22}$$

If Eq. (22) is to hold for each x in the interval $0 \le x \le 1$, then each coefficient in the series must separately be zero; see Problem 3 for a proof of this fact. Hence

$$(\lambda_i - \mu)b_i - c_i = 0, \qquad i = 1, 2, 3, \ldots. \tag{23}$$

If $\mu \ne \lambda_i$ for $i = 1, 2, 3, \ldots$, then

$$b_i = \frac{c_i}{\lambda_i - \mu}, \qquad i = 1, 2, 3, \ldots, \tag{24}$$

and

$$y = \phi(x) = \sum_{i=1}^{\infty} \frac{c_i}{\lambda_i - \mu} \phi_i(x). \tag{25}$$

Equation (25), with c_i given by Eq. (20), is a formal solution of the nonhomogeneous boundary value problem (16) and (2). Our argument does not prove that the series (25) converges. However, any solution of the boundary value problem (16), (2) clearly satisfies the conditions of Theorem 11.4; therefore it is reasonable to expect that the series (25) does converge. This fact can be established even if the function f/r does not satisfy the conditions of Theorem 11.4, but if f is merely continuous, for example.

On the other hand, if μ is equal to one of the eigenvalues, say $\mu = \lambda_j$, then for $i = j$ Eq. (23) is of the form $0 \cdot b_j - c_j = 0$. If $c_j \ne 0$, it is impossible to solve for b_j, while if $c_j = 0$, then b_j is arbitrary. Hence, if $\mu = \lambda_j$, and if $c_j \ne 0$, then there is no solution of the nonhomogeneous boundary value problem (16) and (2), while if $\mu = \lambda_j$ and $c_j = 0$, then the solution $y = \phi(x)$ contains an arbitrary multiple of the corresponding eigenfunction ϕ_j and hence is not unique. The condition $c_j = 0$, under which the boundary value problem (16), (2) can be solved when $\mu = \lambda_j$, imposes a restriction upon the nonhomogeneous term $f(x)$, namely,

$$\int_0^1 f(x)\phi_j(x)\, dx = 0. \tag{26}$$

In other words, if $\mu = \lambda_j$, the nonhomogeneous boundary value problem can be solved only if f is orthogonal to the eigenfunction corresponding to the eigenvalue λ_j.

The results which we have formally obtained are summarized in the following theorem.

Theorem 11.5. *The nonhomogeneous boundary value problem (16), (2) has a unique solution for each continuous f whenever μ is different from all of the eigenvalues of the corresponding homogeneous problem; the solution is given by Eq. (25), and the series converges for each x in $0 \le x \le 1$. If μ is equal to an eigenvalue λ_j, then the nonhomogeneous boundary value problem has no solution unless f is orthogonal to ϕ_j, that is, unless the condition (26) holds; in that case, the solution is not unique and contains an arbitrary multiple of $\phi_j(x)$.*

The content of Theorem 11.5 can also be expressed in the following manner.

Theorem 11.6. *For a given value of μ, either the nonhomogeneous problem (16), (2) has a unique solution for each continuous f (if μ is not equal to any λ_j), or else the homogeneous problem (1), (2) has a nontrivial solution (the eigenfunction corresponding to λ_j).*

This latter form of the theorem is known as the Fredholm* Alternative Theorem. This is one of the basic theorems of mathematical analysis and occurs in many different contexts. The reader is probably familiar with it in connection with sets of linear algebraic equations, where the vanishing or nonvanishing of the determinant of coefficients replaces the statements about μ and λ_i.

The method of eigenfunction expansions described above is one of two main ways of approaching nonhomogeneous boundary value problems. A second method, which leads to a solution expressed as an integral rather than as an infinite series, involves certain functions known as Green's functions. This approach is outlined in Problems 8 to 13.

---

* E. I. Fredholm (1866–1927), a Swedish mathematician, founded the modern theory of integral equations. There are many interrelations between differential and integral equations; see, for example, Sections 2.11 and 2.12.

PROBLEMS

1. Find the normalized eigenfunctions of each of the following problems.

(a) $y'' + \lambda y = 0$, $\quad y(0) = 0$, $\quad y'(1) = 0$

(b) $y'' + \lambda y = 0$, $\quad y'(0) = 0$, $\quad y(1) = 0$

(c) $y'' + \lambda y = 0$, $\quad y'(0) = 0$, $\quad y'(1) = 0$

(d) $y'' + \lambda y = 0$, $\quad y(0) = 0$, $\quad y(1) + y'(1) = 0$

(e) $y^{iv} - \lambda y = 0$, $\quad y(0) = 0$, $\quad y''(0) = 0$, $\quad y(1) = 0$, $\quad y''(1) = 0$

(f) $y^{iv} - \lambda y = 0$, $\quad y(0) = 0$, $\quad y''(0) = 0$, $\quad y(1) = 0$, $\quad y'(1) = 0$

2. Using the eigenfunctions found in Problem 1, determine a formal eigenfunction series expansion for the solution of each of the following problems. State the values of μ for which the solution exists.

(a) $y'' + \mu y = -f(x)$, $\quad y(0) = 0$, $\quad y'(1) = 0$

(b) $y'' + \mu y = -f(x)$, $\quad y'(0) = 0$, $\quad y(1) = 0$

(c) $y'' + \mu y = -f(x)$, $\quad y'(0) = 0$, $\quad y'(1) = 0$

(d) $y'' + \mu y = -f(x)$, $\quad y(0) = 0$, $\quad y(1) + y'(1) = 0$

(e) $y^{iv} - \mu y = f(x)$, $\quad y(0) = 0$, $\quad y''(0) = 0$, $\quad y(1) = 0$, $\quad y''(1) = 0$

(f) $y^{iv} - \mu y = f(x)$, $\quad y(0) = 0$, $\quad y''(0) = 0$, $\quad y(1) = 0$, $\quad y'(1) = 0$

3. If $\sum_{i=1}^{\infty} c_i \phi_i(x)$ converges to $f(x)$, where $f(x) = 0$ for each value of x in $0 \le x \le 1$, show that $c_i = 0$ for each i.
Hint: Multiply by $\phi_j(x)$, integrate, and use Eq. (6).

4. Let L be a second order linear differential operator. Show that the solution $y = \phi(x)$ of the problem

$$L[y] = f(x),$$

$$a_1 y(0) + a_2 y'(0) = \alpha, \qquad b_1 y(1) + b_2 y'(1) = \beta,$$

can be written as $y = u + v$ provided that $u = \phi_1(x)$ and $v = \phi_2(x)$ are solutions of the problems

$$L[u] = 0,$$

$$a_1 u(0) + a_2 u'(0) = \alpha, \qquad b_1 u(1) + b_2 u'(1) = \beta,$$

and

$$L[v] = f(x),$$

$$a_1 v(0) + a_2 v'(0) = 0, \qquad b_1 v(1) + b_2 v'(1) = 0,$$

respectively. Use the principle of superposition.

5. Show that the problem

$$y'' + \pi^2 y = \pi^2 x, \qquad y(0) = 1, \qquad y(1) = 0$$

has the solution

$$y = c_1 \sin \pi x + \cos \pi x + x.$$

Also show that this solution cannot be obtained by splitting the problem as suggested in Problem 4, since neither of the two subsidiary problems can be solved in this case.

6. Consider the problem

$$y'' + p(x)y' + q(x)y = 0,$$

$$y(0) = a, \qquad y(1) = b.$$

Let $y = u + v$, where v is any twice differentiable function satisfying the boundary conditions (but not necessarily the differential equation). Show that u is a solution of the problem

$$u'' + p(x)u' + q(x)u = g(x),$$

$$u(0) = 0, \qquad u(1) = 0,$$

where $g(x) = -[v'' + p(x)v' + q(x)v]$, and is known once v is chosen. Thus nonhomogeneities can be transferred from the boundary conditions to the differential equation. Find a function v for this problem.

7. Using the method of Problem 6, transform the problem

$$y'' + 2y = x, \qquad y(0) = 1, \qquad y(1) + y'(1) = -2$$

into a new problem in which the boundary conditions are homogeneous. Solve the latter problem by reference to Problem 2(d).

Green's* functions.   Problems 8 through 13 indicate an alternate means of solving nonhomogeneous boundary value problems. This method leads to solutions expressed as definite integrals rather than as infinite series.

8. (a) Show by the method of variation of parameters that the general solution of the differential equation

$$-y'' = f(x)$$

can be written in the form

$$y = \phi(x) = c_1 + c_2 x - \int_0^x (x - u)f(u)\, du,$$

where c_1 and c_2 are arbitrary constants.

  (b) Let $y = \phi(x)$ also be required to satisfy the boundary conditions

$$y(0) = 0, \qquad y(1) = 0.$$

Show that in this case

$$c_1 = 0, \qquad c_2 = \int_0^1 (1 - u)f(u)\, du.$$

  (c) Show that, under the conditions of parts (a) and (b), $\phi(x)$ can be written in the form

$$\phi(x) = \int_0^x u(1 - x)f(u)\, du + \int_x^1 x(1 - u)f(u)\, du.$$

---

* Green's functions are named after George Green (1793–1841), of England, who made several significant contributions to the theory of boundary value problems.

(d) Defining

$$G(x, u) = \begin{cases} u(1 - x), & 0 \le u \le x, \\ x(1 - u), & x \le u \le 1, \end{cases}$$

show that the solution takes the form

$$\phi(x) = \int_0^1 G(x, u) f(u) \, du.$$

The function $G(x, u)$ appearing under the integral sign is a Green's function. The usefulness of a Green's function solution rests on the fact that the Green's function is independent of the nonhomogeneous term in the differential equation; thus once the Green's function is determined, the solution of the boundary value problem is obtained by a single integration regardless of the nature of $f(x)$. Note further that no determination of arbitrary constants is required, since $\phi(x)$ as given by the Green's function integral formula automatically satisfies the boundary conditions.

9. By a procedure similar to that in the previous problem show that the solution of the boundary value problem

$$-(y'' + y) = f(x),$$

$$y(0) = 0, \qquad y(1) = 0,$$

is

$$y = \phi(x) = \int_0^1 G(x, u) f(u) \, du,$$

where

$$G(x, u) = \begin{cases} \dfrac{\sin u \sin (1 - x)}{\sin 1}, & 0 \le u \le x, \\[2mm] \dfrac{\sin x \sin (1 - u)}{\sin 1}, & x \le u \le 1. \end{cases}$$

10. It is possible to show that the Sturm-Liouville problem

$$L[y] = -[p(x)y']' + q(x)y = f(x), \tag{i}$$

$$a_1 y(0) + a_2 y'(0) = 0, \qquad b_1 y(1) + b_2 y'(1) = 0, \tag{ii}$$

has a Green's function solution

$$y = \phi(x) = \int_0^1 G(x, u) f(u) \, du, \tag{iii}$$

provided that $\lambda = 0$ is not an eigenvalue of $L[y] = \lambda y$ subject to the boundary conditions (ii). Further, $G(x, u)$ is given by

$$G(x, u) = \begin{cases} -y_1(u)y_2(x)/p(x)W(y_1, y_2)(x), & 0 \le u \le x, \\ -y_1(x)y_2(u)/p(x)W(y_1, y_2)(x), & x \le u \le 1, \end{cases} \tag{iv}$$

where y_1 is a solution of $L[y] = 0$ which satisfies the boundary condition at $x = 0$, y_2 is a solution of $L[y] = 0$ which satisfies the boundary condition at $x = 1$, and $W(y_1, y_2)$ is the Wronskian of y_1 and y_2.

(a) Verify that the Green's functions obtained in Problems 8 and 9 are given by the formula (iv).

(b) Show that $p(x)W(y_1, y_2)(x)$ is a constant, by showing that its derivative is zero.

(c) Using Eq. (iv) and the result of part (b), show that $G(x, u) = G(u, x)$.

11. Solve each of the following boundary value problems by determining the appropriate Green's function and expressing the solution as a definite integral. Use Eqs. (i) to (iv) of Problem 10.

(a) $-y'' = f(x)$, $y'(0) = 0$, $y(1) = 0$

(b) $-y'' = f(x)$, $y(0) = 0$, $y(1) + y'(1) = 0$

(c) $-(y'' + y) = f(x)$, $y'(0) = 0$, $y(1) = 0$

(d) $-y'' = f(x)$, $y(0) = 0$, $y'(1) = 0$

*12. Consider the boundary value problem

$$L[y] = -[p(x)y']' + q(x)y = f(x),\tag{i}$$

$$a_1 y(0) + a_2 y'(0) = 0,\qquad b_1 y(1) + b_2 y'(1) = 0.\tag{ii}$$

According to the text, the solution $y = \phi(x)$ is given by Eq. (25), with $\mu = 0$, where c_i is defined by Eq. (20). The solution $y = \phi(x)$ is also given by Eq. (iii) of Problem 8.

(a) Show that if these two expressions for $\phi(x)$ are to be equivalent, then

$$G(x, u) = \sum_{i=1}^{\infty} \frac{\phi_i(x)\phi_i(u)}{\lambda_i},\tag{iii}$$

where λ_i and ϕ_i are the eigenvalues and eigenfunctions, respectively, of Eqs. (1), (2) of the text.

(b) Derive Eq. (iii) directly by assuming that $G(x, u)$ has the eigenfunction expansion

$$G(x, u) = \sum_{i=1}^{\infty} a_i(x)\phi_i(u);\tag{iv}$$

determine $a_i(x)$ by multiplying Eq. (iv) by $r(u)\phi_j(u)$ and integrating with respect to u from $u = 0$ to $u = 1$.

Hint: Show first that λ_i and ϕ_i satisfy the equation

$$\phi_i(x) = \lambda_i \int_0^1 G(x, u)r(u)\phi_i(u)\, du.\tag{v}$$

*13. Consider the boundary value problem

$$-\frac{d^2 y}{du^2} = \delta(u - x),\qquad y(0) = 0,\qquad y(1) = 0,$$

where u is the independent variable, $u = x$ is a definite point in the interval $0 < u < 1$, and δ is the Dirac delta function (see Section 6.4). Show that the solution of this problem is the Green's function $G(x, u)$ obtained in Problem 8.

In solving the given problem, note that $\delta(u - x) = 0$ in the intervals $0 \le u < x$ and $x < u \le 1$. Note further that $-dy/du$ experiences a jump of magnitude 1 as u passes through the value x.

This problem illustrates a general property, namely, that the Green's function $G(x, u)$ can be identified as the response at the point u to a unit impulse at the point x. A more general nonhomogeneous term f on $0 \leq x \leq 1$ can be regarded as a set of impulses with $f(x)$ giving the magnitude of the impulse at the point x. The solution of a nonhomogeneous boundary value problem in terms of a Green's function integral can then be interpreted as the result of superposing the responses to the set of impulses represented by the nonhomogeneous term $f(x)$.

*11.5   SINGULAR STURM-LIOUVILLE PROBLEMS

In the preceding sections of this chapter we have considered Sturm-Liouville boundary value problems: the differential equation

$$-[p(x)y']' + q(x)y = \lambda r(x)y, \qquad 0 < x < 1, \tag{1a}$$

or

$$L[y] = \lambda r(x)y, \tag{1b}$$

together with boundary conditions of the form

$$a_1 y(0) + a_2 y'(0) = 0, \tag{2a}$$

$$b_1 y(1) + b_2 y'(1) = 0. \tag{2b}$$

Until now we have always assumed that p is differentiable, that q and r are continuous, and that $p(x) > 0$ and $r(x) > 0$ at all points in the interval $[0, 1]$. However, in many equations of physical interest some of these conditions are not satisfied.

For example, if we wish to study Bessel's equation, which we can write as

$$-(xy')' + \frac{v^2}{x} y = xy, \tag{3}$$

on $0 < x < 1$, then $p(x) = x$, $q(x) = v^2/x$, and $r(x) = x$. Thus $p(0) = 0$ and $q(x)$ is unbounded and hence discontinuous as $x \to 0$. However, the given conditions are satisfied elsewhere in the interval. Similarly, in Legendre's equation,

$$-[(1 - x^2)y']' = \alpha(\alpha + 1)y, \tag{4}$$

$p(x) = 1 - x^2$, $q(x) = 0$, and $r(x) = 1$. Here the stated conditions are met in the interval $0 \leq x \leq 1$ except at $x = 1$ where p is zero.

We will use the term singular Sturm-Liouville problem to refer to a certain class of boundary value problems for the differential equation (1) in which the functions p, q, and r satisfy the conditions previously laid down on the open interval $0 < x < 1$, but fail to satisfy them at one or both of the boundary points. We will also prescribe suitable separated boundary conditions, of a kind to be described in more detail later in this section.

As an example, consider the equation

$$xy'' + y' + \lambda xy = 0, \tag{5a}$$

or

$$-(xy')' = \lambda xy, \tag{5b}$$

on the interval $0 < x < 1$, and suppose that $\lambda > 0$. This equation arises in the study of free vibrations of a circular elastic membrane, and is discussed further in Section 11.6. If we introduce the new independent variable t defined by $t = \sqrt{\lambda}\, x$, then

$$\frac{dy}{dx} = \sqrt{\lambda}\,\frac{dy}{dt}, \qquad \frac{d^2y}{dx^2} = \lambda\frac{d^2y}{dt^2}.$$

Hence Eq. (5a) becomes

$$\frac{t}{\sqrt{\lambda}}\,\lambda\frac{d^2y}{dt^2} + \sqrt{\lambda}\,\frac{dy}{dt} + \lambda\frac{t}{\sqrt{\lambda}}\,y = 0$$

or, cancelling the common factor $\sqrt{\lambda}$ in each term,

$$t\frac{d^2y}{dt^2} + \frac{dy}{dt} + ty = 0. \tag{6}$$

Equation (6) is Bessel's equation of order zero; see Section 4.7. The general solution of Eq. (6) for $t > 0$ is

$$y = c_1 J_0(t) + c_2 Y_0(t),$$

and hence the general solution of Eq. (5a) for $x > 0$ is

$$y = c_1 J_0(\sqrt{\lambda}\, x) + c_2 Y_0(\sqrt{\lambda}\, x), \tag{7}$$

where J_0 and Y_0 denote the Bessel functions of the first and second kinds of order zero. From Eqs. (7) and (14) of Section 4.7 we have

$$J_0(\sqrt{\lambda}\, x) = 1 + \sum_{m=1}^{\infty}\frac{(-1)^m\lambda^m x^{2m}}{2^{2m}(m!)^2}, \qquad x > 0 \tag{8}$$

$$Y_0(\sqrt{\lambda}\, x) = \frac{2}{\pi}\left[\left(\gamma + \ln\frac{\sqrt{\lambda}\, x}{2}\right)J_0(\sqrt{\lambda}\, x) + \sum_{m=1}^{\infty}\frac{(-1)^{m+1}H_m\lambda^m x^{2m}}{2^{2m}(m!)^2}\right], \qquad x > 0, \tag{9}$$

where $H_m = 1 + \frac{1}{2} + \cdots + 1/m$, and $\gamma = \lim_{m\to\infty}(H_m - \ln m)$. The graphs of $y = J_0(x)$ and $y = Y_0(x)$ are given in Figure 4.2.

Suppose that we seek a solution of Eq. (5a) that also satisfies the boundary conditions

$$y(0) = 0, \tag{10a}$$
$$y(1) = 0, \tag{10b}$$

which are typical of those we have met in other problems in this chapter.

Since $J_0(0) = 1$ and $Y_0(x) \to -\infty$ as $x \to 0$, the condition $y(0) = 0$ can be satisfied only by choosing $c_1 = c_2 = 0$ in Eq. (7). Thus the boundary value problem (5), (10) has only the trivial solution.

One interpretation of this result is that the boundary condition (10a) at $x = 0$ is too restrictive for the differential equation (5). This illustrates the general situation, namely, that at a singular boundary point it is necessary to consider a modified type of boundary condition. In the present problem, suppose that we require only that the solution (7) of Eq. (5) and its derivative remain bounded. In other words, we take as the boundary condition at $x = 0$ the requirement:

$$y, \ y' \text{ bounded as } x \to 0. \tag{11}$$

This condition can be satisfied by choosing $c_2 = 0$, so as to eliminate the unbounded solution Y_0. The second boundary condition $y(1) = 0$ then yields

$$J_0(\sqrt{\lambda}) = 0. \tag{12}$$

It is possible to show* that Eq. (12) has an infinite set of discrete roots, which yield the eigenvalues $0 < \lambda_1 < \lambda_2 < \cdots < \lambda_n < \cdots$ of the given problem. The corresponding eigenfunctions are

$$\phi_n(x) = J_0(\sqrt{\lambda_n}\, x), \tag{13}$$

determined only up to a multiplicative constant. The boundary value problem (5), (10b), and (11) is an example of a singular Sturm-Liouville problem. This example illustrates that if the boundary conditions are relaxed in an appropriate way, then a singular Sturm-Liouville problem may have a sequence of eigenvalues and eigenfunctions, just as a regular Sturm-Liouville problem does.

Because of their importance in applications, it is worthwhile to investigate singular boundary value problems a little further. There are two main questions with which we will concern ourselves.

(i) Precisely what type of boundary conditions will be permitted to occur in a singular Sturm-Liouville problem?

(ii) To what extent do the eigenvalues and eigenfunctions of a singular problem share the properties of eigenvalues and eigenfunctions of regular Sturm-Liouville problems? In particular, are the eigenvalues real, are the eigenfunctions orthogonal, and can a given function be expanded as a series of eigenfunctions?

Both of these questions can be answered by a study of the self-adjointness relation

$$\int_0^1 \{vL[u] - uL[v]\}\, dx = 0. \tag{14}$$

---

* The function J_0 is well-tabulated; the roots of Eq. (12) can be found in various tables, for example, Jahnke and Emde. The first three roots of Eq. (12) are $\sqrt{\lambda} = 2.405,\ 5.520,$ and 8.653, respectively, to four significant figures.

We will therefore investigate the conditions under which this relation holds for singular problems, where the integral in Eq. (14) may now have to be examined as an improper integral. To be definite we will consider the differential equation (1a) and will assume that $x = 0$ is a singular boundary point, but that $x = 1$ is not. The boundary condition (2b) will be imposed at the nonsingular boundary point $x = 1$, but we will leave unspecified, for the moment, the boundary condition at $x = 0$. Indeed, our principal object is to determine what kinds of boundary conditions are allowable at a singular boundary point if Eq. (14) is to hold.

Since the boundary value problem under investigation is singular at $x = 0$, we will consider the integral $\int_{\epsilon}^{1} vL[u]\,dx$, instead of $\int_{0}^{1} vL[u]\,dx$, as in Section 11.3, and afterwards let ϵ approach zero. Assuming that u and v have at least two continuous derivatives on $\epsilon \le x \le 1$, and integrating twice by parts, we find that

$$\int_{\epsilon}^{1} \{vL[u] - uL[v]\}\,dx = -p(x)[u'(x)v(x) - u(x)v'(x)]\Big|_{\epsilon}^{1}. \tag{15}$$

The boundary term at $x = 1$ is again eliminated if both u and v satisfy the boundary condition (2b), and thus

$$\int_{\epsilon}^{1} \{vL[u] - uL[v]\}\,dx = p(\epsilon)[u'(\epsilon)v(\epsilon) - u(\epsilon)v'(\epsilon)]. \tag{16}$$

Taking the limit as $\epsilon \to 0$ yields

$$\int_{0}^{1} \{vL[u] - uL[v]\}\,dx = \lim_{\epsilon \to 0} p(\epsilon)[u'(\epsilon)v(\epsilon) - u(\epsilon)v'(\epsilon)]. \tag{17}$$

Hence the self-adjointness condition (14) holds if and only if, in addition to the assumptions stated previously,

$$\lim_{\epsilon \to 0} p(\epsilon)[u'(\epsilon)v(\epsilon) - u(\epsilon)v'(\epsilon)] = 0 \tag{18}$$

for every pair of functions u and v in the class under consideration. Equation (18) is therefore the criterion that determines what boundary conditions are allowable at $x = 0$ if that point is a singular boundary point. A similar condition applies at $x = 1$ if that boundary point is singular, namely

$$\lim_{\epsilon \to 0} p(1 - \epsilon)[u'(1 - \epsilon)v(1 - \epsilon) - u(1 - \epsilon)v'(1 - \epsilon)] = 0. \tag{19}$$

In summary, a singular boundary value problem for Eq. (1) is said to be *self-adjoint* if Eq. (14) is valid, possibly as an improper integral, for each pair of functions u and v, which are twice continuously differentiable on the open interval $0 < x < 1$, which satisfy a boundary condition of the form (2) at each regular boundary point, and which satisfy a boundary condition sufficient to insure Eq. (18) if $x = 0$ is a singular boundary point, or Eq. (19)

if $x = 1$ is a singular boundary point. If at least one boundary point is singular, then the differential equation (1), together with two boundary conditions of the type just described, are said to form a *singular Sturm-Liouville problem*.

For example, for Eq. (5) we have $p(x) = x$. If both u and v satisfy the boundary condition (11) at $x = 0$ it is clear that Eq. (18) must hold. Hence the singular boundary value problem, consisting of the differential equation (5), the boundary condition (11) at $x = 0$, and any boundary condition of the form (2b) at $x = 1$, is self-adjoint.

If a singular Sturm-Liouville problem has a sequence of eigenvalues and eigenfunctions, then Eq. (14) can be used, just as in Section 11.3, to prove that the eigenvalues of such a problem are real, and that the eigenfunctions are orthogonal with respect to the weight function r. The expansion of a given function in terms of a series of eigenfunctions then follows as in Section 11.4.

For instance, the eigenfunctions $\phi_n(x) = J_0(\sqrt{\lambda_n}\, x)$ of the differential equation (5)

$$-(xy')' = \lambda xy,$$

subject to the boundary conditions (11) and (10b)

$$y, y' \text{ bounded as } x \to 0,$$
$$y(1) = 0,$$

satisfy the orthogonality relation

$$\int_0^1 x\phi_m(x)\phi_n(x)\, dx = 0, \qquad m \neq n \tag{20}$$

with respect to the weight function $r(x) = x$. Then, if f is a given function, we assume that

$$f(x) = \sum_{n=1}^{\infty} c_n J_0(\sqrt{\lambda_n}\, x). \tag{21}$$

Multiplying Eq. (21) by $xJ_0(\sqrt{\lambda_m}\, x)$ and integrating term by term from $x = 0$ to $x = 1$ yields

$$\int_0^1 xf(x)J_0(\sqrt{\lambda_m}\, x)\, dx = \sum_{n=1}^{\infty} c_n \int_0^1 xJ_0(\sqrt{\lambda_m}\, x)J_0(\sqrt{\lambda_n}\, x)\, dx. \tag{22}$$

Because of the orthogonality condition (20), the right-hand side of Eq. (22) collapses to a single term, and hence

$$c_m = \frac{\displaystyle\int_0^1 xf(x)J_0(\sqrt{\lambda_m}\, x)\, dx}{\displaystyle\int_0^1 xJ_0^2(\sqrt{\lambda_m}\, x)\, dx}, \tag{23}$$

which determines the coefficients in the series (21).

The convergence of the series (21) is established by an extension of Theorem 11.4 to cover this case. This theorem can also be shown to hold for other sets of Bessel functions which are solutions of appropriate boundary value problems, for Legendre polynomials, and for solutions of a number of other singular Sturm-Liouville problems of considerable interest. However, the general theory of singular boundary value problems is very difficult, and the properties of their eigenvalues and eigenfunctions are frequently established separately for each equation.

It must be emphasized that the singular problems mentioned here are not necessarily typical. In general, singular boundary value problems (which also occur when the basic interval extends to infinity in one or both directions) are characterized by continuous, rather than discrete, sets of eigenvalues. That is, there may be an interval $a \leq \lambda \leq b$ such that each value of λ in this interval is an eigenvalue. The corresponding sets of eigenfunctions are therefore not denumerable, and series expansions of the type described in Theorem 11.4 do not exist.

PROBLEMS

1. Find a formal solution of the nonhomogeneous boundary value problem

$$-(xy')' = \mu xy + f(x),$$

$$y, y' \text{ bounded as } x \to 0, \qquad y(1) = 0,$$

where f is a given continuous function on $0 \leq x \leq 1$, and μ is not an eigenvalue of the corresponding homogeneous problem.
Hint: Use a series expansion similar to those in Section 11.4.

2. Consider the boundary value problem

$$-(xy')' = \lambda xy,$$

$$y, y' \text{ bounded as } x \to 0, \qquad y'(1) = 0.$$

(a) Show that the eigenfunctions of this problem are given by $\phi_n(x) = J_0(\sqrt{\lambda_n}\, x)$, where $\sqrt{\lambda_n}$ is the nth positive root (in increasing order) of the equation $J_0'(\sqrt{\lambda}) = 0$. It is possible to show that there is an infinite sequence of such roots.
(b) Show that

$$\int_0^1 xJ_0(\sqrt{\lambda_n}\, x)J_0(\sqrt{\lambda_m}\, x)\, dx = 0, \qquad m \neq n.$$

(c) Find a formal solution of the nonhomogeneous problem

$$-(xy')' = \mu xy + f(x),$$

$$y, y' \text{ bounded as } x \to 0, \qquad y'(1) = 0,$$

where f is a given continuous function on $0 \leq x \leq 1$, and μ is not an eigenvalue of the corresponding homogeneous problem.

*3. Consider the problem

$$-(xy')' + \frac{m^2}{x} y = \lambda x y,$$

$$y, y' \text{ bounded as } x \to 0, \qquad y(1) = 0,$$

where m is a positive integer.

(a) Using the substitution $t = \sqrt{\lambda}\, x$, show that the above differential equation reduces to Bessel's equation of order m; see Problem 6 of Section 4.7. One solution is $J_m(t)$; a second linearly independent solution, denoted by $Y_m(t)$, is unbounded as $t \to 0$.

(b) Show that the eigenvalues $\lambda_1, \lambda_2, \ldots$ of the given problem are the squares of the zeros of $J_m(\sqrt{\lambda})$, and the corresponding eigenfunctions are $\phi_i(x) = J_m(\sqrt{\lambda_i}\, x)$. It is possible to show that there is an infinite sequence of such zeros.

(c) Show that the eigenfunctions $\phi_i(x)$ satisfy the orthogonality relation

$$\int_0^1 x \phi_i(x) \phi_j(x)\, dx = 0, \qquad i \neq j.$$

(d) Determine the coefficients in the formal series expansion

$$f(x) = \sum_{i=1}^{\infty} a_i \phi_i(x).$$

(e) Find a formal solution of the nonhomogeneous problem

$$-(xy')' + \frac{m^2}{x} y = \mu x y + f(x),$$

$$y, y' \text{ bounded as } x \to 0, \qquad y(1) = 0,$$

where f is a given continuous function on $0 \leq x \leq 1$, and μ is not an eigenvalue of the corresponding homogeneous problem.

4. Consider Legendre's equation (see Problems 10 and 11 of Section 4.2.1)

$$-[(1 - x^2)y']' = \lambda y$$

subject to the boundary conditions

$$y(0) = 0, \qquad y, y' \text{ bounded as } x \to 1.$$

The eigenfunctions of this problem are the odd Legendre polynomials $\phi_1(x) = P_1(x)$, $\phi_2(x) = P_3(x), \ldots, \quad \phi_n(x) = P_{2n-1}(x), \ldots$ corresponding to the eigenvalues $\lambda_1 = 2, \lambda_2 = 4 \cdot 3, \ldots, \lambda_n = 2n(2n - 1), \ldots$.

(a) Show that $\int_0^1 \phi_m(x) \phi_n(x)\, dx = 0$ if $m \neq n$.

(b) Find a formal solution of the nonhomogeneous problem

$$-[(1 - x^2)y']' = \mu y + f(x),$$

$$y(0) = 0, \qquad y, y' \text{ bounded as } x \to 1,$$

where f is a given continuous function on $0 \leq x \leq 1$, and μ is not an eigenvalue of the corresponding homogeneous problem.

5. The equation

$$(1 - x^2)y'' - xy' + \lambda y = 0 \tag{i}$$

is Tchebycheff's equation; see Problem 4 of Section 4.2.1.

(a) Show that Eq.(i) can be written in the form

$$-[(1 - x^2)^{\frac{1}{2}}y']' = \lambda(1 - x^2)^{-\frac{1}{2}}y, \qquad -1 < x < 1. \tag{ii}$$

(b) Consider the boundary conditions

$$y, y' \text{ bounded as } x \to -1, \qquad y, y' \text{ bounded as } x \to 1. \tag{iii}$$

Show that the boundary value problem (ii), (iii) is self-adjoint.

(c) It can be shown that the boundary value problem (ii), (iii) has the eigenvalues $\lambda_0 = 0$, $\lambda_1 = 1$, $\lambda_2 = 4, \ldots,$ $\lambda_n = n^2, \ldots.$ The corresponding eigenfunctions are the Tchebycheff polynomials $T_n(x)$. Show that

$$\int_{-1}^1 \frac{T_m(x)T_n(x)}{(1 - x^2)^{\frac{1}{2}}} \, dx = 0, \qquad m \neq n. \tag{iv}$$

Note that this is a convergent improper integral.

*11.6 FURTHER REMARKS ON THE METHOD OF SEPARATION OF VARIABLES; A BESSEL SERIES EXPANSION

In Chapter 10 we discussed a number of classical problems in partial differential equations. For each problem we constructed a set of fundamental solutions, involving suitable trigonometric functions, which satisfied the linear homogeneous partial differential equation and all of the homogeneous boundary or initial conditions. Finally, it was possible to satisfy the remaining nonhomogeneous boundary or initial condition by superposing fundamental solutions and using a Fourier series expansion of the given function in the boundary or initial condition.

The usefulness of the method of separation of variables is not limited to cases in which trigonometric functions can be used in the representation of the solution. More generally, upon reducing the partial differential equation to a set of ordinary differential equations, one obtains a Sturm-Liouville problem in at least one of the independent variables. The eigenfunctions of this Sturm-Liouville problem then play the same role as the trigonometric functions in the problems in Chapter 10. An expansion of a given function in the initial or boundary conditions in a series of eigenfunctions replaces the Fourier series expansions used previously. The study of Sturm-Liouville problems and the expansion theorems associated with them has been stimulated to a large degree by their relation to some of the basic partial differential equations of mathematical physics.

Because of its relative simplicity, as well as the considerable physical significance of many problems to which it is applicable, the method of separation of variables merits its important place in the theory and application of partial differential equations. However, the method of separation of variables is not universally applicable. It requires that the problem involved have certain characteristics. In the first place, the problem must be linear, and some parts of it (usually the partial differential equation and some of the initial or boundary conditions) must be homogeneous. Otherwise the principle of superposition cannot be invoked to construct additional solutions by forming linear combinations of the fundamental solutions.

Furthermore, the geometry of the region involved in the problem is subject to rather severe restrictions. On the one hand, a coordinate system must be employed in which the variables can be separated, and the partial differential equation replaced by a set of ordinary differential equations. For Laplace's equation there are about a dozen such coordinate systems; only rectangular, circular cylindrical, and spherical coordinates are likely to be familiar to most readers of this book. On the other hand, the boundary of the region of interest must consist of coordinate curves or surfaces; that is, of curves or surfaces on which one variable remains constant. Thus, at an elementary level, one is limited to regions bounded by straight lines or circular arcs in two dimensions, or by planes, circular cylinders, circular cones, or spheres in three dimensions.

As a practical matter, we must also be able to solve the ordinary differential equations, obtained after separating the variables, in a reasonably convenient manner. In many problems to which the method of separation of variables can be applied in principle, it is of very limited practical value due to lack of information about the solutions of the ordinary differential equations that appear.

In three-dimensional problems the separation of variables in Laplace's operator $u_{xx} + u_{yy} + u_{zz}$ leads to the equation $y'' + \lambda y = 0$ in rectangular coordinates, to Bessel's equation in cylindrical coordinates, and to Legendre's equation in spherical coordinates. It is this fact that is largely responsible for the intensive study that has been made of these equations, and the functions defined by them. It is also noteworthy that two of the three most important situations lead to singular, rather than regular, Sturm-Liouville problems. Thus, singular problems are by no means exceptional and may be of even greater interest than regular ones. The remainder of this section is devoted to an example involving an expansion of a given function as a series of Bessel functions.

The Vibrations of a Circular Elastic Membrane. In Section 10.7 [Eq. (7)] it was noted that the transverse vibrations of a thin elastic membrane are governed by the two-dimensional wave equation

$$a^2(u_{xx} + u_{yy}) = u_{tt}. \tag{1}$$

To study the motion of a circular membrane it is convenient to write Eq. (1)

in polar coordinates:

$$a^2\left(u_{rr} + \frac{1}{r}u_r + \frac{1}{r^2}u_{\theta\theta}\right) = u_{tt}. \tag{2}$$

We will assume that the membrane has unit radius, that it is fixed rigidly around its circumference, and that it initially occupies a displaced position independent of the angular variable θ, from which it is released at time $t = 0$. Because of the circular symmetry of the initial and boundary conditions, it is natural to assume also that u is independent of θ; that is, u is a function of r and t only. In this event the differential equation (2) becomes

$$a^2\left(u_{rr} + \frac{1}{r}u_r\right) = u_{tt}, \qquad 0 < r < 1, \qquad t > 0. \tag{3}$$

The boundary condition at $r = 1$ is

$$u(1, t) = 0, \qquad t \geq 0, \tag{4}$$

and the initial conditions are

$$u(r, 0) = f(r), \qquad 0 \leq r \leq 1, \tag{5}$$

$$u_t(r, 0) = 0, \qquad 0 \leq r \leq 1, \tag{6}$$

where $f(r)$ describes the initial configuration of the membrane. For consistency we also require that $f(1) = 0$. Finally, we will state explicitly the requirement that $u(r, t)$ is to be always finite for $r \leq 1$.

Assuming that $u(r, t) = R(r)T(t)$, and substituting for $u(r, t)$ in Eq. (3) gives

$$\frac{R'' + (1/r)R'}{R} = \frac{1}{a^2}\frac{T''}{T} = \sigma. \tag{7}$$

As in Chapter 10 we consider all possible cases for the separation constant σ. We find that to obtain nontrivial bounded solutions satisfying the homogeneous boundary and initial conditions we must have $\sigma < 0$. Hence we let $\sigma = -\lambda^2$ with $\lambda > 0$. Then Eq. (7) yields

$$r^2R'' + rR' + \lambda^2 r^2 R = 0, \tag{8}$$

$$T'' + \lambda^2 a^2 T = 0. \tag{9}$$

Thus

$$T(t) = k_1 \sin \lambda at + k_2 \cos \lambda at. \tag{10}$$

Introducing the new independent variable $\xi = \lambda r$ into Eq. (8), we obtain

$$\xi^2 \frac{d^2R}{d\xi^2} + \xi \frac{dR}{d\xi} + \xi^2 R = 0, \tag{11}$$

which is Bessel's equation of order zero. Thus

$$R = c_1 J_0(\xi) + c_2 Y_0(\xi), \tag{12}$$

where J_0 and Y_0 are Bessel functions of the first and second kinds, respectively, of order zero; see Section 11.5. In terms of r we have

$$R = c_1 J_0(\lambda r) + c_2 Y_0(\lambda r). \tag{13}$$

Hence

$$u(r, t) = R(r)T(t) = [c_1 J_0(\lambda r) + c_2 Y_0(\lambda r)](k_1 \sin \lambda at + k_2 \cos \lambda at). \tag{14}$$

The finiteness condition requires that $c_2 = 0$, since $Y_0(\lambda r) \to -\infty$ as $r \to 0$. The boundary condition (4) then requires that

$$J_0(\lambda) = 0. \tag{15}$$

Consequently, the allowable values of the separation constant are obtained from the roots of the transcendental equation (15). Recall from Section 11.5 that $J_0(\lambda)$ has an infinity of discrete positive zeros, which we will denote by $\lambda_1, \lambda_2, \lambda_3, \ldots, \lambda_n, \ldots$, ordered in increasing magnitude. Further, the functions $J_0(\lambda_n r)$ are the eigenfunctions of a singular Sturm-Liouville problem, and can be used as the basis of a series expansion for the given function f. The fundamental solutions of this problem, satisfying the partial differential equation (3), the boundary condition (4), and the finiteness condition, are

$$u_n(r, t) = J_0(\lambda_n r)(k_n \sin \lambda_n at + c_n \cos \lambda_n at), \qquad n = 1, 2, \ldots. \tag{16}$$

In order to satisfy the initial condition $u_t(r, 0) = 0$ it is necessary to choose $k_n = 0$ for all n. Superposing the fundamental solutions (16) with $k_n = 0$, we have

$$u(r, t) = \sum_{n=1}^{\infty} c_n J_0(\lambda_n r) \cos \lambda_n at, \tag{17}$$

whose coefficients c_n are determined so that the initial condition

$$u(r, 0) = \sum_{n=1}^{\infty} c_n J_0(\lambda_n r) = f(r) \tag{18}$$

is satisfied. From Eq. (23) of Section 11.5 we obtain

$$c_k = \frac{\displaystyle\int_0^1 rf(r)J_0(\lambda_k r)\, dr}{\displaystyle\int_0^1 r[J_0(\lambda_k r)]^2\, dr}. \tag{19}$$

Thus the solution of the partial differential equation (3), satisfying the boundary condition (4) and the initial conditions (5) and (6), is given by Eq. (17) with the coefficients defined by Eq. (19).

PROBLEMS

1. Consider Laplace's equation $u_{xx} + u_{yy} = 0$ in the parallelogram whose vertices are $(0, 0), (2, 0), (3, 2),$ and $(1, 2)$. Suppose that on the side $y = 2$ the boundary condition is $u(x, 2) = f(x)$ for $1 \le x \le 3$, and that on the other three sides $u = 0$. See Figure 11.2.

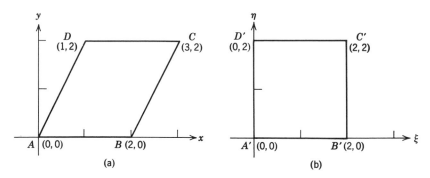

FIGURE 11.2

(a) Show that there are no nontrivial solutions of the partial differential equation of the form $u(x, y) = X(x)Y(y)$ that also satisfy the homogeneous boundary conditions.

(b) Let $\xi = x - \frac{1}{2}y$, $\eta = y$. Show that the given parallelogram in the xy plane transforms into the square $0 \le \xi \le 2, 0 \le \eta \le 2$ in the $\xi\eta$ plane. Show that the differential equation transforms into

$$\tfrac{5}{4}u_{\xi\xi} - u_{\xi\eta} + u_{\eta\eta} = 0.$$

How are the boundary conditions transformed?

(c) Show that in the $\xi\eta$ plane the differential equation possesses no solutions of the form

$$u(\xi, \eta) = U(\xi)V(\eta).$$

Thus in the xy plane the shape of the boundary precludes a solution by the method of separation of variables, while in the $\xi\eta$ plane the region is acceptable but the variables in the differential equation can no longer be separated.

2. Find the displacement $u(r, t)$ in a vibrating circular elastic membrane of radius one that satisfies the boundary condition

$$u(1, t) = 0, \qquad t \ge 0,$$

and the initial conditions

$$u(r, 0) = 0, \qquad 0 \le r \le 1,$$

$$u_t(r, 0) = g(r), \qquad 0 \le r \le 1,$$

where $g(1) = 0$.

Hint: The differential equation to be satisfied is Eq. (3) of the text.

3. Find the displacement $u(r, t)$ in a vibrating circular elastic membrane of radius one that satisfies the boundary condition

$$u(1, t) = 0, \qquad t \geq 0,$$

and the initial conditions

$$u(r, 0) = f(r), \qquad 0 \leq r \leq 1,$$
$$u_t(r, 0) = g(r), \qquad 0 \leq r \leq 1,$$

where $f(1) = g(1) = 0$.

4. The wave equation in polar coordinates is

$$u_{rr} + \frac{1}{r} u_r + \frac{1}{r^2} u_{\theta\theta} = \frac{1}{a^2} u_{tt}.$$

Show that if $u(r, \theta, t) = R(r)\Theta(\theta)T(t)$, then R, Θ, and T satisfy the ordinary differential equations

$$r^2 R'' + r R' + (\lambda^2 r^2 - n^2) R = 0,$$
$$\Theta'' + n^2\Theta = 0,$$
$$T'' + \lambda^2 a^2 T = 0.$$

5. In the circular cylindrical coordinates r, θ, z defined by

$$x = r \cos \theta,$$
$$y = r \sin \theta,$$
$$z = z,$$

Laplace's equation takes the form

$$u_{rr} + \frac{1}{r^2} u_{\theta\theta} + u_{zz} + \frac{1}{r} u_r = 0.$$

(a) Show that if $u(r, \theta, z) = R(r)\Theta(\theta)Z(z)$, then R, Θ, and Z satisfy the ordinary differential equations

$$r^2 R'' + r R' + (\lambda^2 r^2 - n^2) R = 0,$$
$$\Theta'' + n^2\Theta = 0,$$
$$Z'' - \lambda^2 Z = 0.$$

(b) Show that if $u(r, \theta, z)$ is independent of θ, then the first equation in part (a) becomes

$$r^2 R'' + r R' + \lambda^2 r^2 R = 0,$$

the second is omitted altogether, and the third is unchanged.

6. Find the steady state temperature in a semiinfinite rod $0 < z < \infty$, $0 \leq r < 1$, if the temperature is independent of θ and approaches zero as $z \to \infty$. Assume that the temperature $u(r, z)$ satisfies the boundary conditions

$$u(1, z) = 0, \qquad z > 0,$$
$$u(r, 0) = f(r), \qquad 0 \leq r \leq 1.$$

Hint: Refer to Problem 5.

7. Consider the wave equation in two space variables

$$a^2(u_{xx} + u_{yy}) = u_{tt}.$$

(a) Suppose that $u(x, y, t) = v(x, y)T(t)$. Show that v satisfies

$$v_{xx} + v_{yy} + k^2v = 0.$$

This equation is known as the Helmholtz (1821–1894) equation, and k is called the wave number.

(b) In polar coordinates the Helmholtz equation becomes

$$v_{rr} + \frac{1}{r^2}v_{\theta\theta} + \frac{1}{r}v_r + k^2v = 0.$$

If $v(r, \theta) = R(r)\Theta(\theta)$ show that R and Θ satisfy the ordinary differential equations

$$r^2R'' + rR' + (k^2r^2 - \lambda^2)R = 0,$$

$$\Theta'' + \lambda^2\Theta = 0.$$

(c) Find the solution of the Helmholtz equation in the circle $r < c$, which remains bounded at all points in the circle, and which satisfies the boundary condition $v(c, \theta) = f(\theta)$, where f is a given function on $0 \le \theta < 2\pi$.
Hint: The equation for R is a Bessel equation. See Problem 3 of Section 11.5.

8. Consider the flow of heat in an infinitely long cylinder of radius one: $0 \le r < 1, 0 \le \theta < 2\pi, -\infty < z < \infty$. Let the surface of the cylinder be held at temperature zero, and the initial temperature distribution be a function of the radial variable r only. Then the temperature u is a function of r and t only, and satisfies the heat conduction equation

$$\alpha^2\left(u_{rr} + \frac{1}{r}u_r\right) = u_t, \qquad 0 < r < 1, \qquad t > 0,$$

and the following initial and boundary conditions:

$$u(r, 0) = f(r), \qquad 0 \le r \le 1,$$
$$u(1, t) = 0, \qquad\quad t > 0.$$

Show that

$$u(r, t) = \sum_{n=1}^{\infty} c_n J_0(\lambda_n r)e^{-\alpha^2\lambda_n^2 t}$$

where $J_0(\lambda_n) = 0$. Find a formula for c_n.

9. In the spherical coordinates ρ, θ, ϕ defined by the equations

$$x = \rho\cos\theta\sin\phi,$$

$$y = \rho\sin\theta\sin\phi,$$

$$z = \rho\cos\phi,$$

Laplace's equation takes the form

$$\rho^2 u_{\rho\rho} + 2\rho u_\rho + (\csc^2\phi)u_{\theta\theta} + u_{\phi\phi} + (\cot\phi)u_\phi = 0.$$

(a) Show that if $u(\rho, \theta, \phi) = P(\rho)\Theta(\theta)\Phi(\phi)$, then P, Θ, and Φ satisfy ordinary differential equations of the form

$$\rho^2 P'' + 2\rho P' - n^2 P = 0,$$

$$\Theta'' + m^2\Theta = 0,$$

$$(\sin^2 \phi)\Phi'' + (\sin \phi \cos \phi)\Phi' + (n^2 \sin^2 \phi - m^2)\Phi = 0.$$

The first of these equations is of the Euler type, while the third is related to Legendre's equation.

(b) Show that if $u(\rho, \theta, \phi)$ is independent of θ, then the first equation in part (a) is unchanged, the second is omitted, and the third becomes

$$(\sin^2 \phi)\Phi'' + (\sin \phi \cos \phi)\Phi' + (n^2 \sin^2 \phi)\Phi = 0.$$

(c) Show that if a new independent variable s is defined by $s = \cos \phi$, then the equation for Φ becomes

$$(1 - s^2)\frac{d^2\Phi}{ds^2} - 2s\frac{d\Phi}{ds} + n^2\Phi = 0.$$

Note that this is Legendre's equation.

10. Find the steady state temperature $u(\rho, \phi)$ in a sphere of unit radius if the temperature is independent of θ and satisfies the boundary condition

$$u(1, \phi) = f(\phi), \qquad 0 \le \phi \le \pi.$$

Hint: Refer to Problem 9 and to Problems 10 through 16 of Section 4.2.1.

11. The wave equation in spherical coordinates is

$$\rho^2 u_{\rho\rho} + 2\rho u_\rho + (\csc^2 \phi)u_{\theta\theta} + u_{\phi\phi} + (\cot \phi)u_\phi = \frac{1}{a^2} u_{tt}.$$

Assuming that u is independent of θ, and that $u(\rho, \phi, t) = P(\rho)\Phi(\phi)T(t)$, show that P, Φ, and T satisfy the ordinary differential equations

$$\rho^2 P'' + 2\rho P' - \mu^2 P = 0,$$

$$\Phi'' + (\cot \phi)\Phi' + (\lambda^2 + \mu^2)\Phi = 0,$$

$$T'' + \lambda^2 a^2 T = 0.$$

Show that if ϕ is replaced by the new variable s defined by $s = \cos \phi$, then the differential equation for Φ becomes

$$(1 - s^2)\frac{d^2\Phi}{ds^2} - 2s\frac{d\Phi}{ds} + (\lambda^2 + \mu^2)\Phi = 0.$$

This equation is Legendre's equation.

*11.7 SERIES OF ORTHOGONAL FUNCTIONS; MEAN CONVERGENCE

In Section 11.4 we stated that under certain restrictions a given function f can be expanded in a series of eigenfunctions of a Sturm-Liouville boundary value problem, the series converging to $f(x)$ at each point in the interval. In this section we will describe a different kind of convergence that is especially useful for series of orthogonal functions, such as eigenfunctions.

Suppose that we are given the set of functions $\phi_1, \phi_2, \ldots, \phi_n$, which are continuous on the interval $0 \le x \le 1$ and satisfy the orthonormality condition

$$\int_0^1 r(x)\phi_i(x)\phi_j(x)\, dx = \begin{cases} 0, & i \neq j, \\ 1, & i = j, \end{cases} \tag{1}$$

where r is a nonnegative weight function. Suppose also that we wish to approximate a given function f, defined on $0 \le x \le 1$, by a linear combination of $\phi_1, \ldots, \phi_n$. That is, if

$$S_n(x) = \sum_{i=1}^n a_i\phi_i(x), \tag{2}$$

we wish to choose the coefficients $a_1, \ldots, a_n$ so that the function S_n will best approximate f on $0 \le x \le 1$. The first problem that we must face in doing this is to state precisely what we mean by "best approximate f on $0 \le x \le 1$." There are several reasonable meanings that can be attached to this phrase.

(a) We can choose n points $x_1, \ldots, x_n$ in the interval $0 \le x \le 1$, and require that $S_n(x)$ have the same value as $f(x)$ at each of these points. The coefficients $a_1, \ldots, a_n$ are found by solving the set of linear algebraic equations

$$\sum_{i=1}^n a_i\phi_i(x_j) = f(x_j), \qquad j = 1, \ldots, n. \tag{3}$$

This procedure is known as the *method of collocation*. If the points $x_1, \ldots, x_n$ are well-chosen, and if n is fairly large, then presumably $S_n(x)$ will not only be equal to $f(x)$ at the chosen points but will be reasonably close to it at other points as well. However, collocation has several deficiencies. One is that the coefficients a_i are found by solving a set of linear equations, not a simple thing to do if n is large. Further, the a_i depend on the location of the points $x_1, \ldots, x_n$, and it is not clear how best to select these points.

(b) Alternatively, we can consider the difference $|f(x) - S_n(x)|$ and try to make it as small as possible. The trouble here is that $|f(x) - S_n(x)|$ is a function of x as well as of the coefficients $a_1, \ldots, a_n$, and it is not obvious what criterion should be used in selecting the a_i. The choice of a_i that makes $f(x) - S_n(x)$ small at one point may make it large at another. One way to proceed is to consider instead the least upper bound of $|f(x) - S_n(x)|$ for x in $0 \le x \le 1$, and then to choose $a_1, \ldots, a_n$ so as to make this quantity as small as possible. That is, if

$$E_n(a_1, \ldots, a_n) = \text{l.u.b.}_{0 \le x \le 1} |f(x) - S_n(x)|, \tag{4}$$

then choose $a_1, \ldots, a_n$ so as to minimize E_n. The difficulty is that it is usually very hard, if not impossible, to write down the expression $E_n(a_1, \ldots, a_n)$; hence this approach may not be very effective in practice.

(c) Another way to proceed is to consider

$$I_n(a_1, \ldots, a_n) = \int_0^1 r(x) \, |f(x) - S_n(x)| \, dx. \tag{5}$$

If $r(x) = 1$, then I_n is the area between the graphs of $y = f(x)$ and $y = S_n(x)$; see Figure 11.3. We can then determine the coefficients a_i so as to minimize

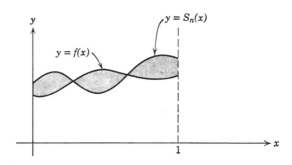

FIGURE 11.3

I_n. To avoid the complications resulting from calculations with absolute values, it is more convenient to consider instead

$$R_n(a_1, \ldots, a_n) = \int_0^1 r(x)[f(x) - S_n(x)]^2 \, dx \tag{6}$$

as our measure of the quality of approximation of the linear combination $S_n(x)$ to $f(x)$. While R_n is clearly similar in some ways to I_n, it lacks the simple geometrical interpretation of the latter. Nevertheless, it is much easier mathematically to deal with R_n than with I_n. The quantity R_n is called the *mean square error* of the approximation S_n to f. If $a_1, \ldots, a_n$ are chosen so as to minimize R_n, then S_n is said to best approximate f in the mean square sense.

In order to choose $a_1, \ldots, a_n$ so as to minimize R_n, we must satisfy the necessary conditions

$$\frac{\partial R_n}{\partial a_i} = 0, \qquad i = 1, \ldots, n. \tag{7}$$

Writing out Eq. (7), and noting that $\partial S_n(x; a_1, \ldots, a_n)/\partial a_i$ is equal to $\phi_i(x)$, we obtain

$$-\frac{\partial R_n}{\partial a_i} = 2 \int_0^1 r(x)[f(x) - S_n(x)]\phi_i(x) \, dx = 0. \tag{8}$$

Substituting for $S_n(x)$ from Eq. (2) and making use of the orthogonality relations (1) leads to

$$a_i = \int_0^1 r(x)f(x)\phi_i(x)\,dx, \qquad i = 1, \ldots, n. \tag{9}$$

The coefficients defined by Eq. (9) are called the Fourier coefficients of f with respect to the orthonormal set $\phi_1, \phi_2, \ldots, \phi_n$ and the weight function r. Since the conditions (7) are only necessary and not sufficient for R_n to be a minimum, a separate argument is required to show that R_n is actually minimized if the a_i are chosen by Eq. (9). This argument is outlined in Problem 2. Note that the coefficients (9) are the same as those in the eigen-function series whose convergence, under certain conditions, was stated in Theorem 11.4. Thus $S_n(x)$ is the nth partial sum in this series, and con-stitutes the best mean square approximation to $f(x)$ that is possible with the functions $\phi_1, \ldots, \phi_n$. We will assume hereafter that the coefficients a_i in $S_n(x)$ are given by Eq. (9).

Equation (9) is noteworthy in two other important respects. In the first place, it gives a formula for each a_i *separately*, rather than a set of linear algebraic equations for $a_1, \ldots, a_n$, as in the method of collocation, for example. This is due to the orthogonality of the base functions $\phi_1, \ldots, \phi_n$. Further, the formula for a_i is *independent* of n, the number of terms in $S_n(x)$. The practical significance of this is as follows. Suppose that, in order to obtain a better approximation to f, we desire to use an approximation with more terms, say k terms, where $k > n$. It is then unnecessary to recompute the first n coefficients in $S_k(x)$. All that is required is to compute the coefficients arising from the additional base functions $\phi_{n+1}, \ldots, \phi_k$.

Now let us suppose that there is an infinite sequence of functions $\phi_1, \ldots, \phi_n, \ldots$, which are continuous and orthonormal on the interval $0 \leq x \leq 1$. Suppose further that as n increases without bound the mean square error R_n approaches zero. In this event the infinite series

$$\sum_{i=1}^{\infty} a_i \phi_i(x)$$

is said to *converge in the mean square sense* (or, more simply, *in the mean*) to $f(x)$. Mean convergence is an essentially different type of convergence than the pointwise convergence considered up to now. A series may converge in the mean without converging at each point. This is plausible geometrically because the area between two curves, which behaves in the same way as the mean square error, may be zero even though the functions are not the same at every point. They may differ on any finite set of points, for example, without affecting the mean square error. It is less obvious, but also true, that even if an infinite series converges at every point, it may not converge in the mean. Indeed, the mean square error may even become unbounded. An example of this phenomenon is given in Problem 1.

Now suppose that we wish to know what class of functions, defined on $0 \leq x \leq 1$, can be represented as an infinite series of the orthonormal set ϕ_i, $i = 1, 2, \ldots$. The answer depends upon what kind of convergence we require. We say that the set $\phi_1, \ldots, \phi_n, \ldots$ is *complete* with respect to mean square convergence for a set of functions $\mathcal{F}$, if for each function f in $\mathcal{F}$, the series

$$f(x) = \sum_{i=1}^{\infty} a_i \phi_i(x), \tag{10}$$

with coefficients given by Eq. (9), converges in the mean. There is a similar definition for completeness with respect to pointwise convergence.

Theorems having to do with the convergence of series such as that in Eq. (10) can now be restated in terms of the idea of completeness. For example, Theorem 11.4 can be restated as follows: The eigenfunctions of the Sturm-Liouville problem

$$-[p(x)y']' + q(x)y = \lambda r(x)y, \qquad 0 < x < 1, \tag{11}$$

$$a_1 y(0) + a_2 y'(0) = 0, \qquad b_1 y(1) + b_2 y'(1) = 0, \tag{12}$$

are complete with respect to ordinary pointwise convergence for the set of functions which are continuous on $0 \leq x \leq 1$, have a piecewise continuous derivative there, and (if necessary) satisfy certain boundary conditions at $x = 0$ and $x = 1$, as explained in Theorem 11.4.

If pointwise convergence is replaced by mean convergence, Theorem 11.4 can be considerably generalized. Before we state such a companion theorem to Theorem 11.4, we first define what is meant by a square integrable function. A function f is said to be *square integrable* on the interval $0 \leq x \leq 1$ if both f and f^2 are integrable* on that interval. The following theorem is similar to Theorem 11.4 except that it involves mean convergence.

Theorem 11.7. *The eigenfunctions ϕ_i of the Sturm-Liouville problem (11), (12) are complete with respect to mean convergence for the set of functions which are square integrable on $0 \leq x \leq 1$. In other words, given any square integrable function f, the series (10) whose coefficients are given by Eq. (9), converges to $f(x)$ in the mean square sense.*

It is significant that the class of functions specified in Theorem 11.7 is very large indeed. The class of square integrable functions contains some functions with many discontinuities, including some kinds of infinite discontinuities, as well as some functions that are not differentiable at any point. All

---

* For the Riemann integral that is used in elementary calculus the hypotheses that f and f^2 are integrable are independent; that is, there are functions such that f is integrable but f^2 is not, and conversely. See Problem 3. A generalized integral, known as the Lebesgue integral, can be defined and has the property (among others) that if f^2 is integrable, then f is also necessarily integrable. The term square integrable came into common use in connection with this type of integration.

of these functions have mean convergent expansions in the eigenfunctions of
the boundary value problem (11), (12). However, in many cases these series
do not converge pointwise, at least not at every point. Thus mean convergence
is more naturally associated with series of orthogonal functions than ordinary
pointwise convergence.

The theory of Fourier series discussed in Chapter 10 is just a special case
of the general theory of Sturm-Liouville problems. For instance, the
functions $\phi_n(x) = \sqrt{2}\sin n\pi x$ are the normalized eigenfunctions of the
Sturm-Liouville problem $y'' + \lambda y = 0$, $y(0) = 0$, $y(1) = 0$. Thus, if f is a
given square integrable function on $0 \le x \le 1$, then according to Theorem
11.7, the series

$$f(x) = \sum_{n=1}^{\infty} b_n \phi_n(x) = \sqrt{2}\sum_{n=1}^{\infty} b_n \sin n\pi x, \tag{13}$$

where

$$b_n = \int_0^1 f(x)\phi_n(x)\,dx = \sqrt{2}\int_0^1 f(x)\sin n\pi x\,dx, \tag{14}$$

converges in the mean. The series (13) is precisely the Fourier sine series
discussed in Section 10.5. If f satisfies the further conditions stated in
Theorem 11.4, then this series converges pointwise as well as in the mean.

Theorem 11.7 can be extended to cover self-adjoint boundary value
problems having periodic boundary conditions, such as the problem

$$y'' + \lambda y = 0, \tag{15}$$

$$y(-l) - y(l) = 0, \qquad y'(-l) - y'(l) = 0, \tag{16}$$

considered at the end of Section 11.3. The eigenfunctions of the problem
(15), (16) are $\phi_n(x) = \cos(n\pi x/l)$ for $n = 0, 1, 2, \ldots,$ and $\psi_n(x) = \sin(n\pi x/l)$ for $n = 1, 2, \ldots.$ If f is a given square integrable function on
$-l \le x \le l$, then its expansion in terms of the eigenfunctions ϕ_n and ψ_n is
of the form

$$f(x) = \frac{a_0}{2} + \sum_{n=1}^{\infty}\left(a_n \cos\frac{n\pi x}{l} + b_n \sin\frac{n\pi x}{l}\right), \tag{17}$$

where

$$a_n = \frac{1}{l}\int_{-l}^{l} f(x)\cos\frac{n\pi x}{l}\,dx, \qquad n = 0, 1, 2, \ldots, \tag{18}$$

$$b_n = \frac{1}{l}\int_{-l}^{l} f(x)\sin\frac{n\pi x}{l}\,dx, \qquad n = 1, 2, \ldots. \tag{19}$$

This expansion is exactly the Fourier series for f discussed in Sections 10.3
and 10.4. According to the generalization of Theorem 11.7, the series (17)
converges in the mean for any square integrable function f even though f may
not satisfy the conditions of Theorem 10.3, which assure pointwise convergence.

PROBLEMS

1. In this problem we show that pointwise convergence of a sequence $S_n(x)$ does not imply mean convergence, and conversely.

(a) Let $S_n(x) = n\sqrt{x}\,e^{-nx^2/2}$, $0 \le x \le 1$. Show that $\lim_{n \to \infty} S_n(x) = 0$ for each x in $0 \le x \le 1$. Show also that

$$R_n = \int_0^1 [0 - S_n(x)]^2\, dx = \frac{n}{2}(1 - e^{-n}),$$

and hence that $\lim_{n \to \infty} R_n = \infty$. Thus pointwise convergence does not imply mean convergence.

(b) Let $S_n(x) = x^n$ for $0 \le x \le 1$ and let $f(x) = 0$ for $0 \le x \le 1$. Show that

$$R_n = \int_0^1 [f(x) - S_n(x)]^2\, dx = \frac{1}{2n + 1},$$

and hence $S_n(x)$ converges to $f(x)$ in the mean. Also show that $S_n(x)$ does not converge to $f(x)$ pointwise throughout $0 \le x \le 1$. Thus mean convergence does not imply pointwise convergence.

2. Suppose that the functions $\phi_1, \ldots, \phi_n$ satisfy the orthonormality relation (1), and that a given function f is to be approximated by $S_n(x) = c_1\phi_1(x) + \cdots + c_n\phi_n(x)$, where the coefficients c_i are not necessarily those of Eq. (9). Show that the mean square error R_n given by Eq. (6) may be written in the form

$$R_n = \int_0^1 r(x)f^2(x)\, dx - \sum_{i=1}^{n} a_i^2 + \sum_{i=1}^{n} (c_i - a_i)^2,$$

where the a_i are the Fourier coefficients given by Eq. (9). Show that R_n is minimized if $c_i = a_i$ for each i.

3. In this problem we show by examples that the (Riemann) integrability of f and f^2 are independent.

(a) Let $f(x) = \begin{cases} x^{-1/2}, & 0 < x \le 1, \\ 0, & x = 0. \end{cases}$

Show that $\int_0^1 f(x)\, dx$ exists as an improper integral, but $\int_0^1 f^2(x)\, dx$ does not.

(b) Let $f(x) = \begin{cases} 1, & x \text{ rational}, \\ -1, & x \text{ irrational}. \end{cases}$

Show that $\int_0^1 f^2(x)\, dx$ exists, but $\int_0^1 f(x)\, dx$ does not.

4. Suppose that it is desired to construct a set of polynomials $f_0(x)$, $f_1(x)$, $f_2(x), \ldots, f_k(x), \ldots$, where $f_k(x)$ is of degree k, which are orthonormal on the interval $0 \le x \le 1$. That is, the set of polynomials must satisfy

$$\int_0^1 f_j(x)f_k(x)\, dx = \delta_{jk}.$$

(a) Find $f_0(x)$ by choosing the polynomial of degree zero such that

$$\int_0^1 f_0^2(x)\, dx = 1.$$

(b) Find $f_1(x)$ by determining the polynomial of degree one such that

$$\int_0^1 f_0(x)f_1(x)\, dx = 0 \quad \text{and} \quad \int_0^1 f_1^2(x) = 1.$$

(c) Find $f_2(x)$.

(d) The normalization condition $\int_0^1 f_k^2(x)\, dx = 1$ is somewhat awkward to apply. Let $g_0(x)$, $g_1(x)$, ..., $g_k(x)$ be the sequence of polynomials which are orthogonal on $0 \le x \le 1$ and which are normalized by the condition $g_k(1) = 1$. Find $g_0(x)$, $g_1(x)$, and $g_2(x)$ and compare them with $f_0(x)$, $f_1(x)$, and $f_2(x)$.

5. Suppose that it is desired to construct a set of polynomials $P_0(x)$, $P_1(x)$, ..., $P_k(x)$, ..., where $P_k(x)$ is of degree k, which are orthogonal on the interval $-1 \le x \le 1$. Suppose further that $P_k(x)$ is normalized by the condition $P_k(1) = 1$. Find $P_0(x)$, $P_1(x)$, $P_2(x)$, and $P_3(x)$. Note that these are the first four Legendre polynomials; see Problem 11 of Section 4.2.1.

6. This problem develops some further results associated with mean convergence. Let $R_n(a_1, \ldots, a_n)$, $S_n(x)$, and a_i be defined by Eqs. (6), (2), and (9), respectively.

(a) Show that

$$R_n = \int_0^1 r(x)f^2(x)\, dx - \sum_{i=1}^n a_i^2.$$

Hint: Substitute for $S_n(x)$ in Eq. (6) and integrate, using the orthogonality relation (1).

(b) Show that $\sum_{i=1}^n a_i^2 \le \int_0^1 r(x)f^2(x)\, dx$. This result is known as Bessel's inequality.

(c) Show that $\sum_{i=1}^\infty a_i^2$ converges.

(d) Show that $\lim_{n\to\infty} R_n = \int_0^1 r(x)f^2(x)\, dx - \sum_{i=1}^\infty a_i^2$.

(e) Show that $\sum_{i=1}^\infty a_i \phi_i(x)$ converges to $f(x)$ in the mean if and only if

$$\int_0^1 r(x)f^2(x)\, dx = \sum_{i=1}^\infty a_i^2.$$

This result is known as Parseval's equation.

In Problems 7 through 9 let ϕ_1, ϕ_2, ..., ϕ_n, ... be the normalized eigenfunctions of the Sturm-Liouville problem (11), (12).

7. Show that if a_n is the nth Fourier coefficient of a square integrable function f, then $\lim_{n\to\infty} a_n = 0$.

Hint: Use Bessel's inequality, Problem 6(b).

8. Show that the series

$$\phi_1(x) + \phi_2(x) + \cdots + \phi_n(x) + \cdots$$

cannot be the eigenfunction series for any square integrable function.
Hint: See Problem 7.

9. Show that the series

$$\phi_1(x) + \frac{\phi_2(x)}{\sqrt{2}} + \cdots + \frac{\phi_n(x)}{\sqrt{n}} + \cdots$$

is not the eigenfunction series for any square integrable function.
Hint: Use Bessel's inequality, Problem 6(b).

   Problems 10 and 11 are concerned with Parseval's equation; see Problem 6(e). In each of these problems suppose that the functions ϕ_i satisfy the orthonormality relation (1).

10. Show that Parseval's equation is obtained formally by squaring the series (10) corresponding to f, multiplying by the weight function r, and integrating term by term.

11. Let f and g be two square integrable functions having mean convergent series expansions with respect to the functions ϕ_i, the coefficients being denoted by a_i and b_i, respectively. Show that

$$\int_0^1 r(x)f(x)g(x)\,dx = \sum_{i=1}^{\infty} a_i b_i.$$

This is a generalization of Parseval's equation and reduces to the result of Problem 6(e) if $f(x) = g(x)$.
Hint: Write Parseval's equation for the functions $f + g$ and $f - g$ and then subtract one from the other.

REFERENCES

The following books were mentioned in the text in connection with certain theorems about Sturm-Liouville problems.

Birkhoff, G. and Rota, G.-C., *Ordinary Differential Equations*, Ginn, Boston, 1962.
Sagan, H., *Boundary and Eigenvalue Problems in Mathematical Physics*, Wiley, New York, 1961.
Weinberger, H., *A First Course in Partial Differential Equations*, Blaisdell, New York, 1965.

The following book is a convenient source of numerical and graphical data about Bessel and Legendre functions.

Jahnke, E. and Emde, F., *Tables of Functions with Formulae and Curves*, Teubner, Leipzig, 1938.

The following books also contain much information about Sturm-Liouville problems.

Dettman, J. W., *Mathematical Methods in Physics and Engineering*, McGraw-Hill, New York, 1962.
Hochstadt, H., *Differential Equations: A Modern Approach*, Holt, Rinehart, and Winston, New York, 1964.
Tricomi, F. G., *Differential Equations*, Hafner, New York, 1961.

Answers to Problems

CHAPTER ONE

Page 7

1. (a) 2nd order, linear   (b) 2nd order, nonlinear
   (c) 4th order, linear   (d) 1st order, nonlinear
   (e) 2nd order, nonlinear   (f) 3rd order, linear
3. (a) $r = -2$ (b) $r = \pm 1$ (c) $r = 2, -3$ (d) $r = 0, 1, 2$
4. (a) $r = -1, -2$ (b) $r = 1, 4$
5. (a) 2nd order, linear   (b) 2nd order, linear
   (c) 2nd order, linear   (d) 2nd order, nonlinear
   (e) 4th order, linear   (f) 2nd order, nonlinear

CHAPTER TWO

Section 2.1, Page 15

1. $y = ce^{-3x} + \dfrac{x}{3} - \dfrac{1}{9} + e^{-2x}$ 2. $y = ce^{2x} + \dfrac{x^3}{3}e^{2x}$

3. $y = ce^{-x} + 1 + \dfrac{x^2}{2}e^{-x}$ 4. $y = \dfrac{c}{x} + \dfrac{3\cos 2x}{4} + \dfrac{3}{2}\sin 2x$

5. $y = 3e^x + 2(x - 1)e^{2x}$ 6. $y = \frac{1}{2}(x^2 - 1)e^{-2x}$

7. $y = e^{-x}\displaystyle\int_0^x \dfrac{e^t}{1 + t^2}\, dt$ 8. $y = \dfrac{\sin x}{x^2}$

9. $x = ce^{-y} + \frac{1}{2}e^y$

14. (a) See Problem 2.   (b) See Problem 4.

Section 2.2, Page 20

1. $y = \dfrac{c}{x} + \dfrac{\sin x}{x} - \cos x$ 2. $y = \dfrac{c}{x^3} - \dfrac{\cos x}{x^3}$

3. $y = (c - 2x\cos x + 2\sin x)\cos x$ 4. $y = \dfrac{c + (x - 1)e^x}{x^2}$

5. $y = \dfrac{1}{12}\left(3x^2 - 4x + 6 + \dfrac{1}{x^2}\right), \qquad x > 0$

6. $y = \dfrac{1}{x}(e^x + 1 - e)$, $x > 0$ 7. $y = \dfrac{2x + 1 - \pi}{\sin x}$, $0 < x < \pi$

8. $y = \dfrac{\sin x - x \cos x}{x^2}$, $x > 0$

9. $y = \dfrac{c}{x^2} + \dfrac{1}{x}$; $\lim\limits_{x \to 0} |y| = \infty$ for all c

10. $y = cx + x^2$; $\lim\limits_{x \to 0} y = 0$ for all c

11. $y = cx + 2x^{3/2}$; $\lim\limits_{x \to 0} y = 0$ for all c, but y'', y''', $\ldots$, all $\to \pm\infty$ as $x \to 0$

12. $y = \dfrac{c + \sin x}{x}$; $\lim\limits_{x \to 0} y = \begin{cases} \pm\infty, & c \neq 0 \\ 1, & c = 0 \end{cases}$

13. $y = \frac{1}{2}(1 - e^{-2x})$ for $0 < x < 1$; $y = \frac{1}{2}(e^2 - 1)e^{-2x}$ for $x > 1$

14. $y \to 0$ as $x \to \infty$. Note that $a = \lambda$ and $a \neq \lambda$ must be considered separately.

16. $y = (\frac{2}{5}x^{-1} + cx^4)^{-1/2}$

Section 2.3, Page 28

1. (a) $2x + 5y > 0$ or $2x + 5y < 0$ (b) $x^2 + y^2 < 1$
   (c) Everywhere   (d) $x + y > 0$ or $x + y < 0$
   (e) $1 - x^2 + y^2 > 0$, $x \neq 0, y \neq 0$ (f) Everywhere

   or

   $1 - x^2 + y^2 < 0$, $x \neq 0, y \neq 0$

2. $|x| < 1$ 3. $y = [2(x - \frac{7}{8})]^{-1/2}$; $x > \frac{7}{8}$

4. $x > -(1 - e^{-3/2})^{1/3}$

5. For given c, solutions are valid for $|x| < |c|/2$.
   $(0, 4)$: $y = (16 - 4x^2)^{1/2}$
   $(1, -1)$: $y = -(5 - 4x^2)^{1/2}$

6. (a) $y_1(x)$ is solution for $x > 2$; $y_2(x)$ is solution for all x
   (b) f_y is not continuous at $(2, -1)$.

8. (c) $y = 3 - x$ 9. (c) $y = \dfrac{x^2}{2} + x + 1$

10. (c) $y = e^{-x^2/2} \displaystyle\int_1^x e^{t^2/2}\, dt$ 11. (c) $y = (1 - x)e^x - 1$

12. (a) $\lim\limits_{x \to \infty} \phi(x; y_0) = 1$ if $y_0 < 2$; $\phi(x; 2) = 2$ for all x;

   $\phi(x; y_0) \to \infty$ as x approaches some finite value if $y_0 > 2$

   (b) $\lim\limits_{x \to \infty} \phi(x; y_0) = -1$ if $y_0 < 0$; $\phi(x; 0) = 0$ for all x;

   $\lim\limits_{x \to \infty} \phi(x; y_0) = 1$ if $y_0 > 0$

   (c) $\lim\limits_{x \to \infty} \phi(x; y_0) = 0$ for every y_0

   (d) $\lim\limits_{x \to \infty} \phi(x; y_0) = \epsilon/\sigma$ if $y_0 > 0$; $\phi(x; 0) = 0$ for all x;

   $\phi(x; y_0) \to -\infty$ as x approaches some finite value if $y_0 < 0$

Section 2.4, Page 32

1. $3y^2 - 2x^3 = c;$ $y \neq 0$

2. $3y^2 - 2\ln|1 + x^3| = c;$ $1 + x^3 \neq 0;$ $y \neq 0$

3. $\dfrac{1}{y} + \cos x = c$ if $y \neq 0;$ also $y = 0;$ everywhere

4. $\arctan y - x - \dfrac{x^2}{2} = c;$ everywhere

5. $2\tan 2y - 2x - \sin 2x = c$ if $\cos 2y \neq 0;$ also $y = \pm\dfrac{(2n+1)\pi}{4}$ for any integer $n;$ everywhere

6. $y = \sin[\ln|x| + c]$ if $x \neq 0$ and $|y| < 1;$ also $y = \pm 1;$ $x \neq 0$ and $|y| < 1$

7. $y^2 - x^2 + 2(e^y - e^{-x}) = c;$ $y + e^y \neq 0$

8. $3y + y^3 - x^3 = c;$ everywhere

9. $y = \frac{1}{3}\arcsin(3\cos^2 x),$ $0.95 < x < 2.19$ approximately

10. $y = [2(1 - x)e^x - 1]^{1/2},$ $-1.68 < x < 0.77$ approximately

11. $r = 2e^\theta,$ $-\infty < \theta < \infty$

12. $y = -[2\ln(1 + x^2) + 4]^{1/2},$ $-\infty < x < \infty$

13. $y = [3 - 2\sqrt{1 + x^2}]^{-1/2},$ $|x| < \frac{1}{2}\sqrt{5}$

14. $y = -\frac{1}{2} + \frac{1}{2}\sqrt{4x^2 - 15},$ $x > \frac{1}{2}\sqrt{15}$

15. $2y^3 - 3(\arcsin x)^2 = c$

16. $y = \dfrac{a}{c}x + \dfrac{bc - ad}{c^2}\ln|cx + d| + k;$ $c \neq 0,$ $cx + d \neq 0$

17. $x = \dfrac{c}{a}y + \dfrac{ad - bc}{a^2}\ln|ay + b| + k;$ $a \neq 0,$ $ay + b \neq 0$

18. $|y + 2x|^3 |y - 2x| = c$

19. (a) $y = y_0 e^{\epsilon t}$

   (b) $y = \dfrac{\epsilon/\sigma}{1 + \left(\dfrac{\epsilon}{\sigma y_0} - 1\right)e^{-\epsilon t}};$ $y_0 \neq 0, \epsilon/\sigma$

Section 2.5, Page 37

1. $x^2 + 3x + y^2 - 2y = c$ 2. Not exact

3. $3x^3 + xy - x - 2y^2 = c$ 4. $x^2y^2 + 2xy = c$

5. $ax^2 + 2bxy + cy^2 = k$ 6. Not exact

7. $e^x \sin y + 2y\cos x = c;$ also $y = 0$ 8. Not exact

9. $e^{xy}\cos 2x + x^2 - 3y = c$ 10. $y\ln x + 3x^2 - 2y = c$

11. Not exact   12. $x^2 + y^2 = c$

13. (a) $b = 3;$ $x^2y^2 + 2x^3y = c$
    (b) $b = 1;$ $e^{2xy} + x^2 = c$

14. $\displaystyle\int^y N(x, t)\, dt + \int^x \left[M(s, y) - \int^y N_s(s, t)\, dt\right] ds = c$

Section 2.6, Page 42

1. $x^2 + 2\ln|y| - \dfrac{1}{y^2} = c$; also $y = 0$ 2. $e^x \sin y + 2y \cos x = c$

3. $xy^2 - (y^2 - 2y + 2)e^y = c$
4. $\mu(x) = e^{3x}$; $(3x^2 y + y^3)e^{3x} = c$
5. $\mu(x) = e^{-x}$; $y = ce^x + 1 + e^{2x}$
6. $\mu(y) = y$; $xy + y \cos y - \sin y = c$
7. $\mu(y) = e^{2y}/y$; $xe^{2y} - \ln|y| = c$;   also $y = 0$
8. $\mu(y) = \sin y$; $e^x \sin y + y^2 = c$
9. $\mu(x, y) = xy$; $x^3 y + 3x^2 + y^3 = c$

11. $\mu(t) = \exp\displaystyle\int^t R(s)\,ds$, where $t = xy$

Section 2.7, Page 45

1. $y = cx + x\ln|x|$

2. $y = cx^2$

3. $\arctan \dfrac{y}{x} - \ln|x| = c$

4. $x^2 + y^2 - cx^3 = 0$

5. $|y - x| = c\,|y + 3x|^5$

6. $|y + x|\,|y + 4x|^2 = c$

7. $-\dfrac{2x}{x + y} = \ln c\,|x + y|$

8. $\dfrac{x}{x + y} + \ln|x| = c$

9. (a) $|y - x| = c\,|y + x|^3$
   (b) $|y - x + 3| = c\,|y + x + 1|^3$

10. $|y + x + 4|\,|y + 4x + 13|^2 = c$

11. $-2\dfrac{x - 2}{x + y - 3} = \ln c\,|x + y - 3|$

12. $x^2 y^2 + 2x^3 y = c$

14. (b) Let $z = x + \dfrac{b}{c}\,y$

15. (a) No   (b) Yes   (c) Yes   (d) No

Section 2.8, Page 47

1. $y = \dfrac{c}{x^2} + \dfrac{x^3}{5}$

2. $\arctan \dfrac{y}{x} - \ln \sqrt{x^2 + y^2} = c$

3. $x^2 + xy - 3y - y^3 = 0$

4. $x = ce^y + ye^y$

5. $x^2 y + xy^2 + x = c$

6. $y = \dfrac{1 - e^{1-x}}{x}$

7. $(x^2 + y^2 + 1)e^{-y^2} = c$

8. $y = \dfrac{4 + \cos 2 - \cos x}{x^2}$

9. $x^2 y + x + y^2 = c$

10. $\dfrac{y^2}{x^3} + \dfrac{y}{x^2} = c$

11. $\dfrac{x^3}{3} + xy + e^y = c$

12. $y = ce^{-x} + e^{-x}\ln(1 + e^x)$

13. $2\left(\dfrac{y}{x}\right)^{1/2} - \ln|x| = c$

14. $x^2 + 2xy + 2y^2 = 34$

15. $y = \dfrac{c}{\cosh^2(x/2)}$

16. $\dfrac{2}{\sqrt{3}}\tan^{-1}\dfrac{2y - x}{\sqrt{3}\,x} - \ln|x| = c$

17. $y = ce^{3x} - e^{2x}$

18. $y = \dfrac{c}{x^2} - x$

19. $3y - 2xy^3 - 10x = 0$ 20. $e^x + e^{-y} = c$

21. $e^{-y/x} + \ln|x| = c$ 22. $y^3 + 3y - x^3 + 3x = 2$

23. $\dfrac{1}{y} = x \displaystyle\int^x \dfrac{e^{2t}}{t^2}\,dt + cx$; also $y = 0$ 24. $\sin^2 x \sin y = c$

25. $\dfrac{x^2}{y} + \arctan\dfrac{y}{x} = c$ 26. $x^2 + 2x^2y - y^2 = c$

27. $\sin x \cos 2y - \frac{1}{2}\sin^2 x = c$ 28. $2xy + xy^3 - x^3 = c$

29. $2\arcsin\dfrac{y}{x} - \ln|x| = c$ 30. $xy^2 - \ln|y| = 0$

31. $x + \ln|x| + \dfrac{1}{x} + y - 2\ln|y| = c$;   also $y = 0$

32. $x^3y^2 + xy^3 = -4$

34. $x + e^{-y} = c$ 37. $y = cx - \dfrac{c^3}{3}$; $y^2 = \frac{4}{9}x^3$

38. $y = cx - e^c$; $y = x\ln x - x$, $x > 0$

40. (a) $y = x + \dfrac{1}{c - x}$,   (b) $y = \dfrac{1}{x} + \dfrac{2x}{x^2 + 2c}$

(c) $y = \sin x + (c\cos x - \frac{1}{2}\sin x)^{-1}$

Section 2.9, Page 57

1. $t = (\ln 2)/k$ years, where k is the interest rate

2. In six months: four million dollars. After only one year, his wealth will be infinite.

3. $M = 100\exp\left(-\dfrac{t}{20}\ln\dfrac{5}{4}\right)$;   half life $= \dfrac{20\ln 2}{\ln\frac{5}{4}}$ years

4. $t = \dfrac{2\ln 10}{\ln 2}$ hours

5. (a) $k = -\dfrac{\ln 2}{5568} \cong -1.245 \times 10^{-4}$

(b) $Q = Q_0 e^{-t\ln 2/5568} \cong Q_0 e^{-(1.245\times 10^{-4})t}$

(c) $t = \dfrac{5568\ln 5}{\ln 2}$ years $\cong 12{,}930$ years

6. $p = (2.5 \times 10^8)e^{(t\ln 10)/300}$;   A.D. 2250

7. (a) $p = p_0 e^{\epsilon t}$; $\lim\limits_{t\to\infty} p = \infty$

(b) $p = \dfrac{p_0 e^{\epsilon t}}{1 + \dfrac{k}{\epsilon}p_0(e^{\epsilon t} - 1)}$; $\lim\limits_{t\to\infty} p = \dfrac{\epsilon}{k}$

8. (a) $u = u_0 + (u_1 - u_0)e^{kt}$ (b) $t = \dfrac{\ln\frac{13}{8}}{\ln\frac{13}{12}}$ min $\cong 6.07$ min

9. $r = 3 - t$ mm, $0 < t < 3$ 10. $t = 100\ln 100$ min

11. $Q = 50e^{-0.2}(1 - e^{-0.2})$ lb

12. $Q = 200 + t - \dfrac{100(200)^2}{(200 + t)^2}$ lb; $t < 300$

$c = \frac{121}{125}$ lb/gal; $\lim\limits_{t \to \infty} c = 1$ lb/gal

13. (a) $x = pq[e^{z(q-p)t} - 1]/[qe^{z(q-p)t} - p]$ (b) $x = p^2\alpha t/(p\alpha t + 1)$

14. $x = px_0/[(p - x_0)e^{-p\alpha t} + x_0]$

15. (a) $x = 0.04(1 - e^{-t/12000})$ (b) $t^* \cong 36$ minutes

16. (a) $c(t) = k + (P/r) + [c_0 - k - (P/r)]e^{-rt/V}$
$\lim\limits_{t \to \infty} c(t) = k + (P/r)$

(b) $T = \dfrac{V}{r} \ln 2$; $T = \dfrac{V}{r} \ln 10$

(c) Superior, $T = 430$ years; Michigan, $T = 71.4$ years;
Erie, $T = 6.05$ years; Ontario, $T = 17.6$ years

17. (a) $y^2 - x^2 = c$ (b) $x^2 + y^2 = cy$
(c) $x - y = c(x + y)^3$ (d) $x^2 - 2cy = c^2$; $c > 0$

18. (a) $y - 3x = c$
(b) $\ln \sqrt{x^2 + y^2} + \arctan(y/x) = c$, or $r = ke^{-\theta}$

19. $y - b = c(x - a)$ 20. $(x - 2)^2 + y^2 = 9$

21. $x = cy^2$

Section 2.10, Page 67

1. (a) $x_m = v_0^2/2g$ (b) $t_m = v_0/g$ (c) $t = 2v_0/g$

2. $v = \dfrac{mg}{k} + \left(v_0 - \dfrac{mg}{k}\right)e^{-kt/m}$; $\lim\limits_{t \to \infty} v = \dfrac{mg}{k}$

3. $t = \dfrac{m}{k} \ln 10$

4. (a) $v = 5(1 - e^{-0.2t})$ ft/sec   (b) $\lim\limits_{t \to \infty} v = 5$ ft/sec

5. $2\dfrac{m}{k}(\sqrt{v_0} - \sqrt{v}) + 2\dfrac{m^2 g}{k^2} \ln\left|\dfrac{mg - k\sqrt{v_0}}{mg - k\sqrt{v}}\right| = t$; $v_l = \left(\dfrac{mg}{k}\right)^2$

6. $v = \sqrt{\dfrac{mg}{k}} \dfrac{e^{2\sqrt{kg/m}\,t} - 1}{e^{2\sqrt{kg/m}\,t} + 1}$; $\lim\limits_{t \to \infty} v = \sqrt{\dfrac{mg}{k}}$

7. $v_l = \left(\dfrac{mg}{k}\right)^{1/r}$

8. (a) $x_m = -\dfrac{m^2 g}{k^2} \ln\left(1 + \dfrac{kv_0}{mg}\right) + \dfrac{mv_0}{k}$ (b) $t_m = \dfrac{m}{k} \ln\left(1 + \dfrac{kv_0}{mg}\right)$

9. $v_l = \dfrac{2}{9} \dfrac{a^2 g(\rho - \rho')}{\mu}$

10. (a) $w \cong 64$ lb   (b) $w_m \cong 16.9$ lb

11. $\dfrac{x_m}{R} = -1 + \left(1 - \dfrac{v_0^2}{v_e^2}\right)^{-1} = \dfrac{v_0^2}{v_e^2}\left(1 + \dfrac{v_0^2}{v_e^2} + \dfrac{v_0^4}{v_e^4} + \cdots\right)$

12. $v_e = \left(\dfrac{2gR}{1 + \xi}\right)^{\frac{1}{2}}$;   altitude $\simeq 1536$ miles

13. $v = 5011$ ft/sec

14. $v = \dfrac{s\beta - mg}{k}\left[1 - \left(\dfrac{m_0 - \beta t}{m_0}\right)^{k/\beta}\right]$

CHAPTER THREE

Section 3.1, Page 89

1. (a) $y = c_1 x^{-1} + c_2 + \ln x$ (b) $y = c_1 \ln x + c_2 + x$

  (c) $y = \dfrac{1}{c_1} \ln \dfrac{x - c_1}{x + c_1} + c_2$

  (d) $y = \pm\tfrac{2}{3}(x - 2c_1)\sqrt{x + c_1} + c_2$;   *Hint:* $\mu(v) = v^{-3}$ is an integrating factor.

2. (a) $y^2 = c_1 x + c_2$

  (b) $y = c_1 \sin (x + c_2) = k_1 \sin x + k_2 \cos x$

  (c) $\dfrac{y^3}{3} - 2c_1 y + c_2 = 2x$ (d) $x + c_2 = \pm\tfrac{2}{3}(y - 2c_1)(y + c_1)^{\frac{1}{2}}$

3. (a) $y = \tfrac{4}{3}(x + 1)^{\frac{3}{2}} - \tfrac{1}{3}$ (b) $y = \dfrac{2}{(1 - x)^2}$

  (c) $y = c_1 \tan^{-1} x + c_2 + 3 \ln x - \tfrac{3}{2} \ln (x^2 + 1)$

  (d) $y = \tfrac{1}{2}x^2 + \tfrac{3}{2}$

4. (a) Any interval not containing $x = 0$
  (b) Any interval
  (c) Any interval not containing $x = 0$ or $x = 1$
  (d) Any interval not containing $x = 0$
  (e) Any interval
  (f) Any interval not containing $x = (2n + 1)\pi/2$, $n = 0, \pm 1, \pm 2, \ldots$

5. $\phi''(0) = -p(0)a_1 - q(0)a_0$,
  $\phi'''(0) = [p^2(0) - p'(0) - q(0)]a_1 + [p(0)q(0) - q'(0)]a_0$,
  yes

6. (a) $y'' - y = 0$ (b) $y'' + y = 0$
  (c) $y'' = 0$ (d) $y'' - 2y' + y = 0$
  (e) $x^2 y'' - 2xy' + 2y = 0$ (f) $y'' - y = 0$
  (g) $(1 - x \cot x)y'' - xy' + y = 0$ (h) $y'' + 3y' = 0$

Section 3.2, Page 97

2. $y = \tfrac{2}{3}e^x + \tfrac{1}{3}e^{-2x}$, $y = 0$

8. (a) $b + cx$ (b) $(c - a) \sin x + b \cos x$
  (c) $(ar^2 + br + c)e^{rx}$ (d) $ar(r - 1)x^{r-2} + brx^{r-1} + cx^r$

9. (a) $(2a + 2b + c)x^2$ (b) $(ar^2 x^2 + brx + c)e^{rx}$
  (c) $[ar^2 + (b - a)r + c]x^r$

11. (a) $(n - m)e^{(m+n)x}$ (b) -1 (c) $x^2 e^x$ (d) $-e^{2x}$
  (e) 0

12. (a) $-\infty < x < \infty$ (b) $-\infty < x < \infty$
    (c) $-\infty < x < \infty$ (d) $x > 0$ or $x < 0$

13. (a) $y = \dfrac{e^x - e^{-x}}{2}$ (b) $y = \sinh x$

    (c) $y = 4e^{-2x} - 3e^{-3x}$ (d) $y = 1 - e^{-(x-1)}$

16. If x_1 is an inflection point and $y = \phi(x)$ is a solution, then from the differential
    equation $p(x_1)\phi'(x_1) + q(x_1)\phi(x_1) = 0$.

17. (a) Yes, $y = c_1 e^{-x^2/2} \displaystyle\int^x e^{t^2/2}\, dt + c_2 e^{-x^2/2}$

    (b) No

    (c) Yes, $y = \dfrac{1}{\mu(x)}\left[c_1 \displaystyle\int^x \mu(t)\, dt + c_2 \right]$ where $\mu(x) = \displaystyle\int^x \left(\dfrac{1}{t} + \dfrac{\cos t}{t} \right) dt$

    (d) Yes, $y = c_1 x^{-1} + c_2$

18. (a) $x^2\mu'' + 3x\mu' + (1 + x^2 - \nu^2)\mu = 0$
    (b) $(1 - x^2)\mu'' - 2x\mu' + \alpha(\alpha + 1)\mu = 0$
    (c) $\mu'' - x\mu = 0$
    (d) $x^2\mu'' + 2x\mu' + (-x^2 + kx + \frac{9}{4} - m^2)\mu = 0$

20. The Legendre equation and the Airy equation are self-adjoint.

Section 3.3, Page 102

5. $W(c_1 y_1, c_2 y_2) = c_1 c_2 W(y_1, y_2) \neq 0$

9. If y_1 and y_2 are linearly independent, then $W(y_1, y_2)$ cannot change sign. Show
   that $W(y_1, y_2)$ will change sign if y_1 has none or more than one zero between
   consecutive zeros of y_2.

Section 3.4, Page 105

1. $y_2(x) = e^{-2x}$ 2. $y_2(x) = xe^{-x}$

3. $y_2(x) = x^{-1}$, $x > 0$ or $x < 0$ 4. $y_2(x) = x^{-2}$, $x > 0$ or $x < 0$

5. $y_2(x) = \sin x$ 6. $y_2(x) = \dfrac{3x}{4} + \dfrac{3x^2 - 1}{8} \ln \dfrac{x - 1}{x + 1}$

7. $y_2(x) = x^{-\frac{1}{2}} \cos x$ 9. $y_2(x) = x^{-2}$

Section 3.5, Page 109

1. $y = c_1 e^x + c_2 e^{-3x}$ 2. $y = c_1 e^{-x/2} + c_2 x e^{-x/2}$
3. $y = c_1 e^{x/2} + c_2 e^{-x/3}$ 4. $y = c_1 e^{x/2} + c_2 e^x$
5. $y = c_1 e^x + c_2 e^{-x}$ 6. $y = c_1 e^x + c_2 x e^x$
7. $y = c_1 + c_2 e^{-5x}$ 8. $y = c_1 e^{(9+3\sqrt{5})x/2} + c_2 e^{(9-3\sqrt{5})x/2}$
9. $y = c_1 e^{(1+\sqrt{3})x} + c_2 e^{(1-\sqrt{3})x}$ 10. $y = c_1 e^{-x} + c_2 x e^{-x}$
11. $y = e^x$ 12. $y = 2x e^{3x}$
13. $y = \frac{1}{10} e^{-9(x-1)} + \frac{9}{10} e^{x-1}$

Section 3.5.1, Page 113

1. $y = c_1 e^x \cos x + c_2 e^x \sin x$
2. $y = c_1 e^x \cos \sqrt{5}\, x + c_2 e^x \sin \sqrt{5}\, x$

3. $y = c_1 e^{2x} + c_2 e^{-4x}$

4. $y = c_1 e^{-x} \cos x + c_2 e^{-x} \sin x$

5. $y = c_1 e^{x/3} + c_2 x e^{x/3}$

6. $y = e^{-3x}(c_1 \cos 2x + c_2 \sin 2x)$

7. $y = \frac{1}{2} \sin 2x$

8. $y = e^{-2x} \cos x + 2e^{-2x} \sin x$

14. $\pm 2^{1/4} e^{i\pi/8};$ $\quad \pm 2^{1/4} e^{-i\pi/8};$ $\quad \pm e^{i\pi/4} = \pm \dfrac{1+i}{\sqrt{2}}$

15. (a) $y = c_1 e^{ix} + c_2 e^{-2ix} = (c_1 \cos x + c_2 \cos 2x) + i(c_1 \sin x - c_2 \sin 2x)$, no
   (b) $y = c_1 e^{r_1 x} + c_2 e^{r_2 x}$ where $r_1 = -1 + 2^{1/4} e^{-i\pi/8}$ and $r_2 = -1 - 2^{1/4} e^{-i\pi/8}$,
   no

17. (a) Yes, $y = c_1 \cos z + c_2 \sin z,$ $\quad z = \displaystyle\int^x e^{-t^2/2}\, dt$

   (b) No

   (c) Yes, $y = c_1 e^{-x^2/4} \cos \dfrac{\sqrt{3}}{4} x^2 + c_2 e^{-x^2/4} \sin \dfrac{\sqrt{3}}{4} x^2$

18. $y = c_1 \cos \ln x + c_2 \sin \ln x$

Section 3.6.1, Page 123

1. $y = e^x - \frac{1}{2} e^{-2x} - x - \frac{1}{2}$

2. $y = c_1 e^{3x} + c_2 e^{-x} - \frac{1}{2} e^{2x}$

3. $y = \frac{7}{10} \sin 2x - \frac{19}{40} \cos 2x + \frac{1}{4} x^2 - \frac{1}{8} + \frac{3}{5} e^x$

4. $y = c_1 + c_2 e^{-2x} + \frac{3}{2} x - \frac{1}{2} \sin 2x - \frac{1}{2} \cos 2x$

5. $y = c_1 \cos 3x + c_2 \sin 3x + \frac{1}{18}(x^2 - \frac{2}{3}x + \frac{1}{9})e^{3x} + \frac{2}{3}$

6. $y = 4xe^x - 3e^x + \frac{1}{6}x^3 e^x + 4$

7. $y = c_1 e^{-x} + c_2 e^{-x/2} + (x^2 - 6x + 14) - \frac{3}{10} \sin x - \frac{9}{10} \cos x$

8. $y = c_1 \cos x + c_2 \sin x - \frac{1}{3}x \cos 2x - \frac{5}{9} \sin 2x$

9. $y = c_1 e^{-x} + c_2 x e^{-x} + \frac{1}{25} e^x (3 \cos x + 4 \sin x)$

10. $u = c_1 \cos \omega_0 t + c_2 \sin \omega_0 t + \dfrac{1}{\omega_0^2 - \omega^2} \cos \omega t$

11. $u = c_1 \cos \omega_0 t + c_2 \sin \omega_0 t + \dfrac{1}{2\omega_0} t \sin \omega_0 t$

12. $u = e^{-\mu t/2}(c_1 \cos \sqrt{4\omega_0^2 - \mu^2}\, t + c_2 \sin \sqrt{4\omega_0^2 - \mu^2}\, t)$
   $\qquad\qquad + \dfrac{(\omega_0^2 - \omega^2) \cos \omega t + \mu\omega \sin \omega t}{(\omega_0^2 - \omega^2)^2 + \mu^2\omega^2}$

13. $y = c_1 e^{-x/2} \cos \dfrac{\sqrt{3}}{2} x + c_2 e^{-x/2} \sin \dfrac{\sqrt{3}}{2} x + \frac{1}{2} - \frac{1}{13} \sin 2x + \frac{3}{26} \cos 2x$

14. $y = c_1 e^{-x/2} \cos \dfrac{\sqrt{15}}{2} x + c_2 e^{-x/2} \sin \dfrac{\sqrt{15}}{2} x + \frac{1}{6}e^x - \frac{1}{4}e^{-x}$

15. $y = c_1 e^{-x} + c_2 e^{2x} + \frac{1}{6}xe^{2x} + \frac{1}{8}e^{-2x}$

16. $y_p(x) = x(A_0 x^4 + A_1 x^3 + A_2 x^2 + A_3 x + A_4) + x(B_0 x^2 + B_1 x + B_2)e^{-3x}$
   $\qquad\qquad + D \sin 3x + E \cos 3x$

17. $y_p(x) = A_0 x + A_1 + x(B_0 x + B_1) \sin x + x(D_0 x + D_1) \cos x$

18. $y_p(x) = e^x(A \cos 2x + B \sin 2x) + (D_0 x + D_1)e^{2x} \sin x + (E_0 x + E_1)e^{2x} \cos x$

19. $y_p(x) = Ae^{-x} + x(B_0 x^2 + B_1 x + B_2)e^{-x} \cos x + x(D_0 x^2 + D_1 x + D_2)e^{-x} \sin x$

20. $y_p(x) = A_0 x^2 + A_1 x + A_2 + x^2(B_0 x + B_1)e^{2x} + (D_0 x + D_1) \sin 2x$
   $\qquad\qquad + (E_0 x + E_1) \cos 2x$

21. $y_p(x) = x(A_0x^2 + A_1x + A_2) \sin 2x + x(B_0x^2 + B_1x + B_2) \cos 2x$

22. $y_p(x) = (A_0x^2 + A_1x + A_2)e^x \sin 2x + (B_0x^2 + B_1x + B_2)e^x \cos 2x$
$\qquad\qquad + e^{3x}(D \cos x + E \sin x) + Fe^x$

23. $y = c_1 \cos \lambda x + c_2 \sin \lambda x + \sum_{m=1}^{N} \dfrac{a_m}{\lambda^2 - m^2\pi^2} \sin m\pi x$

25. $y = \begin{cases} t, & 0 \le t \le \pi \\ -\left(1 + \dfrac{\pi}{2}\right) \sin t - \dfrac{\pi}{2} \cos t + \dfrac{\pi}{2} e^{(\pi - t)}, & t > \pi \end{cases}$

26. (i) $y_p(x) = e^{(\alpha+\beta)x}(A_0x^n + \cdots + A_n) + e^{(\alpha-\beta)x}(B_0x^n + \cdots + B_n)$

(ii) $y_p(x) = e^{(\alpha+\beta)x}(A_0x^{n+1} + \cdots + A_nx) + e^{(\alpha-\beta)x}(B_0x^n + \cdots + B_n)$

(iii) $y_p(x) = e^{(\alpha+\beta)x}(A_0x^{n+1} + \cdots + A_nx) + e^{(\alpha-\beta)x}(B_0x^{n+1} + \cdots + B_nx)$

(iv) Replace $e^{\beta x}$ by $\cosh \beta x + \sinh \beta x$ and $e^{-\beta x}$ by $\cosh \beta x - \sinh \beta x$.

Section 3.6.2, Page 127

1. $y_p(x) = e^x$
2. $y_p(x) = -\frac{2}{3}xe^{-x}$
3. $y_p(x) = \frac{3}{2}x^2e^{-x}$
4. $y_p(x) = -(\cos x) \ln (\tan x + \sec x)$
5. $y_p(x) = (\sin 3x) \ln (\tan 3x + \sec 3x) - 1$
6. $y_p(x) = -e^{-2x} \ln x$
7. $y_p(x) = \frac{3}{4}(\sin 2x) \ln \sin 2x - \frac{3}{2}x \cos 2x$
8. $y = c_1x^{-1/2} \cos x + c_2x^{-1/2} \sin x - \frac{3}{2}x^{1/2} \cos x$
9. $y = c_1e^x + c_2x - \frac{1}{2}e^{-x}(2x - 1)$

10. $y_p(x) = \displaystyle\int^x [e^{3(x-t)} - e^{2(x-t)}]g(t)\, dt$

11. $y_p(x) = x^{-1/2} \displaystyle\int^x \dfrac{g(t) \sin (x - t)}{t^{3/2}}\, dt$

14. (a) $y = c_1x + c_2x^2 + 4x^2 \ln x$ \qquad (b) $y = c_1x^{-1} + c_2x^{-5} + \frac{1}{12}x$

Section 3.7.1, Page 136

1. $u = \frac{1}{4} \cos 8t$ ft, $\frac{1}{4}$ ft, 8 rad/sec, $\dfrac{\pi}{4}$ sec; t in sec

2. $u = \frac{5}{7} \sin 14t$ cm; t in sec

3. $u = \dfrac{1}{4\sqrt{2}} \sin 8\sqrt{2}\, t - \dfrac{1}{12} \cos 8\sqrt{2}\, t$ ft, $\dfrac{\sqrt{22}}{24}$ ft, $8\sqrt{2}$ rad/sec, $\dfrac{\pi\sqrt{2}}{8}$ sec; t in sec

5. Approximately 1% \qquad\qquad 6. $c = \sqrt{10}/2$ lb sec/ft

7. $r = \sqrt{A^2 + B^2}$, $r \cos \theta = A$, $r \sin \theta = -B$; \quad $R = r$; \quad $\delta = \theta + \dfrac{(4n + 1)\pi}{2}$

$n = 0, 1, 2, \ldots$

8. $\omega_0 = \sqrt{k/m}$; \qquad (a) $u = u_0 \cos \omega_0 t$ \qquad (b) $u = \dfrac{\dot{u}_0}{\omega_0} \cos \left(\omega_0 t - \dfrac{\pi}{2}\right)$

(c) $u = \sqrt{u_0^2 + \left(\dfrac{\dot{u}_0}{\omega_0}\right)^2} \cos (\omega_0 t - \delta)$, \qquad $\delta = \tan^{-1} \dfrac{\dot{u}_0/\omega_0}{u_0}$

9. $2\pi\sqrt{l/g}$

10. $u = e^{-10t}\left(2 \cos 4\sqrt{6}\, t + \dfrac{5}{\sqrt{6}} \sin 4 \sqrt{6}\, t\right)$ cm; t in sec

11. $u = \dfrac{1}{8\sqrt{31}} e^{-2t} \sin 2\sqrt{31}\, t$ ft; t in sec

12. $c > 8$ lb sec/ft, overdamped; $c = 8$ lb sec/ft, critically damped;
    $c < 8$ lb sec/ft, underdamped

13. $\mu = \dfrac{\sqrt{4km - c^2}}{2m}$

(a) $u = u_0 \sqrt{1 + \left(\dfrac{c}{2m\mu}\right)^2}\, e^{-ct/2m} \cos(\mu t - \delta)$, $\delta = \tan^{-1}\dfrac{c}{2m\mu}$

(b) $u = \dfrac{\dot{u}_0}{\mu} e^{-ct/2m} \cos\left(\mu t - \dfrac{\pi}{2}\right)$

(c) $u = \sqrt{u_0^2 + \left(\dfrac{\dot{u}_0}{\mu} + \dfrac{cu_0}{2m\mu}\right)^2}\, e^{-ct/2m} \cos(\mu t - \delta)$,

$\delta = \tan^{-1} \dfrac{\dot{u}_0/\mu + cu_0/2\mu m}{u_0}$

15. $\dot{u}_0 < \dfrac{-cu_0}{2m}$

16. (a) $2\pi/\sqrt{31}$ (b) $c = 5$ lb sec/ft

Section 3.7.2, Page 141

1. $-2 \sin 8t \sin t$ 2. $2 \sin \dfrac{t}{2} \cos \dfrac{13t}{2}$

3. $u = \frac{151}{1482} \cos 16t + \frac{16}{247} \cos 3t$ ft, t in sec; $\omega = 16$ rad/sec
4. $u = \frac{64}{45}(\cos 7t - \cos 8t) = \frac{128}{45} \sin \frac{1}{2}t \sin \frac{15}{2}t$ ft; t in sec
5. $\omega_0 = \sqrt{k/m}$

(a) $u = \left[u_0 - \dfrac{F}{m(\omega_0^2 - \omega^2)}\right] \cos \omega_0 t + \dfrac{F}{m(\omega_0^2 - \omega^2)} \cos \omega t$

(b) $u = \dfrac{\dot{u}_0}{\omega_0} \sin \omega_0 t + \dfrac{F_0}{m(\omega_0^2 - \omega^2)}(\cos \omega t - \cos \omega_0 t)$

(c) $u = \left[u_0 - \dfrac{F}{m(\omega_0^2 - \omega^2)}\right] \cos \omega_0 t + \dfrac{\dot{u}_0}{\omega_0} \sin \omega_0 t + \dfrac{F}{m(\omega_0^2 - \omega^2)} \cos \omega t$

7. $u = \begin{cases} 0, & t \le 0 \\ (F_0/m)(t - \sin t), & 0 < t \le \pi \\ (F_0/m)[(2\pi - t) - 3 \sin t], & \pi < t \le 2\pi \\ -(4F_0/m) \sin t, & 2\pi < t \end{cases}$

8. $u = \frac{8}{901}(30 \cos 2t + \sin 2t)$ ft, t in sec; $m = 4$ slugs

9. $u = e^{-ct/2m}(c_1 \cos \mu t + c_2 \sin \mu t) + \dfrac{F_0}{\Delta} [m(\omega_0{}^2 - \omega^2) \sin \omega t - c\omega \cos \omega t]$

$\mu = \dfrac{\sqrt{4km - c^2}}{2m}$, $\omega_0{}^2 = \dfrac{k}{m}$, $\Delta = m^2(\omega_0{}^2 - \omega^2)^2 + c^2\omega^2$

(a) $c_1 = u_0 + \dfrac{c\omega F_0}{\Delta}$, $c_2 = \dfrac{cu_0}{2m\mu} + \dfrac{F_0\omega}{\mu\Delta}\left[\dfrac{c^2}{2m} - m(\omega_0{}^2 - \omega^2)\right]$

(b) $c_1 = \dfrac{c\omega F_0}{\Delta}$, $c_2 = \dfrac{\dot{u}_0}{\mu} + \dfrac{F_0\omega}{\mu\Delta}\left[\dfrac{c^2}{2m} - m(\omega_0{}^2 - \omega^2)\right]$

(c) $c_1 = u_0 + \dfrac{c\omega F_0}{\Delta}$, $c_2 = \dfrac{\dot{u}_0}{\mu} + \dfrac{cu_0}{2m\mu} + \dfrac{F_0\omega}{\mu\Delta}\left[\dfrac{c^2}{2m} - m(\omega_0{}^2 - \omega^2)\right]$

Section 3.8, Page 146

4. (a) $Q = 10^{-6}(2e^{-500t} - e^{-1000t})$ coulombs; t in sec
   (b) $Q = 10^{-6}(1 - 500t)e^{-500t}$ coulombs; t in sec
   (c) $Q = 10^{-6}e^{-100t}(\cos 200t + \frac{1}{2}\sin 200t)$ coulombs; t in sec
5. $R = 10^3$ ohms
6. $Q = \psi(t) = 10^{-6}(e^{-4000t} - 4e^{-1000t} + 3)$ coulombs; t in sec
   $\psi(0.001) \cong 1.52 \times 10^{-6}$; $\psi(0.01) \cong 3 \times 10^{-6}$; $Q \to 3 \times 10^{-6}$ as $t \to \infty$
7. $I \cong 0.11 \cos(120\pi t + \delta)$ amperes, $\delta = \tan^{-1}\dfrac{386}{360\pi}$; t in sec
8. $\omega = 1/\sqrt{LC}$
9. (c) $I = \dfrac{E_0}{\sqrt{R^2 + (\omega L - 1/\omega C)^2}} \sin(\omega t - \delta)$, $\delta = \tan^{-1}\dfrac{\omega L - 1/\omega C}{R}$

CHAPTER FOUR

Section 4.1, Page 151

1. (a) $\rho = 1$ (b) $\rho = 2$ (c) $\rho = \infty$
   (d) $\rho = \frac{1}{2}$ (e) $\rho = \frac{1}{2}$ (f) $\rho = 1$

2. (a) $\displaystyle\sum_{n=0}^{\infty} \dfrac{(-1)^n x^{2n+1}}{(2n+1)!}$, $\rho = \infty$ (b) $\displaystyle\sum_{n=0}^{\infty} \dfrac{x^n}{n!}$, $\rho = \infty$
   (c) $1 + (x - 1)$, $\rho = \infty$ (d) $1 - 2(x + 1) + (x + 1)^2$, $\rho = \infty$
   (e) $\displaystyle\sum_{n=1}^{\infty} (-1)^{n+1}\dfrac{(x - 1)^n}{n}$, $\rho = 1$ (f) $\displaystyle\sum_{n=0}^{\infty} (-1)^n x^n$, $\rho = 1$
   (g) $\displaystyle\sum_{n=0}^{\infty} x^n$, $\rho = 1$ (h) $\displaystyle\sum_{n=0}^{\infty} (-1)^{n+1}(x - 2)^n$, $\rho = 1$

3. $y' = 1 + 2^2 x + 3^2 x^2 + 4^2 x^3 + \cdots + (n + 1)^2 x^n + \cdots$
   $y'' = 2^2 + 3^2 \cdot 2x + 4^2 \cdot 3x^2 + 5^2 \cdot 4x^3 + \cdots + (n + 2)^2(n + 1)x^n + \cdots$
4. $y' = a_1 + 2a_2 x + 3a_3 x^2 + 4a_4 x^3 + \cdots + (n + 1)a_{n+1} x^n + \cdots$

   $\quad = \displaystyle\sum_{n=1}^{\infty} na_n x^{n-1} = \sum_{n=0}^{\infty} (n + 1)a_{n+1} x^n$

   $y'' = 2a_2 + 6a_3 x + 12a_4 x^2 + 20a_5 x^3 + \cdots + (n + 2)(n + 1)a_{n+2} x^n + \cdots$

   $\quad = \displaystyle\sum_{n=2}^{\infty} n(n - 1)a_n x^{n-2} = \sum_{n=0}^{\infty} (n + 2)(n + 1)a_{n+2} x^n$

Section 4.2, Page 158

1. (a) $a_{n+2} = \dfrac{a_n}{(n+2)(n+1)}$

$$y_1(x) = 1 + \frac{x^2}{2!} + \frac{x^4}{4!} + \frac{x^6}{6!} + \cdots = \sum_{n=0}^{\infty} \frac{x^{2n}}{(2n)!} = \cosh x$$

$$y_2(x) = x + \frac{x^3}{3!} + \frac{x^5}{5!} + \frac{x^7}{7!} + \cdots = \sum_{n=0}^{\infty} \frac{x^{2n+1}}{(2n+1)!} = \sinh x$$

(b) $a_{n+2} = \dfrac{a_n}{n+2}$

$$y_1(x) = 1 + \frac{x^2}{2} + \frac{x^4}{2 \cdot 4} + \frac{x^6}{2 \cdot 4 \cdot 6} + \cdots = \sum_{n=0}^{\infty} \frac{x^{2n}}{2^n n!}$$

$$y_2(x) = x + \frac{x^3}{3} + \frac{x^5}{3 \cdot 5} + \frac{x^7}{3 \cdot 5 \cdot 7} + \cdots = \sum_{n=0}^{\infty} \frac{2^n n! \, x^{2n+1}}{(2n+1)!}$$

(c) $(n+2)a_{n+2} - a_{n+1} - a_n = 0$

$$y_1(x) = 1 + \tfrac{1}{2}(x-1)^2 + \tfrac{1}{6}(x-1)^3 + \tfrac{1}{6}(x-1)^4 + \cdots$$

$$y_2(x) = (x-1) + \tfrac{1}{2}(x-1)^2 + \tfrac{1}{2}(x-1)^3 + \tfrac{1}{4}(x-1)^4 + \cdots$$

(d) $a_{n+4} = -\dfrac{k^2 a_n}{(n+4)(n+3)}; \qquad a_2 = a_3 = 0$

$$y_1(x) = 1 - \frac{k^2 x^4}{3 \cdot 4} + \frac{k^4 x^8}{3 \cdot 4 \cdot 7 \cdot 8} - \frac{k^6 x^{12}}{3 \cdot 4 \cdot 7 \cdot 8 \cdot 11 \cdot 12} + \cdots$$

$$= 1 + \sum_{m=0}^{\infty} \frac{(-1)^{m+1}(k^2 x^4)^{m+1}}{3 \cdot 4 \cdot 7 \cdot 8 \cdots (4m+3)(4m+4)}$$

$$y_2(x) = x - \frac{k^2 x^5}{4 \cdot 5} + \frac{k^4 x^9}{4 \cdot 5 \cdot 8 \cdot 9} - \frac{k^6 x^{13}}{4 \cdot 5 \cdot 8 \cdot 9 \cdot 12 \cdot 13} + \cdots$$

$$= x \left[1 + \sum_{m=0}^{\infty} \frac{(-1)^{m+1}(k^2 x^4)^{m+1}}{4 \cdot 5 \cdot 8 \cdot 9 \cdots (4m+4)(4m+5)} \right]$$

Hint: Let $n = 4m$ in the recurrence relation, $m = 1, 2, 3, \ldots$.

(e) $(n+2)(n+1)a_{n+2} - n(n+1)a_{n+1} + a_n = 0, \qquad n \geq 1; \qquad a_2 = -\tfrac{1}{2}a_0$

$$y_1(x) = 1 - \tfrac{1}{2}x^2 - \tfrac{1}{6}x^3 - \tfrac{1}{24}x^4 + \cdots$$

$$y_2(x) = x - \tfrac{1}{6}x^3 - \tfrac{1}{12}x^4 + \cdots$$

(f) $a_{n+2} = -\dfrac{(n^2 - 2n + 4)a_n}{2(n+1)(n+2)}, \qquad n \geq 2; \qquad a_2 = -a_0, \qquad a_3 = -\tfrac{1}{4}a_1$

$$y_1(x) = 1 - x^2 + \tfrac{1}{6}x^4 - \tfrac{1}{30}x^6 + \cdots$$

$$y_2(x) = x - \tfrac{1}{4}x^3 + \tfrac{7}{160}x^5 - \tfrac{19}{1920}x^7 + \cdots$$

2. $y(x) = x + \dfrac{x^3}{3} + \dfrac{x^5}{3 \cdot 5} + \dfrac{x^7}{3 \cdot 5 \cdot 7} + \cdots = \displaystyle\sum_{n=0}^{\infty} \frac{2^n n! \, x^{2n+1}}{(2n+1)!}$

3. $y_1(x) = 1 - \tfrac{1}{3}(x-1)^3 - \tfrac{1}{12}(x-1)^4 + \tfrac{1}{18}(x-1)^6 + \cdots$

$y_2(x) = (x-1) - \tfrac{1}{4}(x-1)^4 - \tfrac{1}{20}(x-1)^5 - \tfrac{1}{28}(x-1)^7 + \cdots$

Section 4.2.1, Page 164

1. (a) $\phi''(0) = -1$, $\phi'''(0) = 0$, $\phi^{iv}(0) = 3$
   (b) $\phi''(0) = 0$, $\phi'''(0) = -2$, $\phi^{iv}(0) = 0$
   (c) $\phi''(1) = 0$, $\phi'''(1) = -6$, $\phi^{iv}(1) = 42$
   (d) $\phi''(0) = 0$, $\phi'''(0) = -a_0$, $\phi^{iv}(0) = -4a_1$

2. (a) $\rho = \infty$, $\rho = \infty$ (b) $\rho = 1$, $\rho = 3$, $\rho = 1$
   (c) $\rho = 1$, $\rho = \sqrt{3}$ (d) $\rho = 1$

3. (a) $\rho = \infty$ (b) $\rho = \infty$ (c) $\rho = \infty$
   (d) $\rho = \infty$ (e) $\rho = 1$ (f) $\rho = \sqrt{2}$

4. (a) $y_1(x) = 1 - \dfrac{\alpha^2}{2!} x^2 - \dfrac{(2^2 - \alpha^2)\alpha^2}{4!} x^4 - \dfrac{(4^2 - \alpha^2)(2^2 - \alpha^2)\alpha^2}{6!} x^6 - \cdots$

$$- \frac{[(2m)^2 - \alpha^2] \cdots (2^2 - \alpha^2)\alpha^2}{(2m)!} x^{2m} - \cdots$$

$$y_2(x) = x + \frac{1 - \alpha^2}{3!} x^3 + \frac{(3^2 - \alpha^2)(1 - \alpha^2)}{5!} x^5 + \cdots$$

$$+ \frac{[(2m + 1)^2 - \alpha^2] \cdots (1 - \alpha^2)}{(2m + 1)!} x^{2m+1} + \cdots$$

(b) $y_1(x)$ or $y_2(x)$ terminates with x^n as $\alpha = n$ is even or odd.

(c) $n = 0, y = 1$; $n = 1, y = x$; $n = 2, y = 1 - 2x^2$;
   $n = 3, y = x - \frac{4}{3}x^3$

5. $y_1(x) = 1 - \dfrac{x^3}{3!} + \dfrac{x^5}{5!} + \dfrac{x^6}{2 \cdot 3 \cdot 5 \cdot 6} + \cdots$

$$y_2(x) = x - \frac{x^4}{3 \cdot 4} + \frac{x^6}{2 \cdot 3 \cdot 5 \cdot 6} + \cdots$$

6. $y_1(x) = 1 - \frac{1}{6}x^3 - \frac{1}{12}x^4 - \frac{1}{40}x^5 + \cdots$, $y_2(x) = x - \frac{1}{12}x^4 + \frac{1}{20}x^5 + \cdots$
   $\rho = \infty$

7. Cannot specify arbitrary initial conditions at $x = 0$; hence $x = 0$ must be a singular point.

8. $f'(0) = \lim\limits_{h \to 0} \dfrac{e^{-1/h^2} - 0}{h} = 0$, $f''(0) = \lim\limits_{h \to 0} \dfrac{(2/h^3)e^{-1/h^2} - 0}{h} = 0$,   etc.

9. (a) $y = 1 + x + \dfrac{x^2}{2!} + \cdots + \dfrac{x^n}{n!} + \cdots = e^x$

   (b) $y = 1 + \dfrac{x^2}{2} + \dfrac{x^4}{2 \cdot 4} + \dfrac{x^6}{2 \cdot 4 \cdot 6} + \cdots + \dfrac{x^{2n}}{2^n \cdot n!} + \cdots$

   (c) $y = 1 + x + \frac{1}{2}x^2 + \frac{1}{2}x^3 + \cdots$

   (d) $y = 1 + x + x^2 + \cdots + x^n + \cdots = \dfrac{1}{1 - x}$

(e) $y = a_0 \left(1 + x + \dfrac{x^2}{2!} + \cdots + \dfrac{x^n}{n!} + \cdots \right)$

$$+ 2! \left(\dfrac{x^3}{3!} + \dfrac{x^4}{4!} + \cdots + \dfrac{x^n}{n!} + \cdots \right)$$

$$= a_0 e^x + 2 \left(e^x - 1 - x - \dfrac{x^2}{2} \right) = ce^x - 2 - 2x - x^2$$

(f) $y = a_0 \left(1 - \dfrac{x^2}{2} + \dfrac{x^4}{2^2 2!} - \dfrac{x^6}{2^3 3!} + \cdots + \dfrac{(-1)^n x^{2n}}{2^n n!} + \cdots \right)$

$$+ \left(x + \dfrac{x^2}{2} - \dfrac{x^3}{3} + \dfrac{x^4}{2 \cdot 4} + \dfrac{x^5}{3 \cdot 5} + \cdots \right)$$

$$= a_0 e^{-x^2/2} + \left(x + \dfrac{x^2}{2} - \dfrac{x^3}{3} + \dfrac{x^4}{2 \cdot 4} + \dfrac{x^5}{3 \cdot 5} + \cdots \right)$$

Section 4.3, Page 170

$x = -1$	$x = 0$	$x = 1$
1. ordinary	regular singular	ordinary
2. regular singular	regular singular	regular singular
3. regular singular	irregular singular	regular singular
4. regular singular	irregular singular	regular singular
5. irregular singular	ordinary	regular singular
6. ordinary	ordinary	irregular singular
7. ordinary	ordinary	ordinary
8. regular singular	regular singular	irregular singular

11. (a) regular singular point   (b) irregular singular point
    (c) irregular singular point   (d) irregular singular point

Section 4.4, Page 175

1. (a) $y = c_1 x^{-1} + c_2 x^{-2}$ (b) $y = c_1 |x|^{-\frac{1}{2}} + c_2 |x|^{-\frac{3}{2}}$
(c) $y = c_1 x^2 + c_2 x^2 \ln |x|$
(d) $y = c_1 x^{-1} \cos (2 \ln |x|) + c_2 x^{-1} \sin (2 \ln |x|)$
(e) $y = c_1 x + c_2 x \ln |x|$ (f) $y = c_1 (x - 1)^{-3} + c_2 (x - 1)^{-4}$
(g) $y = c_1 |x|^{(-5 + \sqrt{29})/2} + c_2 |x|^{(-5 - \sqrt{29})/2}$

(h) $y = c_1 |x|^{\frac{3}{2}} \cos \left(\dfrac{\sqrt{3}}{2} \ln |x| \right) + c_2 |x|^{\frac{3}{2}} \sin \left(\dfrac{\sqrt{3}}{2} \ln |x| \right)$

(i) $y = c_1 x^3 + c_2 x^3 \ln |x|$
(j) $y = c_1 (x - 2)^{-2} \cos (2 \ln |x - 2|) + c_2 (x - 2)^{-2} \sin (2 \ln |x - 2|)$

(k) $y = c_1 |x|^{-\frac{1}{2}} \cos \left(\dfrac{\sqrt{15}}{2} \ln |x| \right) + c_2 |x|^{-\frac{1}{2}} \sin \left(\dfrac{\sqrt{15}}{2} \ln |x| \right)$

(l) $y = c_1 x + c_2 x^4$
3. $\alpha < 1$
5. (a) $y = c_1 x^{-1} + c_2 x^2$ (b) $y = c_1 x^2 + c_2 x^2 \ln x + \frac{1}{4} \ln x + \frac{1}{4}$
(c) $y = c_1 x^{-1} + c_2 x^{-5} + \frac{1}{12} x$ (d) $y = c_1 x + c_2 x^2 + x^2 \ln x + \ln x + \frac{3}{2}$
(e) $y = c_1 \cos (2 \ln x) + c_2 \sin (2 \ln x) + \frac{1}{3} \sin (\ln x)$
(f) $y = c_1 x^{-\frac{3}{2}} \cos (\frac{3}{2} \ln x) + c_2 x^{-\frac{3}{2}} \sin (\frac{3}{2} \ln x)$

7. $x > 0$: $c_1 = k_1$, $c_2 = k_2$
    $x < 0$: $c_1(-1)^{r_1} = k_1$, $c_2 = k_2$

8. (a) $y = c_1 x^{-\frac{1}{2}+i(1+\sqrt{3}/2)} + c_2 x^{-\frac{1}{2}+i(1-\sqrt{3}/2)}$

$$= c_1 x^{-\frac{1}{2}}\left\{\cos\left[\left(1 + \frac{\sqrt{3}}{2}\right)\ln x\right] + i\sin\left[\left(1 + \frac{\sqrt{3}}{2}\right)\ln x\right]\right\}$$

$$+ c_2 x^{-\frac{1}{2}}\left\{\cos\left[\left(1 - \frac{\sqrt{3}}{2}\right)\ln x\right] + i\sin\left[\left(1 - \frac{\sqrt{3}}{2}\right)\ln x\right]\right\}$$

(b) $y = c_1 x^{2i} + c_2 x^{-i}$
    $= c_1[\cos(2\ln x) + i\sin(2\ln x)] + c_2[\cos(\ln x) - i\sin(\ln x)]$

(c) $y = c_1 x^{1+i} + c_2 x^{-1-i}$
    $= c_1 x[\cos(\ln x) + i\sin(\ln x)] + c_2 x^{-1}[\cos(\ln x) - i\sin(\ln x)]$

Section 4.5, Page 182

1. (a) $r(2r - 1) = 0$; $a_n = -\dfrac{a_{n-2}}{(n+r)[2(n+r)-1]}$; $r_1 = \frac{1}{2}, r_2 = 0$

$$y_1(x) = x^{\frac{1}{2}}\left[1 - \frac{x^2}{2\cdot 5} + \frac{x^4}{2\cdot 4\cdot 5\cdot 9} - \frac{x^6}{2\cdot 4\cdot 6\cdot 5\cdot 9\cdot 13} + \cdots\right.$$
$$\left. + \frac{(-1)^n x^{2n}}{2^n n!\, 5\cdot 9\cdot 13\cdots(4n+1)} + \cdots\right]$$

$$y_2(x) = 1 - \frac{x^2}{2\cdot 3} + \frac{x^4}{2\cdot 4\cdot 3\cdot 7} - \frac{x^6}{2\cdot 4\cdot 6\cdot 3\cdot 7\cdot 11} + \cdots$$
$$+ \frac{(-1)^n x^{2n}}{2^n n!\, 3\cdot 7\cdot 11\cdots(4n-1)} + \cdots$$

(b) $r^2 - \frac{1}{9} = 0$; $a_n = -\dfrac{a_{n-2}}{[(n+r)^2 - \frac{1}{9}]}$; $r_1 = \frac{1}{3}, r_2 = -\frac{1}{3}$

$$y_1(x) = x^{\frac{1}{3}}\left[1 - \frac{1}{1!\,(1+\frac{1}{3})}\left(\frac{x}{2}\right)^2 + \frac{1}{2!\,(1+\frac{1}{3})(2+\frac{1}{3})}\left(\frac{x}{2}\right)^4 + \cdots\right.$$
$$\left. + \frac{(-1)^m}{m!\,(1+\frac{1}{3})(2+\frac{1}{3})\cdots(m+\frac{1}{3})}\left(\frac{x}{2}\right)^{2m} + \cdots\right]$$

$$y_2(x) = x^{-\frac{1}{3}}\left[1 - \frac{1}{1!\,(1-\frac{1}{3})}\left(\frac{x}{2}\right)^2 + \frac{1}{2!\,(1-\frac{1}{3})(2-\frac{1}{3})}\left(\frac{x}{2}\right)^4 + \cdots\right.$$
$$\left. + \frac{(-1)^m}{m!\,(1-\frac{1}{3})(2-\frac{1}{3})\cdots(m-\frac{1}{3})}\left(\frac{x}{2}\right)^{2m} + \cdots\right]$$

Hint: Let $n = 2m$ in the recurrence relation, $m = 1, 2, 3, \ldots$.

(c) $r(r - 1) = 0$; $a_n = -\dfrac{a_{n-1}}{(n+r)(n+r-1)}$; $r_1 = 1, r_2 = 0$

$$y_1(x) = x\left[1 - \frac{x}{1!\,2!} + \frac{x^2}{2!\,3!} + \cdots + \frac{(-1)^n}{n!\,(n+1)!}x^n + \cdots\right]$$

(d) $r^2 = 0$; $a_n = \dfrac{a_{n-1}}{(n+r)^2}$; $r_1 = r_2 = 0$

$$y_1(x) = 1 + \frac{x}{(1!)^2} + \frac{x^2}{(2!)^2} + \cdots + \frac{x^n}{(n!)^2} + \cdots$$

(e) $r(3r - 1) = 0$; $a_n = -\dfrac{a_{n-2}}{(n+r)[3(n+r) - 1]}$; $r_1 = \frac{1}{3}, r_2 = 0$

$$y_1(x) = x^{1/3}\left[1 - \frac{1}{1!\,7}\left(\frac{x^2}{2}\right) + \frac{1}{2!\,7\cdot 13}\left(\frac{x^2}{2}\right)^2 + \cdots\right.$$

$$\left. + \frac{(-1)^m}{m!\,7\cdot 13\cdots(6m+1)}\left(\frac{x^2}{2}\right)^m + \cdots\right]$$

$$y_2(x) = 1 - \frac{1}{1!\,5}\left(\frac{x^2}{2}\right) + \frac{1}{2!\,5\cdot 11}\left(\frac{x^2}{2}\right)^2 + \cdots$$

$$+ \frac{(-1)^m}{m!\,5\cdot 11\cdots(6m-1)}\left(\frac{x^2}{2}\right)^m + \cdots$$

Hint: Let $n = 2m$ in the recurrence relation, $m = 1, 2, 3, \ldots$.

(f) $r^2 - 2 = 0$; $a_n = -\dfrac{a_{n-1}}{[(n+r)^2 - 2]}$; $r_1 = \sqrt{2}, r_2 = -\sqrt{2}$

$$y_1(x) = x^{\sqrt{2}}\left[1 - \frac{x}{1(1 + 2\sqrt{2})} + \frac{x^2}{2!\,(1 + 2\sqrt{2})(2 + 2\sqrt{2})} + \cdots\right.$$

$$\left. + \frac{(-1)^n}{n!\,(1 + 2\sqrt{2})(2 + 2\sqrt{2})\cdots(n + 2\sqrt{2})}x^n + \cdots\right]$$

$$y_2(x) = x^{-\sqrt{2}}\left[1 - \frac{x}{1(1 - 2\sqrt{2})} + \frac{x^2}{2!\,(1 - 2\sqrt{2})(2 - 2\sqrt{2})} + \cdots\right.$$

$$\left. + \frac{(-1)^n}{n!\,(1 - 2\sqrt{2})(2 - 2\sqrt{2})\cdots(n - 2\sqrt{2})}x^n + \cdots\right]$$

2. $r^2 = 0$; $r_1 = 0, r_2 = 0$

$$y_1(x) = 1 + \frac{\alpha(\alpha + 1)}{2\cdot 1^2}(x - 1) - \frac{\alpha(\alpha + 1)[1\cdot 2 - \alpha(\alpha + 1)]}{(2\cdot 1^2)(2\cdot 2^2)}(x - 1)^2 + \cdots$$

$$+ (-1)^{n+1}\frac{\alpha(\alpha + 1)[1\cdot 2 - \alpha(\alpha + 1)]\cdots[n(n - 1) - \alpha(\alpha + 1)]}{2^n(n!)^2}(x - 1)^n + \cdots$$

3. $r^2 = 0$; $r_1 = 0, r_2 = 0$; $a_n = \dfrac{(n - 1 - \lambda)a_{n-1}}{n^2}$

$$y_1(x) = 1 + \frac{-\lambda}{(1!)^2}x + \frac{(-\lambda)(1 - \lambda)}{2!}x^2 + \cdots$$

$$+ \frac{(-\lambda)(1 - \lambda)\cdots(n - 1 - \lambda)}{(n!)^2}x^n + \cdots$$

For $\lambda = n$, the coefficients of all terms past x^n are zero.

6. (b) $[(n - 1)^2 - 1]b_n = -b_{n-2}$, and it is impossible to determine b_2.

Section 4.5.1, Page 187

1. (a) $x = 0$; $r(r-1) = 0$; $r_1 = 1, r_2 = 0$
   (b) $x = 0$; $r^2 - 3r + 2 = 0$; $r_1 = 2, r_2 = 1$
   (c) $x = 0$; $r(r-1) = 0$; $r_1 = 1, r_2 = 0$
       $x = 1$; $r(r+5) = 0$; $r_1 = 0, r_2 = -5$
   (d) none
   (e) $x = 0$; $r^2 + 2r - 2 = 0$; $r_1 = -1 + \sqrt{3}, r_2 = -1 - \sqrt{3}$
   (f) $x = 0$; $r(r - \frac{3}{4}) = 0$; $r_1 = \frac{3}{4}, r_2 = 0$
       $x = -2$; $r(r - \frac{5}{4}) = 0$; $r_1 = \frac{5}{4}, r_2 = 0$
   (g) $x = 0$; $r^2 + 1 = 0$; $r_1 = i, r_2 = -i$
   (h) $x = -1$; $r^2 - r + 3 = 0$; $r_1 = \frac{3}{2}, r_2 = -\frac{1}{2}$

2. $y_1(x) = x - \dfrac{x^3}{24} - \dfrac{25}{456} x^5 + \cdots$

3. $r_1 = \frac{1}{2}, r_2 = 0$
   $$y_1(x) = (x-1)^{1/2}[1 - \tfrac{7}{12}(x-1) + \tfrac{43}{480}(x-1)^2 + \cdots], \qquad \rho = 1$$

4. (c) *Hint:* $(n-1)(n-2) + (1 + \alpha + \beta)(n-1) + \alpha\beta$
   $$= (n - 1 + \alpha)(n - 1 + \beta)$$
   (d) *Hint:* $(n-\gamma)(n - 1 - \gamma) + (1 + \alpha + \beta)(n - \gamma) + \alpha\beta$
   $$= (n - \gamma + \alpha)(n - \gamma + \beta)$$

Section 4.7, Page 199

1. (a) $y_1(x) = \displaystyle\sum_{n=0}^{\infty} \frac{(-1)^n x^n}{n!\,(n+1)!}$,

   $$y_2(x) = -y_1(x)\ln x + \frac{1}{x}\left[1 + \sum_{n=1}^{\infty} \frac{H_n + H_{n-1}}{n!\,(n-1)!}(-1)^n x^n\right]$$

   (b) $y_1(x) = \displaystyle\sum_{n=0}^{\infty} \frac{(-1)^n x^n}{(n!)^2}$, $y_2(x) = y_1(x)\ln x - \dfrac{2}{x}\displaystyle\sum_{n=1}^{\infty} \frac{(-1)^n H_n}{(n!)^2} x^n$

   (c) $y_1(x) = \displaystyle\sum_{n=0}^{\infty} \frac{(-1)^n 2^n}{(n!)^2} x^n$, $y_2(x) = y_1(x)\ln x - 2\displaystyle\sum_{n=1}^{\infty} \frac{(-1)^n 2^n H_n}{(n!)^2} x^n$

   (d) $y_1(x) = \dfrac{1}{x}\displaystyle\sum_{n=0}^{\infty} \frac{(-1)^n 2^n}{n!\,(n+1)!} x^n$,

   $$y_2(x) = -2y_1(x)\ln x + \frac{1}{x^2}\left[1 + \sum_{n=1}^{\infty} \frac{H_n + H_{n-1}}{n!\,(n-1)!}(-1)^n 2^n x^n\right]$$

2. $y_1(x) = x^{3/2}\left[1 + \displaystyle\sum_{m=1}^{\infty} \frac{(-1)^m}{m!\,(1 + \frac{3}{2})(2 + \frac{3}{2})\cdots(m + \frac{3}{2})}\left(\frac{x}{2}\right)^{2m}\right]$

   $y_2(x) = x^{-3/2}\left[1 + \displaystyle\sum_{m=1}^{\infty} \frac{(-1)^m}{m!\,(1 - \frac{3}{2})(2 - \frac{3}{2})\cdots(m - \frac{3}{2})}\left(\frac{x}{2}\right)^{2m}\right]$

   Hint: Let $n = 2m$ in the recurrence relation, $m = 1, 2, 3, \ldots$. For $r = -\frac{3}{2}$, $a_1 = 0$ and a_3 is arbitrary.

CHAPTER FIVE

Section 5.1, Page 203

1. $\phi^{(n)}(0) = -p_1(0)y_0^{(n-1)} - \cdots - p_n(0)y_0$
   $\phi^{(n+1)}(0) = p_1(0)[p_1(0)y_0^{(n-1)} + \cdots + p_n(0)y_0] - p_1'(0)y_0^{(n-1)} - \cdots$
   $\qquad - p_n(0)y_0' - p_n'(0)y_0$

2. (a) $y''' = -\cos x$ (b) $y''' + y' = 0$
   (c) $y''' - 2y'' - y' + 2y = 0$ (d) $x^3y''' - 3x^2y'' + 6xy' - 6y = 0$
   (e) $y''' + y' = 1$ (f) $y^{iv} - y'' = 0$

3. (a) $-\infty < x < \infty$ (b) $x > 0$ or $x < 0$
   (c) $x < 1$, or $0 < x < 1$, or $x < 0$ (d) $x > 0$

Section 5.2, Page 206

4. (a) 1   (b) 1   (c) $-6e^{-2x}$
   (d) e^{-2x} (e) $6x$

5. $\sin^2 x = \frac{1}{10}(5) - \frac{1}{2}\cos 2x$

6. (a) $a_0[n(n-1)(n-2)\cdots 1] + a_1[n(n-1)\cdots 2]x + \cdots + a_n x^n$
   (b) $(a_0 r^n + a_1 r^{n-1} + \cdots + a_n)e^{rx}$
   (c) $e^x, e^{-x}, e^{2x}, e^{-2x}$;   yes, $W(e^x, e^{-x}, e^{2x}, e^{-2x}) \neq 0$, $-\infty < x < \infty$

8. (a) $y = c_1 x + c_2 x^2 + c_3 x^3$
   (b) $y = c_1 x^2 + c_2 x^3 + c_3(x+1)$

Section 5.3, Page 212

1. (a) $\sqrt{2}e^{i[(\pi/4)+2m\pi]}$ (b) $2e^{i[(2\pi/3)+2m\pi]}$
   (c) $e^{i(\pi+2m\pi)}$ (d) $e^{i[(3\pi/2)+2m\pi]}$
   (e) $2e^{i[(11\pi/6)+2m\pi]}$ (f) $\sqrt{2}e^{i[(5\pi/4)+2m\pi]}$

2. (a) $1, \frac{1}{2}(-1 + i\sqrt{3}), \frac{1}{2}(-1 - i\sqrt{3})$ (b) $2^{1/4}e^{-\pi i/8}, 2^{1/4}e^{7\pi i/8}$
   (c) $1, i, -1, -i$ (d) $(\sqrt{3} + i)/\sqrt{2}, -(\sqrt{3} + i)/\sqrt{2}$

3. $y = c_1 e^x + c_2 x e^x + c_3 e^{-x}$ 4. $y = c_1 e^x + c_2 x e^x + c_3 x^2 e^x$

5. $y = c_1 e^x + c_2 e^{2x} + c_3 e^{-x}$ 6. $y = c_1 + c_2 x + c_3 e^{2x} + c_4 x e^{2x}$

7. $y = c_1 \cos x + c_2 \sin x + e^{\sqrt{3}x/2}\left(c_3 \cos \dfrac{x}{2} + c_4 \sin \dfrac{x}{2}\right)$
   $\qquad + e^{-\sqrt{3}x/2}\left(c_5 \cos \dfrac{x}{2} + c_6 \sin \dfrac{x}{2}\right)$

8. $y = c_1 e^x + c_2 e^{-x} + c_3 e^{2x} + c_4 e^{-2x}$

9. $y = c_1 e^x + c_2 x e^x + c_3 x^2 e^x + c_4 e^{-x} + c_5 x e^{-x} + c_6 x^2 e^{-x}$

10. $y = c_1 + c_2 x + c_3 e^x + c_4 e^{-x} + c_5 \cos x + c_6 \sin x$

11. $y = c_1 + c_2 e^x + c_3 e^{2x} + c_4 \cos x + c_5 \sin x$

12. $y = c_1 + c_2 e^{2x} + e^{-x}(c_3 \cos \sqrt{3} x + c_4 \sin \sqrt{3} x)$

13. $y = e^x[(c_1 + c_2 x)\cos x + (c_3 + c_4 x)\sin x]$
    $\qquad\qquad\qquad\qquad\qquad + e^{-x}[(c_5 + c_6 x)\cos x + (c_7 + c_8 x)\sin x]$

14. $y = 2 - 2\cos x + \sin x$

15. $y = \frac{1}{2}(\cosh x - \cos x) + \frac{1}{2}(\sinh x - \sin x)$

17. (a) $y = c_1 x + c_2 x^2 + c_3 x^{-1}$ (b) $y = c_1 x + c_2 x \ln x + c_3 x (\ln x)^2$
    (c) $y = c_1 x + c_2 \cos (\ln x) + c_3 \sin (\ln x)$

20. (a) Stable   (b) Not stable   (c) Not stable
    (d) Not stable   (e) Not stable   (f) Stable

Section 5.4, Page 217

1. $y = \frac{3}{16}(1 - \cos 2x) + \frac{1}{8}x^2$
2. $y = c_1 e^x + c_2 x e^x + c_3 e^{-x} + \frac{1}{2}x e^{-x} + 3$
3. $y = c_1 e^{-x} + c_2 \cos x + c_3 \sin x + \frac{1}{2}x e^{-x} + 4(x - 1)$
4. $y = c_1 + c_2 e^x + c_3 e^{-x} \cos x$
5. $y = (x - 4) \cos x - (\frac{3}{2}x + 4) \sin x + 3x + 4$
6. $y = c_1 + c_2 x + c_3 e^{-2x} + c_4 e^{2x} - \frac{1}{3}e^x - \frac{1}{48}x^4 - \frac{1}{16}x^2$
7. $y = c_1 \cos x + c_2 \sin x + c_3 x \cos x + c_4 x \sin x + 3 + \frac{1}{25} \cos 2x$
8. $y = c_1 + c_2 e^x + c_3 e^{2x} + \frac{1}{4}(x^2 + 3x) - xe^x$
9. $y = c_1 + c_2 x + c_3 x^2 + c_4 e^{-x} + e^{x/2}\left(c_5 \cos \frac{\sqrt{3}}{2}x + c_6 \sin \frac{\sqrt{3}}{2}x\right) + \frac{x^4}{24}$
10. $y = c_1 + c_2 x + c_3 x^2 + c_4 e^{-x} + \frac{1}{20} \sin 2x + \frac{1}{40} \cos 2x$
11. $y = c_1 e^x + c_2 e^{-x} + c_3 \cos x + c_4 \sin x - 3x - \frac{1}{4}x \sin x$
12. $y_p(x) = x(A_0 x^3 + A_1 x^2 + A_2 x + A_3) + Bx^2 e^x$
13. $y_p(x) = x(A_0 x + A_1)e^{-x} + B \cos x + C \sin x$
14. $y_p(x) = Ax^2 e^x + B \cos x + C \sin x$
15. $y_p(x) = x(A_0 x^2 + A_1 x + A_2) + (B_0 x + B_1) \cos x + (C_0 x + C_1) \sin x$
16. $y_p(x) = Ax^2 + (B_0 x + B_1)e^x + x(C \cos 2x + D \sin 2x)$
17. $y_p(x) = Ae^x + (B_0 x + B_1)e^{-x} + xe^{-x}(C \cos x + D \sin x)$
18. $t_0 = a_0, \quad t_n = a_0 \alpha^n + a_1 \alpha^{n-1} + \cdots + a_{n-1}\alpha + a_n$

Section 5.5, Page 221

1. $y_p(x) = -\ln \cos x - (\sin x) \ln (\sec x + \tan x)$
2. $y_p(x) = -x^2/2$ 3. $y_p(x) = e^{4x}/30$ 4. $y_p(x) = x^4/15$
5. $y_p(x) = \frac{1}{2}\int^x [e^{x-t} - \sin (x - t) - \cos (x - t)]g(t)\, dt$
6. $y_p(x) = \frac{1}{2}\int^x [\sinh (x - t) - \sin (x - t)]g(t)\, dt$
7. $y_p(x) = \frac{1}{2}\int^x \left(\frac{x}{t^2} - 2\frac{x^2}{t^3} + \frac{x^3}{t^4}\right) g(t)\, dt$

CHAPTER SIX

Section 6.1, Page 227

1. (a) piecewise continuous   (b) neither   (c) continuous

2. (a) $\frac{1}{s^2}, \quad s > 0$ (b) $\frac{2}{s^3}, \quad s > 0$ (c) $\frac{n!}{s^{n+1}}, \quad s > 0$

3. $\frac{s}{s^2 + a^2}, \quad s > 0$

4. (a) $\dfrac{s}{s^2 - b^2}$, $s > |b|$ (b) $\dfrac{b}{s^2 - b^2}$, $s > |b|$

   (c) $\dfrac{s - a}{(s - a)^2 - b^2}$, $s - a > |b|$ (d) $\dfrac{b}{(s - a)^2 - b^2}$, $s - a > |b|$

5. (a) $\dfrac{b}{s^2 + b^2}$, $s > 0$ (b) $\dfrac{s}{s^2 + b^2}$, $s > 0$

   (c) $\dfrac{b}{(s - a)^2 + b^2}$, $s > a$ (d) $\dfrac{s - a}{(s - a)^2 + b^2}$, $s > a$

6. (a) $\dfrac{1}{(s - a)^2}$, $s > a$ (b) $\dfrac{2as}{(s^2 + a^2)^2}$, $s > 0$

   (c) $\dfrac{s^2 + a^2}{(s - a)^2(s + a)^2}$, $s > |a|$ (d) $\dfrac{n!}{(s - a)^{n+1}}$, $s > a$

   (e) $\dfrac{a\, n!\,(2s)^n}{(s^2 + a^2)^{n+1}}$, $s > 0$ (f) $\dfrac{a\, n!\,(2s)^n}{(s^2 - a^2)^{n+1}}$, $s > |a|$

7. (a) converges   (b) converges   (c) diverges

Section 6.2, Page 234

1. $y = \frac{1}{5}(e^{3t} + 4e^{-2t})$ 2. $y = 2e^{-t} - e^{-2t}$

3. $y = e^t \sin t$ 4. $y = e^{2t} - te^{2t}$

5. $y = te^t - t^2 e^t + \frac{2}{3}t^3 e^t$ 6. $y = \cosh t$

7. $y = 2e^t \cosh \sqrt{3}t - \dfrac{2}{\sqrt{3}} e^t \sinh \sqrt{3}t$

8. $y = \dfrac{1}{\omega^2 - 4}[(\omega^2 - 5)\cos \omega t + \cos 2t]$

9. $y = \frac{1}{5}(\cos t - 2 \sin t + 4e^t \cos t - 2e^t \sin t)$

10. $y = \frac{1}{5}(e^{-t} - e^t \cos t + 7e^t \sin t)$

11. $Y(s) = \dfrac{s}{s^2 + 4} + \dfrac{1 - e^{-s}}{s(s^2 + 4)}$

12. $Y(s) = \dfrac{1}{s^2(s^2 + 1)} - \dfrac{e^{-s}(s + 1)}{s^2(s^2 + 1)}$

15. (a) $F(s) = \dfrac{n!}{(s - a)^{n+1}}$ (b) $F(s) = \dfrac{6s^2 - 2}{(s^2 + 1)^3}$ (c) $F(s) = \dfrac{n!}{s^{n+1}}$

17. (a) $Y' - s^2 Y = -s$

   (b) $s^2 Y'' + 2s Y' - [s^2 + \alpha(\alpha + 1)]Y = -1$

18. $\mathscr{L}\{\mathrm{erfc}(t)\} = \dfrac{1}{s}[1 - e^{s^2/4}\mathrm{erfc}(s/2)]$

Section 6.3, Page 242

2. (a) $F(s) = \dfrac{2e^{-2s}}{s^3}$ (b) $F(s) = \dfrac{e^{-s}(s^2 + 2)}{s^3}$

   (c) $F(s) = \dfrac{e^{-\pi s}}{s^2} - \dfrac{e^{-2\pi s}}{s^2}(1 + \pi s)$ (d) $F(s) = \dfrac{1}{s}(e^{-s} + 2e^{-3s} - 6e^{-4s})$

(e) $F(s) = \dfrac{1}{s^2}[(1 - s)e^{-2s} - (1 + s)e^{-3s}]$

3. (a) $f(t) = t^3 e^{2t}$

(b) $f(t) = \frac{1}{3}u_2(t)[e^{t-2} - e^{-2(t-2)}]$

(c) $f(t) = 2u_2(t)e^{t-2}\cos(t - 2)$

(d) $f(t) = u_2(t)\sinh 2(t - 2)$

(e) $f(t) = u_1(t)e^{2(t-1)}\cosh(t - 1)$

5. (a) $f(t) = 2(2t)^n$

(b) $f(t) = 2e^{-t}\cos t - e^{-t}\sin t$

(c) $f(t) = \frac{1}{6}e^{t/3}(e^{2t/3} - 1)$

(d) $f(t) = \dfrac{e^2}{2}u_4(t)e^{(t-4)/2}$

6. (a) $F(s) = \dfrac{1}{s}(1 - e^{-s}), \qquad s > 0$

(b) $F(s) = \dfrac{1}{s}(1 - e^{-s} + e^{-2s} - e^{-3s}), \qquad s > 0$

(c) $F(s) = \dfrac{1}{s}[1 - e^{-s} + \cdots + e^{-2ns} - e^{-(2n+1)s}]$

$= \dfrac{1 - e^{-(2n+2)s}}{s(1 + e^{-s})}, \qquad s > 0$

(d) $F(s) = \dfrac{1}{s}\displaystyle\sum_{n=0}^{\infty}(-1)^n e^{-ns} = \dfrac{1/s}{1 + e^{-s}}, \qquad s > 0$

8. (a) $\mathscr{L}\{f(t)\} = \dfrac{1/s}{1 + e^{-s}}, \qquad s > 0$

(b) $\mathscr{L}\{f(t)\} = \dfrac{1 - e^{-s}}{s(1 + e^{-s})}, \qquad s > 0$

(c) $\mathscr{L}\{f(t)\} = \dfrac{1 - (1 + s)e^{-s}}{s^2(1 - e^{-2s})}, \qquad s > 0$

(d) $\mathscr{L}\{f(t)\} = \dfrac{1 + e^{-s\pi}}{(1 + s^2)(1 - e^{-s\pi})}, \qquad s > 0$

9. (a) $\mathscr{L}\{f(t)\} = \dfrac{1}{s}(1 - e^{-s}), \qquad s > 0$

(b) $\mathscr{L}\{g(t)\} = \dfrac{1}{s^2}(1 - e^{-s}), \qquad s > 0$

(c) $\mathscr{L}\{h(t)\} = \dfrac{(1 - e^{-s})^2}{s^2}, \qquad s > 0$

10. (b) $\mathscr{L}\{p(t)\} = \dfrac{1 - e^{-s}}{s^2(1 + e^{-s})}, \qquad s > 0$

Section 6.3.1, Page 248

1. $y = 1 - \cos t + \sin t - u_{\pi/2}(t)[1 - \sin t]$

2. $y = e^{-t}\sin t + \frac{1}{2}u_\pi(t)[1 + e^{-(t-\pi)}\cos t + e^{-(t-\pi)}\sin t]$
$- \frac{1}{2}u_{2\pi}(t)[1 - e^{-(t-2\pi)}\cos t - e^{-(t-2\pi)}\sin t]$

3. $y = \frac{1}{6}[1 - u_{2\pi}(t)](2 \sin t - \sin 2t)$

4. $y = \frac{1}{6}[1 - u_\pi(t)](2 \sin t - \sin 2t)$

5. $y = 1 - u_1(t)[1 - e^{-(t-1)} - (t - 1)e^{-(t-1)}]$

6. $y = e^{-t} - e^{-2t} + u_2(t)[\frac{1}{2} - e^{-(t-2)} + \frac{1}{2}e^{-2(t-2)}]$

7. $y = \cos t + u_\pi(t)(1 + \cos t)$

8. $y = 1 + \sum_{n=1}^{\infty} (-1)^n u_{n\pi}(t)[1 - \cos (t - n\pi)]$

9. (a) $F(s) = \dfrac{1 - e^{-s}}{s^2}$

   (b) $y = t - u_1(t)[t - 1 - \sin (t - 1)]$

Section 6.4, Page 253

1. $y = e^{-t} \cos t + e^{-t} \sin t - u_\pi(t)e^{-(t-\pi)} \sin t$

2. $y = \frac{1}{2}u_\pi(t) \sin 2t - \frac{1}{2}u_{2\pi}(t) \sin 2t$

3. $y = 2te^{-t} + u_{2\pi}(t)[1 - e^{-(t-2\pi)} - (t - 2\pi)e^{-(t-2\pi)}]$

4. $y = \cosh t + 2u_1(t) \sinh (t - 1)$

5. $y = \dfrac{1}{\sqrt{2}} e^{-t} \sin \sqrt{2}\, t + \frac{1}{4}e^{-t} \cos \sqrt{2}\, t + \frac{1}{4}(\sin t - \cos t)$

$$+ \dfrac{1}{\sqrt{2}} u_\pi(t)e^{-(t-\pi)} \sin \sqrt{2}(t - \pi)$$

6. $y = \cos \omega t - \dfrac{1}{\omega} u_{\pi/\omega}(t) \sin \omega t$ 7. $y = [1 + u_\pi(t)] \sin t$

Section 6.5, Page 256

3. $\sin t * \sin t = \frac{1}{2}(\sin t - t \cos t)$ is negative when $t = 2\pi$, for example.

4. (a) $F(s) = \dfrac{2}{s^2(s^2 + 4)}$ (b) $F(s) = \dfrac{1}{(s + 1)(s^2 + 1)}$ (c) $F(s) = \dfrac{1}{s^2(s - 1)}$

5. (a) $f(t) = \dfrac{1}{6}\displaystyle\int_0^t (t - u)^3 \cos u \, du$ (b) $f(t) = \displaystyle\int_0^t e^{-(t-u)} \cos 2u \, du$

   (c) $f(t) = \dfrac{1}{2}\displaystyle\int_0^t (t - u)e^{-(t-u)} \sin 2u \, du$ (d) $f(t) = \displaystyle\int_0^t \sin (t - u)g(u) \, du$

6. $y = \frac{1}{2}(1 - e^{-t} \sin t - e^{-t} \cos t) - \frac{1}{2}u_{2\pi}(t)[1 - e^{-(t-2\pi)} \sin t - e^{-(t-2\pi)} \cos t]$

7. $y = \displaystyle\int_0^t e^{-(t-u)} \sin (t - u) \sin \alpha u \, du$

8. $\Phi(s) = \dfrac{F(s)}{1 + K(s)}$

9. (c) $\phi(t) = \frac{1}{3}(4 \sin 2t - 2 \sin t)$ (d) $u(t) = \frac{1}{3}(2 \sin t - \sin 2t)$

10. (a) $\Phi(s) = \dfrac{2s}{s^3 + 2}$ (b) $\Phi(s) = \dfrac{(1 - e^{-2\pi s})(s^2 + 1)}{s(s^2 + 2)}$

   (c) $\Phi(s) = \dfrac{2(s^2 + 2s + 2)}{(s^2 + 4)(s^2 + 3s + 3)}$ (d) $\Phi(s) = -\dfrac{s(2s^2 - s + 2)}{(s^2 + 1)(s^2 + 2s + 2)}$

CHAPTER SEVEN

Section 7.1, Page 265

2. $x_1' - x_2 = 0$, $x_1(0) = u_0$
   $x_2' + p(t)x_2 + q(t)x_1 = g(t)$, $x_2(0) = u_0'$

Section 7.2, Page 270

1. $x_1 = c_1 e^{-3t} + c_2 e^{2t}$
   $x_2 = -4c_1 e^{-3t} + c_2 e^{2t}$

2. $x_1 = c_1 e^{3t} + c_2 e^{-t} + \frac{1}{4} e^t$
   $x_2 = 2c_1 e^{3t} - 2c_2 e^{-t} - 2e^t$

3. $x_1 = -\frac{2}{3}\cos t - \frac{4}{3}\sin t + \frac{2}{3}\sin 2t + \frac{2}{3}\cos 2t - 5t$
   $x_2 = \qquad -\frac{2}{3}\sin t + \frac{1}{3}\sin 2t \qquad\qquad - 2t + 1$

4. $x_1 = c_1 e^{2t} + c_2(t-1)e^{2t} + \frac{1}{8} + \frac{1}{2}t + \frac{3}{4}t^2$
   $x_2 = -c_1 e^{2t} - c_2 t e^{2t} \qquad - \frac{3}{8} - t - \frac{1}{4}t^2$

5. $x_1 = e^t + 7te^t + 3t^2 e^t$
   $x_2 = -e^t + 2te^t + \frac{3}{2}t^2 e^t$

6. $x_1 = c_1 + c_2 t \qquad\qquad\qquad + \frac{4}{3}t^3$
   $x_2 = 2c_1 + c_2(2t - \frac{1}{2}) + t - 2t^2 + \frac{8}{3}t^3$

7. $x_1 = c_1 e^t \cos 2t + c_2 e^t \sin 2t + \frac{4}{13}e^{-t}\sin t - \frac{7}{13}e^{-t}\cos t$
   $x_2 = c_1 e^t(\cos 2t + \sin 2t) + c_2 e^t(-\cos 2t + \sin 2t) - \frac{2}{13}e^{-t}\sin t - \frac{16}{13}e^{-t}\cos t$

8. $x_1 = e^{-2t}\cos t + 3e^{-2t}\sin t$
   $x_2 = \qquad 2e^{-2t}\sin t$

9. $x_1 = \qquad c_2 e^t$
   $x_2 = -\sqrt{2}c_1 e^{-2t} + \qquad c_3 e^t$
   $x_3 = \qquad c_1 e^{-2t} + \sqrt{2}c_3 e^t$

10. $x_1 = c_1 e^t + c_2 e^{-2t} + c_3 e^{3t}$
    $x_2 = -4c_1 e^t - c_2 e^{-2t} + 2c_3 e^{3t}$
    $x_3 = -c_1 e^t - c_2 e^{-2t} + c_3 e^{3t}$

11. $x_1 = 4c_1 e^{-2t} + 3c_2 e^{-t}$
    $x_2 = -5c_1 e^{-2t} - 4c_2 e^{-t} + c_3 e^{2t}$
    $x_3 = -7c_1 e^{-2t} - 2c_2 e^{-t} - c_3 e^{2t}$

13. $x_1 = c_1 + 2c_2 e^t + c_3 e^{2t}$
    $x_2 = 2c_1 + c_2 e^t$

14. $x_1 = c_1 e^{-2t} \qquad + \frac{1}{2}t - \frac{5}{4}$
    $x_2 = -\frac{3}{2}c_1 e^{-2t} + c_2 + \frac{1}{4}t^2 + \frac{1}{4}t$

15. $x_1 = c_1 e^{-t} + c_2 e^{2t} + 3c_3 e^{4t} + \frac{1}{4}$
    $x_2 = 3c_1 e^{-t} \qquad - c_3 e^{4t} + \frac{1}{4}$

16. $x_1 = -\cos t - \sin t$
    $x_2 = \qquad - \sin t$

17. $x_1 = c_1 e^{2t}$
    $x_2 = \qquad c_2 e^{-2t}$

18. No solutions

19. Infinitely many solutions: x_1 arbitrary; $x_2 = \frac{1}{4}(e^{2t} - e^{-2t}) - x_1$
20. No solutions
21. Infinitely many solutions: any solution of $(D + 1)x_1 + Dx_2 = 0$
23. (a) Five   (b) Three

Section 7.3, Page 279

1. (a) $\begin{pmatrix} 6 & -6 & 3 \\ 5 & 9 & -2 \\ 2 & 3 & 8 \end{pmatrix}$

(b) $\begin{pmatrix} -15 & 6 & -12 \\ 7 & -18 & -1 \\ -26 & -3 & -5 \end{pmatrix}$

(c) $\begin{pmatrix} 6 & -12 & 3 \\ 4 & 3 & 7 \\ 9 & 12 & 0 \end{pmatrix}$

(d) $\begin{pmatrix} -8 & -9 & 11 \\ 14 & 12 & -5 \\ 5 & -8 & 5 \end{pmatrix}$

2. (a) $\begin{pmatrix} -2 & 1 & 2 \\ 1 & 0 & -1 \\ 2 & -3 & 1 \end{pmatrix}$ (b) $\begin{pmatrix} 1 & 3 & -2 \\ 2 & -1 & 1 \\ 3 & -1 & 0 \end{pmatrix}$ (c), (d) $\begin{pmatrix} -1 & 4 & 0 \\ 3 & -1 & 0 \\ 5 & -4 & 1 \end{pmatrix}$

3. $\begin{pmatrix} 10 & 6 & -4 \\ 0 & 4 & 10 \\ 4 & 4 & 6 \end{pmatrix}$

4. (a) $\begin{pmatrix} 7 & -11 & -3 \\ 11 & 20 & 17 \\ -4 & 3 & -12 \end{pmatrix}$ (b) $\begin{pmatrix} 5 & 0 & -1 \\ 2 & 7 & 4 \\ -1 & 1 & 4 \end{pmatrix}$ (c) $\begin{pmatrix} 6 & -8 & -11 \\ 9 & 15 & 6 \\ -5 & -1 & 5 \end{pmatrix}$

6. $x_1 = -\frac{1}{3}, x_2 = \frac{7}{3}, x_3 = -\frac{1}{3}$ 7. No solution

8. $x_1 = -c, x_2 = c + 1, x_3 = c$, where c is arbitrary

9. $x_1 = c, x_2 = -c, x_3 = -c$, where c is arbitrary

10. $x_1 = 0, x_2 = 0, x_3 = 0$

11. (a) Linearly independent   (b) $\mathbf{x}^{(1)} - 5\mathbf{x}^{(2)} + 2\mathbf{x}^{(3)} = 0$

(c) $2\mathbf{x}^{(1)} - 3\mathbf{x}^{(2)} + 4\mathbf{x}^{(3)} - \mathbf{x}^{(4)} = 0$

(d) Linearly independent   (e) $\mathbf{x}^{(1)} + \mathbf{x}^{(2)} - \mathbf{x}^{(4)} = 0$

13. (a) $\begin{pmatrix} 7e^t & 5e^{-t} & 10e^{2t} \\ -e^t & 7e^{-t} & 2e^{2t} \\ 8e^t & 0 & -e^{2t} \end{pmatrix}$

(b) $\begin{pmatrix} 2e^{2t} - 2 + 3e^{3t} & 1 + 4e^{-2t} - e^t & 3e^{3t} + 2e^t - e^{4t} \\ 4e^{2t} - 1 - 3e^{3t} & 2 + 2e^{-2t} + e^t & 6e^{3t} + e^t + e^{4t} \\ -2e^{2t} - 3 + 6e^{3t} & -1 + 6e^{-2t} - 2e^t & -3e^{3t} + 3e^t - 2e^{4t} \end{pmatrix}$

(c) $\begin{pmatrix} e^t & -2e^{-t} & 2e^{2t} \\ 2e^t & -e^{-t} & -2e^{2t} \\ -e^t & -3e^{-t} & 4e^{2t} \end{pmatrix}$ (d) $(e-1)\begin{pmatrix} 1 & 2/e & \dfrac{e+1}{2} \\ 2 & 1/e & -\dfrac{e+1}{2} \\ -1 & 3/e & e+1 \end{pmatrix}$

14. (a) $3\mathbf{x}^{(1)}(t) - 6\mathbf{x}^{(2)}(t) + \mathbf{x}^{(3)}(t) = 0$ (b) Linearly independent

Section 7.4, Page 286

2. (c) $W(t) = c \exp [p_{11}(t) + p_{22}(t)]$

6. (a) $W(t) = t^2$

(b) $\mathbf{x}^{(1)}$ and $\mathbf{x}^{(2)}$ are linearly independent at each point except $t = 0$; they are linearly independent on every interval.

(c) At least one coefficient must be discontinuous at $t = 0$.

(d) $\mathbf{x}' = \begin{pmatrix} 0 & 1 \\ -\dfrac{2}{t^2} & \dfrac{2}{t} \end{pmatrix}\mathbf{x}$

7. (a) $W(t) = t(t - 2)e^t$

(b) $x^{(1)}$ and $x^{(2)}$ are linearly independent at each point except $t = 0$ and $t = 2$; they are linearly independent on every interval.

(c) There must be at least one discontinuous coefficient at $t = 0$ and $t = 2$.

(d) $x' = \begin{pmatrix} 0 & 1 \\ 2 - 2t & t^2 - 2 \\ t^2 - 2t & t^2 - 2t \end{pmatrix} x$

Section 7.5, Page 292

1. $x = c_1 \begin{pmatrix} 1 \\ 2 \end{pmatrix} e^{-t} + c_2 \begin{pmatrix} 2 \\ 1 \end{pmatrix} e^{2t}$

2. $x = c_1 \begin{pmatrix} 3 \\ 4 \end{pmatrix} + c_2 \begin{pmatrix} 1 \\ 2 \end{pmatrix} e^{-2t}$

3. $x = c_1 \begin{pmatrix} 1 \\ 1 \end{pmatrix} e^t + c_2 \begin{pmatrix} 1 \\ 3 \end{pmatrix} e^{-t}$

4. $x = c_1 \begin{pmatrix} 1 \\ -4 \end{pmatrix} e^{-3t} + c_2 \begin{pmatrix} 1 \\ 1 \end{pmatrix} e^{2t}$

5. $x = c_1 \begin{pmatrix} 4 \\ -5 \\ -7 \end{pmatrix} e^{-2t} + c_2 \begin{pmatrix} 3 \\ -4 \\ -2 \end{pmatrix} e^{-t} + c_3 \begin{pmatrix} 0 \\ 1 \\ -1 \end{pmatrix} e^{2t}$

6. $x = c_1 \begin{pmatrix} 1 \\ -4 \\ -1 \end{pmatrix} e^t + c_2 \begin{pmatrix} 1 \\ -1 \\ -1 \end{pmatrix} e^{-2t} + c_3 \begin{pmatrix} 1 \\ 2 \\ 1 \end{pmatrix} e^{3t}$

7. $x = -\frac{3}{2} \begin{pmatrix} 1 \\ 3 \end{pmatrix} e^{2t} + \frac{7}{2} \begin{pmatrix} 1 \\ 1 \end{pmatrix} e^{4t}$

8. $x = \frac{1}{2} \begin{pmatrix} 1 \\ 1 \end{pmatrix} e^{-t} + \frac{1}{2} \begin{pmatrix} 1 \\ 5 \end{pmatrix} e^{3t}$

9. $x = \begin{pmatrix} 0 \\ -2 \\ 1 \end{pmatrix} e^t + 2 \begin{pmatrix} 1 \\ 1 \\ 0 \end{pmatrix} e^{2t}$

10. $x = \frac{62}{17} \begin{pmatrix} 1 \\ 2 \\ -1 \end{pmatrix} e^t + \frac{27}{17} \begin{pmatrix} 1 \\ -2 \\ 1 \end{pmatrix} e^{-t} + \frac{15}{17} \begin{pmatrix} 2 \\ 1 \\ -8 \end{pmatrix} e^{4t}$

12. $x = c_1 \begin{pmatrix} 1 \\ 1 \end{pmatrix} t + c_2 \begin{pmatrix} 1 \\ 3 \end{pmatrix} t^{-1}$

13. $x = c_1 \begin{pmatrix} 1 \\ 3 \end{pmatrix} t^2 + c_2 \begin{pmatrix} 1 \\ 1 \end{pmatrix} t^4$

14. $x = c_1 \begin{pmatrix} 3 \\ 4 \end{pmatrix} + c_2 \begin{pmatrix} 1 \\ 2 \end{pmatrix} t^{-2}$

15. $x = c_1 \begin{pmatrix} 1 \\ 2 \end{pmatrix} t^{-1} + c_2 \begin{pmatrix} 2 \\ 1 \end{pmatrix} t^2$

18. $x = c_1 \begin{pmatrix} 1 \\ 1 \end{pmatrix} e^{-3t} + c_2 \left[\begin{pmatrix} 1 \\ 1 \end{pmatrix} te^{-3t} - \begin{pmatrix} 0 \\ \frac{1}{4} \end{pmatrix} e^{-3t} \right]$

19. $x = c_1 \begin{pmatrix} 2 \\ 1 \end{pmatrix} e^t + c_2 \left[\begin{pmatrix} 2 \\ 1 \end{pmatrix} te^t + \begin{pmatrix} 1 \\ 0 \end{pmatrix} e^t \right]$

Section 7.6, Page 298

1. $\begin{pmatrix} \frac{3}{11} & -\frac{4}{11} \\ \frac{2}{11} & \frac{1}{11} \end{pmatrix}$

2. $\begin{pmatrix} \frac{1}{6} & \frac{1}{12} \\ -\frac{1}{2} & \frac{1}{4} \end{pmatrix}$

3. $\begin{pmatrix} 1 & -3 & 2 \\ -3 & 3 & -1 \\ 2 & -1 & 0 \end{pmatrix}$

4. $\begin{pmatrix} \frac{1}{3} & \frac{1}{3} & 0 \\ \frac{1}{3} & -\frac{1}{3} & \frac{1}{3} \\ -\frac{1}{3} & 0 & \frac{1}{3} \end{pmatrix}$

5. Singular

6. $\begin{pmatrix} \frac{1}{2} & -\frac{1}{4} & \frac{1}{8} \\ 0 & \frac{1}{2} & -\frac{1}{4} \\ 0 & 0 & \frac{1}{2} \end{pmatrix}$

7. $\begin{pmatrix} \frac{1}{10} & \frac{3}{10} & \frac{1}{10} \\ -\frac{2}{10} & \frac{4}{10} & -\frac{2}{10} \\ -\frac{7}{10} & -\frac{1}{10} & \frac{3}{10} \end{pmatrix}$

8. Singular

9. $\begin{pmatrix} 1 & 1 & 0 & 1 \\ 1 & 0 & 1 & 1 \\ 1 & 1 & 1 & 1 \\ 0 & 1 & 0 & 1 \end{pmatrix}$

10. $\begin{pmatrix} 6 & \frac{13}{5} & -\frac{8}{5} & \frac{2}{5} \\ 5 & \frac{11}{5} & -\frac{6}{5} & \frac{4}{5} \\ 0 & -\frac{1}{5} & \frac{1}{5} & \frac{1}{5} \\ -2 & -\frac{4}{5} & \frac{4}{5} & -\frac{1}{5} \end{pmatrix}$

13. $\lambda_1 = 2$, $\mathbf{x}^{(1)} = \begin{pmatrix} 1 \\ 3 \end{pmatrix}$; $\lambda_2 = 4$, $\mathbf{x}^{(2)} = \begin{pmatrix} 1 \\ 1 \end{pmatrix}$

14. $\lambda_1 = 1 + 2i$, $\mathbf{x}^{(1)} = \begin{pmatrix} 1 \\ 1 - i \end{pmatrix}$; $\lambda_2 = 1 - 2i$, $\mathbf{x}^{(2)} = \begin{pmatrix} 1 \\ 1 + i \end{pmatrix}$

15. $\lambda_1 = \lambda_2 = -3$, $\mathbf{x}^{(1)} = \begin{pmatrix} 1 \\ 1 \end{pmatrix}$

16. $\lambda_1 = 1$, $\mathbf{x}^{(1)} = \begin{pmatrix} 1 \\ -4 \\ -1 \end{pmatrix}$; $\lambda_2 = -2$, $\mathbf{x}^{(2)} = \begin{pmatrix} 1 \\ -1 \\ -1 \end{pmatrix}$; $\lambda_3 = 3$, $\mathbf{x}^{(3)} = \begin{pmatrix} 1 \\ 2 \\ 1 \end{pmatrix}$

17. $\lambda_1 = 1$, $\mathbf{x}^{(1)} = \begin{pmatrix} 2 \\ -3 \\ 2 \end{pmatrix}$; $\lambda_2 = 1 + 2i$, $\mathbf{x}^{(2)} = \begin{pmatrix} 0 \\ 1 \\ -i \end{pmatrix}$;

$\lambda_3 = 1 - 2i$, $\mathbf{x}^{(3)} = \begin{pmatrix} 0 \\ 1 \\ i \end{pmatrix}$

18. $\lambda_1 = 2$, $\mathbf{x}^{(1)} = \begin{pmatrix} 0 \\ 0 \\ 1 \end{pmatrix}$; $\lambda_2 = \lambda_3 = 1$, $\mathbf{x}^{(2)} = \begin{pmatrix} 0 \\ 1 \\ -6 \end{pmatrix}$

19. $\lambda_1 = 1$, $\mathbf{x}^{(1)} = \begin{pmatrix} 1 \\ 0 \\ -1 \end{pmatrix}$; $\lambda_2 = 2$, $\mathbf{x}^{(2)} = \begin{pmatrix} -2 \\ 1 \\ 0 \end{pmatrix}$; $\lambda_3 = 3$, $\mathbf{x}^{(3)} = \begin{pmatrix} 0 \\ 1 \\ -1 \end{pmatrix}$

20. $\lambda_1 = \lambda_2 = \lambda_3 = 2$, $\mathbf{x}^{(1)} = \begin{pmatrix} 0 \\ 1 \\ -1 \end{pmatrix}$

21. $\lambda_1 = -1$, $\mathbf{x}^{(1)} = \begin{pmatrix} 1 \\ 0 \\ -1 \end{pmatrix}$; $\lambda_2 = -1$, $\mathbf{x}^{(2)} = \begin{pmatrix} 0 \\ 2 \\ -1 \end{pmatrix}$; $\lambda_3 = 8$, $\mathbf{x}^{(3)} = \begin{pmatrix} 2 \\ 1 \\ 2 \end{pmatrix}$

Section 7.7, Page 305

1. $\Phi(t) = \begin{pmatrix} -\frac{1}{3}e^{-t} + \frac{4}{3}e^{2t} & \frac{2}{3}e^{-t} - \frac{2}{3}e^{2t} \\ -\frac{2}{3}e^{-t} + \frac{2}{3}e^{2t} & \frac{4}{3}e^{-t} - \frac{1}{3}e^{2t} \end{pmatrix}$ 2. $\Phi(t) = \begin{pmatrix} 3 - 2e^{-2t} & -\frac{3}{2} + \frac{3}{2}e^{-2t} \\ 4 - 4e^{-2t} & -2 + 3e^{-2t} \end{pmatrix}$

3. $\Phi(t) = \begin{pmatrix} \frac{3}{2}e^{t} - \frac{1}{2}e^{-t} & -\frac{1}{2}e^{t} + \frac{1}{2}e^{-t} \\ \frac{3}{2}e^{t} - \frac{3}{2}e^{-t} & -\frac{1}{2}e^{t} + \frac{3}{2}e^{-t} \end{pmatrix}$

4. $\Phi(t) = \begin{pmatrix} \frac{1}{5}e^{-3t} + \frac{4}{5}e^{2t} & -\frac{1}{5}e^{-3t} + \frac{1}{5}e^{2t} \\ -\frac{4}{5}e^{-3t} + \frac{4}{5}e^{2t} & \frac{4}{5}e^{-3t} + \frac{1}{5}e^{2t} \end{pmatrix}$

5. $\Phi(t) = \left(\begin{array}{cc} -2e^{-2t} + 3e^{-t} & -e^{-2t} + e^{-t} \\ \frac{5}{2}e^{-2t} - 4e^{-t} + \frac{3}{2}e^{2t} & \frac{5}{4}e^{-2t} - \frac{4}{3}e^{-t} + \frac{13}{12}e^{2t} \\ \frac{7}{2}e^{-2t} - 2e^{-t} - \frac{3}{2}e^{2t} & \frac{7}{4}e^{-2t} - \frac{2}{3}e^{-t} - \frac{13}{12}e^{2t} \end{array}\right.$

$\left.\begin{array}{c} -e^{-2t} + e^{-t} \\ \frac{5}{4}e^{-2t} - \frac{4}{3}e^{-t} + \frac{1}{12}e^{2t} \\ \frac{7}{4}e^{-2t} - \frac{2}{3}e^{-t} - \frac{1}{12}e^{2t} \end{array}\right)$

6. $\Phi(t) = \begin{pmatrix} \frac{1}{6}e^{t} + \frac{1}{3}e^{-2t} + \frac{1}{2}e^{3t} & -\frac{1}{3}e^{t} + \frac{1}{3}e^{-2t} & \frac{1}{2}e^{t} - e^{-2t} + \frac{1}{2}e^{3t} \\ -\frac{2}{3}e^{t} - \frac{1}{3}e^{-2t} + e^{3t} & \frac{4}{3}e^{t} - \frac{1}{3}e^{-2t} & -2e^{t} + e^{-2t} + e^{3t} \\ -\frac{1}{6}e^{t} - \frac{1}{3}e^{-2t} + \frac{1}{2}e^{3t} & \frac{1}{3}e^{t} - \frac{1}{3}e^{-2t} & -\frac{1}{2}e^{t} + e^{-2t} + \frac{1}{2}e^{3t} \end{pmatrix}$

Section 7.8, Page 311

1. $\mathbf{x} = c_1 e^{t} \begin{pmatrix} \cos 2t \\ \cos 2t + \sin 2t \end{pmatrix} + c_2 e^{t} \begin{pmatrix} \sin 2t \\ -\cos 2t + \sin 2t \end{pmatrix}$

2. $\mathbf{x} = c_1 e^{-t} \begin{pmatrix} \cos \sqrt{2}\,t \\ \sqrt{2} \sin \sqrt{2}\,t \end{pmatrix} + c_2 e^{-t} \begin{pmatrix} \sin \sqrt{2}\,t \\ -\sqrt{2} \cos \sqrt{2}\,t \end{pmatrix}$

3. $\mathbf{x} = c_1 \begin{pmatrix} 5 \cos t \\ 2 \cos t + \sin t \end{pmatrix} + c_2 \begin{pmatrix} 5 \sin t \\ -\cos t + 2 \sin t \end{pmatrix}$

4. $\mathbf{x} = c_1 e^{t/2} \begin{pmatrix} 5 \cos \frac{3}{2}t \\ 3(\cos \frac{3}{2}t + \sin \frac{3}{2}t) \end{pmatrix} + c_2 e^{t/2} \begin{pmatrix} 5 \sin \frac{3}{2}t \\ 3(-\cos \frac{3}{2}t + \sin \frac{3}{2}t) \end{pmatrix}$

5. $\mathbf{x} = c_1 \begin{pmatrix} 2 \\ -3 \\ 2 \end{pmatrix} e^{t} + c_2 e^{t} \begin{pmatrix} 0 \\ \cos 2t \\ \sin 2t \end{pmatrix} + c_3 e^{t} \begin{pmatrix} 0 \\ \sin 2t \\ -\cos 2t \end{pmatrix}$

6. $\mathbf{x} = c_1 \begin{pmatrix} 2 \\ -2 \\ 1 \end{pmatrix} e^{-2t} + c_2 e^{-t} \begin{pmatrix} -\sqrt{2} \sin \sqrt{2}\,t \\ \cos \sqrt{2}\,t \\ -\cos \sqrt{2}\,t - \sqrt{2} \sin \sqrt{2}\,t \end{pmatrix}$

$+ c_3 e^{-t} \begin{pmatrix} \sqrt{2} \cos \sqrt{2}\,t \\ \sin \sqrt{2}\,t \\ \sqrt{2} \cos \sqrt{2}\,t - \sin \sqrt{2}\,t \end{pmatrix}$

7. $\mathbf{x} = e^{-t}\begin{pmatrix} \cos t - 3\sin t \\ \cos t - \sin t \end{pmatrix}$

8. $\mathbf{x} = e^{-2t}\begin{pmatrix} \cos t - 5\sin t \\ -2\cos t - 3\sin t \end{pmatrix}$

9. $\mathbf{x} = c_1 t^{-1}\begin{pmatrix} \cos(\sqrt{2}\ln t) \\ \sqrt{2}\sin(\sqrt{2}\ln t) \end{pmatrix} + c_2 t^{-1}\begin{pmatrix} \sin(\sqrt{2}\ln t) \\ -\sqrt{2}\cos(\sqrt{2}\ln t) \end{pmatrix}$

10. $\mathbf{x} = c_1\begin{pmatrix} 5\cos(\ln t) \\ 2\cos(\ln t) + \sin(\ln t) \end{pmatrix} + c_2\begin{pmatrix} 5\sin(\ln t) \\ -\cos(\ln t) + 2\sin(\ln t) \end{pmatrix}$

Section 7.9, Page 316

1. $\mathbf{x} = c_1\begin{pmatrix} 2 \\ 1 \end{pmatrix}e^t + c_2\left[\begin{pmatrix} 2 \\ 1 \end{pmatrix}te^t + \begin{pmatrix} 1 \\ 0 \end{pmatrix}e^t\right]$

2. $\mathbf{x} = c_1\begin{pmatrix} 1 \\ 2 \end{pmatrix} + c_2\left[\begin{pmatrix} 1 \\ 2 \end{pmatrix}t - \begin{pmatrix} 0 \\ \frac{1}{2} \end{pmatrix}\right]$

3. $\mathbf{x} = c_1\begin{pmatrix} -3 \\ 4 \\ 2 \end{pmatrix}e^{-t} + c_2\begin{pmatrix} 0 \\ 1 \\ -1 \end{pmatrix}e^{2t} + c_3\left[\begin{pmatrix} 0 \\ 1 \\ -1 \end{pmatrix}te^{2t} + \begin{pmatrix} 1 \\ 0 \\ 1 \end{pmatrix}e^{2t}\right]$

4. $\mathbf{x} = c_1\begin{pmatrix} 1 \\ 1 \\ 1 \end{pmatrix}e^{2t} + c_2\begin{pmatrix} 1 \\ 0 \\ -1 \end{pmatrix}e^{-t} + c_3\begin{pmatrix} 0 \\ 1 \\ -1 \end{pmatrix}e^{-t}$

5. $\mathbf{x} = \begin{pmatrix} 3+4t \\ 2+4t \end{pmatrix}e^{-3t}$

6. $\mathbf{x} = \begin{pmatrix} -1 \\ 2 \\ -33 \end{pmatrix}e^t + 4\begin{pmatrix} 0 \\ 1 \\ -6 \end{pmatrix}te^t + 3\begin{pmatrix} 0 \\ 0 \\ 1 \end{pmatrix}e^{2t}$

7. $\mathbf{x} = c_1\begin{pmatrix} 0 \\ 1 \\ -1 \end{pmatrix}e^{2t} + c_2\left[\begin{pmatrix} 0 \\ 1 \\ -1 \end{pmatrix}te^{2t} + \begin{pmatrix} 1 \\ 0 \\ 1 \end{pmatrix}e^{2t}\right]$

   $+ c_3\left[\begin{pmatrix} 0 \\ 1 \\ -1 \end{pmatrix}t^2 e^{2t} + 2\begin{pmatrix} 1 \\ 0 \\ 1 \end{pmatrix}te^{2t} + 2\begin{pmatrix} 1 \\ 0 \\ 2 \end{pmatrix}e^{2t}\right]$

8. $\mathbf{x} = c_1\begin{pmatrix} 2 \\ 1 \end{pmatrix}t + c_2\left[\begin{pmatrix} 2 \\ 1 \end{pmatrix}t\ln t + \begin{pmatrix} 1 \\ 0 \end{pmatrix}t\right]$

9. $\mathbf{x} = c_1\begin{pmatrix} 1 \\ 1 \end{pmatrix}t^{-3} + c_2\left[\begin{pmatrix} 1 \\ 1 \end{pmatrix}t^{-3}\ln t - \begin{pmatrix} 0 \\ \frac{1}{4} \end{pmatrix}t^{-3}\right]$

Section 7.10, Page 320

1. $\mathbf{x} = c_1\begin{pmatrix} 1 \\ 1 \end{pmatrix}e^t + c_2\begin{pmatrix} 1 \\ 3 \end{pmatrix}e^{-t} + \frac{3}{2}\begin{pmatrix} 1 \\ 1 \end{pmatrix}te^t - \frac{1}{4}\begin{pmatrix} 1 \\ 3 \end{pmatrix}e^t + \begin{pmatrix} 1 \\ 2 \end{pmatrix}t - \begin{pmatrix} 0 \\ 1 \end{pmatrix}$

2. $\mathbf{x} = \frac{1}{5}(2t - \frac{3}{2}\sin 2t - \frac{1}{2}\cos 2t + c_1)\begin{pmatrix} 5\cos t \\ 2\cos t + \sin t \end{pmatrix}$

   $+ \frac{1}{5}(-t - \frac{1}{2}\sin 2t + \frac{3}{2}\cos 2t + c_2)\begin{pmatrix} 5\sin t \\ -\cos t + 2\sin t \end{pmatrix}$

3. $\mathbf{x} = c_1\begin{pmatrix}1\\-4\end{pmatrix}e^{-3t} + c_2\begin{pmatrix}1\\1\end{pmatrix}e^{2t} - \begin{pmatrix}0\\1\end{pmatrix}e^{-2t} + \frac{1}{2}\begin{pmatrix}1\\0\end{pmatrix}e^t$

4. $\mathbf{x} = c_1\begin{pmatrix}1\\2\end{pmatrix} + c_2\left[\begin{pmatrix}1\\2\end{pmatrix}t - \frac{1}{2}\begin{pmatrix}0\\1\end{pmatrix}\right] - 2\begin{pmatrix}1\\2\end{pmatrix}\ln t + \begin{pmatrix}2\\5\end{pmatrix}t^{-1} - \begin{pmatrix}\frac{1}{2}\\0\end{pmatrix}t^{-2}$

5. $\mathbf{x} = (-\sin t + c_1)\begin{pmatrix}5\cos t\\2\cos t + \sin t\end{pmatrix}$

$\qquad\qquad + \left(-\ln\left|\tan\dfrac{t}{2}\right| - \cos t + c_2\right)\begin{pmatrix}5\sin t\\-\cos t + 2\sin t\end{pmatrix}$

6. $\mathbf{x} = c_1\begin{pmatrix}1\\1\end{pmatrix}t + c_2\begin{pmatrix}1\\3\end{pmatrix}t^{-1} - \begin{pmatrix}2\\3\end{pmatrix} + \frac{1}{2}\begin{pmatrix}1\\3\end{pmatrix}t - \begin{pmatrix}1\\1\end{pmatrix}t\ln t - \frac{1}{3}\begin{pmatrix}4\\3\end{pmatrix}t^2$

7. $\mathbf{x} = c_1\begin{pmatrix}2\\1\end{pmatrix}t^2 + c_2\begin{pmatrix}1\\2\end{pmatrix}t^{-1} + \begin{pmatrix}3\\2\end{pmatrix}t + \frac{1}{10}\begin{pmatrix}-2\\1\end{pmatrix}t^4 - \frac{1}{2}\begin{pmatrix}2\\3\end{pmatrix}$

11. $\mathbf{x} = c_1\begin{pmatrix}1\\2\end{pmatrix}e^{3t} + c_2\begin{pmatrix}1\\2\end{pmatrix}e^{-t} + \frac{1}{4}\begin{pmatrix}1\\-8\end{pmatrix}e^t$

12. $\mathbf{x} = c_1\begin{pmatrix}5\cos t\\2\cos t + \sin t\end{pmatrix} + c_2\begin{pmatrix}5\sin t\\-\cos t + 2\sin t\end{pmatrix} + \frac{1}{3}\begin{pmatrix}2\\1\end{pmatrix}\sin 2t$

$\qquad\qquad + \frac{2}{3}\begin{pmatrix}1\\0\end{pmatrix}\cos 2t - \begin{pmatrix}5\\2\end{pmatrix}t + \begin{pmatrix}0\\1\end{pmatrix}$

13. $\mathbf{x} = c_1 e^t\begin{pmatrix}\cos t\\\cos t + \sin t\end{pmatrix} + c_2 e^t\begin{pmatrix}\sin t\\-\cos t + \sin t\end{pmatrix} + \begin{pmatrix}\frac{4}{13}\\-\frac{2}{13}\end{pmatrix}e^{-t}\sin t$

$\qquad\qquad - \begin{pmatrix}\frac{7}{13}\\\frac{16}{13}\end{pmatrix}e^{-t}\cos t$

14. $\mathbf{x} = c_1\begin{pmatrix}1\\1\end{pmatrix}e^t + c_2\begin{pmatrix}1\\3\end{pmatrix}e^{-t} + \begin{pmatrix}1\\0\end{pmatrix}e^t + 2\begin{pmatrix}1\\1\end{pmatrix}te^t$

15. $\mathbf{x} = c_1\begin{pmatrix}1\\2\end{pmatrix} + c_2\left[\begin{pmatrix}1\\2\end{pmatrix}t - \frac{1}{2}\begin{pmatrix}0\\1\end{pmatrix}\right] + \begin{pmatrix}0\\1\end{pmatrix}t + \begin{pmatrix}0\\-2\end{pmatrix}t^2 + \frac{4}{3}\begin{pmatrix}1\\2\end{pmatrix}t^3$

16. $\mathbf{x} = c_1\begin{pmatrix}2\\1\end{pmatrix}e^t + c_2\left[\begin{pmatrix}2\\1\end{pmatrix}te^t + \begin{pmatrix}1\\0\end{pmatrix}e^t\right] + \begin{pmatrix}1\\0\end{pmatrix}e^t + \begin{pmatrix}3\\0\end{pmatrix}te^t + \frac{3}{2}\begin{pmatrix}2\\1\end{pmatrix}t^2e^t$

Section 7.11, Page 325

1. $\mathbf{x} = -\frac{1}{5}\begin{pmatrix}1\\-4\end{pmatrix}e^{-3t} + \frac{1}{5}\begin{pmatrix}1\\1\end{pmatrix}e^{2t}$

2. $\mathbf{x} = \begin{pmatrix}\cos 2t + \sin 2t\\2\sin 2t\end{pmatrix}$

3. $\mathbf{x} = \frac{1}{2}\begin{pmatrix}1\\-1\end{pmatrix}e^t + \frac{1}{2}\begin{pmatrix}1\\3\end{pmatrix}e^{-t} + 2\begin{pmatrix}1\\1\end{pmatrix}te^t$

4. $\mathbf{x} = \frac{1}{6}\begin{pmatrix}1\\2\end{pmatrix}e^{-t} + \frac{2}{3}\begin{pmatrix}2\\1\end{pmatrix}e^{2t} - \frac{1}{2}\begin{pmatrix}1\\2\end{pmatrix}e^t + 2\begin{pmatrix}1\\1\end{pmatrix}te^t$

5. $\mathbf{x} = e^{-t}\begin{pmatrix}\cos\sqrt{2}\,t\\\sqrt{2}\sin\sqrt{2}\,t\end{pmatrix}$

6. (a) $x_1(t) = \cos 2t + \sin 2t + \displaystyle\int_0^t [\cos 2(t - u) + \sin 2(t - u)] \sin u \, du$

$\hspace{3.5cm} - \displaystyle\int_0^t \sin 2(t - u) \cos u \, du$

$\hspace{0.7cm} x_2(t) = 2 \sin 2t + 2 \displaystyle\int_0^t \sin 2(t - u) \sin u \, du$

$\hspace{3.5cm} + \displaystyle\int_0^t [\cos 2(t - u) - \sin 2(t - u)] \cos u \, du$

(b) $x_1(t) = \cos 2t + \sin 2t + \displaystyle\int_0^t [\cos 2(t - u) + \sin 2(t - u)]e^{-u} \, du$

$\hspace{0.7cm} x_2(t) = 2 \sin 2t + 2 \displaystyle\int_0^t \sin 2(t - u)e^{-u} \, du$

(c) $x_1(t) = \begin{cases} \frac{1}{2} + \frac{1}{2}\cos 2t + \frac{3}{2}\sin 2t, & t < \pi \\ \cos 2t + \sin 2t, & t \geq \pi \end{cases}$

$\hspace{0.7cm} x_2(t) = \begin{cases} 1 + 2\sin 2t - \cos 2t, & t < \pi \\ 2\sin 2t, & t \geq \pi \end{cases}$

(d) $x_1(t) = \begin{cases} \cos 2t + \sin 2t, & t < \pi \\ \cos 2t, & t > \pi \end{cases}$

$\hspace{0.7cm} x_2(t) = \begin{cases} 2\sin 2t, & t < \pi \\ \sin 2t + \cos 2t, & t > \pi \end{cases}$

7. In all cases the solution is of the form

$$x_1(t) = -5f(t) + \int_0^t h_1(t - u)g_1(u) \, du - 5\int_0^t f(t - u)g_2(u) \, du,$$

$$x_2(t) = h_2(t) + 2\int_0^t f(t - u)g_1(u) \, du + \int_0^t h_2(t - u)g_2(u) \, du,$$

where g_1 and g_2 are given in the problem, and $f(t) = e^{-2t}\sin t$, $h_1(t) = e^{-2t}(\cos t + 3\sin t)$, $h_2(t) = e^{-2t}(\cos t - 3\sin t)$.

8. $\mathbf{x} = \begin{pmatrix} \frac{1}{2} \\ 1 \end{pmatrix} - \begin{pmatrix} 2 \\ 1 \end{pmatrix}e^t + \begin{pmatrix} \frac{3}{2} \\ 0 \end{pmatrix}e^{2t}$

9. $\mathbf{x} = \begin{pmatrix} -\frac{2}{15} \\ -\frac{6}{15} \end{pmatrix}e^{-t} + \begin{pmatrix} \frac{4}{3} \\ 0 \end{pmatrix}e^{2t} + \begin{pmatrix} -\frac{9}{20} \\ \frac{3}{20} \end{pmatrix}e^{4t} + \begin{pmatrix} \frac{1}{4} \\ \frac{1}{4} \end{pmatrix}$

CHAPTER EIGHT

Section 8.2, Page 336

1. (a) $y = \phi(x) = (1 + e^{2x})/2$;   1.111, 1.246, 1.411, 1.613
   (b) 1.1, 1.22, 1.364, 1.537   (c) 1.05, 1.105, 1.166, 1.233
2. (a) $y = \phi(x) = e^{2x} + \frac{1}{2}x$;   1.271, 1.592, 1.972, 2.425
   (b) 1.25, 1.54, 1.878, 2.274   (c) 1.125, 1.260, 1.406, 1.564
3. (a) 1.1, 1.222, 1.375, 1.573   (b) 1.05, 1.105, 1.167, 1.236
4. $y_6 = 8.903824$, $y_7 = 12.505354$
5. 1.595, 2.464

8. (a) $\phi_3(x) = 1 + x + x^2 + \frac{2}{3}x^3$; $\phi_2(0.4) = 1.56$, $\phi_3(0.4) = 1.603$
   (b) $\phi_3(x) = 1 + \frac{5}{2}x + 2x^2 + \frac{4}{3}x^3 - \frac{1}{6}x^4$; $\phi_2(0.4) = 2.299$, $\phi_3(0.4) = 2.401$
   (c) $\phi_2(x) = 1 + x + x^2 + \frac{2}{3}x^3 + \frac{1}{6}x^4 + \frac{2}{15}x^5 + \frac{1}{63}x^7$; $\phi_2(0.4) = 1.608$

Section 8.3, Page 342

1. $e_{n+1} = [2\phi(\bar{x}_n) - 1]h^2$, $|e_{n+1}| \leq \left[1 + 2 \max_{0 \leq x \leq 1} |\phi(x)|\right]h^2$,

   $e_{n+1} = e^{2\bar{x}_n}h^2$, $|e_1| \leq 0.012$, $|e_4| \leq 0.022$

2. $e_{n+1} = [2\phi(\bar{x}_n) - \bar{x}_n]h^2$, $|e_{n+1}| \leq \left[1 + 2 \max_{0 \leq x \leq 1} |\phi(x)|\right]h^2$,

   $e_{n+1} = 2e^{2\bar{x}_n}h^2$, $|e_1| \leq 0.024$, $|e_4| \leq 0.044$
3. $e_{n+1} = [\bar{x}_n + \bar{x}_n^2\phi(\bar{x}_n) + \phi^3(\bar{x}_n)]h^2$

4. (a) $\phi(x) = 1 + \dfrac{1}{5\pi} \sin 5\pi x$ (b) 1.2, 1.0, 1.2

   (c) 1.1, 1.1, 1.0, 1.0   (d) $h < \dfrac{1}{\sqrt{50\pi}} \cong 0.08$

7. (a) $y_1(h = 0.2) = 1.4$, $y_2(h = 0.1) = 1.44$; $\phi(0.2) \cong 1.48$, exact 1.4918
   (b) $y_1(h = 0.2) = 1.2$, $y_2(h = 0.1) = 1.22$; $\phi(0.2) \cong 1.24$, exact 1.246
   (c) $y_1(h = 0.2) = 1.5$, $y_2(h = 0.1) = 1.54$; $\phi(0.2) \cong 1.58$, exact 1.592
   (d) $y_1(h = 0.2) = 1.2$, $y_2(h = 0.1) = 1.222$; $\phi(0.2) \cong 1.244$
9. (a) 56.75310   (b) 62.027322
10. (a) 1.05, 1.11, 1.17, 1.24   (b) 1.13, 1.27, 1.42, 1.58
    (c) 1.05, 1.11, 1.17, 1.24
11. (a) 0   (b) 60   (c) -92.16
12. $0.224 \neq 0.225$
13. (b) $\phi_2(x) - \phi_1(x) = 0.001e^x \rightarrow \infty$ as $x \rightarrow \infty$

Section 8.4, Page 349

1. 1.110, 1.244, 1.408   2. 1.270, 1.589, 1.967
3. 1.111, 1.252, 1.437
5. $e_{n+1} = 304e^{4\bar{x}_n}(h^3/9)$, $|e_{n+1}| \leq 205h^3$ on $0 \leq x \leq 1$, $|e_1| \leq 0.0504$
6. (a) $e_{n+1} = 2e^{2\bar{x}_n}(h^3/3)$, $|e_{n+1}| \leq 4.96h^3$ on $0 \leq x \leq 1$, $|e_1| \leq 0.00081$
   (b) $e_{n+1} = 4e^{2\bar{x}_n}(h^3/3)$, $|e_{n+1}| \leq 9.92h^3$ on $0 \leq x \leq 1$, $|e_1| \leq 0.0016$
8. (a) 1.110, 1.244, 1.408   (b) 1.270, 1.588, 1.965
   (c) 1.110, 1.250, 1.433

Section 8.5, Page 352

1. 1.110, 1.244, 1.408   2. 1.270, 1.588, 1.966
3. 1.110, 1.249, 1.431   4. $y_2 = 2.464$, $y_3 = 3.738$
7. (a) $y_1(h = 0.2) = 1.240$, $y_2(h = 0.1) = 1.244$;
       $\phi(0.2) \cong 1.245$, exact 1.246
   (b) $y_1(h = 0.2) = 1.580$, $y_2(h = 0.1) = 1.588$;
       $\phi(0.2) \cong 1.591$, exact 1.592
   (c) $y_1(h = 0.2) = 1.240$, $y_2(h = 0.1) = 1.249$;
       $\phi(0.2) \cong 1.252$
8. $\phi(1) \cong 64.586856$, exact 64.897803

Section 8.6, Page 356

1. 1.249, 1.598
3. 1.251, 1.698

2. 1.590, 2.423
7. $\phi(1) \cong 64.885876$, exact 64.897803

Section 8.8, Page 364

1. $y_{4p} = 1.61269$, $y_{4c} = 1.61276$
3. $y_{4p} = 1.69412$, $y_{4c} = 1.69604$

2. $y_{4p} = 2.42539$, $y_{4c} = 2.42554$

4. *Hint:* $\phi'(x) \cong y_n' + \dfrac{y_n' - y_{n-1}'}{h}(x - x_n)$

6. (a) $y_2 = 1.244$, $y_3 = 1.408$
   (c) $y_2 = 1.249$, $y_3 = 1.430$

   (b) $y_2 = 1.588$, $y_3 = 1.965$

Section 8.9, Page 367

1. (a) $x_1 = 1.1, x_2 = 1.26$; $y_1 = 0.4, y_2 = 0.76$
   (b) $x_1 = 1.2, x_2 = 1.451$; $y_1 = 1.1, y_2 = 1.32$
   (c) $x_1 = 0.8, x_2 = 0.582$; $y_1 = 1.1, y_2 = 1.18$
2. $1.30, -0.24$
3. (a) $x_1 = 1.30$, $y_1 = 0.76$
   (c) $x_1 = 0.56$, $y_1 = 1.16$

   (b) $x_1 = 1.50$, $y_1 = 1.26$
4. $x_{4p} = 1.99414, y_{4p} = -0.662313$; $x_{4c} = 1.99519, y_{4c} = -0.662427$

5. $\phi_2(t) = 1 + t + \dfrac{5t^2}{2}$, $\psi_2(t) = -t - t^2$

   $\phi_2(0.2) = 1.25, \psi_2(0.2) = -0.24$; $\phi_2(1) = 4.5, \psi_2(1) = -2$
6. $x' = y, y' = -t^2 y - 3x + t$; $x(0) = 1, y(0) = 2$
   $x_1 = 1.2, x_2 = 1.37$; $y_1 = 1.7, y_2 = 1.348$

CHAPTER NINE

Section 9.1, Page 374

1. $A_0 < 0, A \to -\infty$; $A_0 = 0, A = 0$; $0 < A_0 < \dfrac{\epsilon}{\sigma}, A \to \dfrac{\epsilon}{\sigma}$;

   $A_0 = \dfrac{\epsilon}{\sigma}, A = \dfrac{\epsilon}{\sigma}$; $A_0 > \dfrac{\epsilon}{\sigma}, A \to \dfrac{\epsilon}{\sigma}$

2. $A_0 < 0, A \to 0$; $A_0 = 0, A = 0$; $0 < A_0 < \dfrac{\epsilon}{\sigma}, A \to 0$;

   $A_0 = \dfrac{\epsilon}{\sigma}, A = \dfrac{\epsilon}{\sigma}$; $A_0 > \dfrac{\epsilon}{\sigma}, A \to \infty$

3. $A_0 = 0, A = 0$; $A_0 > 0, A \to \infty$

4. $A_0 < -\dfrac{\epsilon}{\sigma}, A \to -\dfrac{\epsilon}{\sigma}$; $A_0 = -\dfrac{\epsilon}{\sigma}, A = -\dfrac{\epsilon}{\sigma}$;

   $-\dfrac{\epsilon}{\sigma} < A_0 < 0, A \to -\dfrac{\epsilon}{\sigma}$; $A_0 = 0, A = 0$; $A_0 > 0, A \to \infty$

5. $A_0 = 0, A = 0$; $0 < A_0 < 1, A \to 1$; $A_0 = 1, A = 1$;
   $1 < A_0 < 2, A \to 1$; $A_0 = 2, A = 2$; $A_0 > 2, A \to \infty$

6. $A_0 = 0, A = 0$; $0 < A_0 < 1, A \to 0$; $A_0 = 1, A = 1$;
   $1 < A_0 < 2, A \to 2$; $A_0 = 2, A = 2$; $A_0 > 2, A \to 2$

9. $A_0 = 0, A = 0$; $A_0 = \dfrac{\epsilon}{\sigma}, A = \dfrac{\epsilon}{\sigma}$;

$$0 < A_0 < \frac{\epsilon}{\sigma}, A = \frac{(\epsilon/\sigma)A_0 e^{\epsilon t}}{A_0 e^{\epsilon t} + (\epsilon/\sigma - A_0)} \to 0 \text{ as } t \to \infty;$$

$$A_0 > \frac{\epsilon}{\sigma}, A = \frac{(\epsilon/\sigma)A_0 e^{\epsilon t}}{A_0 e^{\epsilon t} - (A_0 - \epsilon/\sigma)} \to \infty \text{ as } t \to \frac{1}{|\epsilon|} \ln \frac{A_0}{A_0 - (\epsilon/\sigma)}$$

Section 9.2, Page 380

1. (a) $x = 4e^{-t}, y = 2e^{-2t}$; $y = x^2/2$
   (b) $x = 4e^{-t}, y = 2e^{2t}, y = 2x^{-2}$; $x = 4e^{-t}, y = 0$,
   (c) $x = 4 \cos t, y = 4 \sin t$; $x = -4 \sin t, y = 4 \cos t$
2. (a) $(0, 0)$ (b) $(0, 0), (-\frac{1}{2}, 1)$
   (c) $(0, 0), (1, 0), (0, 2), (\frac{1}{2}, \frac{1}{2})$ (d) $(0, 0)$
   (e) $(\pm n\pi, 0), n = 0, 1, 2, \ldots$ (f) $(0, 0)$
4. (a) $x = Ae^{-t}, y = Be^{-2t}$; $y = Bx^2/A^2, A \neq 0$
   (b) $x = Ae^{-t}, y = Be^{2t}$; $y = BA^2/x^2, A \neq 0$
   (c) $x = Ae^{t}, y = Be^{-2t}$; $y = BA^2/x^2, A \neq 0$
   (d) $x = Ae^{-t}, y = Be^{2t} - Ae^{-t}$; $y = BA^2/x^2 - x, A \neq 0$

Section 9.3, Page 391

1. saddle point, unstable   2. improper node, unstable
3. saddle point, unstable   4. improper node, asymptotically stable
5. spiral point, asymptotically stable   6. center, stable
7. spiral point, unstable   8. improper node, asymptotically stable
9. $x_0 = 1, y_0 = 1$; saddle point, unstable
10. $x_0 = -1, y_0 = 0$; improper node, asymptotically stable
11. $x_0 = -2, y_0 = 1$; spiral point, asymptotically stable
14. $c^2 > 4 \, km$, improper node, asymptotically stable; $c^2 = 4 \, km$, improper node, asymptotically stable; $c^2 < 4 \, km$, spiral point, asymptotically stable

Section 9.4, Page 401

1. spiral point, asymptotically stable   2. can't tell, asymptotically stable
3. spiral point, asymptotically stable   4. spiral point, unstable
5. can't tell   6. saddle point, unstable
7. $\mu < 2$, spiral point, unstable; $\mu = 2$, can't tell, unstable; $\mu > 2$, improper node, unstable
8. spiral point, unstable   9. can't tell
10. improper node, asymptotically stable
11. (a) $(0, 0)$, can't tell, unstable; $(-1, 1)$, saddle point, unstable
    (b) $(1, 1)$, can't tell, asymptotically stable; $(-1, -1)$, saddle point, unstable
    (c) $(0, 0)$, improper node, unstable; $(0, \frac{3}{2})$, improper node, asymptotically stable; $(1, 0)$ saddle point, unstable; $(-1, 2)$, saddle point, unstable
    (d) $(1, 1)$, spiral point, asymptotically stable; $(-1, 1)$, saddle point, unstable

Section 9.6, Page 419

1. (a) $r = 1$, $\theta = t + t_0$, stable limit cycle
   (b) $r = 1$, $\theta = -t + t_0$, semistable limit cycle
   (c) $r = 1$, $\theta = t + t_0$, stable limit cycle; $r = 3$, $\theta = t + t_0$, unstable periodic
       solution
   (d) $r = 1$, $\theta = -t + t_0$, unstable periodic solution;
       $r = 2$, $\theta = -t + t_0$, stable limit cycle
   (e) $r = (2n - 1)$, $\theta = t + t_0$, $n = 1, 2, 3, \ldots$, stable limit cycle;
       $r = 2n$, $\theta = t + t_0$, $n = 1, 2, 3, \ldots$, unstable periodic solution
   (f) $r = 2$, $\theta = -t + t_0$, semistable limit cycle;
       $r = 3$, $\theta = -t + t_0$, unstable periodic solution
3. (a) counterclockwise
   (b) $r = 1$, $\theta = t + t_0$, stable limit cycle;
       $r = 2$, $\theta = t + t_0$, semistable limit cycle;
       $r = 3$, $\theta = t + t_0$, unstable periodic solution
4. $r = \sqrt{2}$, $\theta = -t + t_0$, unstable periodic solution

CHAPTER TEN

Section 10.2, Page 429

1. $\alpha^2 u_{xx} = u_t$, $0 < x < 1, t > 0$ $\alpha^2 = 0.000114 \text{ m}^2/\text{sec}$
   $u(x, 0) = 20$, $0 \leq x \leq 1$ x in meters
   $u(0, t) = 60$, $t > 0$ t in seconds
   $u(1, t) = 20$, $t > 0$

2. $\alpha^2 u_{xx} = u_t$, $0 < x < 2, t > 0$ $\alpha^2 = 0.000171 \text{ m}^2/\text{sec}$
   $u(x, 0) = 30 + 50x - 20x^2$, $0 \leq x \leq 2$ x in meters
   $u(0, t) = 30$, $t > 0$ t in seconds
   $u(2, t) = 50$, $t > 0$

4. $u(x, t) = e^{-400\pi^2 t} \sin 2\pi x - 2e^{-2500\pi^2 t} \sin 5\pi x$

5. $u(x, t) = 2e^{-\pi^2 t/16} \sin \dfrac{\pi x}{2} - e^{-\pi^2 t/4} \sin \pi x + 4e^{-\pi^2 t} \sin 2\pi x$

6. $u(x) = T_1 + \dfrac{T_2 - T_1}{l} x$

7. (a) $xX'' - \lambda X = 0$, $T' + \lambda T = 0$
   (b) $X'' - \lambda x X = 0$, $T' + \lambda t T = 0$
   (c) $X'' - \lambda(X' + X) = 0$, $T' + \lambda T = 0$
   (d) $[p(x)X']' + \lambda r(x)X = 0$, $T'' + \lambda T = 0$
   (e) Not separable
9. $X'' + \mu^2 X = 0$, $Y'' + (\lambda^2 - \mu^2)Y = 0$, $T' + \alpha^2 \lambda^2 T = 0$
10. $r^2 R'' + rR' + (\lambda^2 r^2 - \mu^2)R = 0$, $\Theta'' + \mu^2 \Theta = 0$, $T' + \alpha^2 \lambda^2 T = 0$

Section 10.3, Page 437

1. (a) $T = 2l$ (b) $T = 1$ (c) Not periodic

   (d) $T = 1$ (e) Not periodic   (f) $T = \dfrac{2\pi}{5}$

(g) $T = \dfrac{2\pi}{|m|}$, $m \neq 0$ (h) Not periodic   (i) $T = 2$

(j) $T = 4$

3. $\displaystyle\int_0^x f(t)\, dt$ may not be periodic; for example, let $f(t) = 1 + \cos t$.

5. $f(x) = \dfrac{2l}{\pi} \displaystyle\sum_{n=1}^{\infty} \dfrac{(-1)^n}{n} \sin \dfrac{n\pi x}{l}$

6. $f(x) = \dfrac{1}{2} - \dfrac{2}{\pi}\left[\sin \dfrac{\pi x}{l} + \dfrac{1}{3} \sin \dfrac{3\pi x}{l} + \dfrac{1}{5} \sin \dfrac{5\pi x}{l} + \cdots \right]$

$\quad = \dfrac{1}{2} - \dfrac{2}{\pi} \displaystyle\sum_{n=1}^{\infty} \dfrac{1}{2n-1} \sin \dfrac{(2n-1)\pi x}{l}$

7. $f(x) = \dfrac{2l}{\pi} \displaystyle\sum_{n=1}^{\infty} \dfrac{1}{n} \sin \dfrac{n\pi x}{l}$ 8. $f(x) = \dfrac{2}{\pi} \displaystyle\sum_{n=1}^{\infty} \dfrac{(-1)^{n+1}}{n} \sin n\pi x$

9. $f(x) = \dfrac{1}{2} - \dfrac{2}{\pi}\left[\dfrac{1}{2} \sin 2\pi x + \dfrac{1}{4} \sin 4\pi x + \dfrac{1}{6} \sin 6\pi x + \cdots \right]$

$\quad = \dfrac{1}{2} - \dfrac{2}{\pi} \displaystyle\sum_{n=1}^{\infty} \dfrac{1}{2n} \sin 2n\pi x$

10. $f(x) = \dfrac{4}{\pi} \displaystyle\sum_{n=1}^{\infty} \dfrac{1}{2n-1} \sin \dfrac{(2n-1)\pi x}{2}$

11. $f(x) = 2l - x$ in $l < x < 2l$; $f(x) = -2l - x$ in $-3l < x < -2l$
12. $f(x) = x - 1$ in $1 < x < 2$; $f(x) = x - 8$ in $8 < x < 9$
13. $f(x) = -l - x$ in $-l < x < 0$

Section 10.4, Page 443

1. $f(x) = \dfrac{4}{\pi}\left(\sin \pi x + \dfrac{1}{3} \sin 3\pi x + \dfrac{1}{5} \sin 5\pi x + \cdots \right)$

$\quad = \dfrac{4}{\pi} \displaystyle\sum_{n=1}^{\infty} \dfrac{\sin (2n-1)\pi x}{2n-1}$

2. $f(x) = \dfrac{\pi}{4} - \displaystyle\sum_{n=1}^{\infty}\left[\dfrac{2}{(2n-1)^2 \pi} \cos (2n-1)x + \dfrac{(-1)^n}{n} \sin nx \right]$

3. $f(x) = \dfrac{1}{2} - \dfrac{1}{2} \cos 2x$

4. $f(x) = t + \dfrac{2}{\pi} \displaystyle\sum_{n=1}^{\infty} \dfrac{\sin n\pi t}{n} \cos n\pi x$

5. $f(x) = \dfrac{l}{2} + \dfrac{4l}{\pi^2}\left(\cos \dfrac{\pi x}{l} + \dfrac{1}{9} \cos \dfrac{3\pi x}{l} + \dfrac{1}{25} \cos \dfrac{5\pi x}{l} + \cdots \right)$

$\quad = \dfrac{l}{2} + \dfrac{4l}{\pi^2} \displaystyle\sum_{n=1}^{\infty} \dfrac{1}{(2n-1)^2} \cos \dfrac{(2n-1)\pi x}{l}$

6. $f(x) = \dfrac{2}{3} + \dfrac{4}{\pi^2}\left(\cos \pi x - \dfrac{1}{4} \cos 2\pi x + \dfrac{1}{9} \cos 3\pi x - \cdots \right)$

$\quad = \dfrac{2}{3} + \dfrac{4}{\pi^2} \displaystyle\sum_{n=1}^{\infty} \dfrac{(-1)^{n+1}}{n^2} \cos n\pi x$

7. $f(x) = \dfrac{1}{2} + \dfrac{2}{\pi}\left(\cos x - \dfrac{1}{3}\cos 3x + \dfrac{1}{5}\cos 5x - \cdots\right)$

$\quad = \dfrac{1}{2} + \dfrac{2}{\pi}\displaystyle\sum_{n=1}^{\infty}\dfrac{(-1)^{n-1}}{2n-1}\cos(2n-1)x$

8. $f(x) = \dfrac{a_0}{2} + \displaystyle\sum_{n=1}^{\infty}(a_n\cos n\pi x + b_n\sin n\pi x)$;

$a_0 = \frac{1}{3}, \qquad a_n = \dfrac{2(-1)^n}{n^2\pi^2}, \qquad b_n = \begin{cases} -1/n\pi, & n \text{ even} \\ 1/n\pi - 4/n^3\pi^3, & n \text{ odd} \end{cases}$

9. $x = \dfrac{1}{\omega^2 - n^2}\left(-\dfrac{n}{\omega}\sin \omega t + \sin nt\right), \qquad \omega^2 \neq n^2$

10. $x = \displaystyle\sum_{n=1}^{\infty}\dfrac{b_n}{\omega^2 - n^2}\left(-\dfrac{n}{\omega}\sin \omega t + \sin nt\right), \qquad \omega^2 \neq n^2$

11. $x = \dfrac{4}{\pi}\displaystyle\sum_{n=1}^{\infty}\dfrac{1}{\omega^2 - (2n-1)^2}\left[\dfrac{1}{2n-1}\sin(2n-1)t - \dfrac{1}{\omega}\sin \omega t\right]$

12. $x = \cos \omega t + \dfrac{1}{2\omega^2}(1 - \cos \omega t) + \dfrac{4}{\pi^2}\displaystyle\sum_{n=1}^{\infty}\dfrac{\cos(2n-1)\pi t - \cos \omega t}{(2n-1)^2[\omega^2 - (2n-1)^2]}$

13. $y = c_1 e^{-2x} + c_2 e^{-x} + \displaystyle\sum_{n=1}^{\infty}\dfrac{a_n}{4 + 5n^2 + n^4}[(2 - n^2)\cos nx + 3n\sin nx]$

Section 10.5, Page 449

1. (a) Odd   (b) Odd   (c) Neither   (d) Odd
   (e) Even   (f) Even   (g) Neither   (h) Even
   (i) Even   (j) Even   (k) Neither   (l) Neither

2. (a) 0   (b) $\frac{2}{5}$ (c) $\dfrac{2\pi(-1)^{n+1}}{n}$

   (d) 0   (e) 0   (f) 0

4. $f(x) = \dfrac{1}{2} + \dfrac{2}{\pi}\left(\cos\dfrac{\pi x}{2} - \dfrac{1}{3}\cos\dfrac{3\pi x}{2} + \dfrac{1}{5}\cos\dfrac{5\pi x}{2} - \cdots\right)$

$\quad = \dfrac{1}{2} + \dfrac{2}{\pi}\displaystyle\sum_{n=1}^{\infty}\dfrac{(-1)^{n-1}}{2n-1}\cos\dfrac{(2n-1)\pi x}{2}$

5. $f(x) = \displaystyle\sum_{n=1}^{\infty}\dfrac{2}{n\pi}\left(-\cos n\pi + \dfrac{2}{n\pi}\sin\dfrac{n\pi}{2}\right)\sin\dfrac{n\pi x}{2}$

6. $f(x) = 1$

7. $f(x) = \dfrac{4}{\pi}\left(\sin x + \dfrac{1}{3}\sin 3x + \dfrac{1}{5}\sin 5x + \cdots\right) = \dfrac{4}{\pi}\displaystyle\sum_{n=1}^{\infty}\dfrac{\sin(2n-1)x}{2n-1}$

8. $f(x) = \displaystyle\sum_{n=1}^{\infty}\dfrac{2}{n\pi}\left(\cos\dfrac{n\pi}{3} + \cos\dfrac{2n\pi}{3} - 2\cos n\pi\right)\sin\dfrac{nx}{3}$

9. $f(x) = \dfrac{1}{2} - \dfrac{1}{\pi}\left(\sin 2\pi x + \dfrac{1}{2}\sin 4\pi x + \dfrac{1}{3}\sin 6\pi x + \cdots\right)$

$\quad = \dfrac{1}{2} - \dfrac{1}{\pi}\displaystyle\sum_{n=1}^{\infty}\dfrac{\sin 2n\pi x}{n}$

10. $f(x) = \dfrac{l}{2} + \dfrac{4l}{\pi^2} \sum\limits_{n=1}^{\infty} \dfrac{1}{(2n-1)^2} \cos \dfrac{(2n-1)\pi x}{l}$

11. $f(x) = \dfrac{2l}{\pi} \left(\sin \dfrac{\pi x}{l} + \dfrac{1}{2} \sin \dfrac{2\pi x}{l} + \dfrac{1}{3} \sin \dfrac{3\pi x}{l} + \cdots \right)$

$= \dfrac{2l}{\pi} \sum\limits_{n=1}^{\infty} \dfrac{1}{n} \sin \dfrac{n\pi x}{l}$

16. $\pi \cong 2.895$ 　　　　　　　　　　　　　17. (b) $\pi \cong 3.061$

18. $k(x) = \dfrac{l}{2} + \dfrac{l}{\pi} \sum\limits_{n=1}^{\infty} \dfrac{1}{n} \sin \dfrac{2n\pi x}{l}$

24. Extend $f(x)$ antisymmetrically into $(l, 2l)$; that is, so that $f(2l - x) = -f(x)$ for $0 \le x < l$. Then extend this function as an even function into $(-2l, 0)$.

Section 10.6, Page 458

1. $u(x, t) = \sum\limits_{n=1}^{\infty} c_n e^{-n^2\pi^2\alpha^2 t/l^2} \sin \dfrac{n\pi x}{l}$; 　　$\alpha^2 = 1.14 \text{ cm}^2/\text{sec}, \ l = 100 \text{ cm}$

　(a) $c_n = \dfrac{100(1 - \cos n\pi)}{n\pi}$ 　　　(b) $c_n = \dfrac{400 \sin (n\pi/2)}{n^2\pi^2}$

　(c) $c_n = \dfrac{100[\cos (n\pi/4) - \cos (3n\pi/4)]}{n\pi}$

2. $u(x, t) = \dfrac{400}{\pi} \sum\limits_{n=1}^{\infty} \dfrac{1}{2n-1} e^{-(2n-1)^2\pi^2\alpha^2 t/400} \sin \dfrac{(2n-1)\pi x}{20}$

　(a) $u(10, 30) \cong 35.7°\text{C}$ 　　(b) $u(10, 30) \cong 66.9°\text{C}$ 　　(c) $u(10, 30) \cong 97.2°\text{C}$

3. $t \cong 400(\alpha\pi)^{-2} \ln \dfrac{400}{25\pi}$

　(a) $t \cong 38.7 \text{ sec}$ 　　(b) $t \cong 77.0 \text{ sec}$ 　　(c) $t \cong 552 \text{ sec}$

4. (a) $u(x, t) = \dfrac{60x}{l} + \sum\limits_{n=1}^{\infty} \left(\dfrac{50}{n\pi} + \dfrac{70}{n\pi} \cos n\pi \right) e^{-0.86n^2\pi^2 t/l^2} \sin \dfrac{n\pi x}{l}$

　(b) $u(5, 30) \cong 12.6°\text{C}$; 　　$u(5, 60) \cong 13.7°\text{C}$
　(c) $u(5, 30) \cong 14.1°\text{C}$; 　　11%; 　　third term $\cong -0.006°\text{C}$
　(d) $t \cong 160 \text{ sec}$

5. (a) $f(x) = 2x, \ 0 \le x \le 50$; 　　$f(x) = 200 - 2x, \ 50 < x \le 100$

　(b) $u(x, t) = 20 - \dfrac{x}{5} + \sum\limits_{n=1}^{\infty} c_n e^{-1.14n^2\pi^2 t/(100)^2} \sin \dfrac{n\pi x}{100}$,

　　$c_n = \dfrac{1}{50} \int_0^{100} \left[f(x) - \left(20 - \dfrac{x}{5} \right) \right] \sin \dfrac{n\pi x}{100} \, dx = \dfrac{800}{n^2\pi^2} \sin \dfrac{n\pi}{2} - \dfrac{40}{n\pi}$

6. $u(x, t) = \dfrac{2}{\pi} + \sum\limits_{n=1}^{\infty} c_n e^{-n^2\pi^2\alpha^2 t/l^2} \cos \dfrac{n\pi x}{l}$, where

　$c_n = \dfrac{2}{l} \int_0^l \cos \dfrac{n\pi x}{l} \sin \dfrac{\pi x}{l} \, dx = \begin{cases} 0, & n \text{ odd,} \\ -4/(n^2 - 1)\pi, & n \text{ even}; \end{cases}$

　$\lim\limits_{t \to \infty} u(x, t) = 2/\pi$

7. $v(x) = 0$

8. $v(x) = T$

9. (b) $u(x, t) = \sum_{n=1}^{\infty} c_n e^{-(2n-1)^2 \pi^2 \alpha^2 t/4l^2} \sin \dfrac{(2n-1)\pi x}{2l}$,

$$c_n = \frac{2}{l} \int_0^l f(x) \sin \frac{(2n-1)\pi x}{2l} \, dx$$

10. $u(x, t) = T + \sum_{n=1}^{\infty} c_n e^{-(2n-1)^2 \pi^2 \alpha^2 t/4l^2} \sin \dfrac{(2n-1)\pi x}{2l}$,

$$c_n = \frac{2}{l} \int_0^l [f(x) - T] \sin \frac{(2n-1)\pi x}{2l} \, dx$$

Section 10.7, Page 467

1. $u(x, t) = \dfrac{4Al}{\pi^2} \displaystyle\sum_{n=1}^{\infty} \dfrac{1}{n^2} \sin \dfrac{n\pi}{2} \sin \dfrac{n\pi x}{l} \cos \dfrac{n\pi at}{l}$

2. $u(x, t) = \dfrac{2Al}{\pi^2} \displaystyle\sum_{n=1}^{\infty} \dfrac{1}{n^2} \left(\sin \dfrac{n\pi}{4} + \sin \dfrac{3n\pi}{4} \right) \sin \dfrac{n\pi x}{l} \cos \dfrac{n\pi at}{l}$

3. $u(x, t) = \displaystyle\sum_{n=1}^{\infty} c_n \sin \dfrac{n\pi x}{l} \sin \dfrac{n\pi at}{l}$, $\qquad c_n = \dfrac{2}{n\pi a} \displaystyle\int_0^l g(x) \sin \dfrac{n\pi x}{l} \, dx$

4. $u(x, t) = \dfrac{4Al^2}{a\pi^3} \displaystyle\sum_{n=1}^{\infty} \dfrac{1}{n^3} \sin \dfrac{n\pi}{2} \sin \dfrac{n\pi x}{l} \sin \dfrac{n\pi at}{l}$

6. $u(x, t) = \displaystyle\sum_{n=1}^{\infty} c_n \sin \dfrac{(2n-1)\pi x}{2l} \cos \dfrac{(2n-1)\pi at}{2l}$,

$$c_n = \frac{2}{l} \int_0^l f(x) \sin \frac{(2n-1)\pi x}{2l} \, dx$$

9. $\phi(x + at)$ represents a wave moving in the negative x-direction with speed $a > 0$.

10. 248 ft/sec

14. $X'' + \mu^2 X = 0$, $\qquad Y'' - (\mu^2 - \lambda^2) Y = 0$, $\qquad T'' + \lambda^2 a^2 T = 0$

15. $r^2 R'' + r R' + (\lambda^2 r^2 - \mu^2) R = 0$, $\qquad \Theta'' + \mu^2 \Theta = 0$, $\qquad T'' + \lambda^2 a^2 T = 0$

Section 10.8, Page 476

1. (a) $u(x, y) = \displaystyle\sum_{n=1}^{\infty} c_n \sin \dfrac{n\pi x}{a} \sinh \dfrac{n\pi y}{a}$, $\qquad c_n = \dfrac{2/a}{\sinh (n\pi b/a)} \displaystyle\int_0^a g(x) \sin \dfrac{n\pi x}{a} \, dx$

(b) $u(x, y) = \dfrac{4a}{\pi^2} \displaystyle\sum_{n=1}^{\infty} \dfrac{1}{n^2} \dfrac{\sin (n\pi/2)}{\sinh (n\pi b/a)} \sin \dfrac{n\pi x}{a} \sinh \dfrac{n\pi y}{a}$

2. $u(x, y) = \displaystyle\sum_{n=1}^{\infty} c_n \sin \dfrac{n\pi x}{a} \sinh \dfrac{n\pi(b-y)}{a}$, $\qquad c_n = \dfrac{2/a}{\sinh (n\pi b/a)} \displaystyle\int_0^a h(x) \sin \dfrac{n\pi x}{a} \, dx$

3. $u(x, y) = v(x, y) + w(x, y)$, where $v(x, y)$ is found in Problem 2 and $w(x, y)$ is given by Eq. (12) in the text.

5. $u(r, \theta) = \dfrac{c_0}{2} + \displaystyle\sum_{n=1}^{\infty} r^{-n}(c_n \cos n\theta + k_n \sin n\theta)$;

$$c_n = \frac{a^n}{\pi} \int_{-\pi}^{\pi} f(\theta) \cos n\theta \, d\theta, \qquad k_n = \frac{a^n}{\pi} \int_{-\pi}^{\pi} f(\theta) \sin n\theta \, d\theta$$

6. $u(r, \theta) = \sum_{n=1}^{\infty} c_n r^n \sin n\theta$, $\qquad c_n = \dfrac{2/\pi}{a^n} \int_0^\pi f(\theta) \sin n\theta \, d\theta$

7. (b) $u(x, y) = c_0 + \sum_{n=1}^{\infty} c_n \cosh \dfrac{n\pi x}{b} \cos \dfrac{n\pi y}{b}$,

$$c_n = \dfrac{2/n\pi}{\sinh (n\pi a/b)} \int_0^b f(y) \cos \dfrac{n\pi y}{b} \, dy$$

8. $u(r, \theta) = c_0 + \sum_{n=1}^{\infty} r^n (c_n \cos n\theta + k_n \sin n\theta)$,

$$c_n = \dfrac{1}{n\pi a^{n-1}} \int_{-\pi}^{\pi} g(\theta) \cos n\theta \, d\theta, \qquad k_n = \dfrac{1}{n\pi a^{n-1}} \int_{-\pi}^{\pi} g(\theta) \sin n\theta \, d\theta$$

Necessary condition is $\displaystyle\int_{-\pi}^{\pi} g(\theta) \, d\theta = 0$.

9. $u_{mn}(x, y) = c_{mn} \sin \dfrac{m\pi x}{a} \sin \dfrac{n\pi y}{b} \sinh \left(\dfrac{m^2}{a^2} + \dfrac{n^2}{b^2} \right)^{1/2} \pi z$

CHAPTER ELEVEN

Section 11.2, Page 491

1. $\lambda_n = \left[\dfrac{(2n-1)\pi}{2l} \right]^2$; $\qquad \phi_n(x) = \sin \dfrac{(2n-1)\pi x}{2l}$; $\qquad n = 1, 2, 3, \ldots$

2. $\lambda_n = \dfrac{(2n-1)^2}{4}$; $\qquad \phi_n(x) = \cos \dfrac{(2n-1)x}{2}$; $\qquad n = 1, 2, 3, \ldots$

3. $\lambda_0 = 0$; $\qquad \phi_0(x) = 1$
   $\lambda_n = n^2 \pi^2$; $\qquad \phi_n(x) = \cos n\pi x$; $\qquad n = 1, 2, 3, \ldots$

4. $\lambda_n = -\left[\dfrac{(2n-1)\pi}{2} \right]^2$; $\qquad \phi_n(x) = \sin \dfrac{(2n-1)\pi x}{2}$; $\qquad n = 1, 2, 3, \ldots$

5. $\lambda_0 = 0$; $\qquad \phi_0(x) = 1 - x$
   For $n = 1, 2, 3, \ldots$, $\phi_n(x) = \sin \mu_n x - \mu_n \cos \mu_n x$ and $\lambda_n = -\mu_n^2$, where μ_n are roots of $\mu = \tan \mu$.

   $\lambda_1 \cong -20.2$; $\qquad \lambda_n = -\dfrac{(2n+1)^2 \pi^2}{4}$ for large n.

6. $\phi_n(x) = \sin \sqrt{\lambda_n}\, x$ where $\sqrt{\lambda_n}$ are roots of $\sqrt{\lambda} = -\tan \sqrt{\lambda}\, \pi$; $\qquad \lambda_1 \cong 0.621$;
   $\lambda_n \cong \dfrac{(2n-1)^2}{4}$ for large n.

7. $\phi_n(x) = \cos \sqrt{\lambda_n}\, x$ where $\sqrt{\lambda_n}$ are roots of $\sqrt{\lambda} = \cot \sqrt{\lambda}$; $\qquad \lambda_1 \cong 0.740$;
   $\lambda_n \cong (n-1)^2 \pi^2$ for large n.

8. $\phi_n(x) = \sin \sqrt{\lambda_n}\, x + \sqrt{\lambda_n} \cos \sqrt{\lambda_n}\, x$ where $\sqrt{\lambda_n}$ are roots of
   $(\lambda - 1) \sin \sqrt{\lambda} - 2\sqrt{\lambda} \cos \sqrt{\lambda} = 0$; $\qquad \lambda_1 \cong 1.69$; $\qquad \lambda_n \cong (n-1)^2 \pi^2$
   for large n.

9. $\lambda_n = n^2 \pi^2$; $\qquad \phi_n(x) = e^x \sin n\pi x$; $\qquad n = 1, 2, 3, \ldots$

10. Positive eigenvalues $\lambda = \lambda_n$ where $\sqrt{\lambda_n}$ are roots of $\sqrt{\lambda} = \frac{2}{3} \tan 3\sqrt{\lambda}\, l$; corresponding eigenfunctions are $\phi_n(x) = e^{-2x} \sin 3\sqrt{\lambda_n}\, x$. If $l = \frac{1}{2}$, $\lambda_0 = 0$ is

eigenvalue, $\phi_0(x) = xe^{-2x}$ is eigenfunction; if $l \neq \frac{1}{2}$, $\lambda = 0$ is not eigenvalue. If $l \leq \frac{1}{2}$ there are no negative eigenvalues; if $l > \frac{1}{2}$ there is one negative eigenvalue $\lambda = -\mu^2$ where μ is a root of $\mu = \frac{2}{3} \tanh 3\mu l$; corresponding eigenfunction is $\phi_{-1}(x) = e^{-2x} \sinh 3\mu x$.

11. No real eigenvalues.

12. Only eigenvalue is $\lambda = 0$; eigenfunction is $\phi(x) = x - 1$.

14. (a) $\lambda_n = \mu_n{}^4$, where μ_n is a root of $\sin \mu l \sinh \mu l = 0$, hence $\lambda_n = (n\pi/l)^4$;
$$\phi_n(x) = \sin (n\pi x/l)$$

(b) $\lambda_n = \mu_n{}^4$, where μ_n is a root of $\sin \mu l \cosh \mu l - \cos \mu l \sinh \mu l = 0$;
$$\phi_n(x) = \frac{\sin \mu_n x \sinh \mu_n l - \sin \mu_n l \sinh \mu_n x}{\sinh \mu_n l}$$

(c) $\lambda_n = \mu_n{}^4$, where μ_n is a root of $1 + \cosh \mu l \cos \mu l = 0$;
$$\phi_n(x) = \frac{[(\sin \mu_n x - \sinh \mu_n x)(\cos \mu_n l + \cosh \mu_n l) \\ + (\sin \mu_n l + \sinh \mu_n l)(\cosh \mu_n x - \cos \mu_n x)]}{\cos \mu_n l + \cosh \mu_n l}$$

Section 11.3, Page 499

1. (a) not self-adjoint   (b) self-adjoint
   (c) not self-adjoint   (d) self-adjoint

3. $\lambda_0 = 0$; $\phi_0(x) = 1$
   $\lambda_n = (2n\pi)^2$; $\phi_n(x) = \cos 2n\pi x$, $\psi_n(x) = \sin 2n\pi x$

5. (a) If $a_2 = 0$ or $b_2 = 0$, then the corresponding boundary term is missing.

7. (b) $\lambda_n = 1 + i(2n\pi/\ln 2)$

9. $M_3[v] = -(P_0 v)''' + (P_1 v)'' - (P_2 v)' + P_3 v$
   $M_4[v] = (P_0 v)^{\text{iv}} - (P_1 v)''' + (P_2 v)'' - (P_3 v)' + P_4 v$
   $L_4[v]$ is self-adjoint if and only if $P_1 = 2P_0'$ and $P_3 = -P_0''' + P_2'$

10. (a) $\mu(x) = \dfrac{1}{P_0(x)} \exp\left[\displaystyle\int^x P_1(t)/P_0(t)\, dt\right]$ (b) No

11. $\displaystyle\int_0^1 \{vL[u] - uL[v]\}\, dx = v'''(0)u(0) - v(0)u'''(0)$

12. No. $\displaystyle\int_0^1 \{vL[u] - uL[v]\}\, dx = \lambda[v(1)u'(1) - v'(1)u(1)]$

Section 11.4, Page 507

1. (a) $\phi_n(x) = \sqrt{2} \sin [(2n - 1)\pi x/2]$ for $n = 1, 2, 3, \ldots$
   (b) $\phi_n(x) = \sqrt{2} \cos [(2n - 1)\pi x/2]$ for $n = 1, 2, 3, \ldots$
   (c) $\phi_0(x) = 1$; $\phi_n(x) = \sqrt{2} \cos n\pi x$ for $n = 1, 2, 3, \ldots$

   (d) $\phi_n(x) = \left[\dfrac{4\sqrt{\lambda_n}}{2\sqrt{\lambda_n} - \sin 2\sqrt{\lambda_n}}\right]^{1/2} \sin \sqrt{\lambda_n}\, x$ for $n = 1, 2, \ldots$;

      $\sqrt{\lambda_n}$ are roots of $\sqrt{\lambda} + \tan \sqrt{\lambda} = 0$

   (e) $\phi_n(x) = \sqrt{2} \sin n\pi x$ for $n = 1, 2, 3, \ldots$

   (f) $\phi_n(x) = \dfrac{\sqrt{2}\,(\sin \mu_n x \sinh \mu_n - \sin \mu_n \sinh \mu_n x)}{(\sinh^2 \mu_n - \sin^2 \mu_n)^{1/2}}$ for $n = 1, 2, 3, \ldots$;

      μ_n are roots of $\sin \mu \cosh \mu - \sinh \mu \cos \mu = 0$

2. For each part the solution is

$$y = \sum_{n=1}^{\infty} \frac{c_n}{\lambda_n - \mu} \phi_n(x), \qquad c_n = \int_0^1 f(x)\phi_n(x)\,dx, \qquad \mu \neq \lambda_n$$

where $\phi_n(x)$ is given in Problem 1, and λ_n is corresponding eigenvalue. In part (c) summation starts at $n = 0$.

6. $v(x) = a + (b - a)x$

7. $v(x) = 1 - \frac{3}{2}x$

11. In all cases solution is $y = \int_0^1 G(x, u)f(u)\,du$, where $G(x, u)$ is given below.

(a) $G(x, u) = \begin{cases} 1 - x, & 0 \leq u \leq x \\ 1 - u, & x \leq u \leq 1 \end{cases}$

(b) $G(x, u) = \begin{cases} u(2 - x)/2, & 0 \leq u \leq x \\ x(2 - u)/2, & x \leq u \leq 1 \end{cases}$

(c) $G(x, u) = \begin{cases} \cos u \sin (1 - x)/\cos 1, & 0 \leq u \leq x \\ \sin (1 - u) \cos x/\cos 1, & x \leq u \leq 1 \end{cases}$

(d) $G(x, u) = \begin{cases} u, & 0 \leq u \leq x \\ x, & x \leq u \leq 1 \end{cases}$

Section 11.5, Page 516

1. $y = \sum_{i=1}^{\infty} \frac{c_i}{\lambda_i - \mu} J_0(\sqrt{\lambda_i}\, x), \qquad c_i = \int_0^1 f(x)J_0(\sqrt{\lambda_i}\, x)\,dx \Big/ \int_0^1 xJ_0^2(\sqrt{\lambda_i}\, x)\,dx,$

$\sqrt{\lambda_i}$ are roots of $J_0(\sqrt{\lambda}) = 0$.

2. (c) Same form of solution as in Problem 1; $\sqrt{\lambda_i}$ are now roots of $J_0'(\sqrt{\lambda}) = 0$.

3. (d) $a_i = \int_0^1 xJ_m(\sqrt{\lambda_i}\, x)f(x)\,dx \Big/ \int_0^1 xJ_m^2(\sqrt{\lambda_i}\, x)\,dx$

(e) $y = \sum_{i=1}^{\infty} \frac{c_i}{\lambda_i - \mu} J_m(\sqrt{\lambda_i}\, x), \qquad c_i = \int_0^1 f(x)J_m(\sqrt{\lambda_i}\, x)\,dx \Big/ \int_0^1 xJ_m^2(\sqrt{\lambda_i}\, x)\,dx$

4. (b) $y = \sum_{i=1}^{\infty} \frac{c_i}{\lambda_i - \mu} P_{2i-1}(x), \qquad c_i = \int_0^1 f(x)P_{2i-1}(x)\,dx \Big/ \int_0^1 P_{2i-1}^2(x)\,dx$

Section 11.6, Page 522

1. (b) $u(\xi, 2) = f(\xi + 1), \qquad 0 \leq \xi \leq 2$
$u(\xi, 0) = 0, \qquad 0 \leq \xi \leq 2$
$u(0, \eta) = u(2, \eta) = 0, \qquad 0 \leq \eta \leq 2$

2. $u(r, t) = \sum_{n=1}^{\infty} k_n J_0(\lambda_n r) \sin \lambda_n at, \qquad k_n = \dfrac{1}{\lambda_n a} \dfrac{\displaystyle\int_0^1 rJ_0(\lambda_n r)g(r)\,dr}{\displaystyle\int_0^1 rJ_0^2(\lambda_n r)\,dr}$

3. Superpose the solution of Problem 2, and the solution [Eq. (17)] of the example in the text.

6. $u(r, z) = \sum_{n=1}^{\infty} c_n e^{-\lambda_n z} J_0(\lambda_n r)$,

where $c_n = \int_0^1 r J_0(\lambda_n r) f(r) \, dr \Big/ \int_0^1 r J_0^2(\lambda_n r) \, dr$, and λ_n are roots of $J_0(\lambda) = 0$.

7. (c) $v(r, \theta) = \frac{1}{2} c_0 J_0(kr) + \sum_{m=1}^{\infty} J_m(kr)(b_m \sin m\theta + c_m \cos m\theta)$,

where J_m is the Bessel function of the first kind of order m, and

$$b_m = \frac{1}{\pi J_m(kc)} \int_{-\pi}^{\pi} f(\theta) \sin m\theta \, d\theta; \qquad m = 1, 2, \ldots$$

$$c_m = \frac{1}{\pi J_m(kc)} \int_{-\pi}^{\pi} f(\theta) \cos m\theta \, d\theta; \qquad m = 0, 1, 2, \ldots$$

8. $c_n = \int_0^1 r f(r) J_0(\lambda_n r) \, dr \Big/ \int_0^1 r J_0^2(\lambda_n r) \, dr$

10. $u(\rho, s) = \sum_{n=0}^{\infty} c_n \rho^n P_n(s)$, where $c_n = \int_{-1}^1 f(\cos^{-1} s) P_n(s) \, ds \Big/ \int_{-1}^1 P_n^2(s) \, ds$;

P_n is the nth Legendre polynomial and $s = \cos \phi$.

Section 11.7, Page 531

4. (a) $f_0(x) = 1$ (b) $f_1(x) = \sqrt{3}(1 - 2x)$
   (c) $f_2(x) = \sqrt{5}(-1 + 6x - 6x^2)$
   (d) $g_0(x) = 1$, $g_1(x) = 2x - 1$, $g_2(x) = 6x^2 - 6x + 1$
5. $P_0(x) = 1$, $P_1(x) = x$, $P_2(x) = (3x^2 - 1)/2$, $P_3(x) = (5x^3 - 3x)/2$

Index